HYDROLOGY

for Engineers, Geologists,
and Environmental Professionals

An Integrated Treatment of Surface,
Subsurface, and Contaminant Hydrology

Sergio E. Serrano, Ph.D.

Second Edition, Completely Revised

 HydroScience Inc. Ambler, Pennsylvania

HYDROLOGY FOR ENGINEERS, GEOLOGISTS,
AND ENVIRONMENTAL PROFESSIONALS.
An Integrated Treatment of Surface, Subsurface, and Contaminant Hydrology.
Second Edition, Completely Revised
By Sergio E. Serrano, Ph.D.

Published by:

HydroScience Inc.
1217 Charter Lane
Ambler, PA 19002
Email: hydroscience@earthlink.net
http://home.earthlink.net/~hydroscience
SAN 299-3074

Cover Photo: "La Llovizna" National Park, Caroní River, Venezuela.
Photo courtesy of Ing. Antonio Enrique Seijas

Library of Congress Cataloging-in-Publication Data

Serrano, Sergio E.
  Hydrology for engineers, geologists, and environmental professionals : an integrated treatment of surface, subsurface, and contaminant hydrology / Sergio E. Serrano. -- 2nd ed., completely rev.
      p. cm.
  Includes bibliographical references and index.
  ISBN 978-0-9655643-4-2 (pbk. : alk. paper)
  1. Hydrology. I. Title.
  GB661.2.S47 2010
  551.48--dc22

                                        2010018891

Printed in the United States of America

ISBN 978-0-9655643-4-2

To Carlos E. Molano, an engineer, an outstanding hydrologist, an enthusiastic supporter of new ideas, a heroic field environmental professional, in spite of political and economical adversity, a poet, a philosopher of nature, a classical guitar virtuoso, and a true friend.

"I regard water as the blood of the earth. Its internal process, while not identical to that of our blood, is nonetheless very similar. It is the process that gives water its movement. I would compare this inner motion, the origin of all possible physical movement, to that of a blossoming flower bud. As it unfolds, it creates a vortex-like crown of petals, in the center and at the end of which stands the true secret of motion — life in statu nascendi, in the form of a concentration of movement."

Viktor Schauberger (1885 - 1958)

CONTENTS

PREFACE

Motivated by the positive response from the hydrologic community, I release this second edition of *Hydrology for Engineers, Geologists, and Environmental Professionals*. Based on suggestions and constructive criticism received from reviewers, consulting professionals, and many students, this new edition has been completely revised, enlarged, and updated. Many improvements and new developments are included, while preserving the original philosophy behind the text. Dozens of new examples in numerical applications and graphical visualization have been added.

Thanks to the advance in computing technology, a standard mathematics software, such as Maple (MapleSoft Inc.), is employed as a general analytical and numerical computing platform in hydrology. Many modeling applications which previously required specialized software –such as flow lines and contour plotting, numerical integration, and statistical analysis– are now easily done via a standard mathematics software. However, there is no need of prior knowledge of the software since the book gradually introduces the reader to its use through many applications beginning in the first chapter.

Recent research developments in nonlinear hydrologic science and simulation are included in the new edition. In particular, new solutions of nonlinear infiltration are presented with simple numerical applications (Chapter 4). New developments in analytical decomposition are presented as simple and practical means to complex nonlinear hydrologic problems, such as regional groundwater flow modeling in homogeneous or heterogeneous media, regular or irregularly-shaped domains, steady or transient problems, multiple pumping wells, and nonlinear flow (Chapter 5). For contaminant transport, new applications to the simulation of nonlinear decay, nonlinear sorption, and unsaturated-saturated zones contaminant propagation are presented along with simple programs (Chapter 11).

This book is a response to the need for a hydrology book with a clear, balanced approach to surface, subsurface, and contaminant hydrology. There are several books devoted to surface hydrology, flood frequency analysis, storm water management, storm sewers design, and detention basins design. Those texts are part of the traditional association of hydrology with hydraulic engineering applications in civil engineering programs. Subsurface hydrology, and especially contaminant hydrology, are usually not included in traditional undergraduate hydrology texts. Contamination of rivers, lakes, soils, and groundwater are topics reserved to more advanced graduate courses.

Hydrology has evolved into an independent science with its own object of knowledge among the earth sciences. *Applications* of hydrologic theory are found in several engineering and earth sciences fields, including hydraulics, geology, agricultural science, forestry, and the environmental sciences. For example, environmental engineering is a fertile area for hydrologic applications. Hydrology is a formidable tool to quantitatively and qualitatively assess the environmental impact of development projects. Hydrologic principles may be used in the design of waste water treatment plants, hazardous waste management, aquifer restoration activities, groundwater pollution prediction, and assessment of climate change effects on water resources. *Hydrology for Engineers, Geologists and Environmental Professionals* prepares the reader to analyze and solve the environmental problems of today.

Hydrology for Engineers, Geologists and Environmental Professionals was written based on the following assumptions: (1) Every concept in hydrology may be explained in a simple fashion without losing scientific rigor and without resorting to detailed mathematical, statistical, or numerical analyses. (2) Clarity of presentation is more important than comprehensiveness; mastering of a fundamental concept allows the reader to successfully analyze more difficult problems. (3) Learning is accomplished when the reader develops a sense of familiarity and confidence with the concepts. At that point one acknowledges the *simplicity* of the subject and the desire to study more advanced concepts. (4) Hydrology is a science with applications in many engineering, geology and environmental disciplines, besides the traditional hydraulics and surface-runoff applications. (5) An introduction to hydrology should reflect a balance between surface, subsurface, and contaminant hydrology.

In agreement with the above principles, *Hydrology for Engineers, Geologists and Environmental Professionals* implements many features. The material in each chapter has been carefully selected according to the hydrologic significance of its contents, and not necessarily according to the types of engineering applications. Each of the elements of the hydrologic cycle is covered in one chapter: precipitation, evapotranspiration, infiltration and subsurface flow, groundwater, surface runoff, and the hydrology of extreme events. Considerable effort was spent in assigning consistency of notation and dimensions throughout the entire text. Many of the empirical formulae have been translated for consistency with the rest of the book. Similarly, the SI system is used throughout the entire book. Emphasis is placed on metric units in every solved example. Each numerical calculation has been worked with the corresponding dimensions illustrated.

Most concepts are introduced with a written and graphical description of the problem, and illustrated with a practical numerical example. The supplementary problems are directly related to the concepts presented in each chapter. The level of difficulty of the supplementary problems is very similar to that of the solved examples. This stems from the fact that learning results from the repetitive exposure to the same concept.

In Chapter 1, the reader is introduced to the fundamental concepts behind the hydrologic cycle; a brief history of the evolution of scientific hydrology and its connection with fundamental physical laws transmitted from ancient civilizations; the concept of hydrologic systems and its utilization to investigate environmental impact or to implement engineering applications. All facets of hydrologic systems are illustrated with computational algorithms the reader may easily implement. Precipitation is discussed in Chapter 2 along with programs for the analysis of spatial, temporal, and frequency variability in rainfall. The theory and applications of evapotranspiration are presented in Chapter 3. Chapter 4 is devoted to infiltration, flow in the unsaturated zone, and groundwater recharge. Only a few equations are introduced, each one representative of a modeling category. Each model description is followed by numerical examples designed to illustrate the principles. New explicit solutions to the Green and Ampt equation and of the nonlinear Richard's equation are given along with simple calculations for the estimation of physically-based infiltration rate under variable rainfall.

Chapter 5 covers the theory and applications of saturated groundwater flow. I emphasize the equations derived from Dupuit assumptions, which are useful in hydrologic field applications. New developments in decomposition are used to illustrate simple analytical solutions, which previously required complex numerical manipulation and extensive programming. Examples are presented to various practical modeling scenarios, such as steady and unsteady regional groundwater flow in higher dimensions; irregularly-shaped domains; heterogeneous media; multiple pumping wells; time-dependent boundary conditions; and nonlinear flow. Besides simplicity, the solutions obtained are continuous in space and time, which provides a stable and efficient means to calculate gradients, velocities, and flow rates. Several programs and exercises are given to produce contours, three-dimensional plots, and velocity vectors, which no longer require specialized software. New programs are also introduced for the estimation of aquifer parameters.

Chapter 6 studies the hydrology of surface runoff. Hydrograph analysis is offered as a timeless methodology to obtain information on the surface and subsurface hydrologic regime. Considerable effort is spent on the description of unit hydrograph principles. The fundamental unit hydrograph problems are classified into three distinct types. Each type is identified by a specific application and followed by a set of step-by-step numerical examples. Several computer applications have been added that exploit Maple's ability to fit analytical functions to hydrographs, convolution integrals, and matrix methods in flood forecasting. The focus of chapter 7 is the hydrology of extreme events. The techniques of flood routing in large watersheds are presented as examples of today's computer software. Flood frequency analysis is described with a minimum of probabilistic theory. This edition includes new programs for fitting probability distributions to data using the graphical procedure. Some elementary applications to the design of urban storm sewers are shown in detail.

Chapter 8 introduces the sources of water contamination and the various water quality measures as a preparation for the latter part of the book devoted to contaminant hydrology. Chapters 9, 10, and 11 cover the fundamental hydrologic aspects of river contamination, lake contamination, and soil and groundwater pollution. Descriptions on contaminant loads, mixing processes, dispersion of conservative and non-conservative substances in surface and subsurface aquatic environments are presented along with numerical examples. This edition includes new computer programs for the simulation of system response to contaminant inputs. The reader is illustrated about the tools to assess qualitatively and quantitatively the environmental impact of waste water treatment plants, nuclear power plants, chemical spills, underground storage tanks, sanitary landfills, and well contamination on aquatic media. New applications to the simulation scale-dependent dispersion, nonlinear decay, nonlinear sorption, and unsaturated-saturated zones contaminant propagation are presented along with simple programs. The importance of system nonlinearity –overlooked by most hydrology texts– on plume non-symmetry and shape is emphasized. The first edition of this book included a copy of the KYSPILL software. However, with the rapid advances in standard mathematics software, many of the features of specialized software are now easily accessible with the latter.

Hydrology for Engineers, Geologists and Environmental Professionals was written for the undergraduate student of engineering, geology, geography, forestry, meteorology, or the environmental sciences. It also contains ample advanced material to serve as a first graduate course on hydrology. Because of its integrated focus on surface, subsurface, and contaminant hydrology, the book may be used by the consulting engineer, professional geologist, or environmental professional wishing to review the field of hydrology. Many references to more advanced work are suggested to those readers interested in a more detailed study of a particular aspect of hydrologic science.

Sergio E. Serrano
Philadelphia, May 2010

1 THE HYDROLOGIC CYCLE

1.1 WATER

Water is the most common substance on earth, and yet it is a marvelous entity. Water covers over 70 percent of the earth's surface and participates in all of its processes. It is essential to life on the planet, making up a substantial proportion of every living organism. Water is the only substance on earth that is naturally present on all three phase forms: liquid, solid (ice), and gaseous (water vapor). At the molecular scale, water is composed of two hydrogen atoms sharing electrons with an oxygen atom (H_2O in chemistry notation). This causes an asymmetric distribution of electrons, a corresponding positive charge on one side of the molecule, and a negative one on the other. The polarity results in an electrostatic attraction between molecules and in unique properties affecting planetary processes.

Water possesses a high capacity to absorb heat, a fact that produces many interesting phenomena. The ability of water to absorb large amounts of heat permits solar energy to warm the oceans. This heat is subsequently transferred to the atmosphere. Because the earth's equator is tilted with respect to the plane of its orbit around the sun, seasonal variations in temperature occur. At the same time, the rotation, translation, and precessional movements of the earth create unequal heating on its surface, and differences in atmospheric pressure. Thus, winds, storms, and hurricanes are produced. At the same time, ocean currents warm lands in the northern hemisphere.

Water is a universal solvent. It is slightly acidic and thus dissolves many minerals in its path through the atmosphere, soils, and rivers. Since water is a carrier of substances and has the ability to chemically react with complex organic compounds, it constitutes an essential part of plant and animal nutrients; it actively participates in feeding, assimilation, and excretion processes of living organisms.

Water possesses a high surficial tension. This feature supports many physical and biological processes involving water in small spaces. Water is the only compound whose solid state is lighter than its liquid one. This causes ice to float on liquid water, and permits aquatic life to survive during the winter months. Water transparency permits solar radiation to reach various depths, which allows photosynthesis below the water surface.

1.2 THE NATURE OF HYDROLOGY

Hydrology is the earth science that studies the occurrence, distribution, movement, and properties of the waters of the earth. Hydrology describes and predicts the spatial and temporal variability of water in the terrestrial, oceanic, and atmospheric systems. Hydrology investigates the movement of water on and under the earth's land surfaces, the physical laws inherent to that movement, the transport of contaminant substances in water, and the intervening chemical and biological processes.

Origins and Evolution of Scientific Hydrology

Since the dawn of civilization, humans have depended on the availability of fresh water. Humans understood that water was a pre-requisite to life on the planet, it was essential to health, it affected the production of food, and it was a fundamental means of transportation. In addition, humans observed that water was associated with certain natural phenomena, such as floods and thunderstorms. For these reasons, humans learned to fear, to worship, and to attribute mystic powers to water. Water is part of most mythological and ancient religious traditions of all civilizations in the past.

Parallel to this symbolic representation of water was the necessity to understand and control the environment. Many civilizations in the past attempted to modify the natural distribution of water for their benefit, and in that process many basic facts and empirical laws were learned. For example, about 4000 B.C. a dam was constructed across the Nile to permit reclamation of previously barren lands for agricultural production. The Greeks and especially the Romans built impressive aqueducts that covered vast lands, some of which continued to operate until very recently (e.g., the Segovia aqueduct in Spain operated until the mid twentieth century). The Chinese irrigation and flood control works were also significant projects. The Incas in Peru developed sophisticated water distribution and irrigation systems that permitted the construction of large cities on the top of mountains.

It is suspected that the concept of the hydrologic cycle dates back to ancient Egypt. Preliminary concepts of mass conservation and the relationship between precipitation and streamflow were conceived by early Greek philosophers, such as Thales, Anaxagoras, Herodotus, Hippocrates, Plato and Aristotle. These concepts were based on philosophical analyses and not on physical observation. For this reason, the mechanism of the hydrologic cycle was conceived in a variety of imaginative ways. The theories of the Greek philosophers dominated until the Renaissance. In the mid sixteenth century Leonardo da Vinci in Italy and Bernard Palissy in France asserted, on the basis of field observations, that water in rivers comes from precipitation. In the seventeenth century Pierre Perrault and Edmé Mariotte in France published the first quantitative measurements that verified the rainfall origin of streamflow. Early in the eighteen century the English scientist Edmund Halley extended the quantifying of the hydrologic cycle by estimating the amounts of water involved in the ocean-atmosphere-rivers-ocean cycle of the Mediterranean Sea and surrounding areas.

In the eighteenth century the development of mathematical applications to fluid mechanics and hydraulics brought several important contributions by Europeans, such as Bernoulli, Chézy, Euler, Pitot and others. By about 1800 the modern concepts of evaporation and global hydrologic cycle were established by the English scientist John Dalton. Around that time routine network measurement of precipitation began in Europe, the United States, and India. In the mid nineteenth century the fundamental law of groundwater flow was formulated by the French engineer Henry Darcy. The same century saw many advances in fluid mechanics, hydraulics and sediment transport by Poiseuille, Dupuit, DuBoys, Stokes, Manning, Reynolds, and others whose names have become associated with particular laws or principles.

By the end of the nineteenth century treatises on various aspects of hydrology began to appear. Many of these works examined the relationship between rainfall and streamflow amounts, due to the need to estimate flood magnitudes for the design of bridges, and other structures. This was the beginning of a close association between hydrology and civil engineering, although hydrology has gradually evolved as an independent environmental science related to many other professional disciplines.

The twentieth century saw rapid developments in hydrologic science. With the formation of the Section of Scientific Hydrology in the International Union of Geodesy and Geophysics in 1922, the Hydrology Section in the American Geophysical Union in 1930, and the proliferation of many national and international organizations devoted to the advancement of hydrology, the field has been formally recognized as a scientific discipline. Many individuals have contributed to this rapid expansion of the hydrologic sciences: A. Hazen, E.J. Gumbel, H.E. Hurst, and W.B. Langbein in the applications of statistics to hydrology; O.E. Meinzer, C.V. Theis, C.S. Slichter, and M.K. Hubbert in the development of various concepts of groundwater mechanics; L Prandtl, T. Von Kármán, H. Rouse, V.T. Chow, G.K. Gilbert, and H.A. Einstein in stream hydraulics and sediment transport; R.E. Horton and L.B. Leopold in the development of fundamental knowledge of infiltration, runoff processes and quantitative geomorphology; W. Thornthwaite, and H.E., Penman in the understanding of climate and evapotranspiration; and A. Wolman and R.S. Garrels in the understanding and modeling of water quality.

The advent and rapid development of computer science has provided a unique opportunity to hydrologists involved in the analysis of vast and complex hydrologic data. In addition, computers have made possible the construction and testing of mathematical models representing the different elements of the hydrologic cycle, and their complex inter-relationship. Mathematical analyses and numerical algorithms have found fruitful applications in the simulation of natural hydrologic processes. These have generated not only intrinsic understanding of fundamental laws of hydrology, but also useful tools with practical predictive applications in several engineering design tasks.

For interesting accounts on the origins and evolution of the concept of the hydrologic cycle and the history of hydrology, see Biswas (1970) and Nace (1974). The twentieth century also saw the first discoveries on the relationship between hydrological, environmental, and climatic science. Pioneers like V. Schauberger enunciated basic principles about the health effects of thermal and chemical pollution of water; the consequences of deforestation, river regulation, energy production, and global warming; and the existence of undiscovered subtle energies in water (Bartholomew, 2005; Cobbald, 2006; Schauberger, 1998). Interesting descriptions on the role of hydrology in climate change and the hydrologic effects of global warming can be found in Botkin and Keller (2005).

The Importance of Hydrology

Even though water is the most common substance on earth, 99 percent of it is unsuitable for drinking and other uses. Nearly 97 percent of the earth's waters are in the oceans, and about 2 percent constitute ice caps and glaciers. Thus, the usable water for people, plants, and animals is less than 1 percent of the total. The remaining water resources are being overused or polluted, leading to a growing global water shortage. The increasing shortages are causing famine, economic disruption, and even war in some places. The global society of today is characterized by an intense exploitation of natural resources, and in particular, water resources. The dramatic increase in the world population, accompanied by the rapid industrial and technological development with emphasis on consumption, has placed an unprecedented demand on natural water systems. At the same time, development and construction projects, industrial production and distribution of materials and goods, and the disposal of waste is continuously threatening the quantity and quality of existing surface and subsurface water resources, with the corresponding adverse effects on natural ecosystems and human health. The level of complexity of today's society requires development plans that minimize the damage to natural environmental systems, and remedial actions to restore or counteract the results of poor management practices and accidents of the past.

Because water and environmental issues are inextricably linked, hydrology is a multi-disciplinary science of utmost importance to the environmental fields today. A knowledge of hydrology is fundamental to decision-making processes where water is a component in a system of concern. Hydrologic theory offers valuable tools to understand and quantify physical, chemical, and biological processes related to an engineering or natural system where water is an important player. Development and construction projects, restoration and reclamation activities, and environmental accidents require either an assessment of the effects on related water resources, or specific quantitative information for the purposes of engineering design. Thus, hydrology provides *a priori* or *a posteriori* qualitative or quantitative information that helps the engineer, resource or project manager, scientist, or government official make sound decisions.

Hydrology is an integral part of several disciplines, such as environmental engineering and environmental science, water resources engineering, hydraulic engineering, geotechnical engineering, transportation engineering, chemical engineering, mining engineering, agricultural engineering, agriculture, forestry, geography, geology, toxicology, and biology. Today's hydrologist works in one or more of the above disciplines. He investigates, quantifies, assesses, predicts, or designs for diverse projects where water is an important component. Hydrology provides the tools and the information needed in many applications in engineering analysis and design. Examples of applications are:

- Design of surface water reservoirs
- Design of groundwater reservoirs
- Design of urban storm water sewers and airport drainage systems
- Design of urban water distribution systems

- Design of dikes and other flood control structures
- Design of locks, ports, and other navigational systems
- Design of agricultural irrigation systems
- Design of agricultural drainage systems
- Design of temporary construction and mining drainage systems
- Design of tunnels and underground excavations
- Design of flow control systems for highway development
- Design of bridges and other river foundations
- Design of open channels and other river flow control structures
- Forecasting of flood waves propagation
- Design of soil conservation measures
- Design of sanitary landfills and waste disposal facilities
- Management of rivers, lakes, wetlands, estuaries, and aquifers
- Management of crops, forests, and pasture lands
- Prediction of contamination effects on rivers and lakes
- Prediction of contaminants propagation in soils and groundwaters
- Prediction of effects of drainage on flood flows
- Prediction of environmental impact of water resources projects
- Prediction of environmental impact of deforestation
- Prediction of environmental impact of urbanization
- Prediction of environmental impact of chemical spills
- Prediction of environmental impact of chemical leaks from tanks
- Prediction of environmental impact of leachates from landfills
- Prediction of environmental impact of pesticide application
- Prediction of environmental impact of global climate change
- Design of contaminated-soil remedial systems
- Design of polluted-aquifer containment or restoration systems
- Analysis of the effect of climate change on water resources

As can be seen, hydrologic science has many applications in various fields. It constitutes a discipline for the environmental professional of today. Clearly this book does not intend to cover the details of design procedures for the above applications, which are covered in specialized design texts. Instead, it is a comprehensive introduction to hydrologic science and engineering, and hydrologic analysis. Hydrology provides the qualitative and quantitative analytic tools, which will produce the necessary information for the above applications.

Hydrology is concerned with the identification and analysis of important variables related to a particular project. For example, hydrologic analysis provides the designer of a reservoir with appropriate mathematical models to estimate time distribution of evaporation. Hydrology will also offer objective methods to estimate the probable maximum precipitation in the area, mean streamflow rate and its time variability, emergency peak flow rate, groundwater flow contributions, and minimum flow rates. This information is later used by the engineer in the dimensioning (i.e., the design itself) of the hydraulic structures required, such as the dam location and height, emergency spill way, energy dissipation structures and delivery systems.

Consider the case of a regional groundwater system contaminated by a chemical spill. The hydrologist will be involved in the collection of contaminated water samples, the analysis and quantification of the groundwater flow velocity and direction, the study of regional recharge from rainfall and the areas of natural discharge, and the investigation of the possible paths the contaminant may propagate in the subsoil. The hydrologist will also use mathematical methods to predict the concentration of toxic contaminants at certain sensitive areas in the future. She will then compare these values with maximum permissible concentrations derived from health-risk considerations. Finally, the hydrologist will offer alternatives of containment or remediation and will participate in the design of the respective structures.

1.3 THE HYDROLOGIC CYCLE

As a science focusing on the circulation of water and other substances in the planet, hydrology studies different processes that affect this movement. These processes interact in a complex manner in a particular water-drainage area, called a watershed. The following is a list of the fundamental hydrologic processes:

Precipitation
The fundamental physical process of interest in hydrology is *precipitation* (P), its nature, its occurrence, its spatial distribution at a fixed time, and its time evolution at a fixed location.

Interception
Interception (I_n) is the retention of precipitated water by the vegetation and other forms of cover on the drainage area. This water is temporarily stored on the leaves and other surfaces, and then evaporates back to the atmosphere. Depending on the vegetation type and density, and on the season, interception may be an important variable in the hydrologic cycle of a watershed.

Depression Storage
Precipitation that has reached the ground surface may be temporarily

stored in surface depressions. This process is called *depression storage* (I_d). This water may evaporate or infiltrate after the storm. Depending on the soil hydraulics, vegetation, and topography of the area, depression storage may affect the redistribution of water in the watershed.

Infiltration

Water penetration and redistribution in the soils is called *infiltration* (I). It constitutes one of the most important hydrologic processes affecting not only the partition of water between surface and subsurface components, but also the recharge of aquifers and the transport of contaminants through the subsurface.

Evaporation

Evaporation of water (E) is the change of phase, from liquid to vapor, and the subsequent transport of water from the oceans, lakes, rivers and soils to the atmosphere. Evaporation constitutes an important means of water loss. It depends on several meteorological factors and on the availability of water. Of interest in hydrology and hydrologic applications is the spatial and time distribution of evaporation.

Transpiration

Transpiration (T) is a form of evaporation occurring from the leaves of plants and trees. Transpiration depends on the plant biological processes, species, location, and soil moisture, as well as meteorological factors affecting evaporation.

Streamflow

Streamflow or river flow (Q) is the resultant of contributions from *surface* or *overland flow* (R_o), *subsurface* flow or *interflow* (Q_s), and *groundwater flow* (Q_g). Hydrology studies the relative importance of each of these components and the time distribution of streamflow. Many applications are centered on the analysis of streamflow in a particular watershed.

Flood Routing

Motivated by the need to predict the propagation of catastrophic flood waves through a river system, several techniques have been developed to mathematically simulate this phenomenon. These techniques are called *flood routing*.

Groundwater

Water moving through geologic formations is called *groundwater flow* (Q_g). Hydrology studies the occurrence of groundwater, its seasonal recharge behavior, the movement of water through aquifers, and the discharge of water into streams, lakes, and oceans. Because it controls the low levels in rivers and lakes, and constitutes one of the most important sources of fresh water, groundwater is one of the most studied areas of hydrology.

Snowmelt

The melting of precipitated snow and ice is an important component of the hydrologic cycle in cold climates. Depending on the snow pack characteristics and on the time distribution of air temperature, solar radiation and other variables, *snowmelt* may become an important source of infiltration and streamflow during the spring season.

Sediment Transport

Precipitation, surface runoff, and streamflow are hydrologic processes encouraging the detachment, transport, and deposition of solid particles. *Sediment transport* analysis is of interest to individuals involved in soil conservation in natural and agricultural areas, river channel stability, and reservoir design.

River Pollution

Hydrologic processes affecting streamflow are also important physical processes controlling the transport of contaminants through river systems. Many hydrologic applications today are centered on the prediction of the effect of certain contaminant load, or contaminant spill, on the water quality of a river. The water quality affects the ecology of a river and determines the possible health effects associated with human exposure. Thus hydrology studies the mixing, transport, chemical, and biological processes associated with water flow and contaminant movement in rivers.

Pollution in Lakes

Since lakes and wetlands possess distinct physical hydrologic conditions, lake water quality resulting from various pollution loads are governed by special processes of interest to hydrologists.

Soils and Groundwater Pollution

Water flowing through soils and groundwaters is capable of carrying contaminants resulting from natural dissolution processes, or from human-based contamination products originated from chemical spills, sanitary landfills, or agricultural activities. Modern hydrology investigates the physical, chemical, and biological processes that affect the dispersion of contaminants through the subsurface. There are many applications of hydrologic methods of contaminant propagation prediction to the assessment of contamination, waste containment, and aquifer restoration activities.

The basic mechanism of the global hydrologic cycle is illustrated in Figure 1.1, which represents a portion of the earth profile with some of the most important hydrologic processes. The fundamental driving force of the hydrologic cycle is the radiation from the sun (R). Solar radiation causes the evaporation (E) from the oceans, rivers, lakes, and the soil. The solar radiation also drives the transpiration (T) from the vegetation. The evaporation and transpiration increases the amount of water-vapor present in the air. Masses of air loaded with moisture tend to rise, since they are less dense than dry air. Atmospheric moisture is then subjected to lateral movement by the regional wind velocity (W), which is also the result of atmospheric pressure differences caused by unequal spatial distribution of solar radiation on earth. As the masses of moist air move upward and laterally, they may eventually cool down and begin to condensate to form clouds. When the energy conditions in the cloud are appropriate, water will begin to descend to the surface of the earth to form precipitation (P).

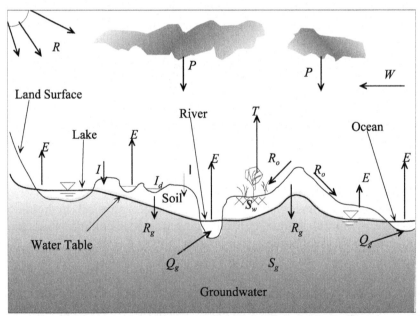

Figure 1.1: General Description of the Hydrologic Cycle

As precipitation approaches the surface of the earth, it is first retained by the leaves of the vegetation and other structures. The amount of water retained in this form is called interception (I_n). If it continues to rain, the excess of precipitation over interception will reach the ground surface and will immediately penetrate the soil via the process of infiltration (I). Infiltrated water will cause an increase in the amount of water present in the soil, called soil moisture or soil-water content (S_w). Water in the soil will move laterally, in the form of subsurface flow or interflow (Q_s), and downward vertically to eventually produce recharge (R_g) to the saturated zone or groundwater zone. Groundwater recharge will cause an increase in the amount of water present in the aquifer (or the groundwater reservoir), called groundwater storage (S_g). Groundwater will slowly move through the aquifer to eventually discharge into rivers, lakes, and the ocean (Q_g).

The excess of precipitation over interception and infiltration (i.e., precipitation that cannot infiltrate), will begin to pond over the ground surface to fill small ground surface depressions. This amount of water is called depression storage (I_d). If it continues to rain, the excess of precipitation over interception, infiltration, and depression storage will begin to flow as overland flow (R_o). Overland flow will eventually discharge into rivers, lakes, and the ocean. Thus, river flow, or streamflow, receives contributions from overland flow, subsurface flow, and groundwater flow. However, each of these contributions has a different proportion and a different arrival time, depending on the precipitation, the soil, the geology, the vegetation and other characteristics of the area.

The above description of the hydrologic cycle is general. Clearly, some of the mechanisms and pathways vary from place to place. For example, in an unforested area the interception might be negligible as compared to that in a forested one. In an urban watershed, the ground surface is practically impervious and the infiltration process might be negligible. On the other hand, a naturally forested area offers the ideal conditions where interception and infiltration are significant. Mountain or steeply sloping watersheds may be controlled by a significant amount of subsurface flow, as compared to overland flow and groundwater flow. Desert areas are characterized by low precipitation, low streamflow, and high evaporation. Karst geology, characterized by units of calcium and magnesium carbonate, offers unique conditions where turbulent groundwater flow coupled with negligible overland flow controls the hydrologic cycle of the area.

The hydrologist needs to investigate local climatic, geologic, topographic, and vegetative characteristics of the watershed in question to understand special conditions of the hydrologic cycle. Geological maps, precipitation data, air temperature data, topographic maps, aerial and satellite pictures are but a few of the available tools in this analysis. A conscientious study of the physical characteristics of a watershed of interest is essential to an understanding of the most important hydrologic processes in place, and to a subsequent quantification of the dominant variables.

Climate Variability and Hydrology

Hydrologists routinely study seasonal and annual fluctuations in precipitation and other weather variables. The repetitive nature and pattern of these fluctuations over a period of many years constitute the characteristic climate of a region. There is increasing evidence that the earth's water resources is undergoing a gradual change impacted by both multiple-year cycles in fluctuating weather patterns and graduate changes in the climate over spans of multiple decades. *El Niño Southern Oscillation* phenomenon is an example of fluctuations in global weather patterns that approximately occurs at cyclical multiple-year intervals. On the other hand, human-induced impacts on *global warming* associated with greenhouse gases is a long-term climate change problem receiving much attention in the scientific community (Lettenmaier, McCabe, and Stakhiv, 1996; National assessment Synthesis Team, 2000).

El Niño Southern Oscillation is the best known anomaly resulting from interactions between weather and oceanic systems. It is a quasicyclic phenomenon that has occurred every 3 to 7 years during the last 450 years (Wurbs and James, 2002). It refers to the abnormally high sea surface temperatures off the coast of Peru. The coastal land of Peru is covered by the Atacama desert, a dry region receiving very little rain. The nearby Pacific Ocean is a very productive fishery. However, El Niño years are marked by a disruption in the usually abundant supply of fish, and flooding rains may fall on the desert. This phenomenon is accompanied by low atmospheric pressure over the eastern Pacific and high atmospheric pressure over the western Pacific. El Niño is the result of large-scale, long-period, waves in the surface of the tropical Pacific Ocean. This produces temporary changes in winds and atmospheric moisture circulation, which cause unusual weather patterns in low and mid-latitude regions around the globe. Some regions may experience unusually warm or cold winters, severe droughts may occur in normally wet agricultural regions, while intense rains may fall over normally dry regions.

The earth's climate has undergone a slow but continuous change throughout its history. Warming and cooling cycles have occurred in the past, each lasting thousands of years. A highly debated issue in the scientific community is the possible effect of human activities on climate change. In particular, there is an ongoing discussion about the possible warming effect of increased concentrations of carbon dioxide and other trace gases in the atmosphere due to the burning of fossil fuels accompanied by increased deforestation of large areas. This topic is known colloquially as the greenhouse effect (Mimikou, 1995). As solar energy reaches the earth, some of it is reflected back, and some of it is absorbed. The outgoing infrared radiation is partially absorbed by clouds, carbon dioxide, water vapor, and other gases. This energy is then radiated in all directions, including back to the earth. The natural greenhouse effect is beneficial to earth because it regulates temperature, which would otherwise be too cold to sustain life. However, human activities now substantially increase the emission of greenhouse gases such as carbon dioxide and nitrous oxide from the burning of fossil fuels. Methane is also added to the atmosphere by agriculture and municipal landfills. Chlorofluorocarbons are released through various means, such as outdated air-conditioning coolants, plastic foams, and aerosol propellants. At the same time, the proportion of forests is substantially decreased. Plants have the natural ability to consume carbon dioxide and release oxygen. Thus, the natural balance of greenhouse gases existing prior to the industrial revolution has been disrupted.

Of interest to the hydrologist is the extent of the effect of global warming resulting from an increase in greenhouse gases on the characteristics of precipitation, soil moisture, surface and groundwater availability, droughts, and floods. Changes in the local hydrologic cycle are possible during the 21st century, and the consequences to water management may be substantial. While climate change occurs at the global scale, the effects of changes in state-atmospheric variables will be felt at the local watershed scales (English et al, 2005; Szép et al, 2005; Li et al, 2004; Laiho et al, 2004; Venugopal, et al 1999). To assess this possibility, previous studies have focused on the coupling of regional climate models with landscape-scale hydrologic models (e.g., Hostetler and Giorgi, 1993). There is a need for an alternate analysis of point precipitation, temperature, and solar radiation coupled with the nonlinear differential equations governing infiltration, soil moisture, deep recharge, and groundwater discharge.

There is evidence of increasing soil-surface temperature due to the complex interaction of increased air temperature and corresponding increased precipitation (Gosnold et al., 1997). Long-term variability in precipitation and air temperature regimes affect the corresponding evapotranspiration and energy balances at the soil surface and will result in possible long-term changes in the soil-moisture regime (Goyal, 2004). The impacts of these changes on the hydrochemical and stream flow regime may be dramatic (Avila et al., 1996). The state variables in the upper soil layers (e.g., the volumetric water content) control, not only vegetation cover and soil fauna (Chadwick, 2003; Tonkov, 2003; Sulkava, and Huhta, 2003), but also the transient variability in output recharge to regional aquifers (slow response) and output overland flow supply (fast response). There is some evidence of an important role of incoming solar radiation and inter-annual precipitation on the nonlinear response of aquifer discharge (Eltahir and Yeh, 1999). Thus, the exploration of long-term quantitative changes in the magnitude and distribution of hydrologic variables due to global changes in temperature and precipitation may be approached via a mechanistic analysis of the fundamental equations governing mass and energy balance in the unsaturated zones (Kay et al, 2005). Some illuminating preliminary studies have been done by performing water budget calculations in the light of various patterns describing precipitation and temperature changes (Panagoulia and Dimou, 1997). Using a conceptual rainfall-runoff model Chiew et al (1995) showed that the potential effects of changes in precipitation and temperature might translate in a significant increase in stream flow. As hydrologic research continues in this arena, knowledge of the impacts of these changes will add to the increasing evidence of the various effects of climate change on ecosystem response (see the review by Fuhrer, 2003).

Hydrologic Systems

It is common in engineering analysis to represent the different components of the hydrologic cycle as components of a complex system. In such a representation, each component acts as a subsystem with clearly defined boundaries. Inside the domain of a system component, certain variables of interest are defined, and their variability with respect to space and time are studied. These domain variables are subject to input functions from other subsystems, and transform the input variables into output variables that subsequently affect other subsystems. Clearly such conceptualization of the hydrologic cycle permits an understanding of the role of each component of the hydrologic cycle on the overall hydrologic response of an area. At the same time, it is possible to conceive the effect other hydrologic functions have on a particular component of interest. Furthermore the systems approach offers a means to quantitatively evaluate the magnitude and characteristics of variables in every system component. This approach has generated a large variety of hydrologic simulation models for multitude of practical applications.

Figure 1.2 shows a simplified systems representation of the hydrologic cycle described above. Each subsystem is represented as a rectangle. The arrows represent relationships between the different subsystems.

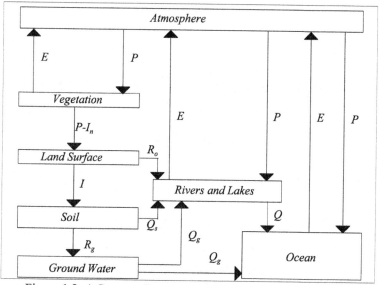

Figure 1.2: A Systems Representation of the Hydrologic Cycle

We remark again that this is a general, simplified, overview of the hydrologic cycle. Applications to particular watersheds require an in depth identification and analysis of the dominant processes, and a corresponding elimination of relatively unimportant ones. Other versions of Figure 1.2 may be applied in regions with different conditions. For example, there might be a snowpack subsystem that inputs snowmelt to the land surface subsystem; the soil subsystem may return some water back to the land surface (a process called exfiltration), where it is subject to evaporation; in the vicinity of a lake or a river, the soil subsystem may receive water from the river during times of high river stage, in which case the direction of the arrows may reverse; a similar phenomenon may occur between the groundwater and the river subsystem.

Therefore, a particular version of the hydrologic cycle system should be constructed to satisfy: (1) the project objectives, and (2) the specific hydrologic conditions of the watershed in question. The objectives to be accomplished determine the type of hydrologic model to use, the variables involved, and the required data to collect. The hydrologic conditions in a region determine the inner structure of the model and the inter-relation between the different system components. In a multi-disciplinary field as hydrology, the objectives of the hydrologic tasks must be clearly stated *a priori*. For example, the determination of the hydrologic regime in an area requires an entirely different model from that needed for the evaluation of the impact of agricultural tile drainage on streamflow.

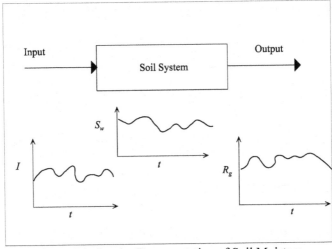

Figure 1.3: System Representation of Soil Moisture

Once the structure of a hydrologic model has been determined, the systems approach method calls for an individual analysis of each subsystem. Figure 1.3 shows an example of the soil subsystem in a watershed. Input variables to the soil system are the infiltration from the land surface, the subsurface flow from nearby rivers and lakes, and the possible capillary rise from the groundwater system. Output variables from the soil system might be composed of groundwater recharge, exfiltration to the land surface system, and subsurface flow to nearby rivers and lakes. The space and time evolution of each of these variables is analyzed and their combined effect on the system variable, in this case soil-water content, is quantified. The output variables are then quantified after determining specific functional relationships between the output variables, the system variable, and the input variables. These functional relationships are derived from the application of fundamental physical, chemical, and biological laws, and the application of mathematical methods. The process is repeated for all the system components. The result is a conceptual model of the hydrologic cycle designed to satisfy a specific set of project objectives. For an in depth treatment of the application of systems theory to hydrology see Singh (1988).

Physical Laws of Application in Hydrology

In the analysis of hydrologic systems, and especially in the determination of functional relationships between input, storage and output variables, several fundamental physical laws are applied. The most important physical laws with application in hydrologic analysis are as follow.

(1) The law of conservation of mass.
Mass is neither created nor destroyed. It is only transformed.

(2) Newton's laws of motion.
Law of conservation of momentum: *the momentum of a body remains constant unless the body is acted upon by a force.*

Force equals mass times acceleration: *the rate of change of momentum of a body is proportional to the net force acting on the body and is in the same direction as the net force.*

Law of action and reaction: *for every net force acting on a body, there is a corresponding force of the same magnitude exerted by the body in the opposite direction.*

(3) Laws of thermodynamics.
Law of conservation of energy: *energy is neither created nor destroyed. It is only transformed.*

Part of the energy transformed into work is lost to other forms of energy: *no process is possible in which the sole result is the absorption of heat and its complete conversion into work.*

(4) Fick's first law of diffusion.
Contaminant substances move from high to low concentration locations: *a diffusion substance moves from where its concentration is larger to where its concentration is smaller at a rate that is proportional to the spatial gradient of concentration.*

Application of these and other biological and chemical laws to different hydrologic processes and systems, in conjunction with the adoption of simplifying assumptions the use of mathematical methods, and the verification with via field experimentation constitutes the scientific method of hydrologic analysis.

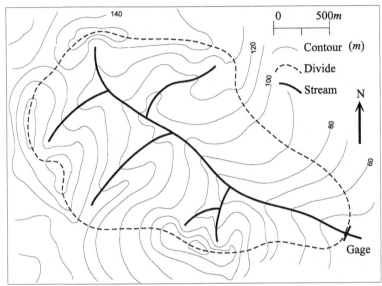

Figure 1.4: Delineation of a Watershed on a Topographic Map

The Concept of a Watershed

In thermodynamics, and in fluid mechanics, you learned that the fundamental laws of physics must be applied to an enclosed system. Similarly, hydrologists usually apply the mass conservation equation and other physical laws to an enclosed geographic region in order to establish its basic hydrologic characteristics. This geographic region is then subdivided into different hydrologic subsystems for specific analyses required by a set of project objectives, as described before. The fundamental geographic unit of hydrologic analysis is the watershed (also called the drainage basin, river basin, or catchment). The watershed is defined as the area that topographically appears to contribute with all the water that flows through a given cross section of a stream. Figure 1.4 shows the watershed contributing to a streamflow gage.

The surface trace of the boundary that delimits a watershed is called a divide, and it marks a boundary between flowing waters. Watershed boundaries do not cut through a stream, and surface waters will not flow through a correctly-drawn divide. In principle, most of the water precipitated within a watershed boundary, eventually passes through the gaging station. The horizontal projection of the area of a watershed is called the drainage area of the stream, or above the stream. The location of the gage is determined by the particular project objectives. Usually a water resource or environmental project is (or will be) near the gage. Once a gage has been located, the delineation of the corresponding watershed is important, since the characteristics of the watershed control many hydrologic processes. In principle, a large portion of the water passing through the stream cross section at the gage originated as precipitation on the drainage area.

To trace the divide of a watershed, a hydrologist needs a topographic map. Starting at the gage, a line is drawn away from the left or right bank, maintaining it always at a 90^0 angle with the contour lines. The hydrologist continues drawing the line until its trend is generally opposite to the direction in which it began and is generally above the headwaters of the stream network. The line is returned to the starting point on the other bank. The divide should pass along the highest points in the region. Mountain tops and mountain ranges should be traced longitudinally along their cliffs. The divide should never cross a stream. By visual inspection, the hydrologist should be able to visualize any drop of water precipitated inside the watershed to eventually appear at the outlet of the watershed (the gage). Delineation of urban watersheds requires storm sewer maps, in addition to topographic maps. In many situations the topographic divide does not coincide with the real divide, because city development may have altered the natural drainage of the watershed to satisfy other technical requirements. Delineation of watershed divides for groundwater studies require geological maps which can provide information of contributing areas from/to surrounding watersheds. Finally, watersheds may be subdivided into sub-watersheds where physical, environmental, or engineering aspects may require more detailed studies of hydrologic characteristics.

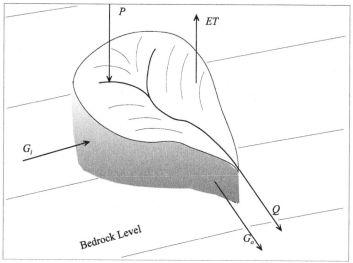

Figure 1.5: General Watershed Water Balance

The Regional Water Balance

The regional water balance is an application of the law of mass conservation to a watershed, a state, a country, a continent or the world (i.e., the global water balance). In the usual case of a watershed water balance (see Figure 1.5), let us imagine that the system boundaries are the watershed boundary, prolonged vertically downward to the bedrock (assuming no significant groundwater flow occurs in the bedrock). Referring to Figure 1.5, a general expression for the watershed water balance is:

$$P + G_i - Q - ET - G_o = \Delta S \qquad (1.1)$$

where

G_i = regional groundwater inflow
G_o = regional groundwater outflow
ET = evapotranspiration (combined evaporation and transpiration)
ΔS = change in the storage of water

Interception has been neglected. The units of each term in equation (1.1) are those of volume (m^3), or volume rate ($m^3/year$, $m^3/month$), in which case these hydrologic quantities report large numbers. However, it is usual to express each of the above quantities in the form of equivalent depth of liquid water assumed uniformly spread over the entire watershed. This is achieved after dividing each quantity by the watershed area expressed in appropriate units. The resulting units are those of depth (mm) or depth rate ($mm/year$, $mm/month$, mm/day, $mm/hour$) depending on the particular application. Water quantities expressed in depth, or depth rate, are smaller and more manageable than those expressed in units of volume. However, small errors in depth translate into large errors in volume.

Example 1.1

A watershed has an area of $A = 350 km^2$ and an estimated mean annual precipitation of $2.4 \times 10^8 m^3/year$. Express the annual precipitation in terms of an equivalent depth of water uniformly spread over the entire watershed.

Solution:

$$P(\frac{mm}{year}) = \frac{P(\frac{m^3}{year})}{A} = \frac{2.4 \times 10^8 \frac{m^3}{year}}{350 km^2 \times \frac{10^6 m^2}{km^2}} \times \frac{1,000 mm}{m} = 685.7 \frac{mm}{year}$$

Thus, an average of 685.7*mm* of precipitation per year would stand over the entire watershed if the water did not infiltrate, evaporate, or runoff.

Example 1.2: Introduction to Maple
Redo Example 1.1 using Maple.

Solution

For all of the computer problems in this book, open the Maple Classic Worksheet, whose commands do not change from version to version. Once open, the Maple worksheet has a series of buttons on the top and a working white area below, just like a word processor. The white portion of the worksheet has a prompt at the cursor, > . If you click the **T** button with the mouse, the prompt disappears and anything you type thereafter is taken as text by Maple. It is always a good idea to type comments prior to each portion of the program. That way a program may be understood by a reader. Go ahead and type a comment. Next, click with the mouse the button that inserts a prompt [>. You will see a prompt > appearing on the next line followed by the cursor. Now you can type a command followed by a semicolon. When the Enter key is pressed, Maple executes the command and displays the output below. Alternatively, if the user wants Maple to execute the command without displaying the output (as when generating thousands of random numbers), a colon must be typed at the end of the command, instead of a semicolon. Below you is a copy of the worksheet.

> **This program expresses precipitation in *mm* of depth**.
> First, enter the data by giving names to the variables and assigning values with a :=
> Area A in km^2, and precipitation P in m^3/year.
> Note that upper case is different from lower case in Maple.
> Spaces between the equal sign and numbers are optional.
> After pressing ENTER, Maple displays the values.
> ```
> > A:=350; P:=2.4E8;
> ```

$$A := 350$$
$$P := 0.24\ 10^9$$

> Express P in depth units by dividing P/A and assign the result to a new variable, lower case p.
> ```
> > p:=P/(A*1.0E6)*1000.;
> ```

$$p := 685.7142857$$

```
> #Note that anything after a pound sign is just a comment
  #Pressing SHIFT-ENTER simultaneously creates a new line
  #Type p followed by a semicolon,
  #and press ENTER to re-check its value
  p;
```

$$685.7142857$$

> Save the worksheet and close.

It is important to remark that, having defined the system and its boundaries, by convention any quantity of water contributing to the system (i.e., any inflow of water) has a positive sign, and any quantity leaving the system (i.e., any outflow of water) has a negative sign. This is important since in certain cases the system boundary is set in such a way that a quantity may have a different sign than that described by equation (1.1). The way in which the system boundary is set depends on the objectives of the project. For example, if the objective is to establish a watershed surface water balance, then the ground surface, rather than the bedrock, should be the lower boundary. In this case the infiltration, I, which does not appear in equation (1.1), is a quantity that represents water leaving the surface, and thus has a negative sign. On the other hand, if the objective is to establish a water balance for the soil system, then the upper boundary should be the ground surface, and the bottom boundary should be the water table. In this case, the infiltration represents water entering the system, and thus has a positive sign. Therefore, consistency between project objectives, system setup, and algebraic signs of hydrologic quantities is important when using water balance calculations.

Another important aspect to remember is that equation (1.1), or any other similar expression involving hydrologic quantities, is a theoretical mass conservation application that assumes accuracy in every quantity. Measurement of hydrologic, climatic, and environmental variables is accomplished through inexact procedures in most practical situations. Even with use of sophisticated instrumentation, most measurement of hydrologic variables is subject to measurement errors varying from 2% to 20%, depending on the quantity, instrument type, and network density. These errors are reflected upon every calculation that uses field-based data. Therefore equation (1.1) is not fully satisfied when real data is substituted into the different variables. In practice, there is a discrepancy term in the right side that accounts for the combined errors in the different measured variables.

Equation (1.1) is the general water balance statement for a watershed. Depending on project objectives, an equivalent water balance equation may be written for a short or a long period of time; for a natural watershed or an artificially-created boundary; for water bodies such as lakes, reservoirs, or groundwater basins; for the region above the ground surface, that below surface, or the entire one. In each case, the system boundaries are different, some hydrologic functions may or may not appear, and the signs of each quantity vary.

Consider for example the water balance of the soil system. Figure 1.7

represents a typical unsaturated zone, or soil profile. The upper boundary is the ground surface, the lower boundary is the water table, and the lateral boundary is the watershed divide. Imagine that the objective of the project is to estimate the effect of a drastic reduction in the watershed infiltration due to a watershed-wide deforestation project. Neglecting the capillary fringe, and the exfiltration flow, and using previously-defined variables, the water balance equation for the soil system is

$$I - ET - Q_s - R_g = \Delta S_w \qquad (1.2)$$

where

ΔS_w = change in soil-water storage

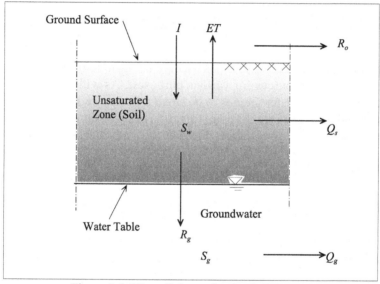

Figure 1.6: Water Balance for the Soil System

Again the units of each variable should be written in the form of depth uniformly spread over the entire watershed. Equation (1.2) could be written on an hourly, daily, monthly of annual basis to observe the time evolution of the different variables. If the balance equation is written for a year, the storage term may be negligible. For instance, if the balance equation is written for a year beginning at the end of the dry season, and ending at the end of the dry season of the following year, there is reason to believe that the net change in the soil-water storage is very small and thus $\Delta S_w \to 0$. This is a typical assumption in annual water balance calculations of surface and subsurface hydrologic systems. In water balance calculations covering shorter periods of time this assumption is not valid.

To estimate the hydrologic effect of deforestation, the hydrologist could set a daily equation (1.2) for a pre-project condition. The daily infiltration based on unaltered soil properties, the overland flow, the soil water content, the groundwater recharge, the subsurface flow, and the groundwater flow are calculated sequentially, using methods later described in this book. Hence, the daily contributions to streamflow are calculated as

$$Q = R_o + Q_s + Q_g \qquad (1.3)$$

Next, the hydrologist would alter the value of the soil parameters according to the perceived effects of deforestation. The calculation above is repeated and a comparison of pre-project versus post-project values of each variable would reveal a possible hydrologic effect of deforestation.

The water balance equation applied to large watersheds and long time intervals (i.e., one annual cycle) is used for the quantitative evaluation of regional water resources for various purposes.. As with the soil water balance, the storage term tends to be small and may be neglected. Thus, if in equation (1.1) we neglect the storage term and assume that for a large watershed and long duration the net groundwater exchange with neighboring watersheds is zero (i.e., $G_i \approx G_o$), then the water balance equation becomes

$$P - ET - Q = 0 \qquad (1.4)$$

Example 1.3
A watershed with a drainage area of $350km^2$ has a mean annual precipitation of 685.7 mm/year. If the mean annual evapotranspiration is 450mm/year, roughly estimate the mean annual watershed streamflow in mm/year and in m^3/year.

Solution
Assuming that the net annual change in storage and the net annual exchange of groundwater with other watersheds is zero, from equation (1.4):

$$Q = P - ET = 685.7 \ \frac{mm}{year} - 450 \ \frac{mm}{year} = 235.7 \ \frac{mm}{year}$$

$$\Rightarrow Q = 235.7\frac{mm}{year} \times \frac{m}{1,000mm} \times 350km^2 \times \frac{10^6 m^2}{km^2} = 82.5 \times 10^6 \frac{m^3}{year}$$

Roughly 82.5 million cubic meters flow annually as streamflow.

Sometimes a water balance equation is used in reservoirs, lakes, streams and groundwater reservoirs for different water-resource purposes. For short periods of time, the change in storage may not be neglected and the water balance equation takes the following form:

$$Q_i - Q_o - E = \frac{\Delta S}{\Delta t} \tag{1.5}$$

where

Q_i = average inflow rate from rivers and groundwater (m^3/s)
Q_o = average outflow rate to rivers and aquifers (m^3/s)
$\Delta S/\Delta t$ = change in storage during Δt (m^3/s)

When equation (1.5) is applied to rivers, the evaporation component may be neglected. For short periods of time Δt (i.e., one day), the groundwater component may be neglected since it constitutes a small component of the total net inflow (outflow).

Example 1.4
The water storage in a river reach at a given time is 50,000 m^3. At the same time the inflow rate into the reach is $25m^3/s$, and the outflow rate is $22m^3/s$. Three hours later, the inflow rate is $23m^3/s$, and the outflow rate is $24m^3/s$. Calculate (1) the change in the storage during the three hours, and (2) the storage volume after the three hours.

Solution
Neglecting groundwater flow (a reasonable assumption for a period of two hours), the average inflow rate is

$$Q_i = \frac{25 \frac{m^3}{s} + 23 \frac{m^3}{s}}{2} = 24 \frac{m^3}{s}$$

Similarly, the average outflow rate is

$$Q_o = \frac{22 \frac{m^3}{s} + 24 \frac{m^3}{s}}{2} = 23 \frac{m^3}{s}$$

From equation (1.5),

$$Q_i - Q_o = \frac{\Delta S}{\Delta t}$$

$$\Rightarrow \Delta S = (Q_i - Q_o)\Delta t$$

$$\Delta S = \left(24 \frac{m^3}{s} - 23 \frac{m^3}{s}\right) \times 3 \ hour \times \frac{3,600 \ s}{hour} = 10,800 \ m^3$$

Note that the change in storage has a positive sign, which implies an increase in storage over the three-hour period. Now the storage after the three hours is calculated from

$$\Delta S = S(t = 3) - S(t = 0)$$

$$\Rightarrow S(t = 3) = S(t = 0) + \Delta S = 50,000 \ m^3 + 10,800 \ m^3 = 60,800 \ m^3$$

Example 1.5
   A lake has a surface area of $18 km^2$. From an inventory of streams flowing into the lake, it is estimated that the average inflow rate in a given day is $45 m^3/s$. In the same day the evaporation rate is about $6.5 mm/day$ and the lake stage (the water level) increases about $15 cm$. Estimate (1) the average flow rate to the main outflowing river in m^3/s, and (2) the outflow volume during the one-day period in m^3.

Solution
   While it is reasonable to neglect groundwater for a short period of one day, the evaporation losses should be considered. From equation (1.5),

$$Q_i - Q_o - E = \frac{\Delta S}{\Delta t}$$

$$\Rightarrow Q_o = Q_i - E - \frac{\Delta s}{\Delta t}$$

$$Q_o = 45 \frac{m^3}{s} - 6.5 \frac{mm}{day} \times \frac{m}{1,000 \ mm} \times \frac{day}{86,400 \ s} \times 18 km^2 \times \frac{10^6 \ m^2}{km^2}$$

$$- 15 \frac{cm}{day} \times \frac{m}{100 \ cm} \times \frac{day}{86,400 \ s} \times 18 \ km^2 \times \frac{10^6 \ m^2}{km^2}$$

$$= 45 \frac{m^3}{s} - 1.35 \frac{m^3}{s} - 31.25 \frac{m^3}{s} = 12.40 \frac{m^3}{s}$$

The outflow volume during one day is

$$Q_o = 12.40 \; \frac{m^3}{s} \times \frac{86,400 \; s}{day} = 1.07 \times 10^6 \; \frac{m^3}{day}$$

Thus, over one million cubic meters of water per day leave the lake. It is also interesting to note that the evaporation rate is about 1.35 $(m^3/s) \times 86,400(s/day) = 116,640(m^3/day)$. This evaporation loss should be included in long term water resources calculation.

Sometimes the objective of a water balance calculation is to estimate the amount of overland runoff (also called direct runoff, effective precipitation, or net rain) for a watershed during a storm. In such case equation (1.1) becomes

$$P - I_n - E - R_o - I - I_d = \Delta S \qquad (1.6)$$

where all the terms are expressed in depth of liquid water uniformly spread over the entire watershed. The change in storage is interpreted as the change in the amount stored in the watershed (including lakes, soils, and aquifers) during the period of the storm. For the short duration of a storm, interception, evaporation, and depression storage are usually neglected and the overland runoff reduces to

$$R_o = P - I - \Delta S \qquad (1.7)$$

For duration periods of longer than the storm duration, it is necessary to include the evapotranspiration, and the calculations are conducted sequentially on a daily, weekly, monthly, or annual basis. Thus, the time coordinate is discretized as $t=0, 1, 2, ,..., i-1, i, i+1, ...$, and the hydrologic variables are estimated for each time interval, i. A large variety of hydrologic models have been developed for this purpose (i.e., Thornthwaite and Mather, 1955; Palmer, 1965; Haan, 1972). We will explore some of these procedures in the following chapters. For the time being, let us introduce a simplified hydrologic model developed by Thomas (1981), called the *abcd* model, for the estimation of streamflow. Referring to Figure 1.6, let us write equation (1.1) as follows:

$$P(i) - ET(i) - I(i) - R_o(i) = \Delta S_w = S_w(i) - S_w(i-1) \qquad (1.8)$$

where the indexes i, $i-1$ represent the hydrologic functions calculated at the end of time i or $i-1$, respectively. Equation (1.8) may be written as

$$\big(P(i) + S_w(i-1)\big) - \big(ET(i) + S_w(i)\big) = R_o(i) + I(i) \tag{1.9}$$

Thomas defined the first two terms in the left side of equation (1.9) as the available water, $W(i)$, at any given time, that is

$$W(i) = P(i) + S_w(i-1) \tag{1.10}$$

and the last two terms in the left side of equation (1.9) as

$$Y(i) = ET(i) + S_w(i) \tag{1.11}$$

During each time interval, the soil moisture is assumed to decay exponentially according to the following equation:

$$S_w(i) = Y(i)e^{-PE(i)/b} \tag{1.12}$$

where
$PE(t)=$*potential evapotranspiration* assuming a wet soil

The difference between potential evapotranspiration, $PE(t)$, and actual evapotranspiration, $ET(t)$, is the amount of water available for evapotranspiration. Potential evapotranspiration is a theoretical, maximum possible, amount assuming an abundant supply of water.

Thomas suggested that the relationship between $W(t)$ and $Y(t)$ is of the form

$$Y(i) = \left(\frac{W(i) + b}{2a}\right) - \left[\left(\frac{W(i) + b}{2a}\right)^2 - \frac{W(i)b}{a}\right]^{0.5} \tag{1.13}$$

where a and b are parameters to be determined from measured precipitation, evapotranspiration, and soil moisture in the watershed. If we substitute equations (1.10) and (1.11) into equation (1.9) we get

$$\big(W(i) - Y(i)\big) = R_o(i) + I(i) \tag{1.14}$$

In other words, the difference between $W(i)$ and $Y(i)$ is split between overland flow $R_o(i)$ and infiltration $I(i)$, which subsequently contributes to groundwater recharge $R_g(i)$. The allocation between overland flow and groundwater recharge is suggested as follows:

$$R_o(i) = (1 - c)\big(W(i) - Y(i)\big)$$
$$R_g(i) = c\big(W(i) - Y(i)\big) \tag{1.15}$$

where c is a parameter related to the fraction of mean streamflow that comes from groundwater. Similarly, the groundwater flow may be expressed as a direct function of the groundwater storage:

$$Q_g(i) = d.S_g(i)$$
(1.16)

where d is a model parameter representing the fraction of groundwater storage discharged. The change in groundwater storage could be expressed as a function of groundwater recharge. The water balance equation for the groundwater reservoir may be written as

$$R_g(i) - Q_g(i) = \Delta S_g = S_g(i) - S_g(i-1)$$
(1.17)

Substituting equation (1.17) into equation (1.16), one obtains an expression for the groundwater storage:

$$S_g(i) = \frac{R_g(i) + S_g(i-1)}{d + 1}$$
(1.18)

Finally, the streamflow contribution at the end of period i is obtained from

$$Q(i) = R_o(i) + Q_g(i)$$
(1.19)

after neglecting the subsurface flow component.

The values of the parameters a, b, c, and d are obtained from calibrating the model from the known data for the water balance components in the watershed. Alley (1984) estimated the following mean monthly values from the study of 10 sites in New Jersey, each having a record of 50 years: $a=0.992$, $b=30$, $c=0.16$, and $d=0.26$. It is found that overland flow estimates are very sensitive to the parameter a.

The application of the Thomas model requires values of precipitation, initial estimates of soil-water storage $S_w(0)$, and groundwater storage $S_g(0)$. Thomas suggests the use of optimized values from the watershed in study. Alley (1984) suggests the adoption of some trial values of $S_w(0)$ and $S_g(0)$, and to simulate data for some period (i.e., a year in monthly calculations) prior to the beginning of the period of interest. The potential evapotranspiration, $PE(i)$, is calculated by the Thornthwaite method (see chapter 3).

Table 1.1: Data for Example 1.6

Month	$P(i)$ (*mm*)	$PE(i)$ (*mm*)
J	55	32
F	72	45
M	101	60
A	110	85
M	220	122
J	135	146
J	43	166
A	25	201
S	78	154
O	97	101
N	140	55
D	99	43

Example 1.6

Table 1.1 shows monthly precipitation and calculated potential evapotranspiration for a 260-km^2 watershed in the year 2007. The Thomas model parameters are a=0.9, b=20mm, c=0.1, and d=0.1. The soil-water content at the end of December, 2006, is estimated as 150mm, and the groundwater storage at the same time is 200mm. For each month calculate (1) the soil-water content, (2) the overland flow, (3) the groundwater recharge, (4) the groundwater storage, (5) the groundwater flow, and (6) the total streamflow. Express all quantities in *mm*.

Solution

Set i=1 for the month of January, 2007. The available water is calculated from equation (1.10) as

$$W(1) = P(1) + S_w(0) = 55 \ mm + 150 \ mm = 205 \ mm$$

From equation (1.13), the consumption of water is

$$Y(1) = \frac{W(1)+b}{2a} - \left[\left(\frac{W(1)+b}{2a} \right)^2 - \frac{W(1)b}{a} \right]^{0.5}$$

$$Y(1) = \frac{205mm+20mm}{2\times0.9} - \left[\left(\frac{205mm+20mm}{2\times0.9} \right)^2 - \frac{205mm\times20mm}{0.9} \right]^{0.5}$$

$$Y(1) = 19.8mm$$

At the end of January, the soil-water content is, from equation (1.12),

$$S_w(1) = Y(1)e^{-PE(1)/b} = 19.8mm \times e^{-32mm/20mm} = 4.0 \ mm$$

At this point, it is possible to calculate the actual evapotranspiration, $ET(1)$, from equation (1.11). However this item is not requested in the problem. The overland flow and groundwater recharge are determined from equations (1.15):

$$R_o(1) = (1 - c)(W(1) - Y(1)) = (1 - 0.1) \times (205mm - 19.8mm) = 166.7mm$$

$$R_g(1) = c(W(1) - Y(1)) = 0.1 \times (205mm - 19.8mm) = 18.5 \ mm$$

The groundwater storage is now estimated from equation (1.18) as

$$S_g(1) = \frac{R_g(1) + S_g(0)}{d + 1} = \frac{18.5mm + 200mm}{0.1 + 1} = 198.6mm$$

The groundwater flow is calculated from equation (1.16) as

$$Q_g(1) = d.S_g(1) = 0.1 \times 198.6mm = 19.9mm$$

Finally, the total streamflow for the month of January is calculated from equation (1.19) as

$$Q(1) = R_o(1) + Q_g(1) = 166.7mm + 19.9mm = 186.6mm$$

This is the total streamflow expressed in units of water depth over the entire watershed. To express it in terms of average flow rate, one has to multiply by the watershed area:

$$Q(1) = 186.6\frac{mm}{month} \times \frac{month}{31day} \times \frac{day}{86,400s} \times \frac{m}{1,000mm} \times 260km^2 \times \frac{10^6m^2}{km^2}$$

$$Q(1) = 18.1\frac{m^3}{s}$$

For the month of February, set $i=2$, use $S_w(1)$ and $S_g(1)$ as the initial soil-water content and groundwater storage, respectively, and repeat all of the above calculations. Table 1.2 summarizes the results as calculated with a spreadsheet. All the values are given in *mm*.

Table 1.2: Results of Example 1.6 (all values in *mm*)

i	1	2	3	4	5	6	7	8	9	10	11	12
M	J	F	M	A	M	J	J	A	S	O	N	D
$W(i)$	205.0	76.0	103.0	111.0	220.0	135.0	43.0	25.0	78.0	97.0	140.0	100.0
$Y(i)$	19.8	19.3	19.5	19.6	19.8	19.7	18.6	16.7	19.4	19.5	19.7	19.5
$S_w(i)$	4.0	2.0	1.0	0.3	0.0	0.0	0.0	0.0	0.0	0.1	1.3	2.3
$R_o(i)$	167.0	51.0	75.2	82.3	181.	104.	22.0	7.5	52.8	69.7	108.0	72.7
$R_g(i)$	18.5	5.7	8.4	9.1	20.1	11.5	2.4	0.8	5.9	7.8	12.0	8.1
$S_g(i)$	199.0	186.0	177.0	169.0	172.0	167.0	154.0	140.0	133.0	128.0	127.0	123.0
$Q_g(i)$	19.9	18.6	17.6	16.9	17.2	16.6	15.4	14.0	13.3	12.8	12.7	12.3
$Q(i)$	187.0	69.6	92.8	99.2	197.7	120.0	37.4	21.5	66.1	82.5	121.0	85.0

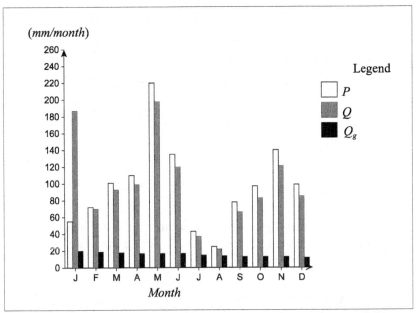

Figure 1.7: Watershed Monthly Streamflow and Groundwater Yield

The results could be used to observe the time evolution of the different components of the hydrologic cycle in the watershed. It is interesting to note that the initial estimate of soil-water storage, as conceived from considerations of soil depth dimensions, is probably too high in this watershed. Assuming the values of the parameters a, b, c, and d are correct (another possibility of error), the calculations suggest that a value of 5 is reasonable. If the initial estimate is correct, then the calculated streamflow values higher than those of precipitation imply that the water comes from storage accumulated from a previous 2006 wet year.

It is also interesting to observe that during the summer months groundwater flow constitutes the most important component of streamflow. This is an important characteristic of groundwater reservoirs in watersheds. Groundwater preserves the flow in rivers during periods of little or no rainfall. Finally, a graphical representation of the above values illustrates the features of the time variability of hydrologic functions. For example, Figure 1.7 shows the monthly values of precipitation, total streamflow, and groundwater flow for this watershed. By repeating the calculations and plotting the results for a typical dry year, an average year, and a wet year, a picture of the hydrologic response of the watershed useful in water management decisions could be obtained. Similar graphs could be produced for the time variability of soil moisture, evapotranspiration and groundwater storage.

Example 1.7

Write a Maple program for Example 1.6 and run it.

Solution

Open the classic Worksheet, enter the data, and write commands for each of the equations as shown below. Figure 1.8 shows the graphics.

```
Program Application of the Thomas Model for Watershed Water Balance
Enter data
> #A=Area (km^2); a, b, c, and d are the parameters.
  A:=260.0: a:=0.9: b:=20.0: c:=0.1: d:=0.1:
  #Swo=initial soil moisture, Sgo=initial groundwater storage
  Swo:=150: Sgo:=200:
  #P[i]=Precipitation vector; note that data is entered
  #inside square parentheses and separated by commas
  P:=[55,72,101,110,220,135,43,25,78,97,140,99]:
  #PE[i]=Potential evapotranspiration vector
  PE:=[32,45,60,85,122,146,166,201,154,101,55,43]:
```

Note that subindex variables go from i=1 to i=12 in Maple.
That is why the initial soil moisture and initial groundwater storage, which would correspond to i=0, were given different names.
As a double check, verify that PE[1]=32 and PE[4]=85 below.

```
> PE[1]; PE[4];
```

$$32$$
$$85$$

The next section calculates all variables for the first month, i=1. All quantities in *mm*
Sw[i]= soil moisture, Ro[i]=overland runoff, Rg[i]=groundwater recharge,
Sg[i]=groundwater storage, Qg[i]=groundwater flow, Q[i]=streamflow
Make sure you always name each variable with the same combination of upper
and lower-case letters. Consistency is paramount.

```
> W[1]:=P[1]+Swo:
  Y[1]:=(W[1]+b)/(2*a)-(((W[1]+b)/(2*a))^2-W[1]*b/a)^0.5:
  Sw[1]:=Y[1]*exp(-PE[1]/b):
  Ro[1]:=(1-c)*(W[1]-Y[1]):
  Rg[1]:=c*(W[1]-Y[1]):
  Sg[1]:=(Rg[1]+Sgo)/(d+1):
  Qg[1]:=d*Sg[1]:
  Q[1]:=Ro[1]+Qg[1]:
```

Repeat all calculations for all months, i=2 to i=12. Note that because Maple does not allow
a subindex i=0, we had to calculate the first month separately.

```
> for i from 2 to 12 do
    W[i]:=P[i]+Sw[i-1]:
    Y[i]:=(W[i]+b)/(2*a)-(((W[i]+b)/(2*a))^2-W[i]*b/a)^0.5:
    Sw[i]:=Y[i]*exp(-PE[i]/b):
    Ro[i]:=(1-c)*(W[i]-Y[i]):
    Rg[i]:=c*(W[i]-Y[i]):
    Sg[i]:=(Rg[i]+Sg[i-1])/(d+1):
    Qg[i]:=d*Sg[i]:
    Q[i]:=Ro[i]+Qg[i]:
  end do:
```

Prepare data for plotting by creating vectors of (x,y) coordinates.
For precipitation, create a vector p:=[[1, P[1]], [2, P[2]], . . . , [12, P[12]].
To do this, use the sequence function, seq(,) *inside* a vector [ ].
The sequence function has two arguments: the first one is a command with subindex variable;
the second argument determines the ranges of values of the subindex variable.

```
> p:=[seq([i,P[i]],i=1..12)];
```

$p := [[1, 55], [2, 72], [3, 101], [4, 110], [5, 220], [6, 135], [7, 43], [8, 25], [9, 78], [10, 97],$
    $[11, 140], [12, 99]]$

Repeat for the other variables.

```
> q:=[seq([i,Q[i]],i=1..12)]:
  sg:=[seq([i,Sg[i]],i=1..12)]:
  qg:=[seq([i,Qg[i]],i=1..12)]:
```

On the same graph plot all functions. To do this, ask Maple to prepare each graph,
end each command line with a colon, and when you are ready to display, ask Maple
to display everything and end the command with a semicolon.

```
> G1:=plot(p,color=black,linestyle=1,legend=["P"]):
  G2:=plot(q,color=black,linestyle=2,legend=["Q"]):
  G3:=plot(sg,color=black,linestyle=3,legend=["Sg"]):
  G4:=plot(qg,color=black,linestyle=4,legend=["Qg"]):
  plots[display](G1,G2,G3,G4,labels=["Month"," (mm)"]);
```

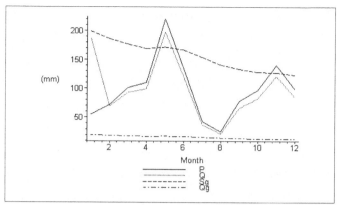

Figure 1.8: Graphics Output of Example 1.7

QUESTIONS AND PROBLEMS

1.1 Cite three other examples of ancient civilizations that achieved an important control of water resources. In each case give the name of the culture, briefly explain the water resources accomplishment, and cite a complete bibliography.

1.2 Cite five examples, not listed in this chapter, of possible applications of hydrology. Write a sentence describing each.

1.3 Write one paragraph describing the relation between hydrology and the environmental sciences.

1.4 What is the difference between hydrology and hydraulics? Qualify your answer with concepts and examples.

1.5 What is the difference between hydrology and water resources engineering? Qualify your answer with concepts and examples.

1.6 Photocopy the map in Figure 1.9, delineate the watershed boundary corresponding to the streamflow gage, and estimate the watershed area in km^2 using the dot grid method: (1) Place a sheet of transparent paper over the topographic map, fix it, and redraw the watershed boundary on the transparent paper. (2) Place a grid of graphics paper under the transparent paper with the watershed boundary and fix it. Count the number of squares or "dots" inside the watershed. For the partial squares, in principle the number of "half" squares outside the boundary would tend to balance with the number of "half" squares inside. (3) Establish a proportionality relation between the scale of the map and the grid; in other words, graphically count the number of grid squares corresponding to $2,500\, km^2$ ($50km$ times $50km$ on the map). (4) Knowing the relationship between the map scale and the grid, proportionally calculate the watershed planimetric area in km^2.

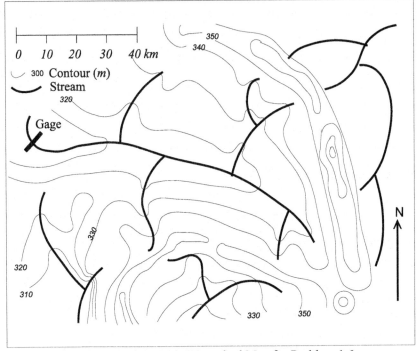

Figure 1.9: Watershed Map for Problem 1.6

1.7 A watershed has an area of A=$220\, km^2$ and an estimated mean annual precipitation of $3.6 \times 10^8 m^3/year$. Express the annual precipitation in terms of an equivalent depth of water uniformly spread over the entire watershed ($mm/year$).

1.8 A watershed has an area of A=$220km^2$ and a mean annual evapotranspiration of $1450mm$. Express it in m^3.

1.9 A watershed has an area of A=$250km^2$, a mean annual precipitation of $1520mm$, and a mean annual evapotranspiration of $1340mm$. Estimate the mean annual watershed streamflow in $mm/year$ and in $m^3/year$.

1.10 The storage in a river reach at a given time is $3 \times 10^6 m^3$. At the same time the inflow rate into the reach is $34m^3/s$, and the outflow rate is $40m^3/s$. Four hours later, the inflow rate is $38m^3/s$, and the outflow rate is $46m^3/s$. Calculate (1) the change in the storage during the four hours, and (2) the storage volume after the four hours.

1.11 The storage in a river reach at a given time is $12\times10^6 m^3$. At the same time the inflow rate into the reach is $14m^3/s$, and the outflow rate is $20m^3/s$. Four hours later, the inflow rate is $18m^3/s$, and the outflow rate is $26m^3/s$. The average groundwater flow to the river is about $9m^3/s$. Calculate (1) the change in the storage during the four hours, and (2) the storage volume after the four hours.

1.12 A lake has a surface area of $15km^2$. From an inventory of streams flowing into a lake, it is estimated that the average inflow rate in a given day is $48m^3/s$. In the same day, the evaporation rate is about $5.0mm/day$ and the lake stage (the water level) increases about $10cm$. Neglecting groundwater flow, estimate (1) the average flow rate to the main outflowing river in m^3/s, and (2) the outflow volume during the one-day period in m^3.

1.13 A lake has a surface area of $15km^2$. The average inflow rate in a given day is $48m^3/s$. In the same day, the evaporation rate is $5.0mm/day$ and the lake level *decreases* $2cm$. Neglecting groundwater flow, estimate (1) the average flow rate to the main outflowing river in m^3/s, and (2) the outflow volume during the one-day period in m^3.

1.14 A lake has a surface area of $15km^2$. The inflow rate from streams is $48m^3/s$ in a given day. In the same day, the evaporation rate is about $5.0mm/day$, the lake level increases about $10cm$, and the average groundwater inflow into the lake is about $3.5m^3/s$. Estimate (1) the average flow rate to the main outflowing river in m^3/s, and (2) the outflow volume during the one-day period in m^3.

1.15 A lake has a surface area of $14km^2$. From an inventory of streams flowing into a lake, it is estimated that the average inflow rate in a given day is $50m^3/s$; the average outflow rate is $25m^3/s$; and in the same day lake stage (the water level) increases $14.7cm$. Neglecting groundwater flow, estimate the average evaporation rate in mm/day.

1.16 A lake has a surface area of $14km^2$. In a given day, the inflow rate from streams is $42m^3/s$; the outflow rate is $25m^3/s$; the groundwater inflow rate is $9m^3/s$; and the lake stage (the water level) increases $14.7cm$. Estimate the average evaporation rate in mm/day.

1.17 Using a spreadsheet, redo Example 1.6 if the parameter values are $a=0.98$, $b=25mm$, $c=0.10$, $d=0.35$, and the rest of the data as before.

1.18 Write a computer program using Maple to solve Example 1.6 if the parameter values are $a=0.98$, $b=25mm$, $c=0.10$, $d=0.35$, and the rest of the data as before.

1.19 For Problem 1. 18, plot P, Q, and Q_g respectively versus time in one graph. State your conclusions about the hydrologic response of the watershed (i.e., describe the "regime": wet months, dry months, importance of groundwater, etc.).

1.20 For problem 1.18, plot in a single graph P, R_o, and R_g. State your conclusions about the hydrologic regime of the partition between overland flow and groundwater recharge.

1.21 For problem 1.18, plot in a single graph R_g, S_g, and Q_g. State your conclusions about the hydrologic regime of the groundwater reservoir.

1.22 For problem 1.18, plot in a single graph P, S_w, R_o, and R_g. State your conclusions about the hydrologic regime of the soil reservoir.

"This that we call rainfall can make days seem short and nights seem long.

"A spring shower is like an imperial decree which confers an honor; a summer shower is like an official pardon for a convicted criminal; an autumn shower is like a dirge.

"A rainy day in the spring is propitious to reading; a rainy day in the summer is good for playing chess; a rainy day in the fall is favorable to organize things in the attic and the basement; and a rainy day in the winter is fortunate to enjoying wine. . ."

"About Rain" From the 17th century epigrams of Chang Ch'ao. In The Importance of Living by Lin Yutang, Sudamericana, Buenos Aires, Argentina, 1943.

2 PRECIPITATION

2.1 THE OCCURRENCE OF PRECIPITATION

Formation of Precipitation

Precipitation is the fundamental hydrologic function. It replenishes rivers, lakes, soil moisture, and aquifers. Of interest to the hydrologist is the form, spatial distribution, and temporal variability of precipitation in a given watershed or geographical region. Qualifying and quantifying these features are of fundamental importance in regime characterization and in many hydrologic applications. While meteorologists study the occurrence of atmospheric moisture and the physics of precipitation as it relates to climatic conditions, hydrologists are mainly concerned with precipitation once it approaches the surface of the earth. Nevertheless, a basic understanding of the origins and formation of precipitation helps in the interpretation and extrapolation of precipitation characteristics.

The formation of precipitation requires an accumulation of water vapor in the atmosphere. Water vapor results from the processes of natural evaporation and water vapor transport caused by the wind. The fraction of water vapor in the atmosphere is very small as compared to quantities of other gases present. A mass of air can hold only certain amount of water vapor. The maximum amount of water vapor the air can hold is called the saturation water vapor. When the amount of water vapor exceeds the saturation water vapor, condensation begins to occur and the process of precipitation may be initiated. The saturation water vapor is a function of air temperature. As the temperature increases, so does the saturation water vapor. Similarly, as the temperature decreases, so does the saturation water vapor. It follows that when a mass of air is cooled, the excess of water vapor over the decreasing amount of saturation water vapor begins to condensate.

From above, the first requisite to the formation of precipitation is the *cooling of moist air masses*. Air can be cooled in several ways. Adiabatic cooling by reduction of pressure through lifting is by far the most important natural process by which large masses of air can be cooled rapidly enough to produce appreciable amounts of precipitation. The rate of precipitation depends on the rate of cooling and on the rate of inflow of water vapor into the air mass to replace the water vapor being transformed into precipitation.

The lifting required for the cooling can be caused by horizontal convergence, frontal lifting, or *orographic lifting*. Horizontal convergence is caused by the flow and concentration of air in a low pressure area, which forces the masses of air upward. Frontal lifting takes place when a warm mass of air flows toward a colder, and denser, mass of air. The colder mass of air acts as a wedge and the warm air is forced upward. The surface of separation between the two different air masses is called a frontal surface. A frontal surface slopes upward toward the colder air mass. This slope is usually so small that the frontal surface covers large portions of the land. The intersection of the frontal surface with the ground is called a front (see Figure 2.1). Orographic lifting occurs when air flowing toward an orographic barrier (i.e., a mountain range) is forced upward in order to pass over it. The slopes of orographic barriers are steeper than those of frontal surface and therefore the air is cooled much faster.

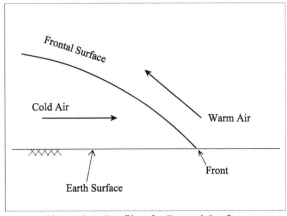

Figure 2.1: Profile of a Frontal Surface

The second requisite for the occurrence of precipitation is the *condensation of water vapor* into liquid or solid form. This is a change of phase from water vapor into liquid droplets, or at low temperatures from water vapor into crystals. This usually results in the formation of clouds, which are airborne liquid-water droplets, ice crystals, or a mixture of the two. Condensation is the result of saturation of air masses. However, condensation requires not only saturation, but also the presence of solid nuclei around which the droplet or crystal begins to grow. There are enough solid particles in the atmosphere to produce condensation when the air reaches saturation. Products of combustion and salt particles from the sea encourage the condensation process. Thus, a byproduct of air pollution is the abnormal enhancement of condensation visually observable in the form of fog near areas of contamination. As an application of this principle, the atmosphere may be seeded with artificial nuclei for the purposes of inducing precipitation over a particular area. Among the legal and environmental issues associated with artificially induced precipitation are the effects such practices have on the mean annual precipitation of an area and its time distribution. Fortunately, humans have learned that although they may affect the rate of condensation, their control over precipitation variables is not direct. This is an active area of research which may yield important results in the future.

The final requisite for the occurrence of precipitation is the growth of *water droplets* of crystals to a critical mass sufficient to overcome the upward currents of air. The rate of precipitation from a cloud depends on the velocity of upward currents producing the cooling, the rate of growth of the raindrops heavy enough to overcome the vertical currents, and the rate of water vapor inflow replacing the precipitated water.

Types of Precipitation

Precipitation may occur in the form of rain, snow, hail, drizzle, and sleet. The form of precipitation depends on the rate of cooling and the air temperature. More important than the form of precipitation is an understanding of the basic storm types, which depend on the cooling conditions. In this respect, the three major categories of precipitation are: *cyclonic precipitation, orographic precipitation,* and *convective precipitation.*

As stated before, cyclonic precipitation is the one associated with horizontal convergence and frontal lifting. It usually produces patterns of precipitation that cover large portions of the land, long storm durations, and low intensities of precipitation. Cyclonic precipitation is a regional event that may be easily tracked by surface or satellite radar sensors. Because of its large size, the generation of cyclonic precipitation systems may be detected early in its development. The system may be observed over a period of time for variables such as precipitation rate, total precipitation depth, and storm duration. Other variables concerning the velocity of movement of the storm and its mean geographical direction may be monitored. This information may be extrapolated with the aid of mathematical models and used for weather forecasting purposes.

Orographic precipitation results from the mechanical lifting of horizontal air currents over natural barriers such as mountain ranges. Factors that are important in this process include land elevation, local slopes, orientation of land slope, and distance from the water vapor source. Elevation above the sea level is an important factor affecting the magnitude of precipitation. Figure 2.2 shows a typical relationship between elevation above the sea level and mean annual precipitation. Precipitation increases with altitude over the first few hundreds of meters of elevation, beyond which there might be a decrease in the precipitation magnitude. Several rain gages in a watershed, each exhibiting good long-term data, may be used to define such a relationship. This relationship may then be used to extrapolate precipitation data to regions with scarce information in the watershed, or to fill in missing data values in existing rain gages. Relationships between monthly precipitation and elevation may not be as well defined and should be used with caution.

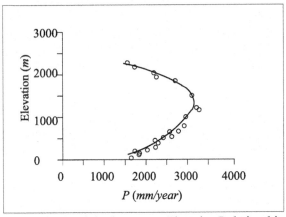

Figure 2.2: Precipitation versus Elevation Relationship

Convective precipitation is typical of tropical regions. It results from the heating of the air at the interface with the ground surface. Heated air expands and loses density, while receiving a substantial amount of water vapor via evaporation from soil moisture. The warm moisture-laden air begins to rise. At the same time, pronounced vertical currents are developed. As the warm air rises, dynamic cooling takes place, causing condensation and precipitation. Convective precipitation usually generates storms of extremely high intensity, but of relatively short duration as compared to cyclonic storms. Convective precipitation covers relatively small areas. Because of its small size and the strong winds accompanying convective precipitation development, highly mobile thunderstorms are usually generated. This results in rainfall phenomena that are difficult to forecast by conventional large-scale measurement devices, and that produces high spatial variability of precipitation amounts.

2.2 MEASUREMENT OF PRECIPITATION

As described in chapter 1, hydrologic variables are measured either in accumulated volume of water, or in liquid-water depth assumed uniformly distributed over a reception area. Precipitation is measured with rain gages. A rain gage is an instrument that captures precipitation and measures its accumulated volume during a certain period of time. The precipitation depth for the same period is equal to the accumulated volume divided by the collection area of the gage. Any open container with vertical sides could be used as a rain gage. However, to compare measurements of precipitation with those obtained elsewhere, it is necessary to use standard equipment with similar characteristics of size and shape.

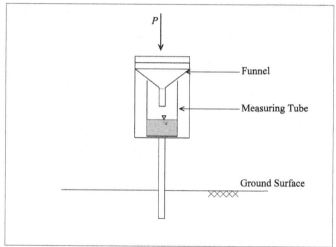

Figure 2.3: Cross Section of a Non-Recording Rain Gage

Rain gages can be of two basic types: non-recording and recording. A non-recording gage measures the total rainfall depth accumulated during a period of time. This period may be 12 hours or one day. There are many kinds of non-recording rain gages, depending on the manufacturer and the standards utilized by the monitoring agency. Figure 2.3 is an illustration of a typical non-recording rain gage. It is an aluminum cylinder of about $25cm$ in diameter located about one meter from the ground surface. Rain is caught by the top collector and funneled into a measuring tube. The cross-sectional area of the measuring tube is one-tenth of that of the collector. Consequently, rainfall depths are amplified ten times as they pass from the collector to the measuring tube, thus increasing the accuracy of the measurement. At measuring time, the observer introduces a stage meter into the measuring tube and records the water depth on a sheet. The stage meter has been properly graduated in millimeters and fractions of millimeters scaled up by a factor of ten. Finally, the measuring tube is emptied. Figure 2.4 shows a plastic rain gage.

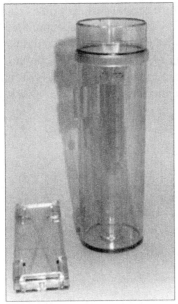 

Figure 2.4: A Plastic Rain Gage   Figure 2.5: Inside of a Tipping Bucket Rain
  (*courtesy of NovaLynx Corp.*)   Gage (*courtesy of NovaLynx Corp.*)

The non-recording rain gages are inexpensive and simple to operate. However, they are only useful when periodic total rain depths are required. A recording rain gage continuously registers the rate of rainfall and its time of occurrence. It provides not only a measure of rainfall depth, but also of rainfall intensity. Recording rain gages can be of the tipping bucket type, the weighing mechanisms type, or the float chamber type. The tipping bucket gage (Figure 2.5) features a two-compartment receptacle, or bucket, pivoted on a knife edge. The gage is calibrated so that when one of the compartments is full of water and the other is empty, the bucket overbalances and tips. First the rain is funneled into one of the compartments, while the second remains empty. When the first compartment is full, the bucket tips, emptying its contents into a container and at the same time placing the second compartment into filling position. The tipping closes an electric circuit, which drives a pen that records on a strip chart attached to a clock-driven revolving drum. Each electrical contact representing a specific amount of rain is recorded. The alternate filling and emptying of the two compartments continue until the rain ceases. Although the tipping bucket gage is durable, simple to operate, and reliable, it does not record properly during periods of intense rainfall.

The weighing gage has a device that weighs the rain or snow collected in a bucket. As it fills with precipitation, the bucket moves downward and its movement is transmitted to a pen on a strip-chart recorder. These gages are useful in cold climates that require measurements of rain as well as snow. However, they are sensitive to wind instability, which produces erratic traces on the chart.

Float gages are water level recording instruments. A float located inside a chamber is connected to a pen on a strip-chart recorder. The float rises as the collected rainwater enters the chamber, and the rise of the float is plotted on the chart. As the level of the water reaches a maximum level, a siphoning mechanism empties the chamber and returns the pen to a zero position on the strip chart. This type of rain gage operates normally in warm climates. In cold climates and during severe storms, water freezing and the siphoning mechanism may produce inaccurate measurements.

Traditional rain gages can be implemented with a telemetric system to automatically transmit rainfall information. This produces a self-reporting gaging station whereby the tipping bucket mechanism generates a digital input signal whenever one millimeter of rainfall drains through the funnel assembly. The signal from the gage is automatically transmitted to a receiving station, where it records the station number and an accumulated amount of rainfall. The receiving station records the time at which the message was received and rainfall rates for desired periods can be calculated accordingly. Self-reporting gages can easily be incorporated into real-time monitoring systems that can be used in a variety of forecasting and simulation modes (Strangeways, 1985).

Weather-radar systems are useful tools for measuring spatial distribution and temporal variability of rain storms. Radar is a device that emits a regular succession of pulses of electro-magnetic radiation from an antenna. In between the emissions, the antenna becomes a receiver of the energy of the emitted pulses scattered by various targets. The returned signals are displayed on the radar scope. The wavelength of the emitted signal may be adjusted to detect raindrops of various sizes (Battan, 1974), and in particular high intense storms, which are likely to produce extreme floods. The importance of the radar lies in its ability to detect at distance and map the distribution of a storm. Subsequent observations of the radar scope produce a reconstructed picture of the storm movement, from which variables such as storm velocity and rainfall intensity are estimated to feed computer simulations of weather forecast. The difficulty with radar measurements is the possibility of missing the target by improperly orienting the radar beam, especially at long ranges. Radar reflectivity could be used to estimate precipitation intensity. However, these estimates have to be calibrated with ground rain gages.

Satellite measurements of precipitation have many of the advantages exhibited by ground-based radar measurements. In addition, satellite-mounted probes can detect a variety of electromagnetic signals from various bands of the spectrum, which form a more detailed picture of the clouds' physics as it relates to the generation of precipitation (Collier, 1985). In addition, the privileged position of the satellite system may detect the origin and evolution of large storm systems, which provide valuable information in weather forecasting. However, estimates of precipitation intensity, like ground-based radar estimates, must be calibrated with conventional rain gages. Remote sensing is a rapidly developing field, and an active area of research. It is expected that some of these limitations will be overcome in the near future.

2.3 ANALYSIS OF POINT PRECIPITATION

As the name implies, the analysis of point precipitation is the study of precipitation information at a fixed location (i.e., an individual rain gage). Two general kinds of analyses are performed: analysis of the quality of precipitation data, and analysis of the time distribution of precipitation.

Quality of Precipitation Data

Precipitation data is available from a multitude of private and governmental organizations. Most countries have a national official institution in charge of the collection of precipitation and other meteorological information. However, depending on the country and the location within a country, institutions with various degrees of interest in meteorological, agricultural, hydrological, and environmental projects are involved in the collection and distribution of precipitation information. Although progress has been made by the World Meteorological Organization towards an adoption of international standard precipitation information practices, there is a wide range of variability in the procedures, accuracy, and instrumentation. Thus, comparison of precipitation information is often a difficult task.

There are many uncertainties associated with precipitation data. Some refer to the type of instrumentation used. For example, precipitation information is related to the size and the orientation of the gage receptacle. Some rain gages are provided with small structures that protect the receptacle from wind instability. The height of the receptacle is another important variable. The location of the rain gage with respect to obstructions such as trees and other structures affect the measurement. During high intensity rainfall events, the splash may affect the readings. Depending on the frequency of gage readings, accuracy may be affected by evaporation of some of the water between subsequent observations. Systematic measurement errors are another source of uncertainty, because of the mechanics of operation of certain instruments. The observer also plays an important role in the generation of random errors of observation, or in systematic errors of reading and transcription. Finally, errors caused by low intensity rain, below the resolution of the instrument are common.

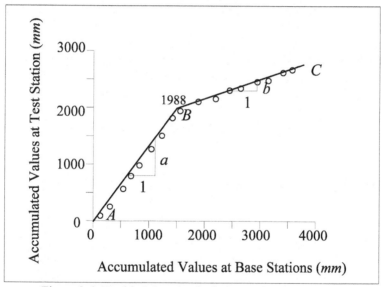

Figure 2.6: Double-Mass Analysis for a Given Rain Gage

Given the importance of precipitation data in any hydrologic calculation, it is crucial to investigate the quality of data reported by each rain gage before it is used. If the information is to be used in the design of a large-scale water resources structure, it is important to employ good quality of precipitation information. Regardless of the degree of sophistication of subsequent hydrologic analysis, the results of any calculation based on poor-quality data are bound to be inaccurate.

It is recommended that the hydrologist begins the analysis of precipitation data by studying the precipitation station itself. In other words, investigate the history of information provided by the rain gage; determine how long it has been in operation; the type of instrumentation used; and the consistency of maintenance and operation. Rain gages operated for short periods of time, are poorly maintained, or are often moved yield unreliable information. Information from these rain gages should be eliminated from the study, or at best used with caution.

The double-mass analysis is a test to detect whether the precipitation data of a station is consistent. The test uncovers significant changes in observation practices. In this analysis, a plot is made of accumulated annual or seasonal precipitation values at a site being studied for consistency (the test station) against the current accumulated values of several surrounding stations (base stations), which exhibit good quality data. Specifically, the mean precipitation is used in the accumulative values for the plot (Figure 2.6). If the data is consistent, a straight line will fit the points. Inconsistent data, on the other hand, will exhibit a change in the slope or a break at a point where changes in observational procedures, instrument moving, or instrument damage occurred. Changes in meteorological conditions will equally affect all stations involved in the test and will not appear in the double-mass graph.

Table 2.1: Annual Precipitation Data for Example 2.1 (*mm*)

Year	P_1	P_2	P_3	P_4	P_5	$\bar{P}_{base}$	$\sum P_1$	$\sum \bar{P}_{base}$
1979	668	759	624	929	808	780	668	780
1980	570	627	833	783	804	762	1238	1542
1981	681	853	822	981	854	878	1919	2420
1982	601	811	660	704	841	754	2520	3174
1983	483	738	746	917	641	761	3003	3935
1984	1186	744	1267	1083	1129	1056	4189	4991
1985	940	785	972	814	978	887	5129	5878
1986	616	546	665	601	810	656	5745	6534
1987	950	659	734	847	923	791	6695	7325
1988	773	845	624	978	912	840	7468	8165
1989	870	637	721	802	663	706	8338	8871
1990	771	897	796	896	932	880	9109	9751
1991	1029	1029	879	791	936	909	10138	10660
1992	876	835	1013	845	1011	926	11014	11586
1993	1027	793	973	1009	960	934	12041	12520
1994	699	700	653	649	753	689	12740	13209

The double mass analysis also provides a means of adjusting the inconsistent data. In the example in Figure 2.6, a break point B occurred in 1988. If the slope of the line AB is a and the slope of the line BC is b, the adjustment of the inconsistent data is made by the ratio of the slopes of the two lines. Thus, it is possible to adjust the data to reflect the conditions that existed prior to the point B. This is done by multiplying each precipitation value at the test station occurring after the break point by the ratio a/b. Alternatively, the data may be adjusted to reflect recent conditions following the break. This is done by multiplying each precipitation value at the test station occurring before the break point by the ratio b/a. An important point to remember is that the double mass analysis should not be used in mountain areas, or to adjust storms of short duration (e.g., daily totals).

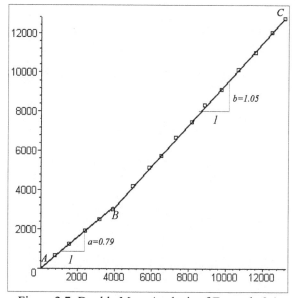

Figure 2.7: Double Mass Analysis of Example 2.1

Example 2.1

Given the annual precipitation values at stations 1, 2, 3, 4, and 5 in Table 2.1, analyze the records of station 1 for consistency and correct its values if necessary.

Solution

Table 2.1 summarizes the calculations. Columns P_1, P_2, P_3, P_4, and P_5 contain the annual precipitation at stations 1, 2, 3, 4, and 5, respectively.

Column $\bar{P}_{base}$ contains the mean annual precipitation at the base stations 2, 3, 4, and 5. Column ΣP_1 contains the cumulative annual precipitation values at station 1 (the test station). Column $\Sigma \bar{P}_{base}$ contains the cumulative values of mean annual precipitation at the base stations 2, 3, 4, and 5.

The cumulative values of the test station, ΣP_1, are plotted against the cumulative values of the base stations, $\Sigma \bar{P}_{base}$, in Figure 2.7. A significant breaking point occurs in 1983 (i.e., point B), thus creating the lines AB of slope a=0.79, and BC of slope b=1.05. A change in observation procedures or instrumentation location occurred in 1983. The ratio of the recent to past slope is b/a=1.05/0.79=1.33. Finally, the data prior to 1983 are corrected by a factor of 1.33 as shown in Table 2.2.

Table 2.2: Adjusted Precipitation of Example 2.1

Year	Recorded P_1	Adjusted P_1
1979	668	888
1980	570	758
1981	681	906
1982	601	799
1983-1994		Not Adjusted

Estimation of Missing Precipitation Data

Sometimes information from a precipitation station is partially missing. For example, a station temporarily malfunctions, or the observer is relocated. In such cases, the hydrologist may attempt to estimate the missing value using information from neighboring stations. A procedure that allows the estimation of a missing precipitation value at one station (e.g., station 1) based on several index stations (e.g., 2, 3, 4, ..., N) is called the normal ratio method:

$$\frac{P_1}{\bar{P}_1} = \frac{1}{(N-1)}\left(\frac{P_2}{\bar{P}_2} + \frac{P_3}{\bar{P}_3} + \frac{P_4}{\bar{P}_4} + ... + \frac{P_N}{\bar{P}_N} \right) \qquad (2.1)$$

where
P_1 = missing precipitation value at station 1
P_2, ..., P_N = precipitation at index stations for the concurrent period
$\bar{P}_1$ = mean annual precipitation at station 1
$\bar{P}_2$, ..., $\bar{P}_N$ = mean annual precipitation at index stations
N = number of index stations (at least three)

Equation (2.1) may be applied to the estimation of a missing precipitation value, or the missing storm depth at a site, by treating P_1, ..., P_N as related to a particular storm. P_1, ..., P_N are normally taken as the mean annual precipitation values as calculated from long-term records. However, they may also be mean monthly precipitation for the corresponding stations. The higher the number of good-quality index stations, the more accurate the estimate is. The index stations should be located as evenly spaced from the missing-data station as possible.

Example 2.2
Estimate the missing precipitation value for June 2007, at a given station, if during the same month the following precipitation values were recorded in four nearby stations: 65, 78, 99, and 88mm. The mean annual precipitation values, based on 20 years of records, for the missing-data station and the index stations are 720, 590, 625, 865, and 742mm, respectively.

Solution
From equation (2.1),

$$\frac{P_1}{\overline{P}_1} = \frac{1}{4}\left(\frac{P_2}{\overline{P}_2} + \frac{P_3}{\overline{P}_3} + \frac{P_4}{\overline{P}_4} + \frac{P_5}{\overline{P}_5}\right)$$

$$\frac{P_1}{720\ mm} = \frac{1}{4}\left(\frac{65\ mm}{590\ mm} + \frac{78\ mm}{625\ mm} + \frac{99\ mm}{865\ mm} + \frac{88\ mm}{742\ mm}\right)$$

$$\Rightarrow P_1 = 84\ mm$$

The U.S. National Weather Service (NWS) has developed an alternate method for estimating missing precipitation values in non-mountainous areas. The method requires four index stations located closest to the missing-data station 1, and in each of four quadrants delimited by North-South and East-West axes drawn through station 1. The estimated precipitation value, P_1 is the weighted average of the values at the four index stations. For each index station, the applicable weight is the reciprocal of the square of its distance D to station 1 (Figure 2.8). The procedure is described by the formula

$$P_1 = \left(\sum_{i=2}^{5} \frac{P_i}{D_i^2} \right) \Bigg/ \left(\sum_{i=2}^{5} \frac{1}{D_i^2} \right)$$ (2.2)

where

P_1 = missing precipitation value at station 1
$P_2, ..., P_5$ = precipitation at index stations for the concurrent period
$D_2, ..., D_5$ = distance between each index station and station one

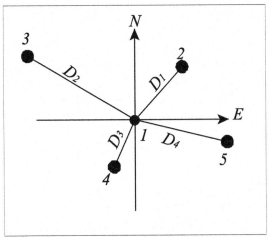

Figure 2.8: Index Stations for the NWS Method

Example 2.3

Rainfall data is missing at a given station 1 for the month of June 2007. During the same month the following precipitation values were recorded in four nearby stations: 65, 78, 99, and 88*mm*. The distance from each index station to station 1 is 12.4, 9.7, 4.3, and 2.6*km*, respectively. Estimate the missing precipitation at station 1 according to the U.S. National Weather Service Method.

Solution

From Equation (2.2),

$$P_1 = \frac{\displaystyle\sum_{i=2}^{5} \frac{P_i}{D_i^2}}{\displaystyle\sum_{i=2}^{5} \frac{1}{D_i^2}} = \frac{\dfrac{65mm}{(12.4km)^2} + \dfrac{78mm}{(9.7km)^2} + \dfrac{99mm}{(4.3km)^2} + \dfrac{88mm}{(2.6km)^2}}{\dfrac{1}{(12.4km)^2} + \dfrac{1}{(9.7km)^2} + \dfrac{1}{(4.3km)^2} + \dfrac{1}{(2.6km)^2}} = 90 \ mm$$

Time Distribution of Precipitation

Recording rain gages provide a continuous graph of precipitation depth with respect to time. A typical portion of a chart from a recording gage is illustrated in Figure 2.9. The solid line shows the level of precipitation, P, in millimeters accumulated at a given time, t. When the precipitated water reaches the maximum level, a siphon mechanism empties the water in the chamber. This is shown by a vertical line in the chart. The cumulative water level with time may be transformed into precipitation intensity, p, or precipitation rate at a given time. At a given time, the slope of the line P versus t is approximated as $\Delta P / \Delta t$, where ΔP is the difference in precipitation depth during a short time interval Δt. If the time interval is $\Delta t = 1 hour$, then the precipitation intensity is simply the difference in precipitation depth during one hour.

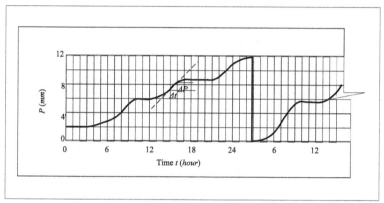

Figure 2.9: A Chart of a Recording Rain Gage

From above, information from recording rain gages is usually digitally processed and archived in the form of precipitation intensity, p (mm/hour), versus time, t (hour). A graph of precipitation intensity versus time is called the rainfall hyetograph. The hyetograph of a storm (Figure 2.10) shows the time distribution of precipitation intensity, and as such it may be used to observe the periods of low intensity, the periods of high intensity, the magnitude of maximum precipitation intensity, p_{max}, and its time of occurrence, the total duration of the storm, t_d, and the total precipitation depth, P (mm).

Example 2.4

Figure 2.10 shows the rainfall hyetograph of a particular storm, as deduced from a continuous recording gage. Estimate the maximum precipitation intensity and its time of occurrence, the total duration of the storm, and the total precipitation depth.

Solution

From Figure 2.10, the storm started at 8:00 AM and ended at 4:00 PM (16 *hours*). There are two periods of rainfall: from 8 to 12 PM, and from 1 to 4 PM, separated by a rainless period from 12 to 1 PM. Precipitation storms are sometimes clustered in several rainfall periods separated by calm intervals in between. Thus, the duration of the storm is $t_d=8hour$. The maximum precipitation intensity is $p_{max}=6mm/hr$, and occurred between 10 and 11 AM. The total precipitation depth of the storm, or cumulative precipitation, is the area under the rainfall hyetograph:

$$P = \sum_{t=8}^{t=16} p_t \, \Delta t = (1+3+6+2+1+5+4) \, \frac{mm}{hour} \times 1 \; hour = 22 \; mm$$

where p_t is the precipitation intensity at time t.

The time evolution of precipitation intensity at a fixed point (i.e., at a rain gage) is of interest in many hydrologic applications. The characteristics of the rainfall hyetograph, particularly during extremely intense events, offer valuable information to the water resources engineer. The design of water resources and hydraulic systems consists in the dimensional definition of structural components such that when fully operational at capacity level the system will be able to function under an extreme precipitation event called the design storm. Urban storm sewers, airport drainage systems, mining and underground excavations are examples of engineering applications of hydrologic analysis of the time distribution of point precipitation.

The time distribution of point precipitation at time scales larger than that of an individual storm supplies information on the seasonal, annual or multi-annual variability of precipitation, and as such it is of interest in a variety of studies in surface hydrology, groundwater analysis, and climate variability. Figure 2.11 shows a monthly time distribution of precipitation at a point. If the graph is built for a particular year, the intensity of precipitation throughout the year indicates the seasonal variability of precipitation, and the severity of the wet and dry months during the year in question. On the other hand, if the graph is built to depict the mean monthly precipitation at a point (i.e., the value for a month is calculated as the average of that month over at least 20 years), then the intensity of precipitation throughout the year indicates the seasonal precipitation regime for the location studied. For example, if Figure 2.11 is actually the mean monthly precipitation at a point, then there is one wet "season" from April to May, and a second less important one from October to November. The dry "seasons" at this location are from June to September and from December to March of the following year. The precipitation intensities indicated are the mean, or the expected, precipitation in an average year.

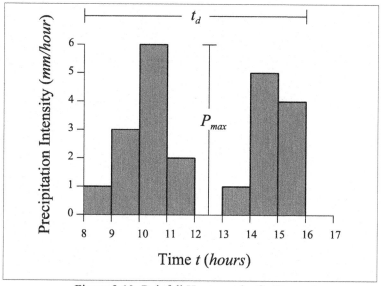

Figure 2.10: Rainfall Hyetograph of a Storm

A similar graph may be built for a typical wet year, or a typical dry year. The visual information offers a simple, yet effective, way to understand the hydrologic regime at a location, and provides valuable information for water resources planning.

Total annual precipitation distribution graphs are plotted for the purpose of observing the long-term variability of precipitation at a location. When this analysis covers several decades, the pattern of natural fluctuation in precipitation responding to climatic conditions may be deduced. The hydrologist takes note of the average duration of dry years and that of wet years, trends in precipitation, and amplitudes in fluctuation of precipitation from wet to dry years. This information is used in connection with water resources planning and management. Figure 2.12 shows an annual distribution of precipitation obtained from one station.

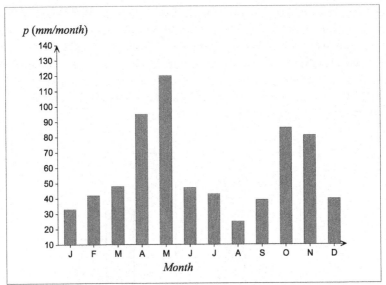

Figure 2.11: Monthly Distribution of Precipitation

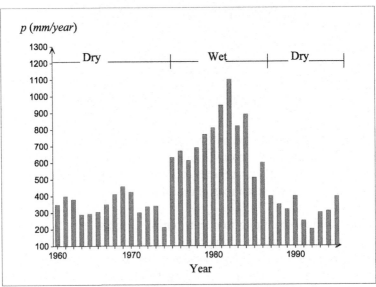

Figure 2.12: Time Distribution of Annual Precipitation

Example 2.5: Long-Term Annual Precipitation in Philadelphia

In the United States, the National Weather Service (NWS) provides atmospheric data on a variety of climatological variables, including precipitation, through the National Oceanic and Atmospheric

Administration (NOAA) National Climatic Data Center (NCDC). This constitutes an excellent source of online climate data for the U.S. (www.ncdc.noaa.gov/oa/climate/climatedata.html). We are interested in the time evolution of annual precipitation in Philadelphia recorded for over a century. This data is available through the NCDC site, or more conveniently through the Franklin Institute of Science and Technology (www.fi.edu/weather/data2/index.html).

Table 2.3: Annual Liquid Precipitation in Philadelphia (*Inches*)

Year i	P_i	Year	P_i	Year	P_i	Year	P_i
1874	46.25	1906	51.87	1938	46.92	1970	39.14
1875	40.22	1907	48.74	1939	45.4	1971	47.79
1876	47.39	1908	38.13	1940	44.61	1972	49.63
1877	37.26	1909	37.36	1941	35.15	1973	46.06
1878	34.53	1910	39.6	1942	43.05	1974	37.78
1879	36.75	1911	51.35	1943	36.77	1975	52.13
1880	33.58	1912	47.0	1944	39.52	1976	33.27
1881	29.91	1913	47.41	1945	46.68	1977	49.42
1882	45.58	1914	39.07	1946	38.35	1978	45.95
1883	39.18	1915	44.83	1947	44.46	1979	52.79
1884	39.34	1916	32.27	1948	49.07	1980	38.8
1885	33.35	1917	39.39	1949	40.48	1981	37.83
1886	37.24	1918	37.73	1950	40.47	1982	40.43
1887	42.17	1919	49.12	1951	41.75	1983	54.41
1888	44.06	1920	46.16	1952	45.84	1984	43.66
1889	50.6	1921	35.45	1953	48.13	1985	35.2
1890	34.02	1922	29.31	1954	34.04	1986	40.42
1891	38.19	1923	39.19	1955	33.03	1987	33.4
1892	34.78	1924	43.11	1956	46	1988	38.41
1893	37.65	1925	32.4	1957	32.2	1989	48.66
1894	40.34	1926	44.91	1958	47.87	1990	35.79
1895	31.01	1927	43.15	1959	38.37	1991	36.22
1896	32.15	1928	39.37	1960	41.15	1992	30.41
1897	42.04	1929	41.56	1961	41.05	1993	42.18
1898	49.23	1930	33.97	1962	42.62	1994	44.92
1899	39.96	1931	39.28	1963	34.95	1995	31.53
1900	40.91	1932	44.52	1964	29.88	1996	56.47
1901	45.54	1933	51.37	1965	29.34	1997	32.52
1902	49.76	1934	38.36	1966	40	1998	31.66
1903	41.5	1935	46.36	1967	44.82	1999	48.5
1904	39.76	1936	38.7	1968	35.45	2000	44.2
1905	41.61	1937	37.4	1969	43.36		

Assume you downloaded a data file in text format that can be read with any word processor. The first two lines of the data file have alphanumeric information describing its contents. Beginning with the third line, the file contains two columns, the left one being the year (from 1874 to 2000) and the right one the recorded liquid precipitation for that year in *inches*. Assume you named the data file PhillyPrecip.txt and stored it in the C drive of your computer at the following path: C:\My Documents\Hydrology_Second_Book\Data\PhillyPrecip.txt. Table 2.3 is a printed replica of a downloaded text file. Write a Maple program to read the data in this file beginning with the third line, transform precipitation data into *mm*, and prepare a single graph with the following curves:(1) The raw annual precipitation data, (2) a 20-year moving average, (3) a graph displaying the mean plus one standard deviation, and (4) a graph displaying the mean minus one standard deviation. State your conclusions about the long-term changes in annual precipitation in Philadelphia.

Solution

The following Maple program describes the procedure. The two-column file is read and stored in an appropriate vector. Precipitation depth is transformed into *mm* by multiplying the second column by 25.4 *mm/inch*. For the *i*-th year, the *m*=20-year average, $\overline{P}_i$, is calculated as the mean precipitation for the *m* years prior to *i* (Serrano, 2011). In other words

$$\overline{P}_i = \frac{1}{m}\sum_{k=0}^{m} P_{i-k}$$

Note that Maple code does not allow a subscript $k=0$. A period of 20 years or longer is generally considered statistically representative for the calculation of the average of a weather variable. This average defines a climate constant. Thus, in the analysis of climate change it is of interest to observe possible long-term changes in these climatic "constants." Now for the *i*-th year, the standard deviation in the *m*=20 preceding years, σ_i, is calculated from the second moment with respect to the mean for the *m* years prior to *i* (Serrano, 2011). In other words

$$\sigma_i = \sqrt{\frac{1}{M-1}\sum_{k=0}^{m}\left(P_{i-k} - \overline{P}_i\right)^2}$$

Figure 2.13 shows the requested graphs. The band $\overline{P}_i \pm \sigma_i$ defines representative precipitation fluctuation bounds. Long-term variation in this band is of interest in studying possible climatic changes.

> **Program for the Analysis of Long-Term Annual Precipitation in Philadelphia**
> Read data file by indicating the path where the text file is located in your disk.
> Notice the double "\\" and that the file has 2 columns.

```
> P_Inches:=readdata("C:\\My
  Documents\\Hydrology_Second_Book\\Data\\PhillyPrecip.txt",2):
```

Data is now stored in a vector P_Inches:=[[year, precipitation], [year, precipitation], . . .].
Year *i* is stored in column 1 of P_Inches[i][1].
Precipitation of year *i* is stored in column 2 of P_Inches[i][2].
Now find the number of data points, Np, and transform inches into mm.
Start in line 3, since the first two lines of data file are just text.

```
> for i from 3 to 2000 do   #2000 is an arbitrary large number
  Np:=i:
  P_mm[i-2]:=[P_Inches[i-2][1],25.4*P_Inches[i-2][2]]:
  end do:                    #Ignore error when the loop is aborted.
Error, invalid subscript selector
```

Create a vector of (x,y) coordinates for plotting purposes, P:=[[year 1, P[1]], [year 2, P[2]], . . .].
Prepare the graph, but do not display it yet.

```
> P:=[seq([P_mm[k][1],P_mm[k][2]],k=1..Np)]:
  G1:=plot(P,color=black,legend=`Annual Precipitation`):
```

Now for each year calculate an M=20-year moving average.
For year *i*, it is the mean of the past 20 years of precipitation.
Store in vector Mean[[year, mean], [year, mean], . . .].
Prepare for plotting.

```
> M:=20:
  for i from M to Np do
  Pbar[i]:=(P_mm[i][2]+sum(P_mm[i-k][2],k=1..M-1))/M;
  end do:
  Mean:=[seq([P_mm[k][1],Pbar[k]],k=M..Np)]:
  G2:=plot(Mean,color=black,thickness=2,
           legend=`Moving Average`):
```

For each year, calculate values of the mean plus one standard deviation,
and the mean minus one standard deviation.
Store in corresponding arrays suitable for plotting.

```
> for i from M to Np do
  sigma[i]:=sqrt((((P_mm[i][2]-Pbar[i])^2
             +sum((P_mm[i-k][2]-Pbar[i])^2,k=1..M-1))/(M-1));
  end do:
  Meanplus:=[seq([P_mm[k][1],Pbar[k]+sigma[k]],k=M..Np)]:
  G3:=plot(Meanplus,color=black,linestyle=3,
           legend=`Mean plus Std. Deviation`):
  Meanminus:=[seq([P_mm[k][1],Pbar[k]-sigma[k]],k=M..Np)]:
  G4:=plot(Meanminus,color=black,linestyle=3,
           legend=`Mean minus Std. Deviation`):
```

Display all of the graphs in a single plot.

```
> plots[display](G1,G2,G3,G4,labels=[`Year`,`P (mm)`],
         labeldirections=[`horizontal`,`vertical`],
         font=[TIMES,ROMAN,16],labelfont=[TIMES,ROMAN,16]);
```

Assuming the data is correct, there seems to be no evidence of increase or decrease in the average annual rainfall depth in Philadelphia during the period from 1874 to 2000. There appears to be a periodic cycle of wet years followed by dry years repeating every 36 years. A longer period of record would corroborate, or negate, these conclusions. Further statistical analysis of the data, including trend, correlation, and spectral analysis, would reveal the presence of trends or periodic cycles with more precision (for more information on the methods see Serrano, 2011).

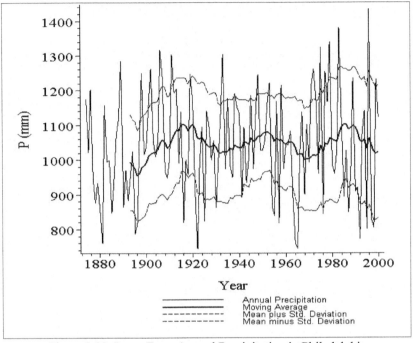

Figure 2.13: Long-Term Annual Precipitation in Philadelphia

Example 2.6: Long-Term Seasonal Precipitation in Philadelphia

Seasonal distribution of precipitation can be analyzed by a simple averaging of recorded amounts during a given month, for several years of record, and repeating for the 12 months of the year. It is of interest the average seasonal distribution for an early period of record as compared to a recent one. When a sufficiently long record exists, such comparison may suggest possible effects of climate change on seasonal distribution of precipitation. Assume you downloaded a file called phl.txt from the Franklin Institute (www.fi.edu/weather/data2/index.html). This data file contains long-term weather data for Philadelphia. Assume this text file is stored in the C drive of your computer at the following path: C:\My Documents\Hydrology_Second_Book\Data\phl.txt. This file contains 7 columns as follows: (1) the month of record (from 1 to 12); (2) the day of record (from 1 to 31, depending on the month); (3) the year of record (from 1873 to 1999); (4) the maximum daily air temperature (°F); (5) the minimum daily air temperature (°F); (6) the daily liquid precipitation (rain plus melted snow in hundredths of an *inch*); and (7) the daily snowfall (tenths of *inches*). Thus, each line in the file contains the date, temperature, precipitation, and snowfall recorded on a day. Sometimes a value -1 appears at a register. This means a "trace" of precipitation was recorded. When the value of -9999 appears, it means the data is unavailable for that day.

Write a Maple program that divides the record into two equal periods, an early one from 1873 to 1936, and a recent one from 1937 to 1999. For each period, calculate and plot the mean seasonal distribution of precipitation. State your conclusions.

Solution

The following Maple program reads the data file, calculates total monthly precipitation depth from column 6, splits the series into two halves, calculates mean monthly precipitation depth for each halved record, and plots the seasonal distribution in a single graph.

```
Maple Program for the Analysis of Seasonal Precipitation in Philadelphia
Read data and store in a 7-column array called Data[]
> Data:=readdata("C:\\My
  Documents\\Hydrology_Second_Book\\Data\\Phl.txt",7):
Scan Data[] file line by line and add the values on the sixth column (daily precipitation values)
for each month. Store monthly values in array P[i][j].
Subindex variables i, j must be integer. The floor( ) command converts them to integer.
> Nmonth:=(2000-1873)*12:
  nd:=1:
  for nm from 1 to Nmonth do
  j:=floor(Data[nd][1]):              #month j
  i:=floor(Data[nd][3]):              #year i
  tot:=0:                             #monthly total
  for k from 1 while Data[nd][1]=j do #begin month loop
      if (Data[nd][6]>0) then         #only positive
          tot:=tot+Data[nd][6]:
      end if:
  nd:=nd+1:
  end do:                             #end month loop
  P[i][j]:=tot*25.4/100;              #convert to mm
  end do:
For the early series (1873 to 1936), calculate the mean precipitation for January.
Store in array PE[ ]. Repeat for each month and prepare for plotting.
> Mid:=floor((1999-1873)/2):
  for j from 1 to 12 do
  PE[j]:=sum(P[m][j],m=1873..1873+Mid)/Mid:
  end do:
  PEarly:=[seq([m,PE[m]],m=1..12)]:   #for plotting
  G1:=plot(PEarly,color=black,thickness=1,
           legend=`1873 to 1936`):
```

For the late series (1937 to 1999), calculate the mean precipitation for January. Store in array PL[ ]. Repeat for each month and prepare for plotting.

```
> for j from 1 to 12 do
    PL[j]:=sum(P[m][j],m=1999-Mid..1999)/Mid:
    end do:
    PLate:=[seq([m,PL[m]],m=1..12)]:        #for plotting
    G2:=plot(PLate,color=black,thickness=2,legend=`1937 to 1999`):
```
Display plots in one graph.
```
> plots[display](G1,G2,labels=[`Month`,
        `Mean Monthly Precipitation (mm/month)`],
    labeldirections=[`horizontal`,`vertical`],
    font=[TIMES,ROMAN,16],labelfont=[TIMES,ROMAN,16]);
```

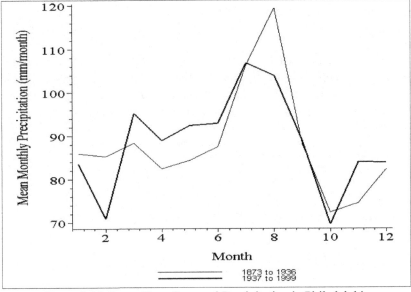

Figure 2.14: Long-Term Seasonal Precipitation in Philadelphia

2.4 SPATIAL DISTRIBUTION OF PRECIPITATION

If the analysis of time distribution of precipitation studies its temporal variability at a fixed point, the spatial distribution analysis studies its regional variability. Given different precipitation depths recorded at several rain gages across a watershed after a storm, a month, a year, or several years, it is often required to estimate an equivalent precipitation depth for the entire watershed during the same duration. For a uniformly spaced, dense, rain-gage network in a flat area, the simplest approach is to use the *arithmetic average*:

$$\bar{P} = \frac{1}{N}\sum_{i=1}^{N} P_i \tag{2.3}$$

where
$\quad\bar{P}$ = average precipitation over a region, during a given time (*mm*)
$\quad P_i$ = precipitation on gage *i* during the same time (*mm*)
$\quad N$ = number of rain gages

The arithmetic average method, although simple, does not take into consideration the rain gage density. The *Thiessen polygons* method is another method of calculating precipitation averages. In this method, an afferent area is assigned to each rain gage, depending on the gage location relative to neighboring ones. Thus, widely spaced gages receive a larger area of influence than closely spaced ones. Within each area, it is assumed that the precipitation magnitude is the one recorded at its gage. A geometrical construction is needed to trace the polygons that delimit each afferent area.

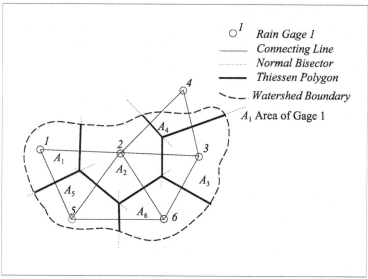

Figure 2.15: Construction of the Thiessen Polygons of a Watershed

Referring to Figure 2.15 as an example, the construction of the Thiessen polygons is as follows:

(1) Connect the stations with straight lines (continuous thin lines in Figure 2.15). Due to lack of precipitation information in certain watersheds, sometimes it is useful to include rain gages outside the

watershed, such as gage 4 in Figure 2.15. The connecting lines will generate a network of triangles. There is more than one way to join the stations. Choose the one that produces triangles without sharp inner angles.

(2) Draw a perpendicular bisector in the middle of each connecting line (dashed lines in Figure 2.15). If the construction is properly done, the three bisectors of each triangle should intersect at a point. The bisectors form the sides of the Thiessen polygons (thick solid lines in Figure 2.15). Prolong them to form the polygons. For a station near the watershed boundary, prolong the polygon sides to the boundary. For a station outside the watershed boundary, such as station 4 in Figure 2.15, consider the portion of the polygon inside the watershed only.

(3) Estimate the area of each polygon corresponding to each gage, using a polar planimeter, the dot grid method, or a computer digitizer. If you use a digitizer or a planimeter, measure each polygon area at least three times and calculate the average area. The summation of all the polygon areas should equal the total watershed area. The error should be less than 10%. It is useful to divide the error among the polygons, allocating the error proportional to each polygon area.

(4) Calculate the average precipitation by the formula

$$\bar{P} = \left(\sum_{i=1}^{N} P_i A_i \right) / \left(\sum_{i=1}^{N} A_i \right) \qquad (2.4)$$

where
    P_i = Precipitation in gage i (mm)
    A_i = area of polygon i (km^2)

The Thiessen polygons method allows the consideration of rain gage network density and the relative distance between gages. However, it should not be applied to mountain regions where orographic control of precipitation is more important than measurement resolution related to gage network density.

Example 2.7
    In Figure 2.15, the watershed area is 309.5 km^2. The polygons' areas in km^2 are: A_1=33.4, A_2=85.6, A_3=62.7, A_4=22.8, A_5=49.9, and A_6=55.1. Estimate the average precipitation if the individual rain gages recorded the following precipitation depths in mm: P_1=17, P_2=24, P_3=8,

$P_4=12$, $P_5=16$, and $P_6=13$.

Solution

From equation (2.4),

$$\bar{P}=\left(\sum_{i=1}^{N} P_i A_i\right) / \left(\sum_{i=1}^{N} A_i\right)$$

$\bar{P}=\{17mm\times33.4km^2+24mm\times85.6km^2+8mm\times62.7km^2$

$+12mm\times22.8km^2+16mm\times49.9km^2+13mm\times55.1km^2\} / 309.5km^2$

$\bar{P}=15.9mm$

One of the most widely used methods to study spatial distribution of precipitation is the *isohyetal method*. The isohyetal method not only permits the calculation of average precipitation over a region or a watershed, but also gives a visual description of the spatial distribution of precipitation. In addition, it may be applied to mountain areas. The method results in the drawing of lines of equal precipitation, called isohyets, across the watershed. Isohyets represent an analogous concept to that of topographic contours, or lines of equal altitude, to observe the spatial variability of relief. Therefore, the construction of isohyetal maps follows the same rules as those of topographic contours, and in fact any computer software designed to draw contours could be used for that purpose. Several ground control points where precipitation is known (i.e., as many rain gages as possible) are needed. Obviously, the higher the rain gage density the higher resolution, and the more accurate, the isohyetal lines are.

Referring to Figure 2.16 as an example, the construction of an isohyetal map is as follows:

(1) Connect the rain gages with straight lines.

(2) Decide the isohyet interval based on the range of precipitation values, the number of precipitation stations and the desired resolution. In Figure 2.16 the minimum precipitation (at gage 3) is **8mm**, and the maximum precipitation (at gage 2) is **24mm**. There are 6 rain gages and thus three isohyets, each drawn at an interval of **5mm**, give a resolution consistent with the number of gages. This will produce

three *isohyets*: one valued at 10*mm*, one at 15*mm*, and one at 20*mm*. Since the construction of isohyets is essentially a linear interpolation of the measured point precipitation, it is unreasonable to select a contour interval inconsistent with the number of gages. For example, with only six rain gages it is not logical to draw an isohyet every millimeter for a total of 15 isohyets. The resulting isohyetal map would be a personal interpretation of the measured values, rather than a reflection of the true spatial variability of rainfall. If a region has 100 rain gages distributed across a watershed, then 40 or 50 isohyets could in principle be drawn, if that is the desired resolution.

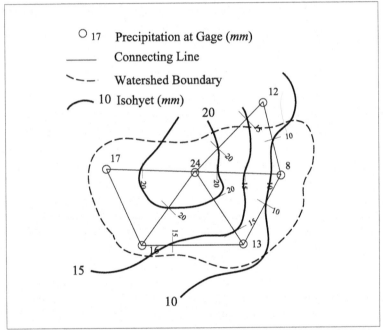

Figure 2.16: Construction of an Isohyetal Map of a Watershed

(3) Locate the points where the selected whole-number isohyets cross the connecting lines between gages. For example, in Figure 2.16 $P_1=17mm$ and $P_2=24mm$. The 20-*mm* isohyet intersects the connecting line between gages 1 and 2. To locate the intersection point, note that the difference in precipitation between the gages is 7 *mm*. Divide the connecting line between gages 1 and 2 in 7 equal intervals, using the usual rules of engineering drafting. Mark the location of 20*mm* on the connecting line. Repeat the procedure for all the connecting lines between gages. Note that some connecting lines are crossed by more than one isohyet.

(4) Join with a smooth curve the points of equal precipitation. This line constitutes the isohyet. Theoretically, all of its points exhibit an equal value of precipitation. Repeat the process until all isohyets are drawn. The isohyetal map gives a visual representation of the areas of high precipitation (around gage 2), and those of low precipitation (around gages 3, 4 and 6).

(5) Estimate the areas between isohyets. Figure 2.17 shows the isohyets with the areas in between them. Note that A_1 and A_4 comprise the areas between the extreme isohyet and the watershed boundary. The summation of the areas must equal the total watershed area.

(6) To calculate the average precipitation, use equation (2.4), with A_i the area between two isohyets, and P_i the precipitation allotted to each area (i.e., precipitation between adjacent isohyets). For example, Figure 2.17, has an isohyet interval of 5mm, the precipitation values are $P_1 = 22.5mm$, $P_2 = 17.5mm$, $P_3 = 12.5mm$, and $P_4 = 7.5mm$.

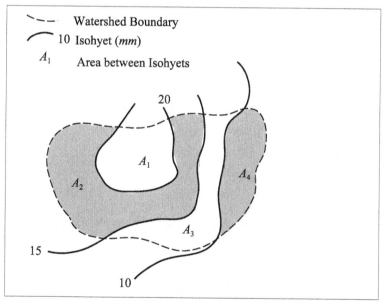

Figure 2.17: Areas between Isohyets

Example 2.8

In Figures 2.16 and 2.17 the areas in between isohyets are $A_1 = 82.5$, $A_2 = 95.1$, $A_3 = 59.6$, and $A_4 = 72.3km^2$. Estimate the mean precipitation depth for the watershed.

Solution
   From equation (2.4)

$$\bar{P} = \left(\sum_{i=1}^{N} P_i A_i \right) \Big/ \left(\sum_{i=1}^{N} A_i \right)$$

$$\bar{P} = \{22.5mm \times 82.5km^2 + 17.5mm \times 95.1km^2$$

$$+ 12.5mm \times 59.6km^2 + 7.5mm \times 72.3km^2\} / 309.5km^2$$

$$\bar{P} = 15.5mm$$

Comparing with the result obtained in Example 2.7 for the same watershed, the difference in the calculated mean precipitation is small in this case.

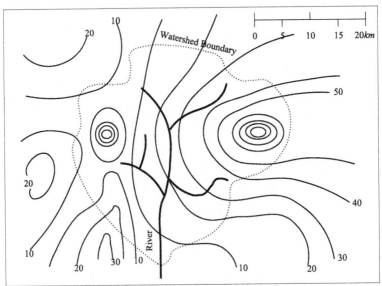

Figure 2.18: Isohyetal Map after an Intense Storm

   Besides the possibility of calculating average precipitation, isohyetal maps offer an interesting view of the spatial distribution of precipitation. Figure 2.18 shows an isohyetal map of total precipitation after a storm built from a network of over 30 rain gages. Note the locations of maximum precipitation depth as represented by the center of the closed isohyets.

Other methods for estimating areal precipitation from point values have been developed. These include eyeball isohyetal method, least-squares surface method, Lagrange-polynomial surface method, spline-surface method, inverse-distance interpolation, multi-quadratic interpolation, optimal interpolation/krigging, empirical orthogonal functions, and hypsometric method (Bonnor, 1975; Creutin and Obled, 1972; Omernik and Kinney, 1983; Shaw, 1988; Shaw and Lynn, 1972; Tabios and Salas, 1985; Wallis and Bowden, 1962).

2.5 FREQUENCY ANALYSIS OF PRECIPITATION

Precipitation Variability, Frequency, Return Period, and Design Rainfall

Precipitation is a climatic variable subject to environmental fluctuations. These fluctuations tend to decrease in magnitude as the hydrologist increases the temporal scale of observation. For example, with the advent of sophisticated electronic instrumentation, it is now possible to measure precipitation intensity by the minute. With these instruments the observer often finds that a typical thunderstorm may register periods of rainfall intensity of over 100$mm/hour$ that lasts for a duration of a minute or two, followed by short periods of significantly lower rainfall intensity (i.e., less than 10$mm/hour$). If the same storm is measured in a standard hourly recording rain gage, the hydrologist may conclude that the hourly precipitation intensity is of the order of 20 or 30$mm/hour$. That is, the hourly precipitation intensity (i.e., the slope on the continuous recording chart; see Figure 2.9) is averaged over a longer period of time and thus the resulting intensity fluctuates less than a hyetograph built with higher temporal resolution. Consequently, a monthly precipitation distribution at the same gage may show less fluctuation in the magnitude of precipitation from month to month. The monthly precipitation is expected to fluctuate around seasonal averages. Similarly, annual point precipitation is expected to show even less fluctuation from year to year. The annual precipitation fluctuates around long term trends governed by global climatic changes.

From the above discussion, the hydrologist should expect less variability, and less resolution, in precipitation as the temporal scale of observation increases. Conversely, one should expect more variability, and more resolution, as the temporal scale of observation decreases. This is especially important since the hydrologist is often not concerned with the prediction of seasonal or annual precipitation regimes, but rather with the objective estimation of a typically adverse rainfall event. The adverse event is then used to design a water resources structure to withstand the occurrence of such a rainfall event. The rainfall event is called the *design rainfall*. Urban storm sewers, mining drainage systems, airport drainage systems, highway box culverts, bridge foundations, and dams are but a few examples of water resources and hydraulic structures which must be designed to withstand an objectively estimated design rainfall. The design rainfall must be quantified based on a conscientious prediction of possible future rainfall events during the service life of the structure. The design event is not the worst possible event one can imagine, for such an approach would produce an expensive design even if the event actually occurs, unless the project in question is a large scale water resources project. Most water resources projects are designed to withstand an event whose magnitude is proportional to the size of the structure. For instance, the failure of a small highway bridge during a particular event may cause some temporary transportation inconvenience, but it is not expected to be a catastrophic accident as that of the failure of a large dam during a flood. The latter would cause enormous human and property losses downstream. Therefore, the magnitude of the design rainfall for a dam should be significantly greater than that of the small bridge. How does the hydrologist predict precipitation in an objective manner?

The occurrence of precipitation depends on many meteorological and geographical variables. The physical interaction between these variables is complex and often difficult to quantify. For these reasons, the prediction of precipitation intensity and its geographical distribution faces practical obstacles. A fundamental problem the hydrologist faces relates to the estimation of the design rainfall under uncertainty. An approach to precipitation prediction is based on a careful evaluation of precipitation data recorded over many years. Although a historical record of precipitation is unlikely to occur again in the future, having good quality rainfall data collected over several decades is by far the best way to study the behavior of an uncertain variable. By studying the historical records of precipitation, it is possible to observe the characteristics of time distribution of precipitation on an hourly, monthly (or seasonal), and annual basis. Relationships between precipitation intensity and duration may be developed. Also monthly (or seasonal) average precipitation values (see Figures 2.11, 2.12, and 2.14) calculated over many years, and mean annual precipitation values (see Figure 2.13) may be estimated. In addition, average deviations (i.e., variances) from the calculated means may be evaluated (see Figure 2.13). In other words, by studying long term records of point precipitation the hydrologist may quantify the statistical properties of precipitation. Since a precipitation amount may not be accurately predicted due to the many uncertainties, at least one may predict it in a broad statistical sense. Furthermore, knowing the statistics of precipitation facilitates the fitting of theoretical probabilistic models (i.e., probability distributions, stochastic processes, random fields, etc.). Probabilistic models are useful in the study of the properties of precipitation, and in extending historical records for the purpose of testing water resources structures with respect to various possible occurrences of precipitation events.

From the above discussion, one must realize that while we are unable to predict the occurrence of a particular rainfall event, at least we can predict the frequency of its occurrence. In other words, a statistical analysis of historical records allows the hydrologist to predict, in all likelihood, *how often* a particular rainfall event may occur during a given period of several years. For instance, the occurrence of a storm with a maximum hourly intensity of 120*mm/hour* may not be determined for a particular year in the life of a structure. However, after collecting long-term precipitation information in the nearest rain gage one can ascertain that this rainfall intensity occurs an average of once every 200 *years*. This average interval of time is called the *return period*, *T*. We remark that this is an average interval between successive occurrences of the event. It does not mean that if the event occurs in a given year, one has to wait 200 years for the next occurrence. A return period of T=200 *years* means that if one had a very long precipitation record (i.e., 1,000 *years* of record, called a *population* in statistics), the event would occur *on an average* of once every 200 *years*.

High intensity rainfall events tend to be less frequent, and correspondingly exhibit long return periods. Similarly, low intensity events are more frequent, and correspondingly exhibit short return periods. This implies that, for a given duration, t_s (*hours*, *min*), there is an inverse relationship between precipitation intensity, *p*, and *T*. The duration is important. Again, as the duration (i.e., the temporal scale of observation) increases the variability of precipitation decreases.

Since there is an intrinsic relationship between precipitation intensity, duration, and frequency (IDF relationship), it follows that an objective criterion to select a design storm under uncertainty is to assign a return period according to the size of the structure. Government organizations, regulatory agencies, and professional experience recommend a given return period for the design of a water resource project. The larger the size of the structure, the higher the magnitude of the design *T*. The hydrologist must establish the IDF relationship for the locality in question to convert the given *T* into the design rainfall *p*. The design rainfall is then used to determine the dimensions and the characteristics of the corresponding hydraulic structures.

Intensity-Duration-Frequency Analysis (IDF)

The IDF relationship at a location constitutes an objective tool to quantify precipitation uncertainty, especially in circumstances when a design rainfall event must be determined for a particular water resources project. To perform the analysis, long-term precipitation data from a recording rain gage must be available. It is recommended that a station with at least twenty years of good quality information be selected, but clearly the longer the record the more accurate the analysis. A record of less than twenty years in length may not offer a statistically representative sample. Furthermore, the length of the record should be commensurate with the design life of the application structure.

The procedure of analysis is as follows:

(1) Select a specific duration of rainfall (e.g., a rainfall interval $t_s = \Delta t = 1$ *hour*).

(2) From the recording gage chart (see Figure 2.9), find the maximum precipitation intensity (*mm/hour*) of the selected duration for every year of record. In other words, determine the maximum slope, $p = \Delta P / t_s$, in the recording gage chart for every year.

(3) Rearrange the maximum annual precipitation intensities found in (2) in decreasing order of magnitude and assign a rank to each value. A rank $m=1$ is assigned to the highest intensity, and a rank $m=N$ to the lowest intensity, where N is the number of years of records.

(4) Estimate the return period corresponding to each intensity by the relative position of p with respect to the ranked series. A commonly used formula is $T=(N+1)/m$.

(5) Repeat steps (1) through (4) for other durations (e.g., 6, 12, 24 *hour*, etc.). A table of precipitation intensity versus return period is obtained for different durations.

(6) Interpolating in the table, select an even return period (e.g., $T=20$ *years*). Plot p versus t_s for the given T, and draw a smooth curve through the points. Repeat for several return periods to obtain the IDF graph.

Table 2.4: Annual Maximum Precipitation Intensity (*mm/hour*)
for Several t_s Durations (*hour*)

Year	$t_s=1$	$t_s=6$	$t_s=24$	Year	$t_s=1$	$t_s=6$	$t_s=24$
1970	20.1	6.7	2.9	1982	35.1	10.7	2.8
1971	42.9	10.6	3.7	1983	38.9	7.7	1.9
1972	38.1	9.1	3.1	1984	23.1	9.3	2.7
1973	30.2	6.8	1.7	1985	16.5	6.6	2.2
1974	25.9	10.2	2.6	1986	21.8	6.9	1.9
1975	35.8	16.6	5.9	1987	45.2	13.7	5.7
1976	28.7	7.2	3.3	1988	39.4	10.8	3.1
1977	27.2	6.1	1.7	1989	40.9	15.8	4.1
1978	52.8	22.1	6.6	1990	39.4	12.0	3.5
1979	26.4	8.6	2.4	1991	44.5	10.5	3.1
1980	52.3	19.4	4.8	1992	29.5	7.8	2.0
1981	46.2	8.7	2.2	1993	58.9	15.5	3.9

Example 2.9

Table 2.4 contains annual maximum precipitation intensities recorded at a station during a period of 24 *years*. For each year, maximum intensities for durations t_s of 1-*hour*, 6-*hour*, and 24-*hour,* respectively, were recorded. Perform an IDF analysis.

Solution

For each duration, the precipitation intensities are arranged in descending order of magnitude (Table 2.5). The highest value is assigned a rank $m=1$, and the lowest value a rank $m=24$, since the number of years of record is $N=24$. The return periods are calculated as $T=(N+1)/m$.

From Table 2.5, select a return period $T=25 years$ and calculate the precipitation intensities, p, corresponding to durations t_s 1, 6, and 24*hour*. Plot p versus t_s (Figure 2.19) and draw a smooth curve through the points. This is the intensity versus duration curve for a return period of 25 *years*. Next, select a return period of $T=10 years$ and interpolate in Table 2.5 to calculate the intensities corresponding to the various durations. Plot p versus t_s points and then a smooth curve through the them in Figure 2.19 to obtain the intensity versus duration curve for a return period of 10 *years*. Repeat the process for $T=5 years$. The resulting collection of curves constitutes the IDF relationship for the gage studied. Observe the basic features of IDF curves: for a given T, p decreases as t_s increases; for a given t_s, p increases as T increases.

Table 2.5: Ranks, *m*, and Return Periods, *T*, for
Annual Maximum Precipitation Intensities (*mm/hour*)

Rank *m*	*T* (year)	t_s=1hour	t_s=6hour	t_s=24hour
1	25	58.9	22.1	6.6
2	12.5	52.8	19.4	5.9
3	8.3	52.3	16.6	5.7
4	6.3	46.2	15.8	4.8
5	5	45.2	15.5	4.1
6	4.2	44.5	13.7	3.9
7	3.6	42.9	12.0	3.7
8	3.1	40.9	10.8	3.5
9	2.8	39.4	10.7	3.3
10	2.5	39.4	10.6	3.1
11	2.3	38.9	10.5	3.1
12	2.1	38.1	10.2	3.1
13	1.9	35.8	9.3	2.9
14	1.8	35.1	9.1	2.8
15	1.7	30.2	8.7	2.7
16	1.6	29.5	8.6	2.6
17	1.5	28.7	7.8	2.4
18	1.4	27.2	7.7	2.2
19	1.3	26.4	7.2	2.2
20	1.3	25.9	6.9	2.0
21	1.2	23.1	6.8	1.9
22	1.1	21.8	6.7	1.9
23	1.1	20.1	6.6	1.7
24	1	16.5	6.1	1.7

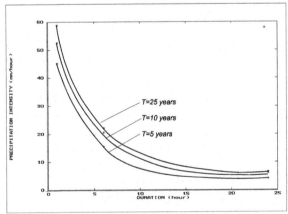

Figure 2.19: IDF Relationship for Example 2.9

Example 2.10: A Design Application

As an application of the previous example, assume that Figure 2.19 is the IDF relationship at the weather station of an airport. Estimate the design precipitation intensity (*mm/hour*) and the design precipitation depth (*mm*)of the airport storm drainage system if according to the size of the airport the required return period is $T=10year$, and the critical duration is $t_s=12hour$. Repeat for $T=15year$.

Solution

In Figure 2.19, for the curve of $T=10year$, read a duration $t_s=12hour$, and a corresponding design intensity $p=9mm/hour$, which corresponds to a depth $P=p \times t_s =9mm/hour \times 12hour=108mm$. Thus, the storm sewer system should be designed to withstand a precipitation depth of 108*mm* in 12 *hour*. Interpolating in Figure 2.19, between the curves $T=10$ and $T=25$, the design rainfall has an intensity of $p=10mm/hour$ and a total depth of $P=120mm$.

Clearly, as the selected return period increases, so does the corresponding design rainfall. For each alternative, the design engineer will dimensionalize the network of canals and collectors and then estimate the cost to build and maintain such system. The cost of each alternative, expressed in annual installments over the service life of the structure, is compared to the cost of damage repairs, flight delays, etc., resulting from not implementing the particular alternative. As the design T increases, the cost of flood protection increases, while the cost of flood damage and airport loss of use decreases. The alternative that offers the least annual cost is the one to select.

In the absence of recording gage data, it is useful to employ regional IDF relationships derived by local, state or national organizations involved in the administration of natural resources or the environment. For example, the U.S. National Weather Service has prepared a series of IDF relationships for the United States for several combinations of T and t_s:

$$p = \frac{a}{t_s + b} \qquad (2.5)$$

where

p = design precipitation intensity (*mm/hour*)
t_s = precipitation duration (*hour*)
a = a function of location and frequency (*mm*)
b = a function of location and frequency (*hour*)

The functions *a* and *b* have been evaluated (Table 2.6) for areas of similar rainfall characteristics within the United States. Figure 2.20 shows an approximate delineation of those areas.

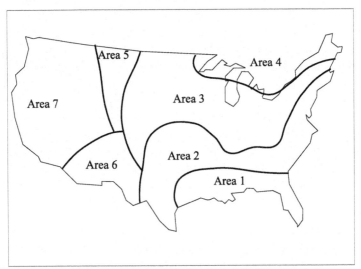

Figure 2.20: U.S. Map of Similar Rainfall Characteristics

Table 2.6: IDF Constants for Equation (2.5) for Various Regions in the U.S.

T (year)		Area 1	Area 2	Area 3	Area 4	Area 5	Area 6	Area 7
2	a =	87.21 mm/hr	59.16	43.18	29.63	29.63	28.79	31.9
2	b =	0.50 in/hr	0.35	0.28	0.22	0.27	0.23	0.18
5	a =	104.52	80.52	55.5	41.02	34.33	31.67	20.32
5	b =	0.48	0.42	0.32	0.27	0.22	0.20	0.20
10	a =	127.0	97.32	71.97	46.99	46.99	51.65	25.32
10	b =	0.60	0.48	0.38	0.27	0.28	0.38	0.22
25	a =	138.35	109.98	97.32	71.97	54.99	65.66	29.59
25	b =	0.55	0.53	0.50	0.45	0.28	0.43	0.17
50	a =	133.35	148.17	105.83	79.16	19.16	67.65	27.52
50	b =	0.47	0.63	0.45	0.40	0.42	0.35	0.13
100	a =	155.32	158.67	122.77	93.13	101.68	88.82	32.68
100	b =	0.55	0.60	0.52	0.47	0.48	0.43	0.17

Source: Steel and McGhee, 1979.

Point IDF relationships are considered representative of a small drainage area (e.g., less than $25\,km^2$). For calculations that involve large drainage areas, an adjustment of the design total precipitation should be made in order to account for the variations in spatial distribution. A depth-area-duration (DAD) of a storm may be conducted for this purpose. The analysis is performed to determine the maximum amounts of precipitation of various durations over areas of various sizes. The procedure is applied to a storm that produces an excessive depth of precipitation (see Gupta, 1989 for details).

Example 2.11: IDF Curves for Miami (Florida)

Prepare the IDF curves similar to Figure 2.19 for the city of Miami (Florida) using equation (2.5), Figure 2.20, and Table 2.6. Determine the design rainfall intensity for a duration of 12*hour* and a return period of 100*year*.

Solution

The city of Miami is located in Area 1 in Figure 2.20. Using the values of *a* and *b* in Table 2.6 corresponding to Area 1 for the various return periods, we write the following Maple program that plots the IDF curves (Figure 2.21) and estimates the design rainfall.

Maple Program for the Derivation of IDF Curves for Miami (Florida)

For T=2 years, enter the values of a and b from Table 2.6, Area 1.
Then use equation (2.5) to define the 2-year IDF curve as a Maple function.
In other words, p2(ts) is a function that maps values of ts into equation (2.5)

```
> a2:=87.21: b2:=0.5:
  p2:=ts->a2/(ts+b2):
```

Repeat for T=10, and 100 years.

```
> a10:=127.0: b10:=0.6: p10:=ts->a10/(ts+b10):
  a100:=155.32: b100:=0.55: p100:=ts->a100/(ts+b100):
```

Estimate the design rainfall intensity in mm/hour for T=100 years and ts=12 hours

```
> p100(12);
```

$$12.37609562$$

In a single graph, plot all of the IDF curves

```
> G1:=plot(p2(ts),ts=0..24,color=black,
          thickness=1,legend=`T=2years`):
  G2:=plot(p10(ts),ts=0..24,color=black,
          thickness=2,legend=`T=10years`):
  G3:=plot(p100(ts),ts=0..24,color=black,
          thickness=3,legend=`T=100years`):
  plots[display](G1,G2,G3,labels=[`Duration ts (hour)`,
      `Precipitation Intensity (mm/hour)`],
      labeldirections=[`horizontal`,`vertical`],
      font=[TIMES,ROMAN,16],labelfont=[TIMES,ROMAN,16]);
```

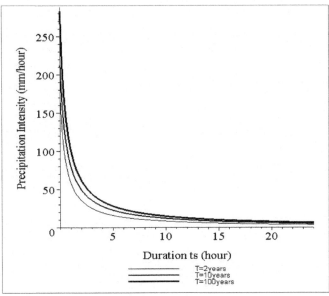

Figure 2.21: IDF Curves of Miami (Florida)

Probable Maximum Precipitation

In situations where the eventual failure of a water resources system may cause the loss of human life besides considerable property damage, structures are not designed according to a specific frequency, but rather to withstand the worst possible precipitation event. This is the case of very large reservoirs, with a storage capacity of over $50 \times 10^6 m^3$. These constructions should be, in principle, permanent structures capable to evacuate the *Probable Maximum Flood* (PMF). For intermediate reservoirs with a storage capacity between 1×10^6 and $50 \times 10^6 m^3$, there is a possibility of a loss of human life. Therefore, intermediate reservoirs should be designed for the *Standard Project Flood* (SPF). The SPF excludes extremely rare storm conditions and thus it is the most severe flood considered reasonably characteristic of a specific region. The magnitude of the peak flow rate of a SPF is between 40 to 60% of that of a PMF for the same watershed.

Since a flood results from precipitation, the PMF is produced by the *Probable Maximum Precipitation* event (PMP). The PMP is defined as the theoretically greatest depth of precipitation for a given duration that is physically possible over a particular drainage area at a certain time of the year. The spatial and temporal distribution of a PMP, determined on the basis of the maximization of factors that operate to produce a maximum storm, leads to the development of the *Probable Maximum Storm* (PMS). A PMS may be used with a precipitation-streamflow relationship (see chapter 5) to compute the PMF hydrograph.

PMP maps are usually provided by national meteorological organizations. For example, in the United States the U.S. National Weather Service (formerly the U.S. Weather Bureau, 1956, 1960; U.S. National Weather service 1978, 1980) has prepared generalized diagrams of PMP based on the rational approach and historic records. PMP values for various durations and corrections for drainage area are given according to the region in the country. See Viessman and Lewis (1996) for examples of application.

A method to estimate the PMP of a particular duration was proposed by Hershfield (1961). This method is based on the statistics of the historical annual maximum precipitation record, for the selected duration, in the study area. For example, the *d-hour* PMP at a point may be computed as

$$P_d = \bar{P} + K_T S_P \tag{2.6}$$

where
P_d = *d-hour* duration PMP (*mm*)
$\bar{P}$ = mean of d duration annual maximum over all the record (*mm*)
K_T = frequency factor of a given return period
S_P = standard deviation of d duration annual maximum (*mm*)

The procedure requires long-term precipitation data from a recording rain gage as follows:

(1) From the recording rain gage chart, select an adverse storm duration d (*hour*) and estimate the maximum precipitation depth (*mm*) for every year of record.

(2) From the annual maximum series, calculate the mean maximum precipitation P and its standard deviation S_P using statistical formulae.

(3) Estimate the frequency factor K_T. It is a function of the probability distribution governing the extreme precipitation series, and the return period. This can be ascertained from the enveloping curve of extreme historic storms. Hershfield recommends a value of K_T=15 for

$d=24hour$.

(4) Estimate the PMP from equation (2.6).

(5) Convert the PMP into a design rainfall hyetograph (time distribution of precipitation). For this purpose, the U.S. National Weather Service (1982) recommends to divide the storm duration into 6-*hour* increments. Next arrange the increments such that they decrease progressively to either side of the greatest 6-*hour* increment. This implies that the lowest increment will be either at the beginning or at the end of the sequence. See Viessman and Lewis (1996) for application examples.

(6) Assume a spatial distribution of the PMP. For drainage areas of less than 2,500 km^2, a uniform depth of precipitation over the entire area may be assumed. For larger areas, it is important to consider the shape of the assumed isohyets, the number of isohyets, the magnitude of the isohyets, and the orientation of the isohyetal map. The U.S. National Weather Service (1982) recommends an elliptical pattern with a major axis-to-minor axis ratio of 2.5:1. This pattern contains 14 isohyets for areas of up to 7,500 km^2, and 19 isohyets for the coverage of an area of 150,000 km^2. The orientation of the isohyetal map should be the one that produces the greatest volume of rainfall within the drainage area. See Viessman and Lewis (1996) for application examples.

Example 2.12
    Derive a 24-*hour* PMS for a watershed of 900 km^2 of drainage area, and propose a design rainfall hyetograph, if the mean annual maximum 24-*hour* precipitation is 135*mm*, and the standard deviation, for the same duration, is 28*mm*.

Solution
    Assuming a value of $K=15$, from equation (2.6) the 24-*hour* PMP is

$$P_{24} = \overline{P} + K_T S_P = 135 \ mm + 15 \times 28 \ mm = 555 \ mm$$

The PMP depth may now be divided into four 6-*hour* rainfall intensity intervals. One possible pattern is to locate the maximum intensity at the third interval with a value of 45% of the PMP, and to gradually decrease the intensities before and after the peak. Specifically, one possible design hyetograph is given in Table 2.6. Note that the total area under the rainfall hyetograph must equal the PMP. In other words

$$P_{24} = \sum_{i=1}^{4} p_i \Delta t$$

P_{24} = (13.9 *mm/hour* + 18.5 *mm/hour* + 41.6 *mm/hour*

+ 18.5 *mm/hour*) × 6 *hour* = 555 *mm*

Table 2.7: PMS for Example 2.12

Time interval (*hour*)	Percentage of PMP	p (*mm/hour*)
0 - 6	15	13.9
6 - 12	20	18.5
12 - 18	45	41.6
18 - 24	20	18.5

Since the drainage area is less than 2,500 km^2, we adopt a uniform spatial distribution for each rainfall intensity. In other words, the rainfall hyetograph above is representative of the entire watershed and constitutes the PMS. The PMS may now be transformed into a PMF by using a precipitation-streamflow relationship, or a unit hydrograph method, or a hydrologic simulation model (see chapter 6).

PROBLEMS

2.1 Given the annual precipitation data for six stations (Table 2.8), check the data of station 1 for consistency and make adjustments to reflect recent conditions.

2.2 Table 2.9 shows the annual precipitation at a station 1 and the mean annual precipitation at 10 base stations nearby. Check the data of station 1 for consistency and make adjustments in the series to reflect recent conditions.

2.3 Estimate the missing precipitation value for May 1995, at a given station, if during the same month the following precipitation values were recorded in four nearby stations: 55, 68, 89, and 78*mm*. The mean annual precipitation values, based on a 20-*year* record, for the missing-data station and the index stations are 735, 605, 640, 880 and 757*mm*, respectively.

2.4 In problem 2.3, the distance from station 1 to each index station (stations 2 through 5) is 12.3, 10.1, 2.9, and 1.9*km*, respectively. Estimate the missing precipitation in station 1 according to the U.S. National Weather Service method.

Table 2.8: Annual Precipitation for Problem 2.1 (*mm*)

Year	P_1	P_2	P_3	P_4	P_5	P_6
1980	349	414	357	359	385	384
1981	514	528	555	535	436	565
1982	476	556	465	557	459	523
1983	515	515	435	484	566	566
1984	385	535	493	438	493	424
1985	435	365	441	396	350	479
1986	387	502	538	343	465	426
1987	475	507	466	404	362	523
1988	308	345	330	366	300	339
1989	470	538	448	535	432	517
1990	593	621	595	697	409	653
1991	241	353	504	410	406	265
1992	300	463	387	363	446	331
1993	340	469	539	448	469	374
1994	285	442	431	458	345	314
1995	334	444	511	331	418	367

Table 2.9: Mean Annual Precipitation for Problem 2.2 (*mm*)

Year	P_1	Base	Year	P_1	Base	Year	P_1	Base
1973	406	411	1981	241	307	1989	296	359
1974	340	359	1981	307	346	1990	351	398
1975	417	361	1983	417	462	1991	274	385
1976	438	360	1984	406	384	1992	428	463
1977	406	385	1985	329	320	1993	395	450
1978	659	541	1986	340	450	1994	351	576
1979	472	359	1987	373	451	1995	329	359
1980	395	333	1988	450	476	1996	418	346

2.5 Given the recording gage chart in Figure 2.22, (1) plot the rainfall hyetograph, (2) calculate the maximum rainfall intensity, (3) calculate the storm duration, and (4) calculate the total precipitation depth.

2.6 Table 2.10 lists the monthly precipitation at a rain gage. Calculate the mean monthly precipitation and plot it with respect to the month of the year. Identify the wet, dry and average months.

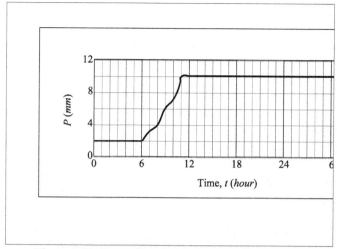

Figure 2.22: Recording Gage Chart for Problem 2.5

Table 2.10: Monthly Precipitation (*mm*) for Problem 2.6

Year	J	F	M	A	M	J	J	A	S	O	N	D
1991	18	36	58	127	110	66	40	15	33	55	77	48
1992	27	43	69	140	128	75	56	21	42	76	88	59
1993	20	38	61	133	118	70	47	19	39	60	80	51
1994	12	21	32	80	96	50	25	8	16	38	56	30
1995	35	51	76	163	139	89	70	37	60	91	101	71

2.7 In problem 2.6, select a wet year and plot the monthly precipitation with respect to the month of the year. In the same graph plot a dry year and an average year. Write your observations about the seasonal variability of rainfall for wet, dry, and average years.

Table 2.11: Annual Precipitation for Problem 2.8 (*mm*)

Year	P	Year	P	Year	P	Year	P
1965	1062	1973	423	1981	188	1989	733
1966	564	1974	127	1982	140	1990	764
1967	653	1975	135	1983	299	1991	937
1968	194	1976	157	1984	517	1992	1102
1969	369	1977	228	1985	575	1993	1025
1970	465	1978	39	1986	779	1994	914
1971	1085	1979	346	1987	736	1995	1080
1972	665	1980	83	1988	849	1996	1213

2.8 Table 2.11 shows annual precipitation data for one station. (1) Plot the precipitation versus time. (2) Calculate the mean annual precipitation $\overline{P}$ (*mm*) and plot it as a straight line on the graph. (3) Identify the wet, medium and dry years. (4) Estimate the average period of precipitation oscillation in years (i.e., number of years between two wet cycles). (5) Assuming that annual precipitation is a random variable, how much is the average fluctuation around the mean (i.e., calculate the standard deviation of precipitation σ_P (*mm*). (6) Add the standard deviation of precipitation to the mean and plot $\overline{P}+\sigma_P$ as a straight dashed line in the graph; repeat for $\overline{P}-\sigma_P$.

2.9 Modify the Maple program of Example 2.5 to produce a single graph with 10, 20, and 30-year moving average curves of annual precipitation in Philadelphia. The data file can be downloaded from the Franklin Institute site (www.fi.edu/weather/data2/index.html). State your conclusions about the effect of different durations in moving averages.

2.10 Modify the Maple program of Example 2.6 to calculate and plot the mean monthly precipitation for the entire series of precipitation in Philadelphia. The data file can be downloaded from the Franklin Institute site (www.fi.edu/weather/data2/index.html

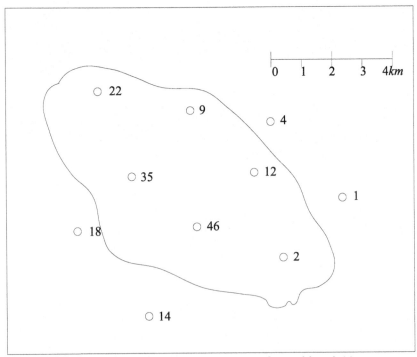

Figure 2.23: Rainfall Data for Problem 2.11

2.11 Figure 2.23 shows a watershed with the total precipitation (*mm*) registered at several rain gages during a storm. Estimate the mean precipitation in the watershed using (1) the arithmetic method, (2) the Thiessen polygons method, and (3) the isohyetal method.

2.12 Calculate the mean precipitation for the watershed in Figure 2.18. Use millimetric paper If you apply the dot grid method of area estimation. Another simple method is to scan the figure into a PDF document and use Adobe's area calculation utility.

2.13 From the Precipitation data at various durations given in Example 2.9, (1) prepare the IDF curves for the 2-*year* and 3-*year* return periods; (2) using these curves, estimate the design rainfall intensity corresponding to a 2-*year* return period and a duration of 12*hour*; (3) estimate the design precipitation intensity of a nearby facility if the required return period is T=2.33*years* (considered the mean annual event), and the critical duration is   .

2.14 Redo the IDF analysis of Example 2.9 as a Depth-Duration-Frequency problem (DDF). Hint: in Table 2.5, transform the precipitation intensity data into precipitation depth by multiplying by the corresponding duration.

2.15 Modify the Maple program of Example 2.11 to prepare the IDF curves for the city of Washington DC, using equation (2.5), Figure 2.20, and Table 2.6. Determine the design rainfall intensity for a duration of 24*hour* and a return period of 25*year*.

2.16 Derive a 24-*hour* Probable Maximum Storm (PMS) for a watershed of 500 km^2 of drainage area, and propose a design rainfall hyetograph, if the mean annual maximum 24-*hour* precipitation depth is 120*mm*, and the standard deviation for the same duration is 18*mm*.

Kama Merú Falls, Canaima National Park, the Grand Savanna, Venezuela.
Photo courtesy of Ing. Antonio Enrique Seijas

"The Philosophers frequently describe this matter. Sendivogius calls it heavenly water, not vulgar, but almost like rain water. When Hermes calls it a bird without wings, figuring thereby its vaporous nature, it is well described. When he calls the sun its father and the moon its mother, he signifies that it is produced by the action of heat upon moisture. When he says the wind carries it in its belly, he only means that the air is its receptacle. When he affirms that which is inferior is like that which is superior, he teaches that the same vapor on the surface of the earth furnishes the rain and dew, wherewith all things are nourished in the vegetable, animal and mineral kingdoms. This now is what the Philosophers call their Mercury and affirm it to be found in all things, as it is in fact."

Alchemist Eirenaei Philalethis, 1668

3 EVAPORATION AND TRANSPIRATION

3.1 IMPORTANCE OF EVAPORATION AND TRANSPIRATION

Evaporation and transpiration constitute the physical and biological processes by which water in the liquid or solid phase, at or near the earth's land surface, becomes atmospheric water vapor. These include evaporation of liquid water from rivers, lakes, soil, and vegetative surfaces; evaporation from within the leaves of plants and trees (transpiration); and sublimation from ice and snow surfaces. *Evapotranspiration* is the collective term for all evaporation and transpiration processes in a region.

The most important source of evaporation is the ocean. Oceans provide a large portion of water vapor to the atmosphere for its subsequent precipitation in various parts of the earth. Continental waters also provide water to the atmosphere. It is estimated that over 60% of the precipitation that falls on the continents of the earth is evapotranspired. This is an average that varies greatly according to the precipitation regime, the season, the soil type, the vegetation, and the land use of the region.

Evapotranspiration is one of the most important quantities in equations simulating hydrologic systems. Since a vast portion of precipitated water is lost through evapotranspiration, a quantitative understanding of the physical processes involved in evapotranspiration is of vital importance in the planning, development, and management of water resources projects. This is easy to see, since the difference between precipitation and evapotranspiration, over a long term, is the water available for human use. The design of surface and shallow groundwater reservoirs are examples of water resources projects where evaporation prediction is a fundamental requisite. Evaporation has a significant influence on the yield of water supply reservoirs and on the economics of building reservoirs of various sizes. Much of the world's food supply is grown on artificially irrigated land. Irrigation constitutes one of the largest users of water around the world. The design of an efficient irrigation system requires a knowledge of crop-water use (transpiration). An irrigation system should aim at providing only the deficit of precipitation necessary for a healthy crop development.

From an environmental point of view, most of the water lost via evapotranspiration is used by plants which form the basis of the earth's land ecosystems. For this reason, an understanding between evapotranspiration and ecosystem type is necessary to predict ecosystem response to climate change. In the analysis of watershed hydrologic response, the amount of precipitation in a storm that becomes surface runoff and groundwater recharge, depends on the soil moisture prior to the storm. The soil moisture is a function of the evapotranspiration during the period of time preceding the rainfall event.

3.2 EVAPORATION FROM FREE WATER BODIES

Fundamental Physical Processes

In its simplest case, evaporation is a change of the phase of water from a liquid to a vapor state through an evaporating surface. The evaporating surface is the upper boundary of a lake, river, or ocean. The driving force in this process is the solar radiation, which provides energy to the molecules of liquid water near the surface. The solar radiation causes an increase in the vibratory kinetic energy of the water molecules. When the amplitude of vibration overcomes the forces of molecular attraction, the water molecules escape from the liquid mass and cross the surface to enter the air immediately above this boundary.

Table 3.1: Latent Heat of Evaporation, L, and Saturated Vapor Pressure, e_s, for Water Under Normal Conditions

Temperature (^{o}C)	L (cal/kg)	e_s (mmHg)	e_s (N/m²)
0	597.3×10^3	4.58	611
5	594.5×10^3	6.54	872
10	591.7×10^3	9.20	1227
15	588.9×10^3	12.78	1704
20	586.0×10^3	17.53	2337
25	583.2×10^3	23.76	3167
30	580.4×10^3	31.83	4243
35	577.6×10^3	42.18	5624
40	574.5×10^3	55.34	7378
50	569.0×10^3	92.56	12.40
60	563.2×10^3	149.46	19.26
70	557.4×10^3	233.79	31169
80	551.4×10^3	355.28	47367
90	545.3×10^3	525.89	70113
100	539.1×10^3	760.00	101325

From above, we note that the first requisite for the occurrence of evaporation is the absorption of energy. Energy is usually provided by solar radiation. However, evaporation may still occur in the absence of sufficient solar energy provided that other atmospheric conditions are favorable. This implies that the required evaporation energy is supplied by the surrounding water or air media. The amount of energy required for the evaporation of one gram of water is called the latent heat of vaporization, L (*cal/g*). The required energy decreases as the temperature of the evaporating water increases. Table 3.1 shows the value of the latent heat of vaporization as a function of temperature of clean water under normal atmospheric conditions. The energy utilized in the process of evaporation is later released in the process of condensation.

Once the molecules of water have absorbed the required amount of energy, they become water vapor. Water vapor is a gas that approximately behaves as an ideal gas. It will occupy the volume of air immediately above the evaporating surface. Thus, if we observed a small control volume just above an evaporating surface (see Figure 3.1), we would note that it is contained by dry air, which is a mixture of oxygen and other gases, and by water vapor. The atmospheric pressure registered by a barometer at this point is the summation of the partial pressure exerted by the dry air, P_{dry}, and the partial pressure exerted by the water vapor, e. Water-vapor pressure, or simply vapor pressure, is a function of the number of water vapor molecules contained in the control volume.

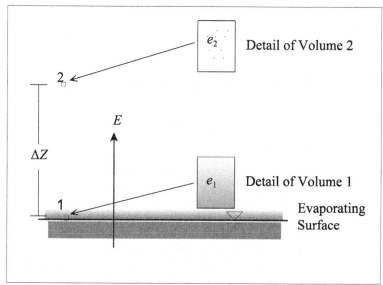

Figure 3.1: Free-Water Evaporation through a Surface

Evaporation is a diffusive process governed by Fick's law of diffusion (see Chapter 1). Therefore, water vapor will move from regions of air mass under high concentration of water vapor (i.e., high number of molecules) to those with a low concentration of it (i.e., low number of molecules). Since vapor pressure is a function of the number of water-vapor molecules present within a volume, the above statement implies that water vapor moves from regions of high vapor pressure to regions of comparatively lower water-vapor pressure. The result will be a transport of water vapor from portions of the air just above an evaporating surface, where water vapor is near liquid water, to upper atmospheric regions of dryer air. The transport of water vapor through air is analogous to other hydrologic processes governed by Fick's law of diffusion and similar thermodynamical concepts. For instance, heat moves from areas of high temperature to regions of low temperature. Pollutants in a lake move from areas of high contaminant concentration to those with a low one. Groundwater moves from areas of high hydraulic head to areas with a low one.

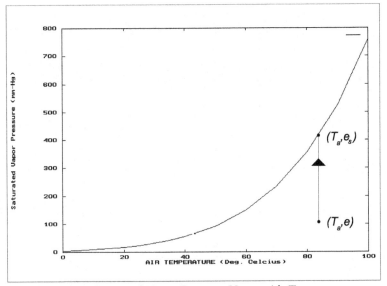

Figure 3.2: Saturated Vapor Pressure Versus Air Temperature

Figure 3.1 illustrates the simple case of free-water evaporation in the absence of wind. Control volume 1 has a given vapor pressure, e_1, and control volume 2, located ΔZ meters above the surface, has a different vapor pressure, e_2. Since volume 1 is closer to the evaporating surface than volume 2, then $e_1 > e_2$, and thus water vapor moves vertically from 1 to 2. More precisely, we say that the evaporation rate is proportional to the vapor pressure gradient, $(e_2 - e_1)/\Delta Z$. The vapor pressure gradient, or the change in vapor pressure per unit distance, is the driving force of the evaporation process.

Some form of atmospheric transport of water vapor is necessary for the evaporation process to continue over time. Returning to Figure 3.1, the initial evaporation causes the migration of water molecules from the water body to the air layers immediately above the surface (control volume 1). If there is not a transport mechanism causing the migration of vapor away from the evaporating surface, then the layers of air immediately above the surface would reach a saturation point. At this point, no more water molecules are admitted into volume 1 and evaporation would cease. This maximum number of molecules held by the air at a given temperature correspond to the so called *saturation vapor pressure*, e_s. The saturation vapor pressure is a function of air temperature (see Table 3.1 and Figure 3.2). Warm air has a higher saturated-vapor pressure (i.e., can hold more moisture) than cold air.

Consider a small volume of air some distance above the evaporating surface (i.e., volume 2 in Figure 3.1) with an air temperature T_a and a (not saturated) vapor pressure e. These coordinates are marked in Figure 3.2. Let us assume that by some means we compress the air while keeping the temperature constant. When this happens, the vapor pressure increases. When the vapor pressure reaches saturation, the air mass has moved its coordinates along the vertical path shown in Figure 3.2. An additional compression of the air would cause the excess of water vapor to condensate. Alternatively, one could decrease the temperature of the air mass, while keeping the pressure constant. When the air temperature intersects the saturated vapor pressure curve (i.e., the dew point temperature), the air reaches saturation. Additional cooling would cause condensation of the excess moisture. In upper atmospheric layers, saturation is reached via a mixture of the above two possibilities: a decrease in temperature accompanied by a change in pressure.

The ratio of the actual, not saturated, vapor pressure to the saturated vapor pressure is the air *relative humidity*:

$$r = \frac{e}{e_s} \times 100 \tag{3.1}$$

where
r=relative humidity of air mass expressed in percentage

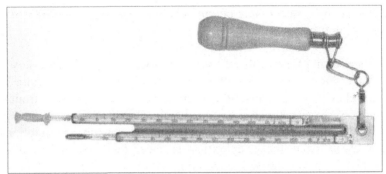

Figure 3.3: Sling Psychrometer with its Handle (*courtesy of Greg Keefer, Hagerstown Maryland Weather Observer*)

Table 3.2: Relative Humidity in Percent with Respect to Wet-Bulb Depression

T_a (°C)	Wet-Bulb Depression (T_a-T_w)(°C)										
	0	1	2	3	4	5	6	7	8	9	10
-10	91	60	31	2							
-8	93	65	39	13							
-6	94	70	46	23	0						
-4	96	74	53	32	11						
-2	98	78	58	39	21	3					
0	100	81	63	46	29	13					
2	100	84	68	52	37	22	7				
4	100	85	71	57	43	29.	16				
6	100	86	73	60	48	35	24	11			
8	100	87	75	63	51	40	29	19	8		
10	100	88	77	66	55	44	34	24	15	6	
12	100	89	78	68	58	48	39	29	21	12	4
14	100	90	79	70	60	51	42	34	26	18	10
16	100	90	81	71	63	54	46	38	30	23	15
18	100	91	82	73	65	57	49	41	34	27	20
20	100	91	83	74	66	59	51	44	37	31	24
22	100	92	83	76	68	61	54	47	40	34	28
24	100	92	84	77	69	62	56	49	43	37	31
26	100	92	85	78	71	64	58	51	46	40	34
28	100	93	85	78	72	65	59	53	48	42	37
30	100	93	86	79	73	67	61	55	50	44	39
32	100	93	86	80	74	68	62	57	51	46	41
34	100	93	87	81	75	69	63	58	53	48	43
36	100	94	87	81	75	70	64	59	54	50	45
38	100	94	88	82	76	71	66	61	56	51	47
40	100	94	88	82	77	72	67	62	57	53	48

Source: Bras (1990); Dept. of Com.-Dept. Def. (1972); Linsley et al. (1982)

Relative humidity is a measure of how much moisture an air mass holds. Relative humidity values of over 80% indicate humid conditions under which evaporation rates are expected to be low. Alternatively, relative humidity values of less than 60% indicate dry conditions under which evaporation rates are expected to be high. Relative humidity is measured with a *psychrometer* (Figure 3.3). This is an instrument with two thermometers. One is a wet-bulb thermometer covered with cloth saturated with water. The other is dry. The temperature on the wet thermometer, T_w, is lower than that of the dry, T_a, because of evaporation. The difference between the two readings is called the wet-bulb depression. Using meteorological tables (Table 3.2), the relative humidity can be found as a function of the wet-bulb depression.

Example 3.1

During a day, the dry-bulb and wet-bulb thermometer readings in a psychrometer indicated 26 and 22°C, respectively. Estimate the relative humidity.

Solution

The wet-bulb depression is $T_a - T_w = 26°C - 22°C = 4°C$. In Table 3.2 the relative humidity corresponding to a wet-bulb depression of 4°C and a dry air temperature of $T_a = 26°C$ is $r = 71\%$

As previously stated, evaporation requires absorption of energy, and a mechanism for the transport of water vapor away from the evaporating surface. The transport mechanism causes a vapor pressure gradient and thus the replacement of moist air with dryer air in the layers immediately above the surface. The naturally diffusive process of water vapor can be greatly affected by the turbulent eddies resulting from the upward movement of moist air. Moist air near the surface is lighter than dry air in layers above. In addition wind currents may also encourage higher vapor pressure gradients by the displacement of moist air away from the evaporating surface. Thus, a general expression of evaporation rate that considers the above factors is Dalton's (1802) law:

$$E = f(u)(e_s - e_a) \qquad (3.2)$$

where

E = evaporation rate (mm/day)

e_s = saturated vapor pressure at the water surface temperature
($mmHg$, N/m^2)
e_a = vapor pressure at a fixed distance above the evaporating surface
($mmHg$, N/m^2)
u=horizontal wind speed ($km/hour$)
$f(u)$= a function of the wind speed and other factors
(($hour.mm$)/($day.km.mmHg$)), or (($hour.mm.m^2$)/($day.km.N$))

Evaporation by Mass Transfer Methods
Many forms of equation (3.2) have been developed for various localities. They all require the saturated vapor pressure at the water surface (the vapor pressure at the surface is considered saturated), and the vapor pressure at a point some distance above the surface. These equations are collectively called mass transfer equations. One widely used was developed by Harbeck (1962) based on a study conducted on 20 reservoirs, each of up to 120 km^2 in surface area:

$$E = kA^{-0.05} W(e_s - e_a) \qquad (3.3)$$

where
E=evaporation rate (mm/day)
A=lake surface area (km^2)
W=wind speed at a point 2m above the water surface ($Km/hour$)
e_s = saturated vapor pressure at water-surface temperature (mm/Hg)
e_a = vapor pressure at a point 2m above the water surface ($mmHg$)
k=mass transfer coefficient equal to 0.054
(($mm.hour$)/($day.km^{0.9}.mmHg$))

The application of equation (3.3) requires an *anemometer* located 2 meters above the lake surface to measure the wind speed, a psychrometer at the same elevation to measure the relative humidity and thermometers to measure the air and surface-water temperature.

Example 3.2
A lake has an average surface area of 45.6 km^2. During a day, the mean water surface temperature is 15°C, the mean air temperature is 20°C, and the mean wind speed at a point 2 meters above the surface of the lake is 9.8$km/hour$. If the relative humidity is 65%, calculate (1) the evaporation rate in mm/day; and (2) The daily volume of water evaporated in m^3/day.

Solution

(1)From Table 3.1 $e_s(T_s)=e_s(15^oC)=12.78$ $mmHg$. From equation (3.1) and Table 3.1,

$$e_a(T_a)=r.e_s(T_a)=r.e_s(20^oC)=0.65\times17.53mmHg=11.39mmHg$$

From equation (3.3),

$$E=kA^{-0.05}W(e_s-e_a)$$

$$E=\frac{0.054mm.hour}{day.km^{0.9}.mmHg}\times(45.6km^2)^{-0.05}\times9.8\frac{km}{hour}$$

$$\times(12.78mmHg-11.39mmHg)$$

$$E=0.61\frac{mm}{day}$$

(2) The total volume of water lost in one day is then

$$E(m^3)=E(\frac{mm}{day}).A_s=0.61\frac{mm}{day}\times\frac{m}{10^3mm}\times45.6km^2\times\frac{10^6m^2}{km^2}=27,816\frac{m^3}{day}$$

Another commonly used method to estimate lake evaporation is the Meyer (1944) equation:

$$E=C\left(1+\frac{W}{16.09}\right)(e_s-e_a) \qquad (3.4)$$

where

E=evaporation rate (mm/day)

e_s, e_a= as previously defined for equation (3.3)

W=wind speed at a point 7.6m above the lake surface ($km/hour$)

C=0.36 for lakes, and 0.50 for wet soils (($mm.hour)/(day.km.mmHg$))

Application of Meyer's equation requires the same instrumentation as that of Harbeck's. An important difference between the two equations is the elevation of the wind speed measurement above the lake surface: 2 meters for the Harbeck's equation, and 7.6 meters for the Meyer's equation. Assuming a logarithmic vertical distribution of wind velocity, the wind velocity, $W(z_1)$, measured at an elevation z_1 may be transformed into an equivalent one, $W(z_2)$, at a different elevation z_2, required by a specific evaporation equation:

$$W(z_2) = W(z_1)\left(\frac{\log(z_2)}{\log(z_1)}\right)$$
(3.5)

Example 3.3

Solve Example 3.2 with Meyer's equation.

Solution

(1) In Example 3.2, the wind speed was measured at $2m$ above the lake; it must now be adjusted to that at an elevation of $7.6m$, as required by Meyer's equation. From equation (3.5),

$$W(7.6m) = W(2.0m)\left(\frac{\log(7.6m)}{\log(2.0m)}\right) = 9.8\frac{km}{hour}\times\left(\frac{0.881}{0.301}\right) = 28.67\frac{km}{hour}$$

From equation (3.4),

(2) The total volume of water lost in one day is then,

$$E(m^3) = E(\frac{mm}{day}).A_s = 1.39\frac{mm}{day}\times\frac{m}{10^3 mm}\times45.6km^2\times\frac{10^6 m^2}{km^2} = 63,384\frac{m^3}{day}$$

In this case the Meyer's equation gives a significantly greater estimate of evaporation losses than Harbeck's. One possible reason is our assumption concerning the wind speed at $7.6m$. If the wind speed is corrected to a value comparable to that at $2m$ of elevation, the two estimates of evaporation are similar.

Measurement of Evaporation Using Pans

   A direct method of measuring lake evaporation is by means of *evaporation pans*. There are several versions. A typical one is a galvanized iron cylindrical container, $1.2m$ in diameter and $25cm$ in depth (see Figure 3.4). It is mounted on a wooden frame about $10cm$ above the ground to allow for air circulation. The pan is re-filled with water daily to a fixed depth of about $20cm$.

Figure 3.4: Evaporation Pan (*courtesy of the U.S. National Weather Service Training Center*)

Figure 3.4 shows an evaporation pan with an anemometer, a water-volume meter to measure the amount of water added, and a thermometer. The water level is measured daily by a hook gage in a stilling well. The evaporation is computed as the difference in observed water levels over a period of time, $\Delta S/\Delta t$, adjusted for any precipitation, P, or any water added to restore levels, Q. Figure 3.5 shows an idealized cross section of an evaporation pan with the variables involved. Thus, applying the water balance equation to the evaporation pan (i.e., equation (1.5), Chapter 1),

$$P + Q - E_p = \frac{\Delta S}{\Delta t}$$ (3.6)

where
   P=total precipitation in one day (*mm/day*)
   Q=water added to a fixed level (*mm/day*)
   E_p= pan evaporation rate (*mm/day*)
   $\Delta S/\Delta t$= measured change in water level in one day (*mm/day*)

The only unknown in equation (3.6) is the pan evaporation rate. The change in water level, ΔS, measured by the observer is positive for an increase in water level with respect to the previous day, and negative for a decrease in level.

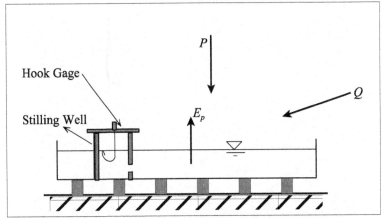

Figure 3.5: Cross Section of an Evaporation Pan

Because of the ideal conditions of the evaporation pan (i.e., metal container, small amounts of water, etc.), the pan evaporation rate is usually higher than that occurring in a nearby lake or reservoir. To estimate the lake evaporation rate, an adjustment must be made according to the equation

$$E = KE_p \qquad (3.7)$$

where
    E=lake evaporation rate (mm/day)
    K=pan coefficient

Average annual or monthly pan coefficients should be used. The pan coefficient varies between 0.6 and 0.8 with an average of 0.7.

Example 3.4
    An observer measured an increase of 21.3mm in the water level of a pan with respect to that recorded the day before. If during the same day she added 20.2mm of water to restore its level, and the station rain gage registered 5.0mm of rain, estimate the pan and lake evaporation rates.

Repeat your calculation for the following day, when she measured a *decrease* of 2.9*mm* in the water level, no water was added to the pan, and no precipitation was registered.

Solution

For the first day the pan evaporation rate is, from equation (3.6),

$$E_p = P + Q - \frac{\Delta S}{\Delta t} = 5.0 \frac{mm}{day} + 20.2 \frac{mm}{day} - 21.3 \frac{mm}{day} = 3.9 \frac{mm}{day}$$

Assuming a pan coefficient of 0.7, the lake evaporation is, from equation (3.7),

$$E = KE_p = 0.7 \times 3.9 \frac{mm}{day} = 2.7 \frac{mm}{day}$$

For the second day, $P=0$, $Q=0$, and $\Delta S/\Delta t = -2.9 mm/day$. Thus, from equation (3.6),

$$E_p = P + Q - \frac{\Delta S}{\Delta t} = 2.9 \frac{mm}{day}$$

and from equation (3.7)

$$E = KE_p = 0.7 \times 2.9 \frac{mm}{day} = 2.0 \frac{mm}{day}$$

An improvement of equation (3.7) to estimate lake evaporation based on pan evaporation considers vapor pressure gradients on the lake and on the pan:

$$E = K \left(\frac{e_s(T_s) - e_a(T_a)}{e_s(T_p) - e_a(T_a)} \right) E_p \qquad (3.8)$$

where

T_s = maximum lake-surface temperature (^oC)
T_p = maximum pan-surface temperature (^oC)
T_a = mean air temperature 4 meters above the lake surface (^oC)
$e_s(T_s)$ = saturated vapor pressure at lake-surface temperature ($mmHg$)
$e_s(T_p)$ = saturated vapor pressure at pan-surface temperature ($mmHg$)
$e_a(T_a)$ = vapor pressure at air temperature ($mmHg$)
K' = 1.5 for U.S. Class A pan (Webb, 1966)

Example 3.5

Calculate the lake evaporation based on the following data recorded during a given day: maximum water temperature at lake surface T_s = 20^oC; maximum water temperature at pan surface T_p = 25^oC; mean air temperature T_a = 23^oC; relative humidity r = 75%; pan coefficient K' = 1.5; and pan evaporation E_p = 4.8mm/day.

Solution

From Table 3.1, $e_s(T_s)$ = 17.53$mmHg$, and $e_s(T_p)$ = 23.76$mmHg$. For the air vapor pressure, we need to interpolate in Table 3.1, and use equation (3.1):

$$e_a(T_a) = e_s(T_a).r = \left[e_s(20^oC) + 3^oC \times \left(\frac{e_s(25^oC) - e_s(20^oC)}{5^oC} \right) \right] \times 0.75$$

$$e_a(23^oC) = \left[17.53mmHg + 3 \times \left(\frac{23.76mmHg - 17.53mmHg}{5} \right) \right] \times 0.75$$

$$= 15.95mmHg$$

Thus, from equation (3.8)

$$E = K' \left(\frac{e_s(T_s) - e_a(T_a)}{e_s(T_p) - e_a(T_a)} \right) E_p$$

$$= 1.5 \times \left(\frac{17.53mmHg - 15.95mmHg}{23.76mmHg - 15.95mmHg} \right) \times 4.8 \frac{mm}{day} = 1.46 \frac{mm}{day}$$

The pan-to-lake coefficient is a major cause of error in the estimation of evaporation. Errors in the range of 10 to 15% of annual estimates and up to 50% for monthly estimates have been reported. Therefore, the pan method is effective when employed in long-term calculations of evaporation.

Evaporation Estimation Using Water Balance Techniques

The most commonly used technique to estimate evaporation involves the application of the hydrologic water balance equation to the reservoir in question. For instance, the application of equation (1.5) requires an inventory of all streams entering and leaving the lake, each with a quantitative evaluation of its flow rate. It is also necessary to measure precipitation in a nearby gage during the period of analysis, and to evaluate the net groundwater contribution, for large lakes. The accuracy of the water balance method is a function of the accuracy of the different variables involved. For annual calculations, average errors between 10 and 20% are normal. This method is usually preferred over other techniques because of its simplicity of application. In addition, many watersheds containing reservoirs are routinely gaged for streamflow and precipitation rates, and thus corresponding evaporation estimates do not require special instrumentation.

Example 3.6

A flood-control reservoir has a surface area of $18km^2$. From an inventory of streams flowing into and out of the lake, it is estimated that the average inflow rate in a given day is $45m^3/s$. The controlled outflow rate is $12.5m^3/s$. During the same day, the lake stage (the water level) increases about $15cm$. Estimate the evaporation rate in mm/day.

Solution

From equation (1.5), neglecting groundwater for a short period of one day,

$$Q_i - Q_o - E = \frac{\Delta S}{\Delta t} \quad \Rightarrow \quad E = Q_i - Q_o - \frac{\Delta s}{\Delta t}$$

Recall that to transform a volume into an equivalent depth over an entire lake one must divide by its surface area,

$$E = \frac{(45m^3/s - 12.5m^3/s) \times \dfrac{86,400s}{day}}{18km^2 \times \dfrac{10^6 m^2}{km^2}} \times \frac{10^3 mm}{m} - 15\frac{cm}{day} \times \frac{10mm}{cm} = 6.0\frac{mm}{day}$$

Evaporation Estimation Using Energy Budget Techniques

As previously stated, evaporation requires absorption of energy. This energy is either supplied by solar radiation, or by the body of the lake itself. Radiation is the emission of energy in the form of electromagnetic waves from all bodies above the absolute zero temperature.

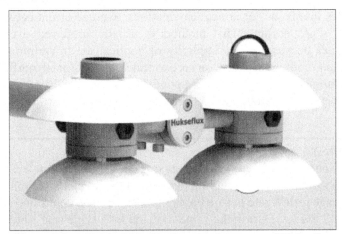

Figure 3.6: A Typical Net Radiometer (*courtesy of Hukseflux Thermal Sensors*)

A *net radiometer* is an instrument used to measure net radiation at the earth's surface in meteorological applications. The name net radiometer reflects the fact that it measures incoming minus reflected radiation in *watt/m²* or *cal/(m².day)*. There are many types of net-radiometers, but the four-component design is a popular one (see Figure 3.6). A four-component net radiometer measures the four separate constituents of the surface radiation balance: (1) short-wave incident or global solar radiation, measured by a *pyranometer* located on the right side of Figure 3.6, above the upper umbrella radiation shield. (2) short-wave reflected solar radiation, measured by a pyranometer located on the right side of Figure 3.6, below the lower umbrella radiation shield. (3) long-wave or infrared radiation emitted by the sky, measured by a *pyrgeometer* located on the left side of Figure 3.6, above the upper umbrella radiation shield. (4) long-wave or infrared radiation emitted by the ground surface. From these, the net radiation (net value of all short-wave and long-wave fluxes) may be estimated. A *pyranometer* is a detector that measures solar radiation flux density with a spectral response from 300 to 2800 nanometers. Its main components are a thermal sensor with a black coating, and a glass dome to shield convective heat. The black coating on the sensor absorbs solar radiation, which is converted to heat flow and thus a voltage output signal proportional to solar radiation. A *pyrgeometer* is a device whose thermal sensor is designed to measure atmospheric infrared radiation spectrum that extends approximately from $4.5\,\mu m$ to $100\,\mu m$.

It is possible to establish an energy balance, or energy budget, equation for a lake, similar to that of a water balance equation. On the left side of this equation, are all forms of caloric energy entering or leaving a lake during a given period of time. Typical positive terms include incoming short-wave solar radiation and incoming long-wave atmospheric radiation. Typical negative terms include reflected short-wave solar radiation; reflected long-wave atmospheric radiation; long-wave radiation emitted by the lake; energy used in the evaporation process; and energy exchanged between the water and the atmosphere as sensible heat because of their temperature differences. The energy transported (or advected) into (positive) or from (negative) the lake by rivers, rainfall, and groundwater may be important. The right side of the energy balance equation represents the change in the lake internal energy during the period of analysis. Thus, the energy balance equation reduces to

$$Q_n - Q_e + Q_h + Q_v = \frac{\Delta Q}{\Delta t} \tag{3.9}$$

where
   Q_n = net radiation (short and long wave) ($cal/(m^2.day)$)
   Q_e = energy used in evaporation ($cal/(m^2.day)$)
   Q_h = energy loss as sensible heat ($cal/(m^2.day)$)
   Q_v = energy advected into or from the lake ($cal/(m^2.day)$)
   ΔQ = change in lake energy ($cal/(m^2)$)
   Δt = period of analysis (day)

To express the sensible heat in terms of the energy used in evaporation, Bowen (1926) suggests the ratio

$$B = \frac{Q_h}{Q_e} = \gamma P \left(\frac{T_s - T_a}{e_s - e_a} \right)$$

(3.10)

where
  B=Bowen's ratio
  γ= psychrometric constant $\approx 0.66 \times 10^{-3} (^{\circ}C^{-1})$
  P=ambient atmospheric pressure at water surface (*mmHg*)

and the rest of the terms as before. The only unknown in the energy balance equation (3.9) is the energy used in evaporation Q_e. To express this energy in terms of evaporation depth, we divide by the density of water and by the latent heat of evaporation. Thus, substituting equation (3.10) into (3.9),

$$E = \frac{C_1}{\rho L (1 + B)} (Q_n + Q_v - \Delta Q / \Delta t)$$

(3.11)

where
  E=evaporation rate (*mm/day*)
  ρ= density of water (kg/m^3)
  L=latent heat of evaporation (*cal/kg*)
  $C_1 = 1000 mm/m$, units conversion constant

The net radiation entering a lake Q_n (i.e., incoming minus reflected, short and long-wave radiation) is evaluated with a net radiometer. The energy advected from streams is evaluated through an inventory of the streams entering or leaving the lake, each with its own flow rate, temperature, and water density. If there is precipitation during the period of analysis, its advected energy must be evaluated. Similarly, for long periods of analysis the advected energy by the evaporated water itself should be included. An approximate expression for the advected energy over the entire lake is given by

$$Q_v = \frac{C_p}{\Delta t} \sum_{i=0}^{N} \rho_i V_i T_i$$

(3.12)

where

Q_v = advected energy over the entire lake (*cal/day*)
C_p = specific heat at constant pressure of water $\approx 1000(cal/(kg.^oC))$
ρ_i = density of component i (kg/m^3)
V_i = volume of component i during $\Delta t (m^3)$
T_i = water temperature of component i (^oC)
N = number of components

If lake-temperature profiles are available, the change in lake energy, $\Delta Q/\Delta t$, is evaluated through a numerical averaging of the lake temperature at different layers, prior and after the period of analysis. For small shallow lakes, equation (3.12) may be applied prior and after the period of analysis.

The most important advantage in using the energy balance method to evaluate evaporation is its accuracy. Less than 10% of errors have been reported. The disadvantage is that it requires special instrumentation and detailed measurement of all the streams, lakes and groundwater surrounding the lake. For a detailed application a discussion on the theoretical basis of the method, see Bruce and Rodgers (1962) and Bras (1990).

Example 3.7
Using radiometers, it has been determined that the net radiation entering a lake (incoming minus reflected, short and long wave) was about $5 \times 10^6 cal/(m^2.day)$ during the period of one day. The surface water temperature during the same day was 13^oC, the air temperature above the lake 9^oC, the relative humidity 85%, and the atmospheric pressure $740mmHg$. There was no appreciable change in the water temperature of the lake and no precipitation was recorded. However, there is a river flowing towards the lake with an average flow rate of $0.5m^3/s$. The river water temperature is 11^oC. The lake has an average surface area of $3.8km^2$. Estimate the evaporation rate in *mm/day*.

Solution
From equation (3.10) and Table 3.1 we first evaluate the Bowen's ratio:

$$B = \gamma P\left(\frac{T_s - T_a}{e_s - e_a}\right)$$

$$B=\frac{0.66}{1000°C}\times740mmHg\left(\frac{13°C-9°C}{11.35mmHg-7.37mmHg}\right)=0.49$$

Note that interpolation in the values of Table 3.1 is needed. Also recall that to obtain the air vapor pressure, one has to multiply the saturated vapor pressure by the relative humidity (see Example 3.2). Since there is no precipitation and no appreciable change in lake temperature, $\Delta Q/\Delta t=0$, and the only component in the advection term is the energy transported from the river to the lake. From equation (3.12),

$$Q_v=\frac{C_p}{\Delta t}\sum_{i=0}^{N}\rho_iV_iT_i$$

$$Q_v=1000\frac{cal}{kg.°C}\times1000\frac{kg}{m^3}\times0.5\frac{m^3}{s}\times\frac{86400s}{day}\times11°C=47.52\times10^{10}\frac{cal}{day}$$

Assuming complete mixing in the lake and dividing by the lake area,

$$Q_v=\frac{47.52\times10^{10}cal/day}{3.8km^2\times\dfrac{10^6m^2}{km^2}}=0.125\times10^6\frac{cal}{m^2.day}$$

Now from equation (3.11) and Table 3.1, the evaporation rate is

$$E=\frac{C_1}{\rho L(1+B)}\left(Q_n+Q_v-\Delta Q/\Delta t\right)$$

$$E=\frac{1000mm/m\times\left(5\times10^6\dfrac{cal}{m^2.day}+0.125\times10^6\dfrac{cal}{m^2.day}\right)}{1000kg/m^3\times590.02\times10^3cal/kg\times(1+0.49)}=5.8\frac{mm}{day}$$

When $\Delta t>24hour$, the change in lake temperature may be significant, and the term $\Delta Q/\Delta t$ must be included in the calculations; this would require an evaluation of the change in the water volume of the lake during the period of analysis.

3.3 TRANSPIRATION FROM VEGETATION

As part of the normal biological activities of plant growth, water and nutrients are transferred from the root zone to the leaf surface. Eventually, the excess of water evaporates to the atmosphere. This process is called *transpiration*. It first begins with the osmotic pressures at the root zone to move water and soil minerals into the roots. From the roots, water is transported through the plant stem to the leaves via an elaborate water transportation system. In the case of trees, this system is so vast that it has made trees deserve the name of "masters of microfluidics" by modern scientists (Holbrook and Zwieniecki, 2008).

In the stem of a large tree, the number of interconnected water transport conduits can exceed hundreds of millions, and their total length can exceed several hundred kilometers. This natural system allows a tree to easily move tens of cubic meters of water from the soil to its leaves on a sunny day, without any moving parts or noise. On a global scale, the moving of water through plants is a major contributor of moisture from the soil to the atmosphere.

The driving water pump of a tree is not in its roots, since trees whose roots have been cut can temporarily provide water to the leaves; it is not in its leaves either, since this air-vacuum pump would limit the maximum suction height, and thus a tree's height, to $10.33m$, failing to explain the existence of trees that surpass the $100m$ in height, like the redwoods in California. Plants transport water to the leaves via an ingenious arrange of capillary vessels. Under capillary, water can be elevated against gravity thanks to the attraction of water molecules to the wettable conduit surface and the ability of water to experience a large surface tension. The diameter in the capillary tubes range from the large ones encountered in the stem, about 50 to 100 μm, to the small ones in the air-water interfaces of the cell walls of the leaves, about 5 to $10nm$. The gradual reduction in tube diameter promotes an efficient flow that reduces viscous losses. Many intriguing questions remain unanswered, such as the ability of a tree to prevent the formation of vapor bubbles, which would render the transport of water useless. While science labors to understand these problems (see Pickard, 1981), we should turn to the explanations given by mystical hydrologists, who focus on the effect of subtle negative (vacuum) energies, and vortex movements. Understanding the principles behind these silent plant engineers may provide the key to a new generation of —efficient, silent, suction-based, non-polluting— motors and water pumps in the future. For illuminating clues on this, please see Bartholomew (2005), and Schauberger (1998).

As water is transported from the roots, air enters the leaves through small surface openings called stomata. Chloroplasts within the leaves consume carbon dioxide from the air and water to synthesize carbohydrates necessary for plant growth. Since the atmospheric concentration of carbon dioxide is low (e.g., 0.038%), then as much as 99% of the water that enters the roots travels through the stem system and escapes through the stomatal orifices to the leaf surfaces where it is available for evaporation (Holbrook and Zwieniecki, 2008). This explains why the demand of water for plants exceeds that of animals.

Transpiration is a continuous process that occurs even without precipitation. However the rate of transpiration may be affected by the rate moisture becomes available to the root system. Furthermore, during a rainfall storm, intercepted water may transfer some of the energy available for evaporation away thereby reducing transpiration.

Transpiration rate is a distinct function of the precipitation regime, the season, the root system depth, the soil type and soil-water content, the density of vegetation, and especially the type of vegetation (i.e., plant species). Vegetation in humid areas has a completely different pattern of transpiration from that in dry or arid areas. The stomatal orifices are sensitive to the solar radiation. In humid areas they open during the day and close at night. In desert areas, where the availability of moisture is limited, the reverse is true. The stomatal orifices close during the day to minimize the loss of precious plant moisture, and open during the night. The season of the year is an important factor affecting transpiration. Transpiration rates, and overall plant activity, is minimal during the winter, and maximum during the summer. In addition, water that migrates to the surface of the leaves through the stomatal orifices is available for evaporation and therefore the normal meteorological factors, such as vapor pressure gradient, radiation, wind velocity, etc., also control transpiration rates.

There are several methods to estimate transpiration for a plant of a given species and stage of development, or a group of plants at a specific field density. These methods are useful in transpiration prediction of small agricultural fields. Alternatively, hydrologists have learned to combine the concept of free-water evaporation with that of transpiration in a single function called *evapotranspiration*. This function offers practical advantages in the determination of combined evaporation and transpiration of watersheds whose vegetation is composed of many types of vegetation, each with different degrees of density and stage of development. The relationship between hydrology and plant development is an active research area called *eco-hydrology* which explores the interface between physical science and biology. For illuminating accounts see Rodríguez-Iturbe (2004).

3.4 EVAPOTRANSPIRATION

Potential Evapotranspiration and Actual Evapotranspiration

Evapotranspiration is a combined function that includes the evaporation from soils, lakes and reservoirs, and transpiration from vegetation. A useful concept in hydrology is that of *potential evapotranspiration, PET*, introduced in chapter 1 after equation (1.12), in water balance calculations. Potential evapotranspiration is a maximum possible evapotranspiration amount that could occur in a watershed given ample supply of water from precipitation. This theoretical maximum would occur under ideal conditions. Potential evapotranspiration tends to be equated to pan evaporation rates. The concept is useful in calculations of actual evapotranspiration in hydrologic models, and in situations such as irrigation systems design. In the latter, a design crop is used in the estimation of the maximum amount of water consumed for optimal plant development. This amount is the potential evapotranspiration, or *consumptive use* as normally called in agricultural engineering. The difference between the potential evapotranspiration and the expected precipitation for a typical dry year is the amount of water to be supplied by the irrigation system. This information is used in the hydraulic design of appropriate water conveyance systems.

For a given period of time, the actual evapotranspiration amount, ET, is in between its potential value and zero. In other words, $0 \le ET \le PET$. Potential evapotranspiration occurs only under a sufficient supply of water from precipitation or soil moisture. Since precipitation may be low, or zero for certain periods of the year, and at the same time the soil moisture is low, ET is usually less than PET.

Evapotranspiration from Water Balance Techniques

In chapter 1 we discussed at length the use of the water balance equation as a fundamental tool in hydrology. This equation is commonly used as a means to evaluate evapotranspiration for a region. For instance, for large watersheds and long durations, equation (1.14) may be used to estimate evapotranspiration, given adequate measures of precipitation and watershed streamflow. Example 1.2 could illustrate this point if evapotranspiration, rather than streamflow, is the unknown. The Thomas model, equations (1.8) through (1.19), constitute a good tool to evaluate the different components of streamflow and evapotranspiration in a watershed (see Example 1.5). Errors involved in the application of water balance techniques are directly related to the accuracy in precipitation, streamflow, and change in storage measurements. Generally, errors between 10 and 20% are normal. In spite of the errors, water balance techniques are usually preferred due to their simplicity.

Table 3.3: Range of Seasonal Crop Coefficients, k_c,
for the Blaney & Criddle Equation (3.13) ($mm/(day.^oC)$)

Crop	Range of k_c	Crop	Range of k_c
Alfalfa	0.90-1.05	Onions	0.25-0.40
Avocado	0.65-0.75	Orange	0.60-0.75
Bananas	0.90-1.05	Potatoes	0.25-0.40
Beans	0.20-0.25	Rice	0.45-0.65
Cocoa	0.95-1.10	Sisal	0.65-0.75
Coffee	0.95-1.10	Sorghum	0.30-0.45
Cotton	0.50-0.65	Soybeans	0.30-0.45
Dates	0.85-1.10	Sugar Beets	0.50-0.65
Deciduous Trees	0.60-0.70	Sugarcane	1.05-1.20
Flax	0.55-0.70	Sweet Potatoes	0.30-0.45
Grains (small)	0.25-0.30	Tobacco	0.30-0.45
Grapefruit	0.70-0.85	Tomatoes	0.30-0.45
Maize	0.30-0.45	Vegetables	0.15-0.30
Oil Seeds	0.25-0.40	Vineyards	0.30-0.55
		Walnuts	0.65-0.75

Source: Ponce (1989).

Temperature Models of Evapotranspiration

Since air temperature is functionally related to the meteorological factors affecting evapotranspiration, and it is an easily measurable variable, several empirical methods relating temperature and evapotranspiration have been developed. One of the most widely used methods in this category is the Blaney and Criddle formula (Blaney and Criddle, 1950, 1962). After a modification by Doorenbos and Pruitt (1977), the potential evapotranspiration, or consumptive use, for a particular crop is given by

$$PET = k_c(a + bf), \quad f = p(0.46T_a + 8.13) \qquad (3.13)$$

where

PET=potential evapotranspiration rate (mm/day)

k_c= seasonal crop coefficients, from Table 3.3 ($mm/(day.^oC)$)

a, b=correction constants, from Table 3.4

p=ratio of mean daily daytime hours for a given month to the total daytime hours in the year as a percent, from Table 3.5

T_a= mean daily air temperature for a given month (^oC)

Table 3.4: Constants a and b in the Blaney and Criddle Equation (3.13)

Insolation Time I_s	Wind Speed $W(km/hour)$	$r<20\%$		$20\%\leq r\leq 50\%$		$r>50\%$	
		a	b	a	b	a	b
Low, I_s<0.6 $_{cloudy}$	W>18	-1.60	1.40	-1.70	1.25	-1.65	0.98
	$7\leq W\leq 18$	-1.80	1.28	-1.85	1.15	-1.55	0.88
	$0\leq W\leq 7$	-2.00	1.15	-2.00	1.05	-1.45	0.80
Medium, $0.6\leq I_s\leq 0.8$	W>18	-1.80	1.73	-2.10	1.52	-1.70	1.16
	$7\leq W\leq 18$	-2.05	1.55	-2.15	1.38	-1.75	1.06
	$0\leq W\leq 7$	-2.30	1.35	-2.20	1.20	-1.80	0.97
High, I_s>0.8 $_{sunny}$	W>18	-2.00	2.06	-2.55	1.82	-1.70	1.31
	$7\leq W\leq 18$	-2.30	1.82	-2.50	1.61	-1.95	1.22
	$0\leq W\leq 7$	-2.60	1.55	-2.40	1.37	-2.15	1.14

Source: Doorenbos and Pruitt (1977).

Table 3.5: Factor p in the Blaney & Criddle Equation (3.13)

Lat. (^oN)	Jan	Feb	Mar	Apr	May	Jun	Jul	Aug	Sep	Oct	Nov	Dec
Lat. (^oS)	Jul	Aug	Sep	Oct	Nov	Dec	Jan	Feb	Mar	Apr	May	Jun
60	0.15	0.20	0.26	0.32	0.38	0.41	0.40	0.34	0.28	0.22	0.17	0.13
50	0.19	0.23	0.27	0.31	0.34	0.36	0.35	0.32	0.28	0.24	0.20	0.18
40	0.22	0.24	0.27	0.30	0.32	0.34	0.33	0.31	0.28	0.25	0.22	0.21
30	0.24	0.25	0.27	0.29	0.31	0.32	0.31	0.30	0.28	0.26	0.24	0.23
20	0.25	0.26	0.27	0.28	0.29	0.30	0.30	0.29	0.28	0.26	0.25	0.25
10	0.26	0.27	0.27	0.28	0.28	0.29	0.29	0.28	0.28	0.27	0.26	0.26
0	0.27	0.27	0.27	0.27	0.27	0.27	0.27	0.27	0.27	0.27	0.27	0.27

Source: Ponce (1989).

Equation (3.13) is adapted to estimate potential evapotranspiration in agricultural fields or watersheds with fairly uniform vegetation. The range of values of the seasonal crop coefficient, k_c, is summarized in Table 3.3. The correction constants, a and b, are in fact functions of the minimum relative humidity, r; the day-time wind speed at 2 meters above the crop, W, and the actual insolation time, I_s. The actual insolation time is defined as the ratio between actual and maximum possible bright sunshine hours.

Table 3.4 summarizes the values of the constants a and b. To read the table, select the appropriate actual insolation time, I_s, from the left column. Then, select the wind speed, W, from the second column. Finally, move horizontally to match the column corresponding to the minimum relative humidity, r. The factor p is summarized in Table 3.5.

Example 3.8

Estimate the potential evapotranspiration for potatoes during the month of May at a watershed with a latitude of $40°N$, and a mean daily air temperature of $22°C$. Assume a high actual insolation time, medium relative humidity, and a mean wind speed of $20km/hour$.

Solution

From Table 3.3, the value of k_c for potatoes with an average consumption rate is $0.32\,mm/(day.°C)$. For a high actual insolation time, medium relative humidity, and wind speed greater than $18km/hour$, Table 3.4 gives the correction factors $a=-2.55$ and $b=1.82$. For a latitude of $40°N$ and the month of May, the value of $p=0.32$ in Table 3.5. Thus, from equation (3.13)

$$f=p(0.46T_a+8.13)=0.32\times(0.46\times22°C+8.13)=5.84°C$$

$$PET=k_c(a+bf)=0.32\frac{mm}{day.°C}\times(-2.55+1.82\times5.84°C)=2.6mm/day$$

Another widely used method to estimate potential evapotranspiration is the one developed by Thornthwaite and Wilm (1944) for humid areas. According to this method, the potential evapotranspiration for a given month is based on the mean monthly air temperature of that month and an annual air temperature efficiency index, which is defined as the sum of 12 monthly values of the heat index:

$$PET_m=k_mk_1\left(\frac{10T_{am}}{J}\right)^{k_2J^3+k_3J^2+k_4J+k_5} \qquad (3.14)$$

where

PET_m = potential evapotranspiration of month m ($mm/month$)
k_m = monthly correction constant function of latitude, from Table 3.6
$k_1 = 16.0 mm/month$
$k_2 = 6.75 \times 10^{-7} (^{o}C^{-3})$
$k_3 = -7.71 \times 10^{-5} (^{o}C^{-2})$
$k_4 = 1.792 \times 10^{-2} (^{o}C^{-1})$
$k_5 = 0.49239$
T_{am} = mean monthly air temperature of month m,
   excluding negative values (^{o}C)

The annual heat index, J, is given by

$$J = k_6 \sum_{m=1}^{12} T_{am}^{1.514} \qquad (3.15)$$

where

J=annual heat index (^{o}C)
$k_6 = 0.0874(^{o}C^{-0.514})$

Table 3.6: Latitude Correction Constant k_m for Thornthwaite's Equation (3.14)

Lat.	Jan	Feb	Mar	Apr	May	Jun	Jul	Aug	Sep	Oct	Nov	Dec
60°N	0.54	0.67	0.97	1.19	1.33	1.56	1.55	1.33	1.07	0.84	0.58	0.48
50°N	0.71	0.84	0.98	1.14	1.28	1.36	1.33	1.21	1.06	0.90	0.76	0.68
40°N	0.80	0.89	0.99	1.10	1.20	1.25	1.23	1.15	1.04	0.93	0.83	0.78
30°N	0.87	0.93	1.00	1.07	1.14	1.17	1.16	1.11	1.03	0.96	0.89	0.85
20°N	0.92	0.96	1.00	1.05	1.09	1.11	1.10	1.07	1.02	0.98	0.93	0.91
10°N	0.97	0.98	1.00	1.03	1.05	1.06	1.05	1.04	1.02	0.99	0.97	0.96
0°	1.00	1.00	1.00	1.00	1.00	1.00	1.00	1.00	1.00	1.00	1.00	1.00
10°S	1.05	1.04	1.02	0.99	0.97	0.96	0.97	0.98	1.00	1.03	1.05	1.06
20°S	1.10	1.07	1.02	0.98	0.93	0.91	0.92	0.96	1.00	1.05	1.09	1.11
30°S	1.16	1.11	1.03	0.96	0.89	0.85	0.87	0.93	1.00	1.07	1.14	1.17
40°S	1.23	1.15	1.04	0.93	0.83	0.78	0.80	0.89	0.99	1.10	1.20	1.25
50°S	1.33	1.19	1.05	0.89	0.75	0.68	0.70	0.82	0.97	1.13	1.27	1.36

Source: Gray, 1973.

Table 3.6 illustrates the values of the correction constant k_m. At the equator, the length of the day equals that of the night and the correction factor is one. The further a place is from the equator (i.e., the greater the latitude), the more marked the inequality between days and nights, and the total number of possible sunshine hours. This difference is reflected in the correction constant, especially during the months of June and December (respectively the Summer and Winter solstices for the Northern hemisphere). During March and September (respectively the Spring and Fall equinox), the correction factor approaches one.

Example 3.9

The first two columns of Table 3.7 show the mean monthly air temperatures for an area located at a latitude of 35^oN. If the growing season for a crop is from May 15 to September 15, determine the monthly and the annual potential evapotranspiration, or consumptive use, of the crop using the Thornthwaite's method.

Table 3.7: Computation of Evapotranspiration for Example 3.9

Month	T_{am} (^oC)	PET_m (mm/month)
Jan	-15.4	-
Feb	-11.6	-
Mar	1.5	2.5
Apr	6.2	19.5
May	17.1	86.0
Jun	26.3	161.9
Jul	29.0	183.1
Aug	30.7	187.4
Sep	14.8	62.3
Oct	6.3	17.3
Nov	2.1	3.4
Dec	-7.4	-

Solution

The annual heat index is calculated from equation (3.15), excluding negative temperatures:

$$I = k_6 \sum_{m=1}^{12} T_{am}^{1.514}$$

$$I = 0.0874^oC^{-0.514} \times [(1.5^oC)^{1.514} + (6.2^oC)^{1.514} + (17.1^oC)^{1.514} + (26.3^oC)^{1.51}$$

$$+ (29.0^oC)^{1.514} + (30.7^oC)^{1.514} + (14.8^oC)^{1.514} + (6.3^oC)^{1.514} + (2.1^oC)^{1.514}]$$

$$I = 57.08^oC$$

Next, calculate the polynomial exponent in equation (3.14):

$$c = k_2 J^3 + k_3 J^2 + k_4 J + k_5$$

$$c = 6.75 \times 10^{-7} \ ^\circ C^{-3} \times (57.08^\circ C)^3 - 7.71 \times 10^{-5} \ ^\circ C^{-2} \times (57.08^\circ C)^2$$

$$+ 1.792 \times 10^{-2} \ ^\circ C^{-1} \times (57.08^\circ C) + 0.49239 = 1.39$$

For the month of March, $T_{am} = 1.5^\circ C$. For a latitude of $35^\circ N$, the correction constant may be found by interpolating from Table 3.6 as $k_m = 0.995$. The potential evapotranspiration is calculated from equation (3.14) as

$$PET_m = k_m k_1 \left(\frac{10 T_{am}}{J} \right)^c = 0.995 \times 16.0 \frac{mm}{month} \left(\frac{10 \times 1.5^\circ C}{57.08^\circ C} \right)^{1.39} = 2.5 \frac{mm}{month}$$

Using Table 3.6 and equation (3.14) sequentially for each month of positive temperature, we find the potential evapotranspiration. The results are summarized in Table 3.7. The annual potential evapotranspiration, for vegetation in general, is found after adding the monthly rates (third column in Table 3.7). For a particular crop under consideration, we only add the evapotranspiration rates that include the crop growing season. Since the growing season starts on May 15 and ends on September 15, we include half of the rate of May and September in the calculations. Thus,

$$PET = \sum_{m=1}^{12} PET_m \times \Delta t = (\frac{86.0}{2} \frac{mm}{month} + 161.9 \frac{mm}{month} + 183.1 \frac{mm}{month}$$

$$+ 187.4 \frac{mm}{month} + \frac{62.3}{2} \frac{mm}{month}) \times 1 month$$

$$PET = 606.6mm$$

Example 3.10

Table 3.8 contains the *mean monthly* temperature, T_{am}, recorded over a long period, and the *2008 monthly* temperature, T_a, for a watershed located at a latitude of $25^\circ N$. Using the Thornthwaite's method, write a Maple program to calculate the mean monthly potential evapotranspiration and the monthly potential evapotranspiration for the year 2008. Plot the two series on a single graph.

Table 3.8: Air Temperature Data for Example 3.10

Month	T_{am} (°C)	T_m (°C)
Jan	0.3	0.6
Feb	2.3	3.3
Mar	5.6	5.1
Apr	9.4	11.4
May	23.0	27.0
Jun	28.6	29.8
Jul	31.3	33.3
Aug	35.7	37.2
Sep	18.2	19.7
Oct	7.9	8.7
Nov	3.9	5.5
Dec	1.1	3.1

Solution

The following Maple program illustrates the procedure and calculations.

```
Maple Program for Example 3.10: PET Thornthwaite's Formulae
Enter constants of Thronthwaite's equation (3.14) and (3.15)
> k1:=16.0: k2:=6.75*10^(-7): k3:=-7.71*10^(-5):
  k4:=1.792*10^(-2): k5:=0.49239: k6:=0.0874:
Create an array with latitude correction factors, Table 3.6
> km:=[0.895,0.945,1.,1.06,1.115,1.14,1.13,1.09,
       1.025,0.95,0.91,0.88]:
Create an array with mean montly air temperature, January through December
> Tam:=[0.3,2.3,5.6,9.4,23.0,28.6,31.3,35.7,18.2,
        7.9,3.9,1.1]:
Create an array with the montly air temperature for the year 2008
> Tm:=[0.6,3.3,5.1,11.4,27.0,29.8,33.3,37.2,19.7,
       8.7,5.5,3.1]:
Calculate annual heat index, equation (3.15)
> J:=k6*sum(Tam[m]^1.514,m=1..12):
Calculate exponent of equation (3.14)
> c:=k2*J^3+k3*J^2+k4*J+k5:
Calculate mean monthly evapotranspiration, equation (3.14); store in an array
> PET_m:=[ seq(km[m]*k1*(10*Tam[m]/J)^c,m=1..12) ]:
Calculate mean annual potential evapotranspiration in mm
> ET_m:=sum(PET_m[m],m=1..12);

                    ET_m := 869.0247958
Calculate monthly potential evapotranspiration for the year 2008; store in an array
> PET_2008:=[seq(km[m]*k1*(10*Tm[m]/J)^c,m=1..12)]:
Calculate annual potential evapotranspiration, year 2008 in mm
> ET_2008:=sum(PET_2008[m],m=1..12);

                    ET_2008 := 986.6675490
```

```
Create an array of coordinates [ [x1,y1], [x2,y2],...] for plotting and display
both plots in one graph
> Meanplot:=[seq([m,PET_m[m]],m=1..12)]:
  Plot2008:=[seq([m,PET_2008[m]],m=1..12)]:
  G1:=plot(Meanplot,color=black,legend=`Mean PET`):
  G2:=plot(Plot2008,color=black,linestyle=3,
          legend=`PET 2008`):
  plots[display](G1,G2,labels=[`Month`,`PET (mm/month)`],
       labeldirections=[`horizontal`,`vertical`],
       font=[TIMES,ROMAN,16],labelfont=[TIMES,ROMAN,16]);
```

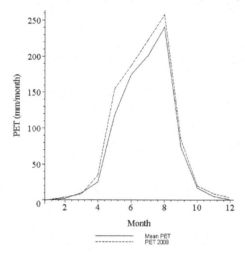

One of the simplest methods for the calculation of annual *actual evapotranspiration* was developed by Turc (1954,1955), based on water balance calculations performed on 254 watersheds representing all the different climates in Europe, Africa, America and the East Indies. The interesting feature is that this model provides estimates of *actual*, as opposed to *potential*, *evapotranspiration*, based solely on precipitation and air temperature data:

$$ET = \dfrac{P}{\left[0.9 + \left(\dfrac{P}{300 + 25T_a + 0.05T_a^3}\right)^2\right]^{1/2}} \tag{3.16}$$

where

ET=annual actual evapotranspiration (*mm/year*)
P=total annual precipitation (*mm/year*)

T_a = mean annual air temperature (^oC)

It should be stressed that equation (3.16) provides approximate estimates of actual evapotranspiration and it should only be sued for preliminary calculations.

Example 3.11: Air Temperature Evolution in Philadelphia

As a preliminary approach to observe possible climate changes, we are interested in the time evolution of mean annual air temperature in Philadelphia recorded for over a century. This data is conveniently available through the Franklin Institute of Science and Technology (http://www.fi.edu/weather/data2/wthrmean.txt). You have downloaded this data file; its first two lines contain alphanumeric information describing its contents. Beginning with the third line, the file contains two columns, the left one is the year (from 1874 to 2000) and the right one the average air temperature in degrees Fahrenheit. Assume you named the data file PhillyTemp.txt and stored it in the C drive of your computer at C:\My Documents\Hydrology_Second_Book\Data\PhillyTemp.txt. Modify the Maple program of Example 2.5 to read the data in this file beginning with the third line, transform temperature data into degrees Celsius, and prepare a single graph with the following curves:(1) The raw annual temperature data, (2) a 20-year moving average, (3) a graph displaying the mean plus one standard deviation, and (4) a graph displaying the mean minus one standard deviation. State your conclusions about the long-term changes in annual air temperature in Philadelphia.

Solution

The following Maple program describes the procedure. The two-column file is read and stored in an appropriate vector. Temperature is transformed to degrees Celsius. For the i-th year, the m=20-year average, T_i, is calculated as the mean precipitation for the m years prior to i (see Example 2.5). Note that Maple code does not allow a subscript k=0. A period of 20 years or longer is generally considered statistically representative for the calculation of the average of a weather variable. This average defines a climate constant. Thus, in the analysis of climate change it is of interest to observe possible long-term changes in these climatic "constants." Now for the i-th year, the standard deviation in the m=20 preceding years, σ_i, is calculated from the second moment with respect to the mean for the m years prior to i (see Example 2.5). The band $T_i \pm \sigma_i$ defines representative precipitation fluctuation bounds. Long-term variation in this band is of interest in studying possible climatic changes.

Assuming the data is correct, there seems to be a slight increase in mean temperature during the period from 1874 to 2000, which would appear visible by drawing a regression line through the series. However, this apparent increase might be a rising limb of a long-term periodic cycle, which would be evident if a longer period of record were available. There appears to be a periodic cycle of cool years followed by warm ones repeating every 90 to 100 years. A longer period of record would corroborate, or negate, these conclusions.

Program for the Analysis of Long-Term Annual Air Temperature in Philadelphia
Read data file by indicating the path where the text file is located in your disk.
Notice the double "\\" and that the file has 2 columns.

```
> TF:=readdata("C:\\My
  Documents\\Hydrology_Second_Book\\Data\\PhillyTemp.txt",2):
```

Data is now stored in a vector TF:=[[year, temperature], [year, temperature], . . .].
Year *i* is stored in column 1 of TF[i][1].
Temperature in year *i* is stored in column 2 of TF[i][2].
Now find the number of data points, Np, and transform degrees Fahrenheit into degrees Celsius.
Start in line 3, since the first two lines of data file are just text.

```
> for i from 3 to 2000 do   #2000 is an arbitrary large number
  Np:=i:
  TC[i-2]:=[TF[i-2][1],(TF[i-2][2]-32)/1.8]:
  end do:            #Ignore error when the loop is aborted.
Error, invalid subscript selector
```

Create a vector of (x,y) coordinates for plotting, T:=[[year 1, TC[1]], [year 2, TC[2]], . . .].
Prepare the graph, but do not display it yet.

```
> T:=[seq([TC[k][1],TC[k][2]],k=1..Np)]:
  G1:=plot(T,color=black,legend=`Annual Temperature`):
```

Now for each year calculate an M=20-year moving average.
For year *i*, it is the mean of the past 20 years of Temperature data.
Store in vector Mean[[year, mean], [year, mean], . . .].
Prepare for plotting.

```
> M:=20:
  for i from M to Np do
  Tbar[i]:=(TC[i][2]+sum(TC[i-k][2],k=1..M-1))/M;
  end do:
  Mean:=[seq([TC[k][1],Tbar[k]],k=M..Np)]:
  G2:=plot(Mean,color=black,thickness=2,
           legend=`Moving Average`):
```

For each year, calculate values of the mean plus one standard deviation,
and the mean minus one standard deviation.
Store in corresponding arrays suitable for plotting.

```
> for i from M to Np do
  sigma[i]:=sqrt(((TC[i][2]-Tbar[i])^2
              +sum((TC[i-k][2]-Tbar[i])^2,k=1..M-1))/(M-1));
  end do:
  Meanplus:=[seq([TC[k][1],Tbar[k]+sigma[k]],k=M..Np)]:
  G3:=plot(Meanplus,color=black,linestyle=3,
          legend=`Mean plus Std. Deviation`):
  Meanminus:=[seq([TC[k][1],Tbar[k]-sigma[k]],k=M..Np)]:
  G4:=plot(Meanminus,color=black,linestyle=3,
          legend=`Mean minus Std. Deviation`):
```

Display all of the graphs in a single plot.

```
> plots[display](G1,G2,G3,G4,labels=[`Year`,`T (Deg. Celsius)`],
         labeldirections=[`horizontal`,`vertical`],
         font=[TIMES,ROMAN,16],labelfont=[TIMES,ROMAN,16]);
```

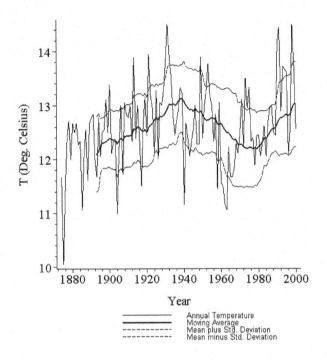

Annual Temperature
Moving Average
Mean plus Std. Deviation
Mean minus Std. Deviation

Further statistical analysis of the data, including trend, correlation, and spectral analysis, would reveal the presence of trends or periodic cycles with more precision (for more information on the methods see Serrano, 2011).

Example 3.12: Evolution of Evapotranspiration in Philadelphia
The availability of 130 years of precipitation and air temperature data for Philadelphia, and the simplicity of Turc's formula, allows a preliminary estimate of long-term annual actual evapotranspiration. Combine the Maple programs in Example 2.5 and Example 3.11 to produce the following plots: (1) annual actual evapotranspiration in *mm/year*, and (2) a 20-year moving average of evapotranspiration.

Solution
The following Maple program combines and modifies the programs in Examples 2.5 and 3.11. The resulting graph illustrates the complex variability expected from the effect of two random variables, precipitation and air temperature. At this preliminary stage, there is no conclusive evidence of any significant trend in the evapotranspiration averages.

Program for the Analysis of Long-Term Evapotranspiration in Philadelphia

Read precipitation and temperature files data files located in your disk.

```
> restart:
  PInch:=readdata("C:\\My
  Documents\\Hydrology_Second_Book\\Data\\PhillyPrecip.txt",2):
  TF:=readdata("C:\\My
  Documents\\Hydrology_Second_Book\\Data\\PhillyTemp.txt",2):
```

Starting in line 3 of each file, find the number of data points, Np, and transform to *mm* and *deg. C*

```
> for i from 3 to 2000 do    #2000 is an arbitrary large number
  Np:=i:
  Pmm[i-2]:=[PInch[i-2][1],25.4*PInch[i-2][2]]:
  TC[i-2]:=[TF[i-2][1],(TF[i-2][2]-32)/1.8]:
  end do:                     #Ignore error when the loop is aborted.
  Error, invalid subscript selector
```

Aplying Equation (3.16), create a vector ETr=[[year 1,ET[year 1]], [year 2,ET[year 2], . . .]

```
> for k from 1 to Np do
  ETr[k]:=[Pmm[k][1],Pmm[k][2]/
  sqrt(0.9+(Pmm[k][2]/(300+25*TC[k][2]+0.05*TC[k][2]^3))^2)]:
  end do:
```

Create a vector of (x,y) coordinates for plotting, ETp:=[[year 1, ET[1]], [year 2, ET[2]], . . .].

Prepare the graph, but do not display it yet.

```
> ETp:=[seq([Pmm[k][1],ETr[k][2]],k=1..Np)]:
  G1:=plot(ETp,color=black,legend=`Annual ET`):
```

Now for each year calculate an M=20-year moving average.

Store in vector Mean[[year, mean], [year, mean], . . .]. Prepare for plotting.

```
> M:=20:
  for i from M to Np do
  ETbar[i]:=(Pmm[i][2]+sum(ETp[i-n][2],n=1..M-1))/M;
  end do:
  Mean:=[seq([Pmm[n][1],ETbar[n]],n=M..Np)]:
  G2:=plot(Mean,color=black,thickness=2,
            legend=`Moving Average`):
```

Display all of the graphs in a single plot.

```
> plots[display](G1,G2,labels=[`Year`,`ET (mm/year)`],
        labeldirections=[`horizontal`,`vertical`],
        font=[TIMES,ROMAN,16],labelfont=[TIMES,ROMAN,16]);
```

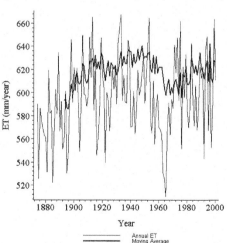

Combination Methods of Evapotranspiration

Penman (1948) combined the use of both the mass-transfer approach (e.g., equation (3.2)) and the energy balance equation method for estimating potential evapotranspiration (e.g., equation (3.9)). The original Penman model provided an estimate of evaporation from a free water surface. However, many studies have suggested that free water surface evaporation and potential evapotranspiration are nearly equal. A close examination of a combination formula for free water evaporation reveals that the energy balance component is actually higher than that of a vegetated area, since the albedo of a free water surface could be 0.05 as compared to about 0.25 for a vegetated area. This alone would justify greater values for the radiation term of free water evaporation as compared to that of evapotranspiration. From turbulence theory, on the other hand, the mass transfer term of a combination model is greater for rough vegetated surfaces and smaller for a smoother surface such as free water. Thus, the two components may compensate each other. Studies have shown that potential evapotranspiration correlates well with combination data. The Penman equation for potential evapotranspiration is given by

$$PET = \frac{\alpha E_n + E_a}{\alpha + 1}$$

(3.17)

where

PET = potential evapotranspiration (mm/day)
α = a function of air temperature, from Table 3.9
E_n = net radiation in evaporation rate units (mm/day)
E_a = mass-transfer evaporation rate (mm/day)

Table 3.9: Values of parameter α for Penman's Equation (3.17)

Air Temperature T_a ($^\circ C$)	α
0	0.68
5	0.93
10	1.25
15	1.66
20	2.19
25	2.86
30	3.69
35	4.73
40	6.00

Source: Ponce, 1989.

E_n is the net radiation, Q_n, expressed in evaporation rate units. Recall that to express radiation $(cal/(m^2.day))$ in terms of liquid-water evaporation rate one must divide by the density of the water and by the latent heat of evaporation (see equation (3.11)):

$$E_n = \frac{C_1 Q_n}{\rho L} \qquad (3.18)$$

where

E_n = evaporation rate from net radiation (mm/day)
Q_n = net radiation ($cal/(m^2.day)$)
ρ = density of water (kg/m^3)
L = latent heat of evaporation (cal/kg)
C_1 = $1000mm/m$, a units conversion constant

The mass transfer evaporation rate in Penman's equation (3.17) is evaluated by an appropriate equation. A formula suggested by Dunne and Leopold (1978) for that purpose is

$$E_a = \left(\frac{100-r}{100}\right)(c_2 + c_3 W)e_s \qquad (3.19)$$

where

E_a = mass-transfer evaporation rate (mm/day)
r = relative humidity
c_2 = $0.1733mm/(day.mmHg)$
c_3 = $0.0512mm.hour/(day.km.mmHg)$
W = wind speed at 2 meters above surface ($km/hour$)
e_s = saturated vapor pressure at surface air temperature ($mmHg$)

Example 3.13

Calculate the potential evapotranspiration using the Penman's method on a day in which the mean air temperature is $20°C$, the relative humidity is 70%, the net radiation is $5.6 \times 10^6 \ cal/(m^2.day)$, and the wind speed at 2 meters above the surface is $8.3km/hour$.

Solution

From Table 3.1 the latent heat of evaporation corresponding to an air temperature $T_a = 20°C$ is $586.0 \times 10^3 cal/kg$. Neglecting the temperature effects on water density, the radiation component in the Penman's method is calculated from equation (3.18) as

$$E_n = \frac{C_1 Q_n}{\rho L} = \frac{1000mm/m \times 5.6 \times 10^6 cal/(m^2.day)}{1000kg/m^3 \times 586.0 \times 10^3 cal/kg} = 9.6mm/day$$

From Table 3.1, the saturated vapor pressure corresponding to an air temperature $T_a = 20°C$ is $e_s = 17.53mmHg$. Thus, from equation (3.19) the mass transfer component is

$$E_a = \left(\frac{100-r}{100}\right)(c_2 + c_3 W)e_s$$

$$E_a = \left(\frac{100-70}{100}\right)\left(0.1733\frac{mm}{day.mmHg} + 0.0512\frac{mm.hour}{day.km.mmHg} \times 8.3\frac{km}{hour}\right)$$

$$\times 17.53mmHg$$

$$E_a = 3.2\frac{mm}{day}$$

From Table 3.9, for an air temperature $T_a = 20°C$ the value of α is 2.19. Finally, from equation (3.17) the potential evapotranspiration is

$$PET = \frac{\alpha E_n + E_a}{\alpha + 1} = \frac{2.19 \times 9.6mm/day + 3.2mm/day}{2.19 + 1} = 7.6mm/day$$

QUESTION AND PROBLEMS

3.1 During a day, the dry-bulb and wet-bulb thermometer readings in a psychrometer indicated 16°C and 14°C, respectively. Estimate the relative humidity.

3.2 From what you have learned about water-vapor pressure and evaporation, explain why during days when the relative humidity is above 90% humans feel uncomfortable.

3.3 Use the saturated vapor pressure versus temperature relationship and the concept of relative humidity to explain why during the winter months the air inside heated houses is very dry.

3.4 Go to the library. Investigate about techniques to control reservoir evaporation. Describe at least two methods, each with advantages and disadvantages. Reference the source consulted.

3.5 A lake has an average surface area of 24 km^2. During a day the mean water surface temperature is 13^oC, the mean air temperature is 16^oC, and the mean wind speed at a point 2 meters above the surface of the lake is $23.2km/hour$. If the relative humidity is 72%, calculate the evaporation rate.

3.6 Solve problem 3.5 with Meyer's equation.

3.7 An observer measured an increase of $17.5mm$ in the level of an evaporation pan with respect to the level recorded the day before. If during the same day he added $14.8mm$ of water to restore the lost water, and the station rain gage registered $7.0mm$ of rain, estimate the pan and lake evaporation rates. Assume a pan coefficient of 0.8. Repeat your calculation for the following day, when he measured a decrease of $4.8mm$ in the water level. No water was added to the pan and no precipitation was registered during the second day.

3.8 Calculate the lake evaporation based on the following data recorded during a given day: maximum water temperature at lake surface $T_s=22^oC$; maximum water temperature at pan surface $T_p=26^0C$; mean air temperature $T_a=24^oC$; relative humidity 69%; pan coefficient $K^{\prime}=1.5$; and pan evaporation $E_p=5.3mm/day$.

3.9 A lake has a surface area of $25km^2$. From an inventory of streams flowing into and out of the lake, it is estimated that the average inflow rate in a given day is $28.5m^3/s$. The average outflow rate is $32.0m^3/s$. During the same day, the lake stage (the water level) decreases about $1.6cm$. Estimate the evaporation rate.

3.10 Solve Example 3.7 if the temperature of the lake is 9^oC, the temperature of the air is 13^oC.

3.11 A nuclear power plant is being planned in the vicinity of the lake in Example 3.7. The reactor cooling water will discharge into the tributary river causing an average increase in the river temperature of about 5^oC. Assuming no net change in lake energy, re-evaluate the new energy advected from the river and the new daily evaporation rate in the lake. Speculate on the possible short-term environmental impact.

3.12 Applying Blaney and Criddle's method, calculate the potential evapotranspiration for soybeans at a watershed located at a latitude of $30°N$, in the month of June, if the mean daily air temperature is $36°C$. Assume a high actual insolation time, medium relative humidity, and a mean wind speed of $25km/hour$.

3.13 The mean monthly air temperatures for an area located at a latitude of $28°N$ are, respectively from January to December, -4.9, 0.6, 4.7, 9.5, 19.0, 28.5, 34.4, 37.2, 17.2, 8.5, 5.3, and $3.1°C$. If the growing season for a crop is from April 21 to October 8, determine the monthly and the annual potential evapotranspiration, or consumptive use, of the crop using the Thornthwaite's method.

3.14 Modify the Maple program of Example 3.12 to generate (1) a graph displaying the mean plus one standard deviation of evapotranspiration, and (2) a graph displaying the mean minus one standard deviation. State your conclusions about the long-term changes in actual evapotranspiration in Philadelphia. *Hint*: Use the equations and adapt the code in Example 2.5, Chapter 2.

3.15 Calculate the potential evapotranspiration using Penman's method on a day in which the mean air temperature is $16°C$, the relative humidity is 65%, the net radiation is $4.8×10^6 cal/(m^2.day)$, and the wind speed at 2 meters above the surface is $12.0km/hour$.

"Y la canción del agua
es una cosa eterna.
Es la savia extrañable
que madura los campos.
Es sangre de poetas
que dejaron sus almas
perderse en los senderos
de la naturaleza."

Federico García Lorca.

4 INFILTRATION AND RECHARGE

4.1 INFILTRATION IN THE HYDROLOGIC CYCLE

During a storm, precipitation that exceeds interception from vegetation reaches the ground surface. Depending on the properties and hydraulic conditions of the soil, part of this water crosses the ground surface and penetrates the soil via a process called *infiltration*. Infiltrated water increases the soil moisture and moves in the unsaturated zone via a process called *redistribution* or *interflow*. During redistribution, the water in the soil may evapotranspirate from upper layers of the soil, it may exfiltrate to streams or surface depressions, it may deep percolate to cause a rise in the *capillary fringe*, or it may recharge the underlying *aquifer*.

Over two thirds of the world's land-area precipitation infiltrates. Therefore, infiltration is quantitatively very important in the global hydrologic cycle. Infiltration naturally provides all the water used by natural and cultivated plants and almost all the water that enters the groundwater reservoirs. For these reasons, understanding of the processes involved in infiltration and redistribution is crucial in water resources management. For example, infiltration and redistribution are integral parts of the design of a crop irrigation system. Water moving in the soil transports dissolved chemicals and other species. Thus, predicting the propagation of nutrients, pesticides, and hazardous chemicals after a spill requires consideration of infiltration and redistribution properties of the soil. Management of groundwater reservoirs, or aquifers, requires a quantitative evaluation of recharge rate and its regime. Many hydrologic applications involve the forecasting of the hydrologic response to rain and snowmelt. Water that does not infiltrate moves relatively fast as overland runoff to the stream, causing a short-term response, and possible flooding. Infiltrated water, on the other hand, moves relatively slowly to the surface water system via subsurface paths. Therefore, a quantitative understanding of infiltration rates and its spatial distribution in a watershed is necessary.

The typical soil profile consists of a matrix of individual soil grains between which are interconnected pore spaces that can contain various proportions of air and water. Referring to Figure 4.1, the soil profile may be subdivided into two broad zones from the hydrologic point of view: the *unsaturated zone* (or *vadose zone*) and the *saturated zone*. In the unsaturated zone the pores are partially filled with water, and in the saturated zone the pores are completely filled with water. Generally, the unsaturated zone occurs between the ground surface and the top of the capillary fringe. The saturated zone, in general, occurs below the top of the capillary fringe. This is a common picture, although one must note that there may be regions in a watershed where there is no saturated zone, or where the saturated zone reaches the ground surface, depending on the geological and topographic conditions.

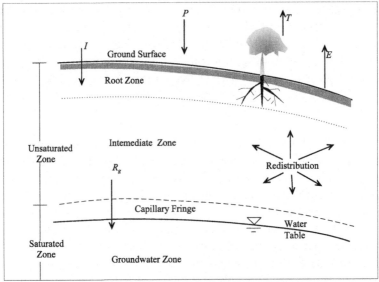

Figure 4.1: A Typical Soil Profile

Within the unsaturated zone, we may distinguish two main subzones: the *root zone* and the *intermediate zone*. The root zone, as the name implies, covers the top 20 or 30cm of the soil where the plants root system develops. The root zone is also called the *A horizon* in agricultural fields. It is characterized by a high content in organic matter, loose soil, animal burrows, and roots. The macropores generated by biological activity make the root zone highly conductive of water and air. As a result, soil-water content in the root zone oscillates widely over time. During periods of precipitation, P, the water content, S_w, increases rapidly in response to infiltration, I. After rainfall ceases, the water content in the root zone decreases rapidly as a result of evaporation, E, and transpiration, T. Below the root zone, one may encounter the intermediate zone, which is characterized by relatively less organic content, and more compacted soil. Hydrologically, the intermediate zone serves as a transmission zone between the root zone and the saturated zone. In the intermediate zone, the redistribution of infiltrated water takes place. Generally speaking, the soil-water content in the intermediate zone oscillates with less amplitude than that in the root zone. As depth increases, the time variability in the soil-water content decreases.

After prolonged redistribution of water in the unsaturated zone, water that has not been drained by gravitational forces remains suspended in the soil due to suction forces that depend on the soil type and texture. The water content corresponding to this condition is called *field capacity*, F_c or *specific retention*. Pressure heads measured with a special kind of manometer (called *tensiometer)* yield values less than that of the surrounding atmospheric pressure. If we take the atmospheric pressure as the reference pressure, it follows that the pressure heads in the unsaturated zone are negative.

The saturated zone covers the region between the top of the capillary fringe and the bottom of the *groundwater zone* (i.e., the *bedrock*). Within the saturated zone, we may distinguish two main subzones: the capillary fringe zone and the groundwater zone. The capillary fringe subzone covers a portion of the soil where water rises from the groundwater zone due to capillary tension forces. Depending on the soil texture, the capillary fringe may range from a few centimeters in depth for sands up to several meters for clays. The groundwater zone covers the portion of the soil between the *water table* (the bottom of the capillary fringe) and the bottom of the aquifer. The water table itself is an imaginary region defined as the surface where the pressure head is equal to that of the surrounding atmosphere. A way to visualize the water table is by introducing *piezometers* in the aquifer and joining those points marked by the static level of the water. It follows that pressure heads in the capillary fringe are below that of the surrounding atmosphere. If we adopt the atmospheric pressure as the reference pressure, the pressure head in the capillary fringe is negative, whereas the pressure head in the groundwater zone is positive. Thus physically, the capillary fringe zone has properties of both the unsaturated and the saturated zones: from the point of view of water content, the capillary fringe belongs to the saturated zone; from the point of view of pressure head, the capillary fringe zone belongs to the unsaturated zone. For these reasons, the capillary fringe zone is often called the *tension saturated zone*.

4.2 SOIL-PHYSICAL PROPERTIES OF INTEREST IN HYDROLOGY

Soil Texture
Consider a typical profile composed of a quasi-homogenous soil

matrix of solid grains and pore spaces. The size of the pores through which water flows is approximately equal to the grain size. Therefore, the distribution of pore sizes is determined largely by the grain-size distribution. Most soils have a mixture of grain sizes. The particle-size distribution is characterized by the *soil texture*, which is determined by the proportions by weight of clay, silt, and sand after gravel particles have been removed. Clay is defined as soil particles whose diameter is less than $0.002mm$. Silt is composed by soil particles between 0.002 and $0.05mm$ in diameter. Sand is composed by soil particles between 0.05 and $2mm$ in diameter. Particles greater than $2mm$ in diameter are classified as gravel.

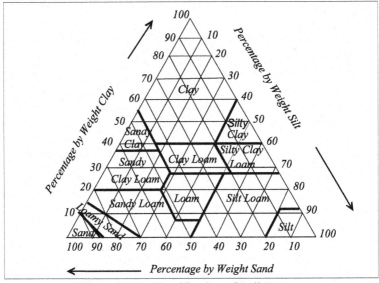

Figure 4.2: A Classification of Soil Texture

Figure 4.2 shows a scheme from the U.S. Department of Agriculture for the definition of soil textures. To classify a soil by texture, the percentages by weight of clay, silt, and sand are read on the left, right, and bottom parts of the graph, respectively. Using the horizontal and diagonal lines of the graph, an intersection between the values of the three scales is found. The soil texture is classified according to the area of the graph where the intersection occurs. Note that the texture is determined by the proportions of sand, silt, and clay after particles larger than sand (i.e., greater than $2mm$) are removed. If a significant portion of the soil is gravel or coarser (e.g.., more than 15%), then the word "gravelly" or "stony" is added to the soil-texture classification. Several soil hydrologic and hydraulic properties depend on soil texture; in particular, hydraulic conductivity, which is a measure of how easily water travels through a soil.

Example 4.1

Grain-size distribution is often portrayed as a cumulative-frequency plot of particle diameter, in logarithmic scale, with respect to weight fraction of grains with smaller diameter. The steeper the slope of such plots, the more uniform the soil-grain distribution. Suppose that from a grain-size distribution plot the information in Table 4.1 was deduced. Define the soil texture.

Table 4.1: Grain-Size Distribution for Example 4.1

Diameter (*mm*)	10.0	5.0	2.0	0.5	0.08	0.05	0.02	0.005	0.002
% Finer	100	85	70	60	55	45	35	15	8

Table 4.2: Soil Proportions for Texture Classification in Example 4.1

	Percentage (total sample)	Percentage (gravel removed)
Gravel (% >2*mm*)	30	-
Sand ($0.05<\%\leq2mm$)	25	36
Silt ($0.002<\%\leq0.05mm$)	37	53
Clay ($\%\leq0.002mm$)	8	11

Solution

From Table 4.1, and using the grain-size classification previously defined, we find the proportions of Table 4.2. Note that in the right column the fraction of gravel has been removed. Reading the percentages of sand, silt, and clay in Figure 4.2, the intersection falls within the silt loam area. However, since more than 15% of the particles are in the gravel range, the soil is classified as gravelly silt loam.

Consider a soil sample of volume V_T (Figure 4.3), and assume that the main components could be separated and amalgamated into the volume of solids V_s, the volume of water V_w, and the volume of air V_a. The volume of voids in the soil sample is $V_v = V_w + V_a$.

Porosity

Porosity, *n*, is the proportion of pore space in a volume of soil:

$$n = \frac{V_v}{V_T} = \frac{V_w + V_a}{V_T} \qquad (4.1)$$

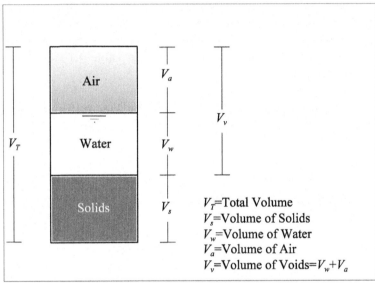

V_T=Total Volume
V_s=Volume of Solids
V_w=Volume of Water
V_a=Volume of Air
V_v=Volume of Voids=$V_w + V_a$

Figure 4.3: Components of a Soil Sample

Table 4.3 shows the range of values of the porosity in soils. Expressed as a ratio, the porosity of a soil is a measure of the maximum volume water would occupy at saturation. For a soil layer of known depth, this maximum storage could be expressed in equivalent depth of liquid water per unit surface area:

$$S_{max} = n.d \qquad (4.2)$$

where
S_{max} = maximum soil-water storage, or soil moisture, in layer (*mm*)
d=soil-layer vertical thickness (*mm*)

Volumetric Water Content

Volumetric water content, θ, is the ratio of water volume to the total volume of the soil sample:

$$\theta = \frac{V_w}{V_T}$$

(4.3)

The water content is a measure of soil moisture. It varies from a value of zero when the soil is completely dry, to a value equal to the soil porosity when the soil is saturated. Thus, $0 \leq \theta \leq n$. However, the range of values for natural soils is not as wide. For a given soil-layer thickness, the water content could be expressed as an equivalent depth of liquid water per unit surface area of the soil:

$$S_w = \theta.d$$

(4.4)

where
   S_w = soil-water content (*mm*)

Table 4.3: Range of Soil Porosity, *n*, for Typical Soils

Material		Range of *n*	Average *n*
Clay		0.33 - 0.65	0.42
Silt		0.33 - 0.61	0.46
	fine	0.25 - 0.53	0.43
Sand	medium	0.27 - 0.49	0.39
	coarse	0.30 - 0.46	0.39
	fine	0.25 - 0.40	0.34
Gravel	medium	0.24 - 0.44	0.32
	coarse	0.24 - 0.35	0.28

Solids Density
   Solids density, ρ_s, or particle density, is the ratio of the mass of solids to the volume of solid grains making up a soil sample:

$$\rho_s = \frac{m_s}{V_s}$$

(4.5)

where
ρ_s = solids density (kg/m^3)
m_s = mass of solid grains (kg)
V_s = volume of solids (m^3)

The solids density depends on the chemical and mineral constituents in the solid grains. The value for mineral quartz, ρ_s=2,650 kg/m^3 is often assumed.

Table 4.4: Soil Dry Bulk Density, ρ_b, for Typical Soils

Material		Range of $\rho_b(kg/m^3)$	Mean $\rho_b(kg/m^3)$
Sandstone	fine	1340 - 2320	1760
	medium	1500 - 1860	1680
Siltstone		2520 - 2890	2650
Claystone		2500 - 2760	2660
Shale		2470 - 2830	2690
	fine	1130 - 1990	1550
Sand	medium	1270 - 1930	1690
	coarse	1420 - 1940	1730
	fine	1600 - 1990	1760
Gravel	medium	1470 - 2090	1850
	coarse	1690 - 2080	1930
Silt		1010 - 1790	1380
Clay		1180 - 1720	1490
Silt Loams		860 - 1670	1320
Clay and Clay		940 - 1540	1300
Sandy Loams		1250 - 1760	1490
Silt Loams		1020 - 1580	1220
Loams		1160 - 1580	1420
All Soils		860 - 1760	1350

Dry Bulk Density

The *dry bulk density*, ρ_b, is the ratio of the mass of solids to the total volume of the dry sample:

$$\rho_b = \frac{m_s}{V_T} \tag{4.6}$$

where
ρ_b = dry bulk density (kg/m^3)

Table 4.4 illustrates typical ranges of the dry bulk density. The solids density and the dry bulk density of a soil are related to the porosity:

$$n = 1 - \frac{\rho_b}{\rho_s} \qquad (4.7)$$

Example 4.2

From a cylindrical sampling tube $6cm$ in diameter, a 12-cm-long sample is taken from a soil. After removal from the tube, the sample has a mass of $0.454kg$. The sample is oven dried at $105^\circ C$. The dry sample now has a mass of $0.415kg$. Estimate the dry bulk density, the porosity, and the water content.

Solution

From the cylindrical dimensions of the sample we calculate the total volume:

$$V_T = 3.1416 \times \left(\frac{6}{2}\right)^2 cm^2 \times 12cm = 339.3cm^3$$

From equation (4.6), the dry bulk density is

$$\rho_b = \frac{m_s}{V_T} = \frac{0.415kg}{339.3cm^3 \times \dfrac{m^3}{10^6 cm^3}} = 1223.1\frac{kg}{m^3}$$

The porosity may be calculated from equation (4.7), assuming $\rho_s = 2650kg/m^3$:

$$n = 1 - \frac{\rho_b}{\rho_s} = 1 - \frac{1223.1 kg/m^3}{2650.0 kg/m^3} = 0.5$$

To calculate the volumetric water content, we apply equation (4.3). Observe that the mass of water is equal to the initial mass of the sample minus that after drying. Thus, the volume of water is equal to mass of water divided by its density.

$$\theta = \frac{V_w}{V_T} = \frac{\dfrac{0.454kg - 0.415kg}{1000kg/m^3}}{339.3cm^3 \times \dfrac{m^3}{10^6cm^3}} = 0.11$$

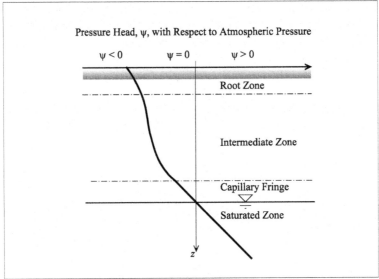

Figure 4.4: Pressure Head Versus Depth Distribution

Soil-Water Pressure

   Soil-water pressure is the force per unit area exerted by water at a point in a soil. For a saturated soil (i.e., point 1 in Figure 4.7) the soil-water pressure is greater than that of the surrounding atmosphere. Soil-water pressure may be expressed as the equivalent column of static liquid water necessary to reach equilibrium. The column of water, called *pressure head*, may be visualized by inserting a piezometer and measuring the vertical depth of static water above the observation point (bottom of piezometer). Thus,

$$\psi = \frac{P_w}{\gamma_w} \tag{4.8}$$

where

ψ = soil-water pressure head (m)
P_w = soil-water pressure (N/m^2)
γ_w = specific weight of water (N/m^3)

Because in many hydrologic problems the specific weight of water is effectively constant, it is convenient to use pressure head. This is not the situation in hydrologic problems that involve important temperature or salinity gradients.

It was previously stated that soil-water pressure in the unsaturated zone is below that of the surrounding atmosphere. If one takes the atmospheric pressure as a reference, the soil-water pressure heads in the unsaturated zone are negative: $\psi<0$ For this reason, soil-water pressure head in the unsaturated zone is often called tension or suction head. In the saturated zone the pressure head is positive: $\psi>0$. Figure 4.4 illustrates an idealized representation of the pressure head distribution with respect to depth, z, in a typical soil profile. Note that above the water table pressure head is negative and nonlinear, whereas below the water table pressure head is positive.

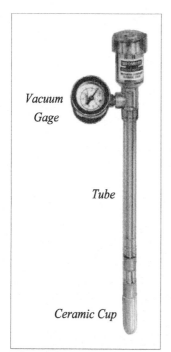

Vacuum
Gage

Tube

Ceramic Cup

Figure 4.5: A Tensiometer
(*courtesy of Irrometer Co.*)

Since pressure head is negative in the unsaturated zone, it can not be measured with piezometers, but rather with tensiometers. A tensiometer consists of a glass or plastic tube (see Figure 4.5). Its bottom is closed by a cup of porous ceramic material and the top has a built-in vacuum gauge. The tube is completely filled with water, inserted into the soil to the depth of measurement, and a hand pump is used to pull a partial vacuum. The water in the tube is initially at a pressure close to that of the surrounding atmosphere. Therefore, there will be a pressure-induced flow through the ceramic cup into the soil. This flow of water will continue until the tension inside the tube equals that of the soil. When equilibrium is reached, the vacuum gage gives the tension in the tube corresponding to the region of soil immediately surrounding the cup. Tensiometers may be placed in clusters at different depths of soil, and their tensions may be recorded in charts. The result is a spatial and temporal distribution of pressure heads in the soil useful in hydrologic studies.

Water Content Versus Pressure Head Relationship

The water content versus pressure head relationship, also called *moisture characteristic curve*, is a highly nonlinear and erratic curve. To understand its behavior, suppose that some water is added to a completely dry soil. Then its pressure head is measured and a sample of soil is taken to obtain its water content. Subsequently, more water is added to the soil, the new pressure head and its increased water content is measured. The process is repeated, always adding water to the soil until saturation is reached. At that point, the water content is equal to the soil porosity and the pressure head is zero. The corresponding curve joining the points of the different water content and pressure head values is called the *main wetting curve* (see Figure 4.6).

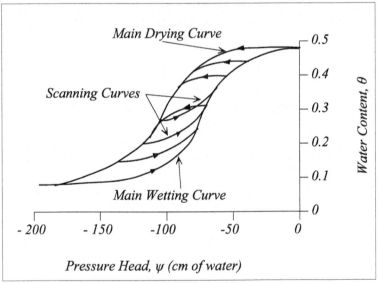

Figure 4.6: Water Content Versus Pressure Head Relationship

The above process could be repeated in reverse (i.e., drying the soil). Starting with a saturated soil, water is gradually removed from the sample, each time measuring the pressure head and the corresponding water content. The process is repeated until the soil is completely dry. The plot of the resulting points constitutes the *main drying curve* (see Figure 4.6). The interesting feature is that the main wetting curve does not normally coincide with the main drying curve, a phenomenon called *hysteresis.* Furthermore, most soils in natural watersheds are not continuously wetted to saturation or continuously dried to the wilting point. Prior to a rain storm, a point in the soil may be near or below field capacity at a location close to the main drying curve in Figure 4.6. When infiltration from rainfall begins, the water content increases rapidly towards the main wetting curve along a path called a *secondary scanning curve*. Most rain storms will not saturated the soil. After infiltration ceases, the soil experiences a decrease in its water content along a different secondary scanning curve. Therefore most natural soils continuously move along secondary scanning curves.

This highly nonlinear, erratic, and hysteretic form of the water content versus pressure head relationship makes the prediction of water content a difficult task. See Freeze and Cherry (1979) for an explanation of the phenomenon. As we shall see, knowledge of the water content versus pressure head relationship is essential to the solution of infiltration differential equations. Many empirical equations that ignore the complexities of hysteresis, heterogeneity, and fingering (preferential flow) have been proposed (e.g., Van Genuchten, 1978; Su and Brooks, 1975; White et al., 1970; Gardner et al., 1970; Laliberte, 1969; Brooks and Corey, 1966; Visser, 1966; Gradner, 1960). A simple adaptation of Gardner et al. (1970) was proposed by Serrano (2004):

$$\theta(\psi) = a\left(\psi - \psi_m\right)^b, \qquad 0 \le \theta \le n < 1, \quad \psi_m < \psi < \psi_a \qquad (4.9)$$

where
   θ = volumetric water content
   ψ = soil-water pressure head (*cm*)
   ψ_m = minimum pressure head at the wilting point (*cm*)
   ψ_a = maximum pressure head at saturation (*cm*)
   a = a constant (cm^{-b})
   b = a constant

Modifying the values of a and b, a variety of soils ranging from clays to sands may be simulated. In general one would expect higher values of b and ψ_m in coarse-texture soils than in fine-texture soils. From (4.9) the porosity may be taken as $n = a(\psi_a - \psi_m)^b$.

Hydraulic Head
   The *hydraulic head* at a point (i.e., point 1 in Figure 4.7) in a soil is the summation of its elevation head plus its pressure head:

$$h = z + \psi \qquad (4.10)$$

where
　　h=hydraulic head at a point (m)
　　z=elevation head at a point (m)

The hydraulic head is a measure of the total mechanical energy at a point. The driving force generating movement of a particle of water in the soil points in the direction of maximum hydraulic head loss. In other words, water moves from locations of high hydraulic head to those of relatively lower hydraulic head. Strictly speaking, the right side of equation (4.10) should include a third term representing the velocity head. However, in most practical situations of laminar flow of water through natural porous formations the velocity head is negligible as compared to the elevation and pressure heads. This observation is not necessarily valid in situations of flow through so-called secondary permeability (i.e., flow through rock fractures), or flow in *karst* aquifers. Depending on the spacing of joints and fractures, a condition of turbulent flow may be present, in which case the velocity head is as important as the elevation and pressure heads.

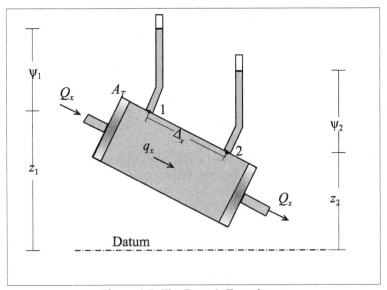

Figure 4.7: The Darcy's Experiment

Darcy's Law

The flow of water in unsaturated or saturated soils is governed by Darcy's law. To explain it, let us consider a soil sample packed in a cylinder of total cross sectional area A_T (Figure 4.7). Water is forced through the cylinder at a constant flow rate Q_x. Two piezometers are inserted at two points, 1 and 2, separated by a distance x. At point 1, the elevation head with respect to a reference plane (e.g., the mean sea level) is z_1, and the pressure head marked by the piezometer is ψ_1. At point 2, the elevation head is z_2, and the pressure head is ψ_2. From equation (4.9), the hydraulic head at point 1 is $h_1 = z_1 + \psi_1$, and at point 2 is $h_2 = z_2 + \psi_2$. The *hydraulic gradient* in the x direction, i_x, is defined as the loss of hydraulic head per unit distance. In other words, $i_x \approx \Delta h / \Delta x = (h_2 - h_1)/\Delta x$. Darcy's law states that the specific discharge in the x direction is proportional to the hydraulic gradient:

$$q_x = -K_x i_x \qquad (4.11)$$

where

q_x = specific discharge in the x direction (volumetric flow rate per unit cross sectional area (*m/month*)

K_x = hydraulic conductivity in the x direction (*m/month*)

i_x = hydraulic gradient in the x direction

It is important to remark that the specific discharge is not an estimate of the actual fluid velocity. The specific discharge is the volumetric flow rate per unit cross-sectional area of porous medium (i.e., $q_x = Q_x / A_T$). This area includes the pores, through which the water flows, and the grains. To obtain an estimate of the average macroscopic *pore velocity* (or filtration, or *seepage velocity*), one must divide by the porosity:

$$u_x = \frac{q_x}{n} \qquad (4.12)$$

where

u_x = mean pore velocity (*m/month*)

Generally, hydrologic studies related to water flow employ the specific discharge, whereas those related to water contamination employ the pore velocity in the calculations.

As the distance between points 1 and 2 tends to zero, in the limit, the hydraulic gradient approaches the derivative of the hydraulic head with respect to distance. Thus, Darcy's law becomes

$$q_x = -K_x \frac{dh}{dx} \qquad (4.13)$$

Because the hydraulic conductivity in unsaturated soils is a strong function of pressure head, as we will see, Darcy's law for unsaturated soils should be written as

$$q_x = -K_x(\psi) \frac{dh}{dx} \qquad (4.14)$$

It is interesting to observe the similarities between Darcy's law and other thermodynamical laws. Equation (4.13) states that groundwater flow, or the work done on a particle of water, occurs in the direction of decreasing hydraulic gradient (note the negative sign). In other words, an energy loss must occur for the movement of water from point 1 to 2 to happen. This concept is analogous to the Fick's law of diffusion, where the movement of contaminant particles occurs in the direction of decreasing concentration gradient. Fourier's law of heat flow states that heat transfer occurs in the direction of decreasing temperature.

Hydraulic Conductivity

The coefficient of proportionality in Darcy's law, equations (4.11) and (4.13), is the *hydraulic conductivity*. It expresses how easily water flows through a soil. In other words, high values of hydraulic conductivity (i.e., those in sands and gravels) indicate that water may travel at relatively high velocities, given appropriate gradients. Conversely, low values of hydraulic conductivity (i.e., those in clays) indicate that water would travel at relatively low velocities through the soil.

Darcy's law illustrates the physical meaning of the flow of water through soils: whereas the hydraulic gradient is the mechanical driving force acting on the fluid particle, the hydraulic conductivity represents the medium and fluid resistance to the movement. Equation (4.11) may be used to define hydraulic conductivity as the specific discharge (or the flow rate per unit cross sectional area) per unit hydraulic gradient. Hydraulic conductivity represents the resistance to the flow. It is a function of the properties of the porous media itself and those of the fluid passing through it:

$$K = \frac{k\gamma}{\mu} \qquad (4.15)$$

where
> K=hydraulic conductivity of a fluid in a porous medium (m/s)
> k=*intrinsic permeability*; a medium property (m^2)
> γ= specific weight of fluid (N/m^3)
> μ= *dynamic viscosity* of fluid ($kg/(m.s)$)

In situations when the fluid in question is not water (e.g., oil contamination), or where the flow regime is subject to strong temperature or solute concentration gradients that affect the density of the fluid, equation (4.15) may be used to calculate the resulting hydraulic conductivity. Hydraulic conductivity expressed in m/s results in very small quantities. In porous media flow, it is more appropriate to convert to m/day or $m/month$.

Several expressions for the hydraulic conductivity in homogeneous saturated soils that ignore hysteresis and heterogeneity have been proposed. A simple adaptation of Gardner's (1960) was proposed by Serrano (2004):

$$K(\psi)=c\left(\psi-\psi_m\right)^m, \qquad \psi_m<\psi<\psi_a \qquad (4.16)$$

where
> $K(\psi)$= hydraulic conductivity ($cm/hour$)
> ψ=soil-water pressure head (cm)
> ψ_m= minimum pressure head at the wilting point (cm)
> ψ_a=maximum pressure head at saturation (cm)
> c=a constant ($cm^{1-m}/hour$)
> m=a constant

By altering the values of c and m a variety of soil types may be represented.

Hydraulic Conductivity Versus Pressure Head Relationship

In the groundwater zone where the soil is saturated, the hydraulic conductivity does not depend on the pressure head. For example, the situation depicted in Figure 4.7 is that of a saturated soil whose hydraulic conductivity does not depend on the pressure head. The saturated hydraulic conductivity of soils in natural watersheds may be a function of orientation and distance, if the soil texture changes spatially, but it does not depend on pressure head. However, in unsaturated soils the hydraulic conductivity is a strong function of pressure head. Figure 4.8 illustrates an example of the hydraulic conductivity versus pressure head relationship of a soil. Note that it exhibits similar features as the water content versus pressure head relationship: nonlinearity and erratic hysteretic loops, depending on the historical path and the direction (i.e., past wetting or drying).

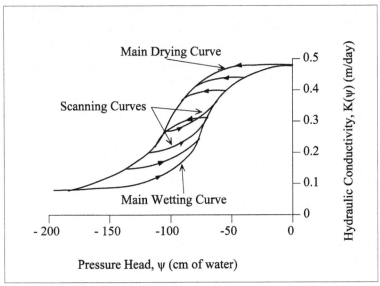

Figure 4.8: Hydraulic Conductivity versus Pressure Head

Table 4.5 illustrates the range of values of the saturated hydraulic conductivity of typical soils.

Table 4.5: Saturated Hydraulic Conductivity for Typical Soils

Material	Range K (*mm/month*)
Clay	0.00025 - 0.026
Soil Bentonite	0.0013 - 0.26
Cement Bentonite	0.026
Silt/Loess	0.0025 - 26.0
Sand fine	26.0 - 260.0
medium	260.0 - 2600.0
coarse	2,600.0 - 26,000.0
Gravel	2,600.0 - 260,000.0

4.3 MODELING OF INFILTRATION

Governing Equation of Vertical Infiltration

In this section we attempt to formulate the fundamental equation describing vertical infiltration in soils. The solution to this equation allows the hydrologist to predict qualitatively and quantitatively the vertical percolation of water subject to various conditions. These predictions are essential in the assessment of groundwater recharge and in the analysis of the propagation of contaminants through soils.

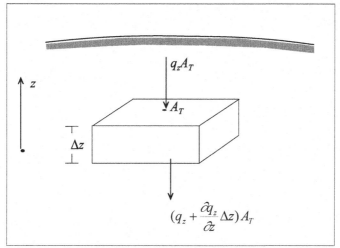

Figure 4.9: Vertical Infiltration through a Control Volume

Consider a small control volume of unsaturated soil experiencing vertical infiltration (Figure 4.9). Designate the volume as $V_T = A_T \times \Delta z$, where A_T is the total cross-sectional area perpendicular to the direction of flow. The vertical coordinate with respect to an arbitrary origin is z. Assuming a constant density of water, the mass rate of water entering the control volume is $q_z \times A_T$. The mass rate of water leaving the control volume is equal to the mass entering it, plus the rate of change of mass with distance times distance. In other words, the mass rate leaving the volume is $[q_z + (\partial q_z/\partial z)\Delta z]A_T$. Now, the net mass rate is the mass rate leaving the volume minus that entering. The net mass rate must equal the change of mass of water within the volume per unit time, $A_T \Delta z(\partial \theta/\partial t)$. Thus, the mass conservation statement for the control volume is

Net mass rate + change of mass within volume = zero

Eliminating $V_T = A_T \Delta z$, this statement may be written mathematically as

$$\frac{\partial q_z}{\partial z} + \frac{\partial \theta}{\partial t} = 0 \qquad (4.17)$$

Darcy's law applied to vertical unsaturated flow is, from equation (4.14),

$$q_z = -K_z(\psi)\frac{\partial h}{\partial z} \qquad (4.18)$$

where
$K_z(\psi)$ = hydraulic conductivity in the z direction ($m/month$)

The hydraulic head is given by equation (4.10) as $h=z+\psi$. Substituting equation (4.18) into (4.17),

$$\frac{\partial \theta}{\partial t} - \frac{\partial}{\partial z}\left(K_z(\psi)\frac{\partial \psi}{\partial z}\right) - \frac{\partial K_z(\psi)}{\partial z} = 0 \qquad (4.19)$$

The water content is a strong function of the pressure head. Thus its time derivative may be expressed as $\partial\theta/\partial t=(d\theta/d\psi)(\partial\psi/\partial t)$. The term $C(\psi)=d\theta/d\psi$ is the slope of the water content versus pressure head relationship. It is called the *specific moisture capacity* and represents the unsaturated storage property of a soil. Thus, equation (4.19) becomes

$$C(\psi)\frac{\partial \psi}{\partial t} - \frac{\partial}{\partial z}\left(K_z(\psi)\frac{\partial \psi}{\partial z}\right) - \frac{\partial K_z(\psi)}{\partial z} = 0 \qquad (4.20)$$

This is called the Richard's equation. Its dependent variable is pressure head. There is another version of the vertical infiltration equation whose dependent variable is water content (Hillel, 1980).

Solutions to the vertical infiltration equation require not only information on the boundary and initial conditions in the soil profile, but also information on the water content versus pressure head relationship and the hydraulic conductivity versus pressure head relationship. As mentioned before, these curves are erratic and hysteretic. Since the parameters of equation (4.20) are functions of the dependent variable (i.e., pressure head), then equation (4.20) is nonlinear. A few solutions to the linearized infiltration equation for specially-controlled laboratory conditions have been reported (i.e., Kuhnel et al., 1990, Boadbridge and White, 1988; Sander et al., 1988; Hillel, 1980; Philip and Knight, 1974; Philip, 1972; Parlange, 1971; Freeze, 1971; Liakopoulos, 1965; Gardner and Mayhugh, 1958; Philip, 1972, 1957, 1955). With the advent of new analytical procedures to solve nonlinear differential equations, such as the method of decomposition (Adomian, 1994), new approaches which consider the hysteretic soil-water physical relationships in statistical terms have being implemented (i.e., Serrano, 1990a, 1990b).

Serrano (2004) proposed a new approximate analytical solution to the nonlinear Richard's equation. He considered a vertical layer of homogeneous soil bounded at the bottom by the water table (or more precisely the air-entry pressure point), with the top soil is limited by the ground surface. Thus, the boundary conditions imposed on equation (4.20) are:

$$\psi(z_a(t),\ t)=\psi_a, \quad 0\le z_a(t), \quad z_a(0)=0$$

$$\psi(l_z,\ t)=\psi_a, \quad \frac{\partial\psi}{\partial z}(l_z,\ t)=-1-\frac{p-e}{K(\psi)}=-1-\frac{p-e}{c(\psi-\psi_m)^m} \quad (4.21)$$

$$\psi(z,\ 0)=\psi_i(z), \quad \psi_m<\psi<\psi_a$$

where
  p=precipitation rate ($cm/hour$)
  e=evapotranspiration rate ($cm/hour$)
  ψ_m = minimum pressure head at the wilting point (cm)
  ψ_a=maximum pressure head at saturation (cm)
  $z_a(t)$= the elevation of the lower boundary (cm)
  $\psi_i(z)$=an arbitrary initial pressure-head condition (cm)
  c=a constant ($cm^{1-m}/hour$) (see equation (4.16))
  m=a constant (see equation (4.16))
  z=vertical elevation upwards, with $z=0$ at the water table (cm)
  l_z= thickness of soil column (cm)

The first line in equations (4.21) represents the pressure head boundary condition, ψ_a, at the bottom of the soil column, which has a changing elevation with time, $z_a(t)$, depending on the recharge conditions. During infiltration $z_a(t)$ increases with time and during redistribution it decreases. The second line in equations (4.21) represents the pressure head and the pressure head gradient at the top of the soil column. In the limiting soil layer at the top, the pressure head varies according to a mass balance between precipitation, evapotranspiration, and infiltration rates. Applying Darcy's law equation (4.14) for vertical infiltration, with the hydraulic head given by equation (4.10), and adopting equation (4.16) to represent the hydraulic conductivity, the pressure head gradient at the top boundary is obtained. The third line in equations (4.21) represents an arbitrary pressure head initial condition, $\psi_i(z)$, distribution.

From the pressure head gradient at the top boundary (second line in equation (4.21)), an approximate solution to the pressure head at the root zone is given as (Serrano, 2004)

$$\psi_b = \psi_a - z + l_z + \left(\frac{2(p-e)}{c(1-m)^2} \right) \left[(\psi_a - z + l_z - \psi_m)^{1-m} - (\psi_a - \psi_m)^{1-m} \right] \quad (4.22)$$

where

ψ_b = pressure head at the top boundary condition (cm)

From equation (4.22) expressions for the pressure head gradient and second derivative at the top boundary can be derived:

$$\frac{\partial \psi_b}{\partial z} = -1 - \frac{2(p-e)}{c(1-m)} (\psi_a - z + l_z - \psi_m)^{-m}$$

$$\varphi_1(z) = \frac{\partial \psi_b}{\partial z} + \left(\frac{\partial \psi_b}{\partial z} \right)^2 \quad (4.23)$$

$$\frac{\partial^2 \psi_b}{\partial z^2} = \varphi_2(z) = -\frac{2(p-e)m}{c(1-m)} (\psi_a - z + l_z - \psi_m)^{-m-1}$$

The solution to the simultaneous equations (4.20) and (4.21) is given by (Serrano, 2004)

$$\psi(z,t)=\psi_i(z)+S(p-e)(\psi_b-\psi_m)\left[\frac{1}{\beta}\left(e^{A_2(z,t)}-1\right)+\frac{1}{(\beta-1)}\left(e^{A_1(z,t)}-1\right)\right]$$

$$A_1(z,t)=\gamma(\beta-1)(\psi_b-\psi_m)^{\beta-2}\varphi_1(z)t, \qquad \psi_m<\psi<\psi_a \tag{4.24}$$

$$A_2(z,\ t)=\alpha\beta(\psi_b-\psi_m)^{\beta-1}\varphi_2(z)t$$

where
   $S(p-e)$=sign function equal to 1 if $p>e$, and equal to -1 if $p<e$
   $\alpha=c/(ab)$
   $\beta=m-b+1$, $m>b$ (See equations (4.9) and (4.16))
   $\gamma=m\alpha$ (See equations (4.9) and (4.16))
   $\varphi_1(z)$, $\varphi_2(z)$= see equations (4.23)

Equations (4.24) are physically-based expressions that preserve the nonlinearity inherent in the differential equation (4.20) and may be easily incorporated into storm water management models for either infiltration during precipitation or redistribution.

Example 4.3: Pressure Head Distribution in an Unsaturated Soil
   A soil has a depth $l_z=100cm$; a maximum pressure head at saturation $\psi_a=0$; a minimum pressure head at the wilting point $\psi_m=-300cm$; the water content versus pressure head relationship was fitted to a curve of the form of equation (4.9) with $a=10^{-8}cm^{-b}$, and $b=3.1$; the hydraulic conductivity versus pressure head relationship was fitted to a curve of the form of equation (4.16) with $c=10^{-10}cm^{1-m}.hour^{-1}$, and $m=4$. Assume that prior to rainfall the initial pressure head distribution was linear and given by $\psi_i(z)=-z$; then it started to rain at a constant rate of $p=3.0cm/hour$; the evaporation rate at the ground surface was a constant $e=0.1cm/hour$. Write a Maple program that implements equations (4.22)-(4.24) and plot in a single graph the pressure head spatial distribution with depth at $t=0$, 1, 3, and 6 hours.

Solution
   The following Maple worksheet shows the program. Any statement after a # sign is an explanatory comment. Figure 4.10 shows the pressure head distribution with head at various times. As time increases, the pressure head at the ground surface approaches that at the atmosphere, while the water table at the bottom rises. For prolonged times, pressure becomes positive at certain points, but equation (4.24) is not valid.

Maple Program for Example 4.3

```
> #restart program
  restart: with(stats[statplots]):
  #enter initial condition
  psii:=z->-z:
  #Pressure head at root zone, equation (4.22)
  psib:=z->psia-z+lz+2*(p-e)/c/((1-m)^2)*(
        (psia-z+lz-psim)^(1-m)-(psia-psim)^(1-m)):
  #enter equations (4.23)
  diff(psib(z),z):        #first derivative of psib(z)
  psib1:=unapply(%,z): #make into a function
  phi1:=psib1(z)+psib1(z)^2:
  diff(psib1(z),z):       #second derivative of psib(z)
  phi2:=unapply(%,z):
  #enter A1 and A2 from equations (4.22)
  A2:=(z,t)->alpha*beta*(psib(z)-psim)^(beta-1)*phi2(z)*t:
  A1:=(z,t)->gama*(beta-1)*(psib(z)-psim)^(beta-2)*phi1(z)*t:
  #pressure-head solution equation (4.22)
  psi:=(z,t)->psii(z)+signum(p-e)*(psib(z)-psim)
        *((exp(A2(z,t))-1)/beta+(exp(A1(z,t))-1)/(beta-1)):
> #enter data
  p:=3.0: e:=0.1: m:=4: psia:=0: psim:=-300:
  lz:=100: a:=10^(-8): c:=10^(-10): b:=3.1:
  alpha:=c/a/b: beta:=m-b+1: gama:=m*alpha:
  #prepare graph of initial condition
  plot(psii(z),z=0..lz,labels=[` psi (cm) `,` z `],
                color=black,linestyle=1,legend=[`t=0`]):
  g0:=xyexchange(%):
  #prepare graphs at t=1, 3, and 6 hours
  plot(psi(z,1),z=0..lz,labels=[` psi (cm) `,` z `],
                color=black,linestyle=2,legend=[`t=1 hour`]):
  g1:=xyexchange(%):
  plot(psi(z,3),z=0..lz,labels=[` psi (cm) `,` z `],
                color=black,linestyle=3,legend=[`t=3 hour`]):
  g3:=xyexchange(%):
  plot(psi(z,6),z=0..lz,labels=[` psi (cm) `,` z `],
                color=black,linestyle=4,legend=[`t=6 hour`]):
  g6:=xyexchange(%):
  #Display all graphs
  plots[display](g0,g1,g3,g6,
        labels=[`Pressure Head (cm)`,`z (cm)`],
        labeldirections=[`horizontal`,`vertical`],
        font=[TIMES,ROMAN,16],labelfont=[TIMES,ROMAN,16]);
```

It is easy to modify the above program to simulate soil–water redistribution after rainfall stops. Simply set $p=0$ and the pressure head spatial distribution when rainfall ceases as the initial condition (e.g., $\psi(z, 6)$). Similarly, the hydraulic head, $h(z, t)$, may be calculated from equation (4.10), and the infiltration rate at any pont in the soil may be easily derived from Darcy's law in the vertical direction, equation (4.18).

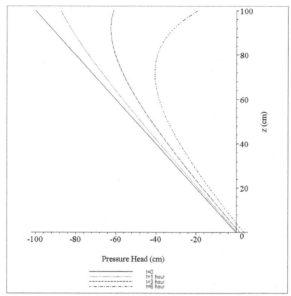

Figure 4.10: Graphics output of Example 4.3

Infiltration Rate Capacity and Actual Infiltration rate

Because the application of solutions of the infiltration equation requires knowledge of difficult-to-measure soil-water physical relationships, traditional hydrology has adopted simplifying and even empirical equations that offer practical tools for infiltration forecasting. These models neglect many of the fundamental physical relationships we have studied and concentrate on simple relationships capable of predicting infiltration rate at the ground surface only. By analogy with evapotranspiration models, where the two concepts of potential evapotranspiration and actual evapotranspiration where used, these models conceive two functions of infiltration: the *infiltration rate capacity* and the *actual infiltration rate*. The infiltration capacity refers to the maximum possible infiltration rate, given the current soil-water content in the root zone and under an ideal supply of abundant precipitation. The actual infiltration rate is usually less than the infiltration capacity owing to the fact that precipitation rate does not normally exceeds the infiltration capacity, unless flood conditions are occurring. In other words, the actual infiltration rate during a period of time, is the minimum between the infiltration capacity and the precipitation rate. Thus, if we denote the actual infiltration rate, $i(t)$, as the specific discharge at the ground surface, that is $i(t)=q_z(z=l_z, t)$, with l_z

the elevation of the ground surface with respect to the origin, then

$$i(t)=\min(f(t),\ p(t)) \tag{4.25}$$

where

min(,)=minimum between the argument values
$i(t)$=actual infiltration rate at the ground surface (*mm/hour*)
$f(t)$=infiltration capacity at the ground surface (*mm/hour*)
$p(t)$=precipitation rate (*mm/hour*)

Thus, the calculation of the actual infiltration rate requires an estimate of the infiltration capacity, $f(t)$.

Green and Amp's Model

The Green and Ampt equation (Green and Ampt, 1911) is a widely-used model of time evolution of infiltration in deep homogeneous soils under ponding conditions that develop during intense rainfall events.

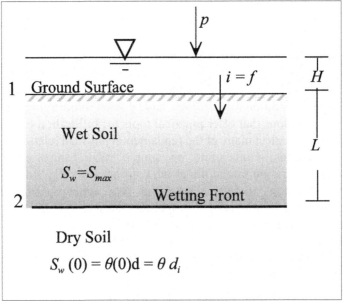

Figure 4.11:Deep Homogeneous Soil under Ponding

Consider infiltration of water into a deep homogeneous soil under an intense constant rainfall rate, p, such that a ponding layer of water of thickness H, has developed on the ground surface at time t_p after rainfall began (Figure 4.11). At any time t after rainfall began, the wetting front is located a vertical distance L from the ground surface. The pressure head at the wetting front, ψ_f, is negative if we take the ambient atmospheric pressure as reference. Neglecting air entrapment, the portion of the soil between the ground surface and the wetting front is saturated and has a volumetric water content, $\theta = n$, where n is the soil porosity. For the portion of the soil deeper than the wetting front at time t, the water content is $\theta = \theta_i$, where θ_i is the initial water content, that is the water content prior to the storm. The water content versus depth relation is shown in Figure 4.12.

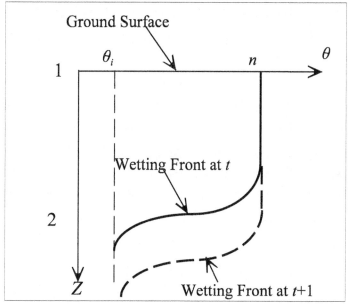

Figure 4.12: Water Content versus Depth under Ponding

At a given time, t, the pressure head at point 1 located at the ground surface (Figures 4.11 and 4.12) is equal to the column of water above it, or $\psi_1 = H$. The pressure head at point 2 located at the wetting front is $\psi_2 = \psi_f$ (Negative). Locating the datum at point 2, the hydraulic head at point 1 is, from equation (4.10), $h_1 = z_1 + \psi_1 = L + H$, where z_1 is the elevation head at point 1. Similarly, the hydraulic head at point 2 is $h_2 = z_2 + \psi_2 = \psi_f$, where $z_2 = 0$ is the elevation head at point 1. From equations (4.11) or (4.13), the hydraulic gradient in the vertical direction may be written as

$$\frac{\partial h}{\partial z} \approx \frac{h_2 - h_1}{L} = \frac{\psi_f - L - H}{L} \qquad (4.26)$$

From equation (4.11) we apply Darcy's law in the vertical direction to obtain he infiltration rate:

$$i=f=-K\frac{\partial h}{\partial z}=\frac{K}{L}\left(-\psi_f+L+H\right)$$ (4.27)

where
  i, f=infiltration rate capacity ($mm/hour$)
  K=saturated hydraulic conductivity ($mm/hour$)

When the layer of water ponding above the ground tends to zero,

$$f=\frac{K}{L}\left(|\psi_f|+L\right)$$ (4.28)

where $|\ .\ |$ denotes the absolute value. If we now integrate the infiltration rate equation (4.28) between 0 and t, we obtain the *cumulative infiltration depth*, or the total layer of liquid water infiltrated since the beginning of the storm:

$$F(t)=\int_0^t f(\tau)d\tau=S_{max}-S_w=(n-\theta_i)L$$ (4.29)

where
  $F(t)$=cumulative infiltration depth (mm)
  $\square_{max}$=maximum soil-water content in mm (see equation(4.2))
  S_w=actual soil-water content in mm (see equation (4.4))

From equation (4.29) we obtain an expression for the saturated depth, L, as

$$L=\frac{F(t)}{(n-\theta_i)}$$ (4.30)

Substituting equation (4.30) into equation (4.28),

$$f(t)=\frac{K}{F(t)/(n-\theta_i)}\left(|\psi_f|+\frac{F(t)}{(n-\theta_i)}\right)=K\left(\frac{a}{F}+1\right) \tag{4.31}$$

where

$$a=|\psi_f|(n-\theta_i)(mm)$$

Expressing $f(t)=dF(t)/dt$ and rearranging, equation (4.31) becomes

$$\frac{dF}{dt}-\frac{aK}{F}-K=0, \quad t\geq t_p, \quad F(t_p)=F_p \tag{4.32}$$

where

$F_p=pt_p=$cumulative infiltration at the time of ponding (mm)
$t_p=$time to ponding (*hour*)

A useful expression for the time to ponding has been given by Digman (1994) as

$$t_p=\frac{K|\psi_f|(n-\theta_i)}{p(p-K)}=\frac{Ka}{p(p-K)} \tag{4.33}$$

Equation (4.32) describes the cumulative infiltration depth at any time $t \geq t_p$. Multiplying by dt, separating variables, integrating t between t_p and t and F between F_p and F; and rearranging, we obtain the traditional Green and Ampt solution:

$$t=\frac{F-F(t_p)}{K}+\frac{a}{K}\ln\left(\frac{F(t_p)+a}{F(t)+a}\right)+t_p, \quad t\geq t_p \tag{4.34}$$

In this equation, F is not given explicitly in terms of t. To obtain the cumulative infiltration function versus time, the hydrologist must select trial values of F and substitute them in equation (4.33) to obtain the corresponding time of occurrence t. In spite of not having an explicit solution, the Green and Ampt model has found many applications in hydrology. It is relatively easy to implement; it is physically based since it arises from a finite difference application of Darcy's Law; it lends itself to applications under transient rainfall conditions (Chu, 1978), time-varying depth of ponding (Freyberg et al., 1980) , and soils in which the hydraulic conductivity changes with depth (Beven, 1984). It has been used as a basic approach to comprehensive models (Schmid, 1990). Serrano (2003b, 2001b) derived an approximate explicit solution to equation (4.32):

$$F(t) \approx F_0(t) + a\ln\left(m_1(t)\right)\left[1 + \frac{m_2(t)}{\left(1 - m_2(t)\right)\left(1 + m_2(t)\ln(m_1(t))\right)}\right], \quad t \geq t_p \quad (4.35)$$

where

$$m_1(t) = (F_0(t) + a)/(F_p + a)$$
$$m_2(t) = a/(F_0(t) + a)$$
$$F_0 = K(t - t_p) + F_p$$

The infiltration rate, f, can now be obtained by differentiating equation (4.35) or simply substituting F from equation (5.35) into equation (4.31).

Example 4.4: Green and Ampt Infiltration Model

A storm with an intensity of $p = 20$ *mm/hour* is falling on a soil with the following properties: the saturated hydraulic conductivity is $K = 10$ *mm/hour*; the pressure head at the wetting front is $\psi_f = -100$ *mm*; the initial water content prior to rainfall is $\theta_i = 0.1$; and the porosity is $n = 0.4$. Using the Green and Ampt model, write a Maple program to calculate and plot the cumulative infiltration rate, F, versus time and the infiltration rate, f, versus time.

Solution

The first portion of the Maple worksheet, shown below, programs equations (4.35) for the cumulative infiltration, F. The time to ponding, t_p, is estimated from equation (4.33). Prior to ponding, the cumulative infiltration depth is simply $F(t) = pt$, $t \leq t_p$, after which equation (4.35) rules (see Figure 4.13). For the calculation of the infiltration rate, f, we use Green and Ampt's equation (4.31), with F given by equation (4.35). Notice again that prior to ponding all of the rainfall infiltrates and $f(t) = p$, $t \leq t_p$. This is shown in Figure 4.14. In this example the infiltration rate capacity, $f(t)$, is equal to the actual infiltration rate, $i(t)$, for the entire storm duration. This is so because the rainfall rate equals or exceeds the infiltration rate at all times and the Green and Ampt model is valid.

Example 4.4: Geen-Ampt Infiltration Model

```
> restart:
  #cumulative infiltration from equation (4.35)
  Fp:=p*tp: F0:=t->K*(t-tp)+Fp: a:=psi*(n-thetai):
  m1:=t->(F0(t)+a)/(Fp+a): m2:=t->a/(F0(t)+a):
  F:=t->F0(t)+a*ln(m1(t))*(1+m2(t)
                    /((1-m2(t))*(1+m2(t)*ln(m1(t))))):
  tp:=K*a/(p*(p-K)):  #equation (4.33)
> #data
  p:=20: K:=10: psi:=100: n:=0.4: thetai:=0.1:
> G0:=plot(p*t,t=0..tp,color=black):  #F=p*t, for t<tp
  G1:=plot(F(t),t=tp..12,color=black):
  plots[display](G0,G1,labels=[`t (hour)`,`F (mm)`],
   labeldirections=[`horizontal`,`vertical`],
   font=[TIMES,ROMAN,16],labelfont=[TIMES,ROMAN,16]);
```

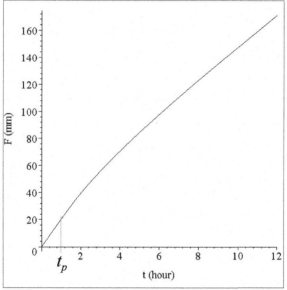

Figure 4.13: Cumulative Infiltration Depth with Time

```
> G0:=plot(p*t,t=0..tp,color=black):  #F=p*t, for t<tp
  G1:=plot(F(t),t=tp..12,color=black):
  plots[display](G0,G1,labels=[`t (hour)`,`F (mm)`],
   labeldirections=[`horizontal`,`vertical`],
   font=[TIMES,ROMAN,16],labelfont=[TIMES,ROMAN,16]);
```

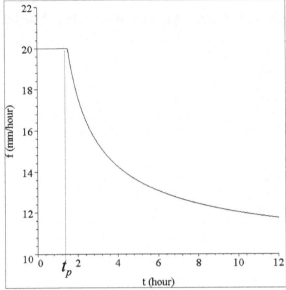

Figure 4.14: Infiltration Rate with Time

Horton's Model

In the absence of values for the physical parameters, many hydrologists opt for the use of empirical infiltration models. One of the most widely used is the Horton (1935) model:

$$f(t) = f_c + (f_0 - f_c)e^{-kt} \tag{4.36}$$

where

f_0 = initial infiltration capacity (*mm/hour*)
f_c = infiltration capacity after prolonged wetting (*mm/hour*)
k = a constant representing the rate of decrease in f (*hour^{-1}*)

The Horton's equation states that the infiltration capacity decreases exponentially between two limiting values, f_0 and f_c (see Figure 4.15). Although simple in form, the Horton's model requires the evaluation of three empirical parameters. In particular, the initial infiltration rate, f_0, and the recession constant, k, are difficult to evaluate. In practice, these parameters are estimated based on *infiltrometer* tests in actual field plots, as seen shortly, or using stream *hydrograph* analyses to independently evaluate the infiltration during different storms (see chapter 6).

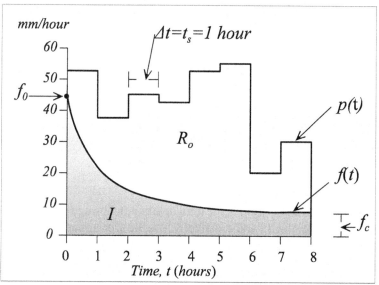

Figure 4.15: Precipitation versus Infiltration During a Storm

Another important limitation of the Horton's model is that it describes the infiltration capacity provided that the rainfall rate, $p(t)$, exceeds the infiltration capacity, $f(t)$, at all times during a storm. In this regard the Horton model has the same limitation as the Green and Ampt's. The moment the precipitation rate is less than the infiltration capacity, the Horton equation is a poor predictor of the infiltration capacity. During periods of a low precipitation rate in a given storm, deep percolation causes an increase in empty pore space. This corresponds to a recovery (i.e., an increase) in the infiltration capacity. The Horton's model does not predict such a recovery. As a rule, the Horton's model should only be used during very high intensity, flood producing, precipitation events when $p(t) > f(t)$, for all t. In such cases, the actual infiltration rate is equal to the infiltration capacity, or $i(t) = f(t)$.

The simplicity of the Horton's model allows us to observe some fundamental hydrologic concepts: the cumulative infiltration depth, as opposed to infiltration rate, and overland flow. Figure 4.15 shows a comparison of point precipitation versus infiltration during a storm. Precipitation intensity, or precipitation rate, $p(t)$, is given at a time interval $\Delta t = t_s = 1\,hour$. Similarly, infiltration rate capacity, $f(t)$, is given by equation (4.36), which is acceptable in this case since the precipitation rate exceeds infiltration capacity throughout the entire storm. Thus, in this situation, the actual infiltration rate equals the infiltration capacity rate: $i(t)=f(t)$ (see equation (4.25). Recall from chapter 2 (see Example 2.4) that cumulative precipitation depth, $P(t)$, or total precipitation is defined as

$$P(t) = \int_0^t p(\tau)d\tau \approx \sum_{j=1}^{j=t} p(j)\Delta t \qquad (4.37)$$

In other words, the precipitation depth is the area under the precipitation rate, or the rainfall hyetograph, curve. Cumulative infiltration may be defined in an analogous way.

Cumulative Infiltration Depth

Cumulative infiltration is the total depth of infiltrated water since the beginning of the storm. Mathematically, it is the area under the infiltration rate. Thus from Figure 4.15,

$$I(t) = \int_0^t i(\tau)d\tau \approx \sum_{j=1}^{j=t} i(j)\Delta t \qquad (4.38)$$

where

$I(t)$=cumulative infiltration depth at time t (*mm* of liquid water)
i=infiltration rate (*mm/hour*)
τ= time dummy variable of integration (*hour*)
j=discrete time variable (*hour*)

Overland Flow or Effective Precipitation

In chapter 1 we defined overland flow, R_o, as the amount of precipitation that does not infiltrate and becomes surface runoff. We may now define it more precisely after comparing total precipitation and total infiltration depths. Overland flow is the excess of precipitation over infiltration:

$$R_o = P - I \qquad (4.39)$$

where

R_o = overland flow during a period of time (*mm*)

Equation (4.39) is essentially the same as the water balance equation (1.7) applied above the ground surface of the watershed, after we neglect evapotranspiration, interception, depression storage, and the change in storage.

Overland flow has other names in the hydrologic literature: *effective precipitation, net rain, storm runoff, direct runoff,* and *surface runoff* are common. They all refer to the portion of precipitation that exceeds infiltration and other losses and contributes to streamflow. In the example depicted in Figure 4.15, where the precipitation intensity is high and its excess over infiltration clearly becomes overland flow, there is no confusion among these terms. It is important to remark, however, that most storms are not flood producing. Most rainfall events exhibit precipitation intensities that may or may not exceed the infiltration capacity. In such instances, the most important fast streamflow component is made of subsurface flow, Q_s. Therefore, the term overland flow may not be an appropriate term to describe the fast-flow streamflow component. For these reasons, the term effective precipitation is a preferred general term, while reserving the term overland flow for the surface flow components, if any.

Example 4.5

Assume that the precipitation and infiltration rates in Figure 4.15 are given in Table 4.6, noting that the period $j=1$ corresponds to a time t between 0 and 1 *hours*; period $j=2$ corresponds to a time t between 1 and 2 *hours*, etc. The infiltration rate for each period is that measured in the middle of the time interval. Calculate: (1) the cumulative precipitation depth for the storm (*mm*); (2) the cumulative infiltration depth for the storm (*mm*); and (3) the effective precipitation depth or overland flow depth (*mm*).

Table 4.6: Precipitation Data for Example 4.5

Time period, j	1	2	3	4	5	6	7	8
p (*mm/hour*)	52	38	45	42	53	55	20	30
I (*mm/hour*)	29	18	12	10	9	8	7.5	7.5

Solution

(1) From equation (4.37), the total precipitation depth is

$$P(t) = \sum_{j=1}^{j=t} p(j)\Delta t$$

$$P(8)=(52\frac{mm}{hour}+38\frac{mm}{hour}+45\frac{mm}{hour}+42\frac{mm}{hour}+53\frac{mm}{hour}$$

$$+55\frac{mm}{hour}+20\frac{mm}{hour}+30\frac{mm}{hour})\times1hour=335mm$$

(2) From equation (4.38) the cumulative infiltration depth is

$$I(t)=\sum_{j=1}^{j=t} i(j)\Delta t$$

$$I(8)=(29\frac{mm}{hour}+18\frac{mm}{hour}+12\frac{mm}{hour}+10\frac{mm}{hour}+9\frac{mm}{hour}$$

$$+8\frac{mm}{hour}+7.5\frac{mm}{hour}+7.5\frac{mm}{hour})\times1hour=101mm$$

Note that this is an approximate numerical integration. Accuracy improves as the time interval decreases. (3) from equation (4.39), the effective precipitation is

$$R_o(8)=P(8)-I(8)=335mm-101mm=234mm$$

Example 4.6

If at the beginning of a storm the infiltration capacity is 38$mm/hour$, the infiltration capacity after 6 hours is 8$mm/hour$, and the Horton's recession constant is 1.11 $hour^{-1}$, calculate (1) the infiltration rate capacity 3 hours after the storm began; and (2) the cumulative infiltration depth 5 hours after the storm began.

Solution

(1) From equation (4.36) The infiltration rate capacity at $t=3hour$ is

$$f(t)=f_c+(f_0-f_c)e^{-kt}=8\frac{mm}{hour}+\left(38\frac{mm}{hour}-8\frac{mm}{hour}\right)e^{-\frac{1.11}{hour}\times3hour}=9.1\frac{mm}{hour}$$

(2) Knowing that cumulative infiltration is equal to the area under the

infiltration rate curve, and by analogy with equation(4.38), the infiltration depth after 5 hours is

$$F(5) = \int_0^5 f(\tau)d\tau = \int_0^5 \left[f_c + (f_0 - f_c)e^{-k\tau} \right] d\tau$$

$$F(5) = f_c\tau\big|_0^5 + (f_0 - f_c)\frac{e^{-k\tau}}{-k}\big|_0^5$$

$$F(5) = f_c \times 5 - (f_0 - f_c)\left(\frac{e^{-k\times 5} - 1}{k} \right)$$

$$F(5) = 8\frac{mm}{hour} \times 5hour - \left(38\frac{mm}{hour} - 8\frac{mm}{hour} \right) \times \left(\frac{e^{-\frac{1.11}{hour} \times 5hour} - 1}{\frac{1.11}{hour}} \right) = 66.9mm$$

Example 4.7

A flooding type infiltration experiment reported an initial infiltration rate of $114.3mm/hour$, an infiltration rate of $12.7mm/hour$ after prolonged wetting, and a cumulative infiltration depth of $476.5mm$ during the 20 hours of the experiment. Assuming that the Horton's model is valid, estimate the recession constant, k.

Solution

Since the infiltration experiment was such that the ground surface was flooded throughout the entire 20-hour period, the infiltration capacity f equals the actual infiltration rate, that is $f(t) = i(t)$. Thus, from equations (4.36) and (4.38), the cumulative infiltration depth is given by

$$I(20) = \int_0^{20} f(\tau)d\tau = \int_0^{20} \left[f_c + (f_0 - f_c)e^{-k\tau} \right] d\tau$$

$$I(20) = f_c\tau\big|_0^{20} + (f_0 - f_c)\frac{e^{-k\tau}}{-k}\big|_0^{20}$$

$$I(20) = 20f_c - (f_0 - f_c)\left(\frac{e^{-20k} - 1}{k} \right)$$

This equation could be written as

$$e^{-20k} + \left(\frac{I(20) - 20f_c}{f_0 - f_c} \right) \times k - 1 = 0$$

Substituting the parameter values,

$$e^{-10k} + \left(\frac{476.49mm - 20hour \times 12.7\dfrac{mm}{hour}}{114.3\dfrac{mm}{hour} - 12.7\dfrac{mm}{hour}} \right) \times k - 1 = 0$$

$$\Rightarrow e^{-10k} + 1.923k - 1 = 0$$

Using a numerical approximation technique (e.g., trial and error, or Newton iteration) we arrive at a value of $k = 0.52 hour^{-1}$.

Example 4.8

Defining $F' = \int_0^{\infty} [f(t) - f_c] dt$, show that the recession constant in the Horton's equation is given by $k = (f_0 - f_c)/F'$.

Solution

First note the interpretation of the parameter F': it is the area under the infiltration capacity curve, and above the line $f = f_c$ (see Figure 4.16). From the definition of F', we have

$$F' = \int_0^{\infty} [f(t) - f_c] dt = \int_0^{\infty} [f_c + (f_0 - f_c) e^{-kt} - f_c] dt$$

$$F' = (f_0 - f_c) \left(\frac{e^{-kt}}{-k} \right) \Big|_0^{\infty} = \frac{f_0 - f_c}{k}$$

$$\Rightarrow k = \frac{f_0 - f_c}{F'}$$

A useful application of the above result is the estimation of k after noisy infiltration rate data from experimental tests. Since the parameter F' is an integral under the infiltration rate curve, its numerical evaluation helps average scattered data points.

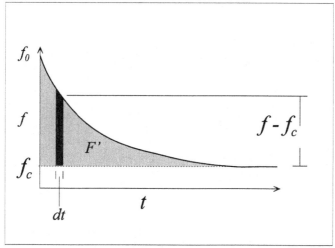

Figure 4.16: Estimation of Horton's k based on F'

Holtan's Model

As stated before, the Horton's model is not applicable to situations when the precipitation rate is less than the infiltration capacity. To circumvent this deficiency, several models have been proposed. One of those is the Holtan's model (Holtan, 1965, 1961; Holtan et al., 1975). In this model, soil storage available for infiltration, rather than time, is the dependent variable:

$$f = G_i . a . S_a^{1.4} + f_c \qquad (4.40)$$

where
   G_i = growth index of vegetation in percentage of maturity
   a = surface-connected porosity parameter ($mm/(hour.mm^{1.4})$)
   S_a = storage available in the root zone (mm of water)

We shall now describe each of the parameters. The growth index parameter, G_i, accounts for the increasing infiltration rates experienced as vegetation develops during the growing season. As plants grow, the root system enlarges its areal and depth coverage, resulting in a greater surface porosity. To estimate the growth index, the hydrologist must first estimate the length of the growing season for the particular crop or type of vegetation coverage in the area. The growth index is then the fraction of time elapsed since the beginning of the growing season, expressed as a percentage of the total length. Table 4.7 gives typical values of the length of the normal growing season for irrigated crops. One must remember that the actual length of the season depends largely on the plant variety and the time of the year when the crop is grown. Annual crops grown during the winter period may take much longer than those in the summer time.

Table 4.7: Typical Length of Normal Growing Season

Crop	Length of Season	Crop	Length of Season
Alfalfa	Between		
Bananas	Full year		
Beans	3 months	Pasture Crops:	
Cocoa	Full Year	Grass	Between Frosts
Coffee	Full year	Ladino White	Between Frosts
Corn (maize)	4 months	Potatoes	3 - 5 months
Dates	Full Year	Rice	3 - 5 months
Grains, small	3 months	Soybeans	140 days
Grain, sorghums	4 - 5 months	Sugar Beets	6 months
Oilseeds	3 - 5 months	Sugarcane	Full year
Orchard Crops:		Tobacco	4 months
Avocado	Full Year	Tomatoes	4 months
Grapefruit	Full Year	Truck Crops, small	2 - 4 months
Orange,	Full Year	Vineyard	5 - 7 months
Walnuts	Between Frosts		
Deciduous	Between Frosts		

Source: U.S. Dept. of Agric., 1970. *Irrigation Water Requirements*. Tech. Release 21.

The parameter a in the Holtan's model has been termed the infiltration capacity of the available storage. It is an index of surface-connected porosity, which depends on the soil-surface condition. It is assumed that the portion of the available storage connected to the surface is a function of the density of plant roots. Thus, a has been determined at plant maturity as the percentage of the ground surface area occupied by plant stems or root crowns. In this manner, the fraction of porosity in the root zone that is surface connected by mature plant roots to form macropores or conduits of air or water is represented. Table 4.8 shows preliminary estimates of this parameter.

Table 4.8: Vegetation Parameter a $(mm/(hour.mm^{1.4}))$ in Holtan's Model

Land use or Cover	Poor Condition[2]	Good Condition[2]
Fallow[1]	0.0274	0.0823
Row crops	0.0274	0.0548
Small Grains	0.0548	0.0823
Hay (legumes)	0.0548	0.1097
Hay (sod)	0.1097	0.1645
Pasture (bunchgrass)	0.0548	0.1097
Temporary pasture (sod)	0.1097	0.1645
Permanent Pasture (sod)	0.2194	0.2742
Woods and Forests	0.2194	0.2742

[1] For fallow land only, poor conditions means after raw crop, and good condition means after sod.

[2] Adjustments needed for weeds and grazing.

Source: U.S. Dept. Agric., Agricultural Research service, 1975.

The S_a variable in equation (4.40) represents the water storage available to infiltrating water in the root zone layer at any given time. Expressed in depth of liquid water, it is the difference between the maximum storage of water, S_{max} (i.e., the soil porosity expressed in depth of water) and the current soil-water content, S_w. Thus, from equations (4.2) and (4.4), the storage available is given as

$$S_a(t) = S_{max} - S_w(t) \qquad (4.41)$$

The infiltration rate after prolonged wetting, f_c, is best obtained from an infiltrometer test. Its magnitude varies from 1.0 to 15.0 $mm/hour$, depending on the soil texture and surface condition.

Since the value of the soil-water storage available, S_a, changes rapidly with time during a storm, Holtan's equation is meant to be applied sequentially to the root-zone layer at discrete intervals of time of about one hour in length. Referring to Figure 4.17, a root-zone layer of thickness d (mm) is subject to precipitation intensity, $p(t)$, as well as other hydrologic functions at a given time t. Given the soil-water content just before time t, there corresponds an equivalent available storage, $S_a(t)$, as given by equation (4.41). According to the storage available the infiltration capacity, $f(t)$, may be estimated from equation (4.40). Then the actual infiltration rate, $i(t)$, is estimated from equation (4.25).

The root zone is subject to evapotranspiration, $ET(t)$. Recall from chapter 3 (section 3.4) that actual evapotranspiration is the minimum between the potential evapotranspiration, $PET(t)$, and the water available to evapotranspiration from precipitation, $p(t)$, and soil moisture, $S_w(t)$. In other words,

$$ET(t) = \frac{\min\left[PET(t)\Delta t,\ p(t)\Delta t + S_w(t)\right]}{\Delta t} \tag{4.42}$$

The potential evapotranspiration may be computed from any of the methods studied in chapter 3.

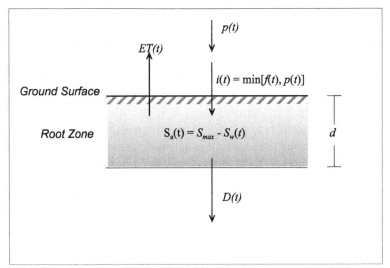

Figure 4.17: Infiltration Functions in the Root Zone Layer

Water may deep percolate, or drain, out of the bottom of the root zone. Thus, the drainage rate, $D(t)$, is assumed zero when the soil-water content is less than the *field capacity*, F_c. Recall that the field capacity is the water content capable of being suspended in the soil against gravitational forces. When the water content exceeds the field capacity, a portion of the water is subject to deep percolation (i.e., drainage). When the water content reaches saturation, the drainage rate is constant and equal to f_c. Thus, the drainage rate may be calculated by a formula such as (Huggins and Monke, 1966)

$$D(t)=0, \qquad\qquad\qquad S_w(t) \le F_c d$$

$$D(t)=f_c\left(1-\frac{S_a(t)}{S_{max}-F_c d}\right)^3, \quad S_w(t)>F_c d \qquad (4.43)$$

where

F_c = field capacity

The field capacity is often defined as the water content corresponding to a pressure head of about -340cm. In the absence of a water content versus pressure head relationship, Table 4.9 could be used for preliminary values.

Table 4.9: Estimates of Field Capacity, F_c

Soil Texture	F_c	Soil Texture	F_c
Coarse Sand	0.067	Loam	0.156
Coarse Sandy Loam	0.087	Silt Loam	0.199
Sand	0.133	Sandy Clay Loam	0.119
Loamy Sand	0.101	Clay Loam	0.127
Loamy Fine Sand	0.054	Silty Clay Loam	0.149
Sandy Loam	0.123	Sandy Clay	0.078
Fine Sandy Loam	0.131	Silty Clay	0.123
Very Fine Sandy Loam	0.117	Clay	0.115

Source: England (1970).

At the end of time step t, the values of soil moisture and storage available change as a result of the above hydrologic activity. By applying a mass balance equation for the root zone we may update these values:

$$S_w(t+\Delta t)=S_w(t)+(i(t)-ET(t)-D(t))\Delta t \qquad (4.44)$$

where

Δt = length of time step (e.g., 1 $hour$)

The storage available is the computed from equation (4.41). We are now ready to repeat the calculations for the time step $t+\Delta t$. The Holtan model applied in this fashion to two layers, the root zone followed by an intermediate zone, may be used to estimate actual infiltration rates at the ground surface, as well as other hydrologic functions of interest. For example, the effective precipitation R_o, the recharge rate R_g (interpreted as the drainage from the second layer), and the streamflow rate may be estimated by this procedure.

Example 4.9

In an agricultural watershed rainfall started at 9:00 AM with an intensity of 25$mm/hour$ and abruptly ceased at 10:00 AM. The soil is mainly planted with several varieties of beans, which were planted about six weeks ago. The soil is composed of a fine sandy loam kept in good condition. The root zone is about 20cm in depth. Assuming an infiltration capacity after prolonged wetting of 10$mm/hour$, a potential evapotranspiration rate of 0.25$mm/hour$, and an initial soil moisture equal to field capacity, estimate the actual infiltration and the effective precipitation for the storm.

Solution

We perform the calculations in the following 8 steps:

(1) We first estimate the initial soil parameters. From Table 4.9, for a fine sandy loam, the field capacity is $F_c=0.131$. Similarly, From Table 4.3, the average porosity for a fine sand is $n=0.43$. From Table 4.8, for row crops with good soil condition, the surface-connected porosity is $a=0.0548mm/(hour.mm^{-1.4})$. From Table 4.7, the average season length for beans is 3 months. Since the beans were planted 1.5 months ago, then the growth index parameter is $G_i=0.5$. The maximum soil-water storage expressed in mm is given by equation (4.2):

$$S_{max}=n.d=0.43\times200mm=86.0mm$$

The initial water content (i.e., the water content immediately before 9:00 AM) is equal to the field capacity, or $\theta(t=9)=F_c=0.131$. To express it as an equivalent depth of liquid water we use equation (4.4):

$$S_w(9)=\theta(9).d=0.131\times200mm=26.2mm$$

Since precipitation rates are given every hour, we use $\Delta t=1\ hour$.

(2) Next, calculate the storage available from equation (4.41):

$$S_a(9)=S_{max}-S_w(9)=86.0mm-26.2mm=59.8mm$$

(3) Now calculate the infiltration capacity from equation (4.40):

$$f(9)=G_i a S_a^{1.4}(9)+f_c=0.5\times\frac{0.0548mm}{hour.mm^{1.4}}\times(59.8mm)^{1.4}+10\frac{mm}{hour}=18.4\frac{mm}{hour}$$

(4) From equation (4.25), the actual infiltration rate is

$$i(9)=min[f(9),\ p(9)]=min\left[18.4\frac{mm}{hour},\ 25.0\frac{mm}{hour}\right]=18.4\frac{mm}{hour}$$

(5) From equation (4.42), the actual evapotranspiration is

$$ET(9)=\frac{min\ [PET(9)\times\Delta t,\ p(9)\times\Delta t+S_w(9)]}{\Delta t}$$

$$ET(9)=\frac{min\left[0.25\frac{mm}{hour}\times 1hour,\ 25\frac{mm}{hour}\times 1hour+26.2mm\right]}{1hour}=0.25\frac{mm}{hour}$$

(6) From equation (4.43) the drainage rate is $D(9)=0mm/hour$, since the soil is at field capacity. For a shallow water table, the value of the drainage rate may be interpreted as the recharge rate.

(7) From equation (4.44), the soil-water content is updated as

$$S_w(10)=S_w(9)+(i(9)-ET(9)-D(9))\Delta t$$

$$S_w(10)=26.2mm+\left(18.4\frac{mm}{hour}-0.25\frac{mm}{hour}\right)\times 1hour=44.4mm$$

With the updated soil-water content calculations, steps (2) through (7) above may be repeated for the next time step, $t=10$. In this example, however, precipitation is composed of only one pulse of rain. It is important to remark that we are evaluating continuous functions of time at discrete intervals Δt. In this example rainfall is given at $\Delta t=1hour$ intervals. This implies that the precipitation rate, $p(t)$, at a given time t is assumed constant for the entire interval Δt (i.e., rainfall intensity is assumed as having a constant intensity of $25mm/hour$ from 9:00 to 10:00 AM). A similar assumption holds for the other hydrologic functions. Clearly, resolution and accuracy improves as Δt decreases.

(8) The effective precipitation for the storm is calculated from equation (1.7):

$$R_o(10)=P(10)-I(10)=\sum_{i=9}^{9} (p(i)-i(i))\times\Delta t=\left(25\frac{mm}{hour} -18.4\frac{mm}{hour}\right)\times1hour$$

$$R_o(10)=6.6mm$$

In this example, only one term in the summation exists. However in storms made of several pulses the summation must be done over all time steps.

Several other infiltration models have been developed in the hydrologic literature. For example the U.S. Soil Conservation Service (1968) developed a widely used curve number procedure that gives indirect estimates of infiltration according to soil type and hydrologic condition (see Viessman, 1989 for application examples). Huggins and Monke (1966) developed a model of infiltration similar to Holtan's, except that it has parameters to calibrate from infiltrometer tests. Many watershed computer simulation models have developed special routines for the calculation of infiltration rate, or a combined *loss rate* from all hydrologic abstractions. For example the Hydrologic Engineering Center of the U.S. Army Corps of Engineers has developed its own loss rate model (see Gupta, 1989 for examples of application).

The hydrologist should carefully examine the assumptions, features, and limitations of each infiltration model. These characteristics should be compared with respect to project objectives. For instance, a hydrologic study that requires a physically-based estimation of infiltration rates should not employ any of the so-called loss-rate models. Similarly, a study of an aquifer recharge regime should also eliminate loss-rate models, since they do not provide an accurate or specific estimation of infiltration. On the other hand, a study of the flooding conditions in a watershed could employ any empirically based or loss-rate model, since the focus of the study is the calculation of effective precipitation during high-intensity storms.

Serrano's Model

A physically-based infiltration model that uses an approximate analytical solution to Richard's equation and is applicable to variable precipitation rate was proposed by Serrano (2004). In hydrologic applications, p is usually provided as constant values within a given time interval, typically one hour, by the weather reporting agencies. In this instance, pressure-head profiles would respond according to the varying precipitation conditions. Of especial interest in storm water management models is the simulation of ground-surface infiltration rates subject to variable hourly precipitation rates, p_j, $j=1$, 2, ... given at discrete times, Δt. The infiltration capacity, f, may be derived from an application of Darcy's law, equation (4.18) to the limiting soil layer at the ground surface, with the hydraulic head given by equation (4.16), the hydraulic conductivity represented by equation (4.10), and the pressure head from equation (4.24). The actual infiltration rate, i, is obtained from equation (4.25) as follows (Serrano, 2004, 1998):

$$i_j = \min\left(f_j,\ (p_j - e)\right) = \min\left(\left[\frac{\psi_a - \psi_m}{\psi_j - \psi_m}\right]^m (p_j - e),\ (p_j - e)\right) \qquad (4.45)$$

where
  i_j= actual infiltration rate at time j (*cm/hour*)
  f_j= infiltration capacity at time j (*cm/hour*)
  p_j= precipitation rate at time j (*cm/hour*)
  e=soil evapotranspiration rate at time j (*cm/hour*)
  ψ_m = minimum pressure head at the wilting point (*cm*)
  ψ_a=maximum pressure head at saturation (*cm*)
  c=a constant ($cm^{1-m}/hour$) (see equation (4.16))
  m=a constant (see equation (4.16))
  ψ_j= pressure head (*cm*) at the root zone at time j due to deeper
     drainage conditions, given from equation (4.24) as

$$\psi_j = \psi_{j-1} + S(p_j - e)(-\psi_m)\left[\frac{1}{\beta}\left(e^{A_2} - 1\right) + \frac{1}{(\beta-1)}\left(e^{A_1} - 1\right)\right]$$

$$A_1 = \gamma(\beta-1)(-\psi_m)^{\beta-2}\varphi_1\Delta t, \qquad \psi_m < \psi_j < \psi_a$$

$$A_2 = \alpha\beta(-\psi_m)^{\beta-1}\varphi_2\Delta t \tag{4.46}$$

$$\varphi_1 = \frac{2(p_j - e)}{c(1-m)}(\psi_a - \psi_m)^{-m} + \left[\frac{2(p_j - e)}{c(1-m)}(\psi_a - \psi_m)^{-m}\right]^2$$

$$\varphi_2 = -\frac{2(p-e)m}{c(1-m)}(\psi_a - \psi_m)^{-m-1}$$

where

    $S(p-e)$=sign function equal to 1 if $p>e$, and equal to -1 if $p<e$
    ψ_{j-1}=pressure head (cm) at the ground surface at previous time j-1
    $\alpha = c/(ab)$
    $\beta = m-b+1$, $m>b$ (See equations (4.9) and (4.16))
    $\gamma = m\alpha$ (See equations (4.9) and (4.16))

Notice that in equation (4.46) A_1 and A_2 are derived from equation (4.24) after setting $z=l_z$ and $t=\Delta t$; φ_1 and φ_2 are similarly derived from equation (4.23). Application of this model requires the sequential (e.g., hourly) updating of ψ_j (equation (4.46)) and its substitution into f_j (equation (4.45)). The pressure head at time step j, ψ_j, becomes the previous pressure head ψ_{j-1} at the following time step.

Example 4.10: Infiltration under Variable Rainfall

A soil has a maximum pressure head at saturation $\psi_a = 0$; a minimum pressure head at the wilting point $\psi_m = -300cm$; the water content versus pressure head relationship was fitted to a curve of the form of equation (4.9) with $a=10^{-8}cm^{-b}$, and $b=3.1$; the hydraulic conductivity versus pressure head relationship was fitted to a curve of the form of equation (4.16) with $c=10^{-10}cm^{1-m}.hour^{-1}$, and $m=4$. Assume that prior to rainfall the initial pressure head distribution at the ground surface was $\psi_0 = -1.0cm$; then it started to rain at the following hourly intensities: 1.0, 4.0, 0.5, 0.0, 2.0, 5.0, 1.0, 0.0, 3.5, 4.5, and 0.2 $cm/hour$, respectively; the evaporation rate at the ground surface was a constant $e=0.0cm/hour$.

Write a Maple program that implements Serrano's model of infiltration and plot in a single graph the precipitation intensity and the corresponding actual hourly infiltration rate for the storm.

Solution

Since p is give hourly, the $\Delta t=1$. The following Maple worksheet programs equations (4.45) and (4.46).

Figure 4.18 shows the graphics output. Prior to the time of ponding, infiltration rates equal those of precipitation. After ponding is achieved during a given interval, infiltration rates decrease. During intervals without precipitation, the pressure head and hydraulic conductivity decrease and thus infiltration rates recover during subsequent rainy periods. Thus equations (4.45) and (4.46) constitute a practical, physically-based, model of infiltration that is applicable to conditions prior or after ponding.

Example 4.10: Infiltration under Variable Rainfall

```
> #initialize and enter data
  restart: with(stats): with(plottools):
  m:=4: psim:=-300: alpha:=c/a/b: beta:=m-b+1:
  gama:=m*c/a/b: Ks:=c*(-psim)^m: a:=10^(-8):
  c:=10^(-10): b:=3.1: psii:=-1:
  p:=[1.0,4.0,0.5,0.0,2.0,5.0,1.0,0.0,3.5,4.5,0.2]:
  N:=describe[count](p):
Warning, the assigned name transform now has a global binding

> #apply equations (4.45) and (4.46) iteratively
  for j from 1 to N do
      phi1[j]:=2*p[j]*(-psim)^(-m)/c/(1-m)
              +(2*p[j]*(-psim)^(-m)/c/(1-m))^2:
      phi2[j]:=-2*p[j]*m*(-psim)^(-m-1)/c/(1-m):
      A2[j]:=alpha*beta*(-psim)^(beta-1)*phi2[j]:
      A1[j]:=gama*(beta-1)*(-psim)^(beta-2)*phi1[j]:
      psi[j]:=psii+signum(p[j])*(-psim)
        *((exp(A2[j])-1)/beta+(exp(A1[j])-1)/(beta-1)):
      i[j]:=min(Ks*p[j]/c/(psi[j]-psim)^m,p[j]):
      psii:=psi[j]:
      #draw lines for p[j] and i[j]
      ii[j]:=line([j-1,i[j]],[j,i[j]],linestyle=3):
      left[j]:=line([j-1,0],[j-1,p[j]]):
      top[j]:=line([j-1,p[j]],[j,p[j]]):
      right[j]:=line([j,p[j]],[j,0]):
  end do:
> #use the sequence command seq( , ) to display the lines
  plots[display](seq(ii[j],j=1..N),seq(left[j],j=1..N),
      seq(top[j],j=1..N),seq(right[j],j=1..N),
      labels=[` t (hour)`,` (cm/hour)`]);
```

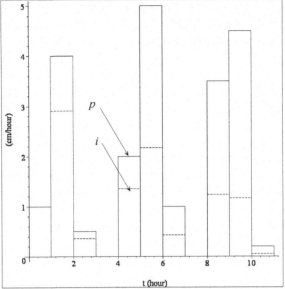

Figure 4.18: Graphics Output for Example 4.10

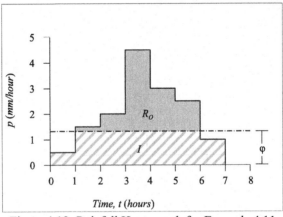

Figure 4.19: Rainfall Hyetograph for Example 4.11

The φ Index Approach

The φ index is an oversimplification of the infiltration problem in a watershed. It ignores all principles of infiltration and assumes that the infiltration rate is constant throughout the entire storm. As such, the φ index has been applied to studies of flood hydrology only, that is to extremely high intensity storms where the aim is the estimation of effective precipitation for storm runoff calculations. Since, comparatively speaking, the proportion of infiltration to effective precipitation is very small during extreme events, errors in the calculation in infiltration are considered negligible.

Example 4.11
   Figure 4.19 shows the rainfall hyetograph of a storm. Knowing that the effective precipitation was about 45% of the total rainfall depth, estimate the φ index.

Solution
   From equation (4.37), the total precipitation depth is

$$P(7)=\sum_{i=1}^{7} p(i)\Delta t$$

$$P(7)=[0.5\frac{mm}{hour}+1.5\frac{mm}{hour}+2.0\frac{mm}{hour}+4.5\frac{mm}{hour}+3.0\frac{mm}{hour}$$

$$+2.5\frac{mm}{hour}+1.0\frac{mm}{hour}]\times 1hour=15.0\ mm$$

From the data the effective precipitation is

$$R_o=0.45\times P(7)=0.45\times 15.0mm=6.75mm$$

   Let us assume that $1\leq\varphi\leq 2mm/hour$, which corresponds to the dashed line drawn in Figure 4.19. According to this assumption, the effective precipitation is, from equations (4.37) through (4.39), or simply by numerically integrating the upper shaded graph in Figure 4.19,

$$R_o=P(7)-I(7)=\sum_{j=1}^{7} p(j)\Delta t-\sum_{j=1}^{7} i(j)\Delta t=\Delta t\sum_{j=1}^{7}\left(p(j)-i(j)\right),\quad p(j) > i(j)$$

$$R_o=\Delta t\sum_{j=2}^{6}\left(p(j)-\varphi\right)=\Delta t\sum_{j=2}^{6} p(j)\Delta t-5\varphi\Delta t$$

$$R_o=\left(1.5\frac{mm}{hour}+2.0\frac{mm}{hour}+4.5\frac{mm}{hour}+3.0\frac{mm}{hour}+2.5\frac{mm}{hour}\right)\times 1hour-5\varphi$$

$$R_o = 13.5mm - 5\varphi$$

$$\Rightarrow \varphi = \frac{13.5mm - R_o}{5hour} = \frac{13.5mm - 6.75mm}{5hour} = 1.35 \frac{mm}{hour}$$

To verify the assumption, calculate the infiltration depth from equations (4.38) and (4.25) or simply integrating the lower shaded area in Figure 4.19:

$$I(7) = \sum_{j=1}^{7} i(j)\Delta t = \sum_{j=1}^{7} \min(p(j), \ i(j))\Delta t = \sum_{j=1}^{7} \min(p(j), \ \varphi)\Delta t$$

$$I(7) = (0.5 \frac{mm}{hour} + 1.35 \frac{mm}{hour} + 1.35 \frac{mm}{hour} + 1.35 \frac{mm}{hour} + 1.35 \frac{mm}{hour}$$

$$+ 1.35 \frac{mm}{hour} + 1.0 \frac{mm}{hour}) \times 1 hour = 8.25mm$$

From equation (4.39) the effective precipitation is

$$R_o(7) = P(7) - I(7) = 15.0mm - 8.25mm = 6.75mm$$

which agrees with the given data. Therefore, our assumption is correct and $\varphi = 1.35 mm/hour$. If the calculated effective precipitation differs from that given by the data, it is necessary to modify the trial range of φ and repeat the above calculations until an agreement is reached. Thus, the procedure reduces to a trial and error routine until the calculated R_o based on the trial φ agrees with the R_o given in the data.

4.4 MEASUREMENT OF INFILTRATION

A common procedure for the direct measurement of infiltration is the use of ring infiltrometers (Bouwer, 1986; Wilcock and Essery, 1984; Tricker, 1979; McQueen, 1963; Johnson, 1963). A ring infiltrometer is a cylindrical impermeable device of about one meter in diameter and a few centimeters in height (see Figure 4.20). The ring is inserted in the ground. By direct flooding or by applying a sufficiently high rate of simulated rainfall a condition of ponding is created. The rate of infiltration may be obtained by (1) measuring the rate at which the level of the ponded surface decreases; (2) measuring the rate at which the water has to be added to maintain a constant level of ponding; or (3) applying a water balance equation to the ponding surface (see Figures 4.20 and 4.21):

$$f(t) = \frac{P(t) - Q(t) - \Delta S(t)}{\Delta t}$$

(4.47)

where

$P(t)$=artificial precipitation applied during Δt (*mm*)
$Q(t)$=ponded water removed from the ring (*mm*)
$\Delta S(t)$= change in the volume of water stored in the ring (*mm*)

The ponded water removed, Q, is usually done via a weir or a small pump. Note that it is expressed in *mm* of water per unit surface area of the plot. Thus, if this amount is given in m^3, one has to divide by the surface are of the ring, $A(m^2)$, to reduce it to *mm*. The change in storage, ΔS, may be expressed as $\Delta S(t) = \Delta z$, where Δz is the change in ponded water level during Δt.

Figure 4.20: Double-Ring Infiltrometer

The water applied to an infiltrometer moves vertically as well as laterally. Since the aim of an infiltrometer test is the estimation of vertical infiltration parameters, a double ring infiltrometer is usually placed in the ground to minimize the effect of horizontal infiltration (see Figures 4.20

and 4.21). The measurements are thus conducted in the inner ring only.

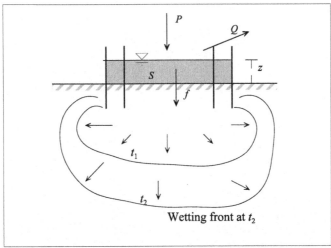

Figure 4.21: Cross Section of a Double-Ring Infiltrometer

By repetitive measurement of Q and ΔS at small intervals of time Δt, and applying equation (4.47), test values of the infiltration capacity are obtained. With certain scatter, these points resemble infiltration capacity curves such as that shown in Figure 4.15. The points may be used to estimate the parameters of infiltration capacity models such as those covered in this chapter. There is a conceptual difficulty in extrapolating the results to conditions when surface ponding does not occur. Another important limitation of infiltrometer tests, is that there is substantial spatial variability in the infiltration properties in a watershed. This variability is a function of the soil properties and land use conditions at different locations within the watershed. The spatial variability should be quantified by conducting several infiltrometer tests covering as much as possible the various field conditions. In this manner, the resulting infiltration model parameters reflect the spatial variability encountered in the field. More information on field measurement with infiltrometers can be found in Herman (1986).

4.5. GROUNDWATER RECHARGE

In chapter 1, recharge to the groundwater reservoir, R_g, was defined as the amount of water that deep percolates through the unsaturated zone and penetrates the saturated zone after crossing the water table during a given period of time. Groundwater recharge is the fundamental source of water to regional aquifers. It is usually a small fraction of the annual precipitation in a watershed. Yet, this amount is important enough to sustain groundwater storage. The groundwater storage, in its turn, is responsible for maintaining a supply of water to springs, streams, lakes, and ultimately the ocean. This supply is important since it keeps the streams flowing during periods without rainfall. In some parts of the world this period may be of the order of months. Therefore, estimation of the hydrologic regime of a groundwater basin requires a spatial and time distribution of groundwater recharge.

Various procedures were described in chapter 1 for the calculation of recharge amounts. In particular, different versions of the water balance equation in combination with soil-layer hydrologic models were discussed. For example, the Thomas model was used to estimate effective precipitation, groundwater recharge, and streamflow components in a watershed.

In this chapter, we explored the application of infiltration capacity models, in combination with root-zone water balance techniques, for the calculation of effective precipitation. We stated that infiltration models may be used for the estimation of groundwater recharge by interpreting the drainage from the root zone, or the drainage from the intermediate zone in a two-layer model, as deep percolation that eventually becomes recharge. For example, the Holtan model may be used for such purpose.

Some researchers (Steenhuis et al., 1985) have found that a simplification of the water balance approach applied to the root zone during periods no longer than one day each gives recharge estimates within 15% of error:

$$R_g(t) = P(t) - ET(t) \qquad\qquad (4.48)$$

where
   $R_g(t)$ = groundwater recharge during day t (mm)
   $P(t)$ = precipitation during day t (mm)
   $ET(t)$ = actual evapotranspiration during day t (mm)

ET is calculated from detailed energy balance measurements at the watershed. Note that overland flow (or effective precipitation) and the change in soil-water storage during the day is neglected. The amount of water moving from the groundwater zone to the capillary fringe is also neglected. This method, with various approaches to model evapotranspiration and soil-water storage, has been successfully applied to several watersheds (i.e., Chiew and McMahon, 1990; Thiery, 1988; Johansson, 1987; Steenhuis and Van Der Molen, 1986; Wellings, 1984).

The precise estimation of groundwater recharge requires a solution to the vertical infiltration equation (4.20) subject to the nonlinear and hysteretic soil-water physical relationships. We presented new solutions to this equation, such as equations (4.22)-(4.24), which could be used to estimate the vertical Darcy velocity, and thus recharge, at a depth near the capillary fringe.

QUESTIONS AND PROBLEMS

4.1 From a grain-size distribution plot the information in Table 4.10 was deduced. Classify the soil according to texture.

Table 4.10: Grain-Size Distribution for Problem 4.1

Diameter (*mm*)	10.0	5.0	2.0	0.5	0.08	0.05	0.02	0.005	0.002
% Finer	100	90	78	66	49	38	29	18	6

4.2 From a cylindrical sampling tube, 5cm in diameter, a 12-cm long sample is taken from a soil. After removal from the tube, the sample has a mass of $0.423kg$. The sample is oven dried at 105°C. The dry sample now has a mass of $0.388kg$. Estimate the dry bulk density, the porosity, and the water content.

4.3 Investigate explanations for the phenomenon of hysteresis in the water content versus pressure head relationship, and in the hydraulic conductivity versus pressure head relationship. Write two paragraphs on the topic and include a complete reference of the source consulted.

4.4 A soil has a depth $l_z=200cm$; a maximum pressure head at saturation $\psi_a=0$; a minimum pressure head at the wilting point $\psi_m=-200cm$; the water content versus pressure head relationship was fitted to a curve of the form of equation (4.9) with $a=10^{-8}cm^{-b}$, and $b=3.1$; the hydraulic conductivity versus pressure head relationship was fitted to a curve of the form of equation (4.16) with $c=10^{-10}cm^{1-m}.hour^{-1}$, and $m=5$. Assume that prior to rainfall the initial pressure head distribution was linear and given by $\psi_i(z)=-z$; then it started to rain at a constant rate of $p=3.5cm/hour$; the evaporation rate at the ground surface was a constant $\underline{e}=0.2cm/hour$. Modify the Maple program in Example 3.3 that implements equations (4.22)-(4.24) and plot in a single graph the pressure head spatial distribution with depth at $t=0$, 2, 4, and 6 *hours*.

4.5 In problem 4.4, rainfall ended at $t=6hours$. Using $\psi(z, 6)$ as initial condition for the redistribution phase, modify the Maple program in Problem 4.4 to calculate and plot in a single graph the pressure head spatial distribution with depth at $t=6$, 48, and 72*hours*.

4.6 Precipitation and infiltration rates for a storm are given in Table 4.11. Calculate: (1) the cumulative precipitation depth for the storm; (2) the cumulative infiltration depth for the storm; and (3) the effective precipitation depth or overland flow depth.

Table 4.11: Precipitation Data for Problem 4.4

Time period j	1	2	3	4	5	6	7	8
p (*mm/hour*)	48	53	23	22	61	33	25	14
i (*mm/hour*)	46	29	19	16	14	13	12	12

4.7 If at the beginning of a storm the infiltration capacity is 68*mm/hour*, the infiltration capacity after 8 hours is 10*mm/hour*, and the Horton's recession constant is $1.22\,hour^{-1}$, calculate (1) the infiltration rate capacity 4 hours after the storm began; and (2) the cumulative infiltration depth 6 hours after the storm began.

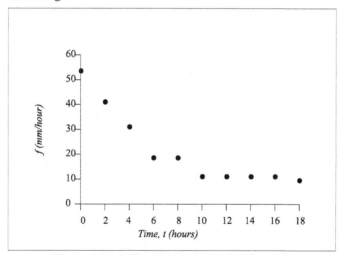

Figure 4.22: Infiltration Data for Problem 4.7

4.8 A flooding type infiltration experiment reported an initial infiltration rate of 98.3*mm/hour*, an infiltration rate of 24.3*mm/hour* after prolonged wetting, and a cumulative infiltration depth of 1227.0*mm* during the 36 hours of the experiment. Assuming that the Horton's model is valid, estimate the recession constant k.

4.9 The points in the Figure 4.22 show the infiltration rates measured after an infiltrometer test. Assuming that the Horton's model is valid, estimate the value of its parameters.

4.10 Assume that in Example 4.9 it continued to rain after 10:00 AM as given in Table 4.12. Write a Maple program that calculates and displays the values of the actual infiltration rates of the storm. In one graph plot the precipitation rate and the actual infiltration rate, all with respect to time.

Table 4.12: Rainfall Data for Problem 4.8

t (hour)	9:00 AM	10:00	11:00	12:00	1:00 PM
$p(t)$ (mm/hour)	25.0	2.5	33.2	28.4	1.2

4.11 In an agricultural watershed rainfall started at 2:00 PM with an intensity of 1.5mm/hour; increased to an intensity of 27.2mm/hour at 3:00; and abruptly ceased at 4:00 PM. The soil is composed of a very fine sandy loam kept in good condition, and it is covered by a fully-matured permanent pasture. The root zone is about 20cm in depth. Assuming an infiltration capacity after prolonged wetting of 10mm/hour, a potential evapotranspiration rate of 0.25mm/hour, and an initial soil moisture equal to field capacity, estimate the actual infiltration and the effective precipitation for the storm using the Holtan's model.

4.12 Rewrite the Maple program that implements Serrano's model of infiltration (Example 4.10), if the hourly rainfall intensities were 2.5, 1.8, 8.9, 0.2, 0.0, 0.0, 4.6, 7.2, 1.8, 0.0, 0.2, 6.5, 5.5, 7.7, and 0.1 cm/hour, respectively; the evaporation rate at the ground surface was a constant e=0.5cm/hour. Use the same soil parameters.

4.12 Solve Example 4.11 if the effective precipitation is 35% of the total rainfall.

4.13 Investigate possible effects of land use changes, such as deforestation, agricultural development, and urbanization on streamflow. Analyze each effect from the point of view of changes in infiltration properties. Write a one-page essay and include the complete bibliography.

4.14 Consult other textbooks on hydrology and describe in two pages the SCS Curve Number model of infiltration with a numerical example of application. Write the complete bibliography.

5 GROUNDWATER

5.1 GROUNDWATER IN THE HYDROLOGIC CYCLE

Importance of Groundwater

Water that percolates through the unsaturated zone may eventually cross the water table through a process called *recharge* (see Figure 4.1). Recharge water increases the storage in the saturated zone or groundwater zone. Recharge may also occur via horizontal or vertical seepage from streams and lakes. Once in the saturated zone, groundwater moves with a very low velocity (i.e., usually much less than $1m/day$) towards discharge zones, such as springs, rivers, lakes, and eventually the ocean. Depending of the depth and geological conditions, groundwater travel times from recharge zone to discharge zones may vary from a few days to centuries and even millennia (see Figure 5.0).

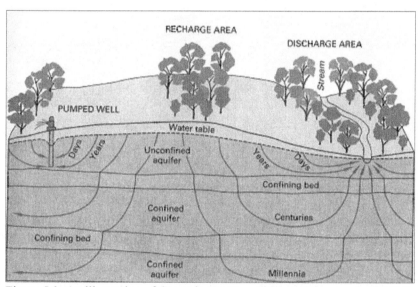

Figure 5.0: An illustration of Groundwater Travel Times (*Courtesy of the U.S. Geological Survey*)

In spite of its slow movement, groundwater constitutes the largest source of fresh water in the world. It is estimated that groundwater constitutes about 30% of the global fresh water and about 99% of its liquid fresh water. Throughout the history of humanity, groundwater has consistently provided an abundant supply of potable water to different civilizations. In today's society, groundwater reservoirs, called *aquifers*, are exploited to satisfy an ever increasing need of water for urban populations, irrigation, and industrial development. Aquifers also play a key role in controlling the regional *hydraulic gradients* and thus the dry-season levels in lakes, springs, and streams. The relatively low flow velocities of groundwater, and its long aquifer residence time, produces a continuous discharge flow rate to streams and lakes. This phenomenon maintains a minimum water level in lakes and a minimum flow rate called *base flow* in streams during periods without rainfall. Base flow may last for several weeks, and even months in some parts of the globe.

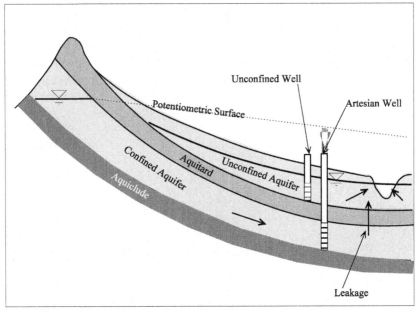

Figure 5.1: Aquifers in Folded Sedimentary Rocks

Because of their size and importance, aquifers are sensitive entities. Demographic explosion, urban and industrial development, and an increasing demand of land resources for a variety of economic activities have endangered the world's groundwater reservoirs. Consequently, excess exploitation and contamination of aquifers are serious concerns today. It is therefore necessary to protect existing aquifers and to restore contaminated sites, to assure an ample supply of fresh water for future generations. This requires management of natural resources and development of projects which minimize the impact on the ground waters. To achieve this, the hydrologist needs to understand the geologic characteristics of aquifers, as well as the physical hydrologic processes affecting groundwater. Aquifers, like surface reservoirs, are subject to the natural processes of the hydrologic cycle, such as natural replenishment from recharge, flow of water through geologic porous formations, and discharge into streams and lakes. It is also important to understand the fundamental processes affecting the transport and dispersion of contaminants in aquifers.

Occurrence of Groundwater

As stated before, groundwater occurs in the saturated zone in regions called *aquifers*. An aquifer is a geologic unit that can store and transmit enough water to be hydrologically significant. If the upper boundary of an aquifer is the *water table*, then it is classified as an *unconfined*, or *phreatic*, aquifer (see Figure 5.1). Recall that by definition the water table is an imaginary surface joining the points where the pressure head is equal to that of the surrounding atmosphere. Pressure head in the saturated zone is greater than the atmospheric pressure. In a mildly-sloping homogeneous aquifer, the water level in an observation well will rise to a level comparable to that of the surrounding water table. Unconfined aquifers are replenished by recharge, which translates into an increase in water table elevation due to additional water occupying voids in the soil. Similarly, exploitation of unconfined aquifers via pumping wells results in a decrease in the water table elevation due to draining of water from the pores.

If an aquifer is saturated throughout its entire thickness and bounded above and below by a formation with significantly lower hydraulic conductivity (called *confining layer* or *aquiclude*), then the aquifer is classified as *confined*. Confined aquifers are natural pressurized flow systems. The water level in an observation well will rise above the upper boundary of the confined aquifer to equilibrate the elevation of the *potentiometric surface*. The potentiometric surface is an imaginary surface delineating the *energy line* consistent with the hydraulic head at the upstream end of the confined aquifer where natural replenishment occurs (see Figure 5.1). If the potentiometric surface elevation is higher than the ground surface, then observation wells drilled through confined aquifers become *artesian* or *free-flowing wells*. Exploitation of confined aquifers via pumping wells do not drain water from pore spaces, as is the case in unconfined aquifers. Instead, pumped water is released from de-pressurization of the aquifer due to the mechanical compression of the grains in the aquifer.

A nearly impervious geologic unit that is unable to transmit groundwater is classified as an *aquiclude*. In practice, a geologic unit is classified as an aquiclude when its hydraulic conductivity is significantly lower than that of regular aquifers. The above classification constitutes an idealization of field conditions. In reality geologic spatial variability produces situations when groundwater flows exhibit characteristics of both confined and unconfined conditions. In fact, most confining layers can transmit some groundwater, called *leakage*, in which case it is classified as an *aquitard*.

Confined aquifers of the kind depicted in Figure 5.1 occur in folded sedimentary rocks that have resulted from the gradual deposition of granular material over many millennia. A *sandstone aquifer* between two confining layers of *shale* is an example of *sedimentary rocks*. On the other hand, unconfined aquifers may result from the sediment deposition in aquatic environments, or meander evolution of mature streams. *Alluvial* deposits are examples of unconfined aquifers. Significant quantities of groundwater may exist in fractured consolidated geologic units. In this situation, groundwater flow occurs through *joints*, *fractures*, and *faults*. This so called *secondary permeability* may produce groundwater flow velocities that in certain cases achieve *turbulent*, as opposed to *laminar*, *hydraulic regime*. If the size of the fractures is large flow velocities are turbulent. Examples of this situation are *karst aquifers*, or aquifers formed as a result of dissolution of *limestone*. The hydrologic regime in highly fractured aquifers is characterized as open channel flow through very complex media. For more information on the geologic aspects of groundwater the reader is referred to the specialized hydrogeologic texts (i.e., Fetter, 1994; Freeze and Cherry, 1979).

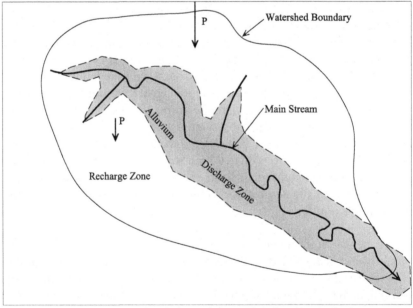

Figure 5.2: Regional Groundwater Flow in a Watershed

5.2. GROUNDWATER FLOW

Recharge and Discharge Zones

In natural watersheds, groundwater flows from *recharge* regions to *discharge* regions. Recharge regions are the portions of the watershed receiving infiltration from rainfall that eventually becomes recharge to the regional aquifer. Depending on the geology and the topography, recharge regions usually include the upper portions and the areas in the watershed subject to deep percolation from the unsaturated zone (see Figures 5.2 and 5.3). Sometimes aquifers are recharged by streams and lakes whose waters percolate deep. This is the situation of aquifers whose hydraulic head in the vicinity is lower than the water level in the stream. By comparing aquifer heads with river water levels near the contact zone, the hydrologist may define a stream as a recharge or discharge region. Alternatively, a stream with a decreasing flow rate as it flows downstream indicates that its waters are recharging the aquifer.

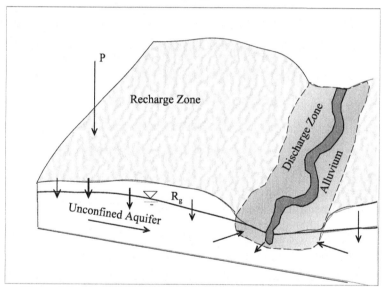

Figure 5.3: Simple Recharge and Discharge Zones in a Watershed

Discharge regions are the portions of the watershed where groundwater exits to the surface. These include natural springs, rivers, lakes, and eventually the oceans. By locating natural springs and seepage faces on a geological or topographic map, the hydrologist may visualize the extent of natural groundwater discharge zones. Often natural springs coincide with abrupt changes in *soil texture* or *rock lithology*. Regional geology (i.e., lithology and structure) and watershed topography are fundamental determining factors of recharge and discharge zones in a watershed. Figure 5.3 shows a sketch representative of simple recharge and discharge zones in a watershed. In this case, recent *alluvium* in the vicinity of a stream is acting as discharge zone, whereas older unconfined aquifer sediments are acting as recharge zone. Note that the ground surface is topographically higher and exhibits higher hydraulic heads in the recharge zone than in the discharge zone.It is also important to note that the surface watershed boundary, which marks the surface runoff limit, often does not coincide with the groundwater boundary. In Figure 5.1, a portion of the land outside the watershed is recharging water to the confined aquifer. The difference between surface and subsurface boundaries may yield important errors in water balance calculations, specially in small watersheds. In large watersheds the portions of the watershed that overestimate flows from incorrect subsurface boundary location tend to compensate with those portions underestimating it.

Storage Properties of Aquifers

As stated previously, exploitation in the form of pumping of unconfined aquifers results in a decrease in the water table elevation due to the draining of water from the pores. The amount of water released from storage is characterized by the aquifer *specific yield* as:

$$S_y = \frac{1}{A}\frac{dV}{dh} \tag{5.1}$$

where
  S_y = aquifer specific yield
  V = volume of drainable pore water (m^3)
  h = water table elevation (m)
  A = surface area of aquifer (m^2)

Equation (5.1) states that the specific yield of an unconfined aquifer is the volume of water drained from the pores per unit decline in water table elevation, per unit surface area of the aquifer. The drained water is that which can flow under gravitational forces. Recall that the water content capable of being suspended in the soil against gravitational forces is called the *field capacity*, F_c. Therefore, the specific yield is equal to the difference between the soil porosity and the field capacity:

$$S_y = n - F_c \tag{5.2}$$

where
   n=soil porosity (see Table 4.3 for typical values)
   F_c= soil field capacity (see Table 4.9 for typical values)

Table 5.1 illustrates typical values of specific yield for soils and rocks.

Table 5.1: Representative Values of Specific Yield for Soils and Rocks

Material	S_y	Material	S_y
Gravel:			
Coarse	0.23	Limestone	0.14
Medium	0.24	Dune Sand	0.38
Fine	0.25	Loess	0.18
Sand:			
Coarse	0.27	Peat	0.44
Medium	0.28	Schist	0.26
Fine	0.23	Siltstone	0.12
Silt	0.08	Till:	
		Predominantly Silt	0.06
Clay	0.03	Predominantly Sand	0.16
Sandstone:		Predominantly Gravel	0.16
Fine-grained	0.21		
Medium-grained	0.27	Tuff	0.21

Source: Todd (1980).

Pumping of confined aquifers results in a decline of its potentiometric surface due to the mechanical compression properties of the water and the soil grains. Therefore, the *storage coefficient* of a confined aquifer is a function of the elastic properties of the water and those of the aquifer. The storage coefficient, also called *storativity*, of a confined aquifer is defined as

$$S = \frac{1}{A}\frac{dV'}{dh}$$

(5.3)

where
   S=storage coefficient
   V'=volume of water released from compression (m^3)
   h=elevation of the potentiometric surface (m)

A=surface area of aquifer (m^2)

Since the storage coefficient in a confined aquifer depends on the mechanical properties of the aquifer, its values tend to be several orders of magnitude lower than the specific yield of a comparable unconfined aquifer. Typical values are of the order of 0.001 and less. When a confined aquifer is pumped, the water released decreases the fluid pressure in the aquifer, which causes an increase in the inter-granular stress and a slight compaction of the aquifer. The storage coefficient is also a function of the aquifer thickness, which may not be a constant for an aquifer. A normalized value of the storage coefficient is called *specific storage* and it is defined as

$$S = bS_s \qquad (5.4)$$

where
  b=aquifer thickness (m)

An expression for specific storage is (Jacob, 1950):

$$S_s = \gamma_w(\alpha + n\beta) \qquad (5.5)$$

where
  S_s = specific storage (m^{-1})
  γ_w = specific weight of water (N/m^3)
  α = aquifer compressibility (m^2/N)
  β = water compressibility (m^2/N)

The first term in equation (5.5) relates to the compressibility of the aquifer (i.e., the inverse of the modulus of elasticity). The second term relates to the compressibility of water. While the latter tends to be a constant at ordinary temperatures, the former may be inferred via consolidation tests in the laboratory. Those tests, however, are difficult to extrapolate to large scale field conditions. For these reasons, the value of the storage coefficient of a confined aquifer is often assumed, or calibrated such that the solution of the flow equations reproduces a set of field-measured values of hydraulic head.

Applicability of Darcy's Law

Darcy's law was introduced in chapter 4 as the fundamental law of groundwater flow. Equations (4.11) and (4.13) state that the specific discharge is a function of the hydraulic gradient, which is the driving force of fluid motion, and of the hydraulic conductivity, which represents the resistance to the motion by the porous media and the fluid itself. Although Darcy's law is widely applicable to groundwater flow problems in natural aquifers, it is only applicable to *laminar flow* conditions. A measure of the hydraulic regime of flow conditions is the *Reynold's* number, which can be defined for porous media flow as

$$\mathbb{R} = \frac{\rho q d_{10}}{\mu} = \frac{q d_{10}}{\nu} \qquad (5.6)$$

where

$\mathbb{R}$ = Reynold's number
ρ = density of fluid (kg/m^3)
q = specific discharge (m/s)
d_{10} = effective size of soil grains (10% are finer) (m)
μ = dynamic viscosity of fluid ($kg/(m.s)$)
ν = kinematic viscosity of fluid (m^2/s)

Darcy's law is strictly applicable to cases when $\mathbb{R} \leq 1$. It is approximately applicable when $1 < \mathbb{R} \leq 10$. If $\mathbb{R} > 10$, the flow regime is *turbulent*, the inertia terms become more important, and Darcy's law is not valid.

Aquifer Heterogeneity and Anisotropy

As stated in chapter 4, hydraulic conductivity is a function of the fluid properties, such as specific weight and viscosity, and of the porous media itself. Soil texture, grain-size distribution, grain orientation and shape are important characteristics affecting the magnitude of the hydraulic conductivity.

Consider a fixed point in an aquifer. Let us denote K_x the horizontal hydraulic conductivity affecting the flow in the horizontal direction, and K_z the hydraulic conductivity affecting the flow in the vertical direction. If $K_x = K_z$, then the aquifer is *isotropic* in the hydraulic conductivity. Otherwise, the aquifer is *anisotropic* in the hydraulic conductivity. Anisotropic aquifers are often encountered in nature, particularly in layered systems, where $K_x > K_z$. This implies that water may travel easier in the horizontal than in the vertical direction.

Another classification of natural aquifers refers to the spatial variability of the hydraulic conductivity. If K is a constant (i.e., it does not change with distance), the aquifer is *homogeneous* in the hydraulic conductivity. If K is a function of the spatial coordinates (i.e., it changes with distance), the aquifer is *heterogeneous* in the hydraulic conductivity. Homogeneous aquifers rarely occur in nature, except for aquifers composed of wind-generated sand dunes, or sedimentary rocks of uniform depositional history. Most aquifers exhibit a certain degree of heterogeneity. Yet, the concept of an equivalent homogeneous aquifer, or an effective hydraulic conductivity value in a heterogeneous aquifer, $\overline{K}$, is of interest to the hydrologist. This stems from the fact that the simplest solutions to the groundwater flow equations are those whose hydraulic conductivity is constant. Solutions of groundwater flow equations in heterogeneous aquifers usually require elaborate analytical techniques, or numerical solution methodologies.

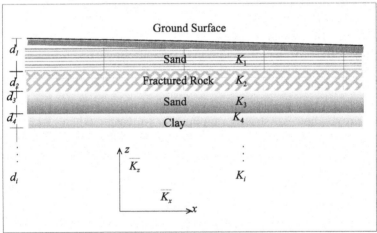

Fig 5.4: Effective Hydraulic Conductivity in Layered Aquifers

From the four possibilities above (i.e., isotropic, anisotropic, homogeneous, heterogeneous), two combinations are frequent in groundwater basins: anisotropic homogeneous aquifers, and isotropic heterogeneous aquifers. Anisotropic homogeneous aquifers in the hydraulic conductivity occur in aquifers characterized by different layers of soil, each with a particular soil texture, hydraulic conductivity, K_i, and thickness, d_i (see Figure 5.4). The total vertical dimension of the aquifer is usually small (e.g., of the order of tens of meters), compared with its horizontal dimensions (e.g., of the order of kilometers). This suggests that an equivalent bulk horizontal hydraulic conductivity, and a bulk vertical hydraulic conductivity is valid for the entire system. The equivalent horizontal hydraulic conductivity may be estimated from

$$\bar{K}_x = \left(\sum_{i=1}^{N} K_i d_i \right) \Big/ \left(\sum_{i=1}^{N} d_i \right) \tag{5.7}$$

where
$\bar{K}_x$ = equivalent bulk horizontal hydraulic conductivity ($m/month$)
K_i = hydraulic conductivity of layer i ($m/month$)
d_i = thickness of layer i (m)
N = number of soil layers in the aquifer

The equivalent vertical hydraulic conductivity may be estimated from

$$\bar{K}_z = \left(\sum_{i=1}^{N} d_i \right) \Big/ \left(\sum_{i=1}^{N} \frac{d_i}{K_i} \right) \tag{5.8}$$

where
$\bar{K}_z$ = equivalent bulk vertical hydraulic conductivity ($m/month$)

Equations (5.7) and (5.8) suggest that the equivalent horizontal hydraulic conductivity is controlled by the layer with the highest individual conductivity, and that the equivalent vertical hydraulic conductivity is controlled by the layer with the lowest conductivity. This explains why in most layered systems $K_x > K_z$ (the bulk conductivities are anisotropic), but the bulk values do not change with distance (homogenous system).

The second commonly occurring aquifer is isotropic heterogeneous. This is the situation in geologic units whose hydraulic conductivity varies erratically with the spatial coordinates (heterogeneous), but without a particular trend in the values (unlayered system) and without a significant difference in the directional components of conductivity (isotropic). Alluvial aquifers without a clear layering pattern are examples of this type.

Example 5.1
An aquifer is composed of a 1.2-m thick layer of sandy loam with a conductivity of 120$m/month$, underlain by a 0.8-m thick layer of silt loam

with a conductivity of 45*m/month*, and a 1.8-*m* thick layer of fine sand with a conductivity of 65*m/month*. Estimate the equivalent bulk values of horizontal and vertical hydraulic conductivity.

Solution

From equation (5.7) the equivalent bulk horizontal conductivity is

$$\bar{K}_x = \frac{\sum\limits_{i=1}^{N} K_i d_i}{\sum\limits_{i=1}^{N} d_i} = \frac{120\dfrac{m}{month} \times 1.2m + 45\dfrac{m}{month} \times 0.8m + 65\dfrac{m}{month} \times 1.8m}{1.2m + 0.8m + 1.8m}$$

$$\bar{K}_x = 78.2 m/month$$

From equation (5.8), the equivalent bulk vertical conductivity is

$$\bar{K}_z = \frac{\sum\limits_{i=1}^{N} d_i}{\sum\limits_{i=1}^{N} \dfrac{d_i}{K_i}} = \frac{1.2m + 0.8m + 1.8m}{\dfrac{1.2m}{120m/month} + \dfrac{0.8m}{45m/month} + \dfrac{1.8m}{65m/month}} = 68.5 m/month$$

Note that $\bar{K}_x > \bar{K}_z$.

Aquifer Transmissivity

Transmissivity is a measure of the ability of water to move horizontally in an aquifer. It is defined as an average value of the hydraulic conductivity integrated over the whole depth of the aquifer:

$$T = \int_0^b K(z)dz \tag{5.9}$$

where

T=aquifer transmissivity ($m^2/month$)
b=total aquifer saturated thickness (b)

Aquifers whose vertical dimensions are small compared to their horizontal ones justify the consideration of only the regional, horizontal, components of groundwater flow. This is achieved by eliminating the vertical coordinate, z, from the equations and adopting an integrated value of conductivity over the whole aquifer depth. If the hydraulic conductivity along the vertical is constant, equation (5.9) reduces to

$$T = \bar{K}b \qquad\qquad (5.10)$$

where
    K=average horizontal hydraulic conductivity ($m/month$)

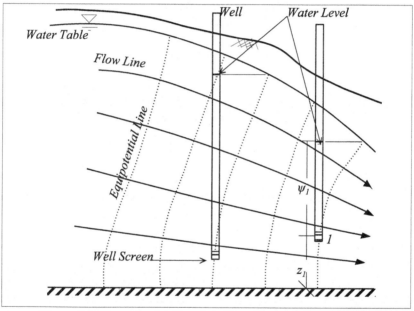

Figure 5.5: Groundwater Flow in a Deep Homogeneous Aquifer

The Groundwater Flow Equation with Dupuit Assumptions

Groundwater flow in aquifers is characterized by flow lines whose general pathways follow a three-dimensional spatial distribution. Consider for example a deep sloping homogenous unconfined aquifer, such as the one depicted in Figure 5.5. The *flow lines* and the velocity vectors have x, y, and z components. The *equipotential lines*, which are perpendicular to the flow lines, are not vertical. The water level at an observation well will rise to an elevation in equilibrium with the equipotential line intersected by the screen at the bottom of the well. Note that the water level at the well will *not* rise to an elevation equal to the water table level (assuming that the well has been properly developed and hydraulically insulated to measure the screen head only). Thus, the hydraulic head h_1 at a point 1 is, from equation (4.10), $h_1 = z_1 + \psi_1$, where z_1 is the elevation head of point 1 with respect to the bottom of the aquifer and ψ_1 is the pressure head at point 1.

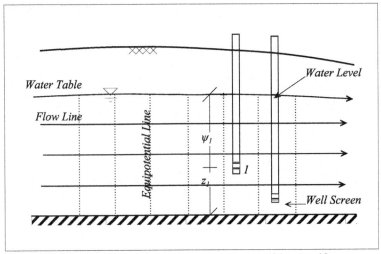

Figure 5.6: Groundwater Flow in a Long, Thin, Aquifer

Many natural aquifers, however, are mildly sloping, long, and thin. These aquifers often contain several layers of soil, each with different texture (Figure 5.4). This results in horizontal hydraulic conductivities, and horizontal flow velocities, of higher magnitude than the vertical values (see Example 5.1). Thus, for mildly sloping, long, and thin aquifers, it appears reasonable to assume that the predominant flow direction is horizontal (see Figure 5.6). In these aquifers, the equipotential lines are almost vertical. The hydraulic head h_1 at a point 1 is, from equation (4.10), $h_1 = z_1 + \psi_1$, where z_1 is the elevation head of point 1 with respect to the bottom of the aquifer and ψ_1 is the pressure head at point 1. The water level in an observation well will rise to an elevation comparable to that of the water table, regardless of the vertical position of the well screen. Therefore, the hydraulic head is the same at any point along the vertical and equal to the elevation of the water table. These are the Dupuit assumptions for horizontal flow, which neglect the vertical components of the flow. Clearly these assumptions are not valid in deep sloping aquifers, in regions near recharge zones, discharge zones, or in the presence of strong vertical hydraulic gradients.

Consider the steady groundwater flow through a vertical section of an unconfined aquifer that satisfies Dupuit assumptions (Figure 5.7). The length of a control volume is Δx and its depth is equal to the total saturated thickness. In Figure 5.7 the slope of the water table is exaggerated (i.e., aquifer thickness is actually the same at each side of the control volume). Since Dupuit assumptions are valid, then the saturated thickness of the aquifer is equal to the hydraulic head, h, at any point along the vertical and equal to the elevation of the water table with respect to the bottom of the aquifer. Thus, the cross-sectional area per unit length of aquifer is $A_T=h\times1$.

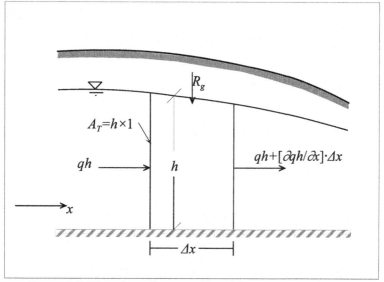

Figure 5.7: Flow through an Aquifer with Dupuit Assumptions

The specific discharge entering the volume is q. The flow rate entering the control volume is the specific discharge times the cross-sectional area, $q\times A_T=q.h$. The flow rate leaving the volume may be expressed as that entering the volume plus its rate of change with respect to distance times the volume length, $qh+[(\partial qh)/(\partial x)]\times\Delta x$. The net flow rate is the rate leaving minus the rate entering the volume. Under steady state conditions (i.e., time independent), the net rate must equal the flow rate entering the volume as recharge from rainfall, or that leaving the system via pumping wells. In words, the conservation of mass statement is

The net mass rate entering the volume minus the increase in mass rate from sources or sinks = zero

The increase in mass rate from recharge is $R_g \Delta x \times 1$, where R_g is the recharge rate (per unit aquifer surface area). Mathematically, the mass conservation equation is

$$\frac{\partial q h}{\partial x} \Delta x - R_g \Delta x = 0 \qquad (5.11)$$

In its present form the continuity equation is not suitable for calculations since field instrumentation to measure specific discharge is usually not readily available. It is more convenient to obtain a flow equation whose dependent variable represents an easily measurable variable, such as hydraulic head. Using Darcy's law we can achieve this. Thus, substituting equation (4.13) into equation (5.11) and eliminating Δx, one obtains

$$\frac{\partial}{\partial x}\left(K_x h \frac{\partial h}{\partial x} \right) = -R_g \qquad (5.12)$$

where
$K_x =$ hydraulic conductivity in the x direction (*m/month*)

In this aquifer with Dupuit assumptions the saturated thickness, b, is equal to the hydraulic head, h. Thus using equation (5.10), equation (5.12) becomes

$$\frac{\partial}{\partial x}\left(T_x \frac{\partial h}{\partial x} \right) = -R_g \qquad (5.13)$$

where
$T_x = K_x h =$ transmissivity in the x direction ($m^2/month$)

Equations (5.12) and (5.13) are nonlinear differential equations, since their parameters are functions of the dependent variables. Consistent with the Dupuit assumptions of mild gradients, one may attempt linearization by assuming that the saturated thickness is almost constant, and $T_x \approx K_x b$, where b is the average saturated thickness. In such case, T_x is not a function of h and the equation is linear. If the aquifer is homogeneous, then $K_x = \bar{K}$, $T = \bar{K}b$, and equation (5.13) reduces to

$$\frac{d^2h}{dx^2} = -\frac{R_g}{T} \tag{5.14}$$

Linearization may not yield accurate results when an aquifer has pumping or injecting wells that generate strong gradients and large changes in saturated thickness. If field conditions approximately reproduce Dupuit assumptions, the linearized equation has been shown to produce reasonably accurate results. Alternatively, if the aquifer is homogeneous, equation (5.12) may be reduced to:

$$\frac{\bar{K}}{2}\frac{d^2h^2}{dx^2} = -R_g \tag{5.15}$$

which is linear in h^2 and may be directly integrated.

A planar two-dimensional version of equation (5.13) may be obtained after repeating the above procedure for the y direction (i.e., horizontal direction perpendicular to x). Hence, the two-dimensional groundwater flow equation in a steady heterogeneous anisotropic aquifer with Dupuit assumptions is

$$\frac{\partial}{\partial x}\left(T_x\frac{\partial h}{\partial x}\right) + \frac{\partial}{\partial y}\left(T_y\frac{\partial h}{\partial y}\right) = -R_g \tag{5.16}$$

where
   T_x = transmissivity in the x direction ($m^2/month$)
   T_y = transmissivity in the y direction ($m^2/month$)

This equation may be linearized as before.

Water exploitation from pumping wells affect the spatial distribution of hydraulic heads. If there are pumping wells in the aquifer, equation (5.16) must be modified to reflect the presence of sources. The two-dimensional groundwater flow equation in a steady heterogeneous anisotropic aquifer with Dupuit assumptions is,

$$\frac{\partial}{\partial x}\left(T_x\frac{\partial h}{\partial x}\right)+\frac{\partial}{\partial y}\left(T_y\frac{\partial h}{\partial y}\right)=-R_g+W \qquad (5.17)$$

where
W=pumping flow rate per unit surface area per unit time (m^{-1})

Pumping or injecting wells may be represented by adding special mathematical functions that specify the coordinates of the well. Consider an aquifer with N wells. Equation (5.17) can now be written as

$$\frac{\partial}{\partial x}\left(T_x\frac{\partial h}{\partial x}\right)+\frac{\partial}{\partial y}\left(T_y\frac{\partial h}{\partial y}\right)=-R_g+\sum_{i=1}^{N}\frac{Q_i}{A_i}\delta(x-x_i)\delta(y-y_i) \qquad (5.18)$$

where
N=number of wells pumping the aquifer
Q_i=pumping rate of well i ($m^3/month$), positive for a pumping well and negative for an injecting one
x_i, y_i=(x, y) coordinates of well i
A_i=cross-section area of well i (m^2)
$\delta(\ )$=the Dirac's delta function with the properties

$$\delta(x)=0, \ x\neq0, \quad \int_{-\infty}^{\infty}\delta(x)dx=0, \quad \int_{-\infty}^{\infty}f(x)\delta(x-a)dx=f(a) \qquad (5.19)$$

The foregoing development assumes steady state conditions. This implies that the solution of the differential equations may be used to simulate time-independent aquifer response. For example, the hydrologist may apply a steady state model to time-averaged, or seasonally-averaged, water management situations, such as the calculation of average hydraulic heads and average groundwater flow velocities. Such conditions are met when a general hydrologic regime is investigated. If project objectives are such that seasonal variability in the recharge, or time variability in the boundary conditions are important, then a transient groundwater model must be used.

Referring to Figure 5.7, the statement of mass conservation for a control volume in an aquifer subject to time variability in the net flow rate becomes

Net mass rate entering the volume minus the increase in mass rate from sources or sinks = rate of change of mass stored in volume

The mass of water stored in the control volume is $S_y h \Delta x \times 1$, where S_y is the unconfined aquifer specific yield. The rate of change is the derivative with respect to time. Repeating the derivation of the steady one-dimensional case, the transient groundwater flow equation in a heterogeneous anisotropic unconfined aquifer with Dupuit assumptions is

$$S_y \frac{\partial h}{\partial t} - \frac{\partial}{\partial x}\left(T_x \frac{\partial h}{\partial x}\right) - \frac{\partial}{\partial y}\left(T_y \frac{\partial h}{\partial y}\right) = R_g \qquad (5.20)$$

This is the Boussinesq equation. It may be linearized as before, if field conditions justify it. Sources or sinks, W, can also be represented as in equation (5.18). It may also be simplified in cases of homogeneous isotropic aquifers as

$$\frac{S_y}{T}\frac{\partial h}{\partial t} - \frac{\partial^2 h}{\partial x^2} - \frac{\partial^2 h}{\partial y^2} = \frac{R_g}{T} - W \qquad (5.21)$$

In all of the above equations, the recharge term, R_g, may also include evapotranspiration from shallow aquifers, in which case the sign of this term changes.

Now, for confined aquifers a procedure similar to the above development may be followed (see Bear, 1979; De Marsily, 1986 for details). The differential equations governing steady or unsteady groundwater flow in confined aquifers with Dupuit assumptions are obtained. In confined aquifers, however, the hydraulic head h does not coincide with the depth of the water table, as in unconfined aquifers, since there is not a water table. With this provision, the steady one-dimensional flow equation in a confined aquifer is the same as equation (5.13), except that the transmissivity is given by equation (5.10), with b the aquifer thickness. The two-dimensional equation is identical to equation (5.16). For the transient equation, considerations on the mechanical properties of water and porous media are necessary. The resulting equation is

$$S\frac{\partial h}{\partial t} - \frac{\partial}{\partial x}\left(T_x\frac{\partial h}{\partial x}\right) - \frac{\partial}{\partial y}\left(T_y\frac{\partial h}{\partial y}\right) = R_g - W \qquad (5.22)$$

This equation is mathematically identical to the unconfined flow equation (5.20), except that instead of the specific yield we use the storage coefficient, S. Sources or sinks can also be added, as in equation (5.18).

The General Groundwater Flow Equation

Until now, we have limited our discussion to the development of the groundwater flow equation with Dupuit assumptions. These assumptions are met by a large variety of highly productive aquifers in semi-flat valleys. However Dupuit assumptions may not be valid in situations where strong hydraulic gradients are present. For instance, aquifers whose vertical dimensions are comparable to their horizontal dimensions (e.g., flow through an earth dam), or aquifers with strong vertical gradients (e.g., vertical flow through a *perched* or *leaking aquifer*) do not satisfy Dupuit assumptions. In such cases the hydrologist should study the principles behind fully three-dimensional flow in aquifers. Applying the law of mass conservation to a control volume in a confined aquifer, using Darcy's law, and taking into consideration the compressibility of the aquifer (i.e., a confined aquifer), the general flow equation is (Bear, 1979)

$$S_s\frac{\partial h}{\partial t} - \frac{\partial}{\partial x}\left(K_x\frac{\partial h}{\partial x}\right) - \frac{\partial}{\partial y}\left(K_y\frac{\partial h}{\partial y}\right) - \frac{\partial}{\partial z}\left(K_z\frac{\partial h}{\partial z}\right) = 0 \qquad (5.23)$$

where
    z=vertical coordinate (m)
    S_s= specific storage (m^{-1})

This is the three-dimensional flow equation in a heterogeneous anisotropic confined aquifer. Unlike the equations with Dupuit assumptions, the vertical coordinate, and the vertical hydraulic conductivity, is needed. If pumping wells, injecting wells, or leakage from adjacent aquitards are present, additional terms are added to the right side of the equation. If steady state conditions prevail, then the time derivative is set to zero. If in addition the aquifer is homogeneous and isotropic, then the equation reduces to the Laplace equation:

$$\frac{\partial^2 h}{\partial x^2} + \frac{\partial^2 h}{\partial y^2} + \frac{\partial^2 h}{\partial z^2} = 0 \qquad (5.24)$$

For unconfined aquifers the compressibility of the porous media is neglected and the equation for homogeneous and isotropic media reduces to the Laplace equation above. This is the governing equation for steady or unsteady flow in unconfined aquifers. Unconfined aquifers subject to steady or unsteady recharge at the water table generate a boundary condition at the water table which reflects this situation. The water table boundary condition is in itself a steady or unsteady nonlinear partial differential equation, which requires special solution techniques (see Serrano, 2003a, 1995a).

Solutions to Groundwater Flow Equations
A *mathematical model* of groundwater flow is constituted by the solution of a governing differential equation (such as one of the equations in the previous section) subject to a set of boundary conditions, and an initial condition if the problem is time dependent. Boundary conditions are the specifications of the dependent variable (e.g., *h*) at the borders of the aquifer. These borders should be chosen to coincide with natural boundaries, such as rivers or abrupt changes in the hydraulic conductivity due to the presence of other geologic units. The *initial condition* is the value of the dependent variable everywhere in the aquifer at *t*=0 when simulations begin.

Mathematical models constitute important tools for groundwater resources management. Natural conditions of an aquifer, pumping wells, injecting wells, underground excavations may all be simulated by a mathematical model. The simulation allows the hydrologist or water resources planner to understand and predict the possible effects of aquifer development projects. Management decisions may be taken based on the forecasted conditions.

Solutions of groundwater flow equations may be obtained analytically or numerically. Analytical solutions provide values of the dependent variable continuously in space and time. They require the application of mathematical methods, but their computational implementation is rather simple (Hermance, 1999; Strack, 1989; De Marsily, 1986; Bear, 1979; Hunt, 1983). Many traditional analytical solutions require regular geometrical domains, aquifer homogeneity, and linearization. As we shall see in this section, these requirements are no longer needed by the new analytical, and approximate analytical, solution.

Numerical solutions of groundwater flow equations provide values of the dependent variable at fixed discrete locations and fixed discrete times. They allow the consideration of irregular aquifer shapes, heterogeneity in the hydraulic conductivity, and discrete linearization (Anderson, 1992; Aral, 1989; Walton, 1989; Bear and Verruijt, 1987; Huyakorn and Pinder, 1983; Ligget and Liu, 1983; Wang and Anderson, 1982; Pinder and Gray, 1977). However, they require vast amounts of information, computer memory, and computer time for its execution. Since numerical solutions are based on space and time discretization and on the numerical approximation of the derivatives in a equation, numerical instability may arise. Numerical solutions are at the heart of the most commonly used computer simulation models today. These models programmed in a computer language, linked with sophisticated graphics for the illustration of the solution, and armed with a friendly end-user interface constitute useful hydrologic analysis tools.

In essence, new analytical solutions, such as the ones described in this section, constitute the best approach for preliminary analyses or for studies with scarce hydrologic information. They no longer require advanced mathematical skills, they can be applied in a variety of practical situations, including irregular domains, heterogeneous aquifers, and nonlinear equations. In addition, with the advent or modern mathematics software such as Maple, the hydrologist can easily implement his or her own model. On the other hand, numerical methods are suitable in complex groundwater modeling scenarios enjoying the availability of large data sets. Advanced analytical solutions and numerical solutions of groundwater equations fall beyond the scope of the present work. The interested hydrologist should consult appropriate texts on partial differential equations (i.e., Myint-U and Debnath, 1987; Powers, 1979) and numerical methods (e.g., Chapra and Canale, 1988). For descriptions on popular groundwater software, such as the USGS MODFLOW program, see Waterloo Hydrogeologic (2004) and Kresic (1997).

Example 5.2: One-Dimensional Flow in a Long Aquifer
    Consider an unconfined aquifer bounded by two rivers flowing parallel to each other (Figure 5.8). The average stage in the left river is $H_1=10m$ with respect to the bottom of the aquifer. The average stage in the right river is $H_2=12m$. The length of the aquifer is $l_x=1100m$. The mean aquifer hydraulic conductivity is $K=50m/month$. The aquifer

receives a mean recharge from rainfall of $R_g=12mm/month$. Calculate (1) the mean hydraulic heads across the aquifer; (2) the flow rate and its direction at the left and right boundaries; and (3) the position of the *groundwater divide* (i.e., point in the aquifer where recharged water splits into that flowing to the left river and that to the right one).

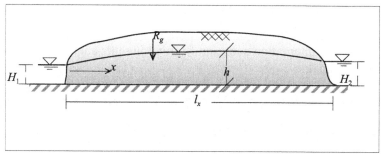

Figure 5.8: Unconfined Aquifer of Example 5.2

Solution
(1) Assuming a homogeneous aquifer and a predominantly horizontal groundwater flow direction between the rivers (x direction), we set $x=0$ at the left boundary. The governing groundwater flow equation is given by equation (5.14):

$$\frac{d^2h}{dx^2}=-\frac{R_g}{T}, \qquad 0\le x\le l_x \tag{5.25}$$

where
$h(x)$=hydraulic head with respect to the bottom of the aquifer (m)

The transmissivity may be estimated as

$$T=\bar{K}b\approx\bar{K}\left(\frac{H_1+H_2}{2}\right)=50\frac{m}{month}\times\left(\frac{10m+12m}{2}\right)=550\frac{m^2}{month}$$

The groundwater flow equation is subject to the following boundary conditions:

$$h(0)=H_1=10, \quad h(l_x)=H_2=12 \tag{5.26}$$

Multiplying both sides of equation (5.25) by dx and integrating indefinitely,

$$\frac{dh}{dx} = -\frac{R_g x}{T} + A \tag{5.27}$$

where A is an integration constant. Multiplying this equation by dx and integrating again

$$h(x) = -\frac{R_g x^2}{2T} + Ax + B \tag{5.28}$$

where B is a constant of integration. This is the general solution of the differential equation. To evaluate the constant B, substitute the left boundary condition equation (5.26) into equation (5.28). Similarly, to evaluate A substitute the right boundary condition equation (5.26) into equation (5.28). The values of the constants are:

$$A = \frac{H_2 - H_1}{l_x} + \frac{R_g l_x}{2T} = \frac{12m - 10m}{1100m} + \frac{0.012m/month \times 1100m}{2 \times 550m^2/month} = 0.0138 \tag{5.29}$$

$$B = H_1 = 10m$$

Plotting the value of h for different distances x, using equation (5.28), it is possible to visualize the shape of the water table (see Figure 5.9).

(2) The hydraulic gradient is obtained by differentiating equation (5.28) with respect to x to give equation (5.27). Substituting equation (5.22) into equation (4.13) we obtain the specific discharge:

$$q(x) = -\bar{K}\frac{dh}{dx} \approx -\frac{T}{b}\frac{dh}{dx} = \frac{2T}{H_1 + H_2}\left(\frac{R_g x}{T} - A\right) \tag{5.30}$$

Substituting $x=0$ and $x=l_x$, respectively, into equation (5.30), one finds the specific discharges $q(0)$ and $q(l_x)$, respectively. Thus, $q(0) = -0.691m/month$. The negative sign means that the direction of the flow is opposite to that of x. Similarly, $q(l_x)=0.509m/month$. Multiply by the cross sectional areas to obtain the flow rates:

$$Q(0)=q(0){\times}H_1{\times}1m=-0.691m/month{\times}10m{\times}1m=-6.91m^3/month$$

$$Q(l_x)=q(l_x){\times}H_2{\times}1m=0.509m/month{\times}12m{\times}1m=6.11m^3/month$$

These are the flow rates discharging to the rivers per meter of aquifer along the river length. By substituting several values of x into equation (5.30) and plotting the resulting specific discharge values, one may visualize the distribution of velocities across the aquifer (Figure 5.9).

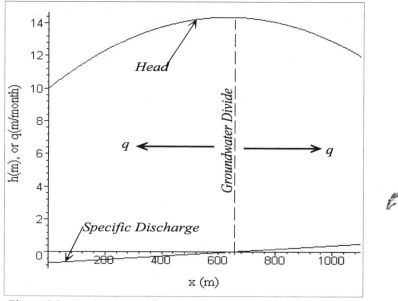

Figure 5.9: Head and Specific Discharge in Aquifer of Example 5.2

(3) The groundwater divide is a point in the aquifer where the horizontal hydraulic gradients are zero (i.e., water table is horizontal), and the specific discharge is zero (see Figure 5.9). Therefore, the location of the divide may be estimated after setting either equation (5.27) or (5.30) to zero and finding the corresponding abscissa x. In either case, the divide is located at approximately $x=632m$. The groundwater divide may or may not coincide with the surface water divide, or watershed boundary, depending on the geologic and hydrologic conditions in the area. The location of the groundwater divide marks the partition of recharged water into either the left or the right discharge areas.

Example 5.3: Impact of a Deep Excavation on Regional Flow

Assume that in the aquifer of Example 5.2 a long excavation between the distances $x_1=450m$ and $x_2=500m$, respectively from the left river, is being planned. The excavation will eventually reach the bottom of the aquifer. (1) Estimate the steady hydraulic heads across the aquifer after the excavation is completed, and evaluate the impact of the construction on the groundwater levels. (2) Calculate the volume of groundwater to be removed to maintain a dry construction site. Assume a specific yield $S_y=0.25$.

Solution

(1) The new construction site will alter the groundwater boundary conditions. After excavation, the aquifer extends from 0 to 450m, and from 500 to 1100m, and the middle portion, from 450 to 500m will be kept at $h=0$. The boundary-value problem for the left portion of the aquifer is, from equation (5.14):

$$\frac{d^2h}{dx^2}=-\frac{R_g}{T'}, \quad 0\le x\le450, \quad h(0)=10, \ h(450)=0$$

The average saturated thickness has changed and the new value of the transmissivity is estimated as $T'=Kb=(50m/month)\times(10/2)m=250$ $m^2/month$. As in Example 5.2, the solution to this equation is given by equation (5.28) as

$$h(x)=-\frac{R_g x^2}{2T'}+A_1x+B_1, \quad 0\le x\le450 \qquad (5.31)$$

As in Example 5.2, equation (5.29), the values of the constants are found after substitution of the boundary conditions:

$$A_1=\frac{0-H_1}{450}+\frac{R_g\times450}{2\times T'}=-0.01142, \quad B_1=10$$

The boundary-value problem for the right portion of the aquifer is, from equation (5.14):

$$\frac{d^2h}{dx^{/2}} = -\frac{R_g}{T^{/}}, \quad x=500+x^{/}, \quad 500 \le x \le 1100, \quad 0 \le x^{/} \le 600$$

$$h(0)=0, \quad h(1100)=12$$

As in Example 5.2, the solution to this equation is given by equation (5.28) as

$$h(x) = -\frac{R_g x^{/2}}{2T^{/}} + A_2 x^{/} + B_2, \quad 500 \le x \le 1100, \ 0 \le x^{/} \le 600 \qquad (5.32)$$

The values of the constants are obtained from the boundary conditions imposed on the right portion of the aquifer (see equation (5.29)):

$$A_2 = \frac{12-0}{600} + \frac{R_g \times 600}{2 \times T^{/}} = 0.0344, \quad B_2 = 0$$

Using equations (5.31) and (5.32), the heads after construction are plotted with respect to distance in Figure 5.10. Using Equation (5.28), the water table before construction is plotted for comparison.

The construction project generates drastic changes in the regional groundwater flow in the aquifer. Before construction, the groundwater flows from the aquifer to the rivers. After the construction project is completed, a flow reversal will occur causing the water to flow from the rivers towards the site. At the construction site, seepage faces discharging water from the aquifer will develop (a condition not considered by the Dupuit assumptions). Equations (5.31) and (5.32) may be used as in Example 5.2 to calculate flow rates from each river into the aquifer per unit length of aquifer. A comparison between the seasonal flow rate in the river with the calculated loss of water to the aquifer will determine whether the river eventually becomes dry. From the water table elevation point of view, the construction will cause a dramatic decrease. The highest drop in water table elevation will occur in the vicinity of the construction site. Certain wells may become dry. It is important to remark that in this case the gradients generated by the construction project are such that Dupuit assumptions may not be valid and the results are only approximate.

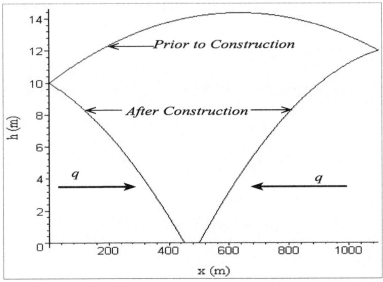

Figure 5.10:Heads before and after Project in Example 5.3

(2) The volume of water stored in the aquifer prior to construction, S_{gi}, is found by integration of the saturated area of the aquifer times the specific yield. Thus from equation (5.28),

$$S_{gi}=S_y\int_0^{l_x}h(x)dx=S_y\int_0^{l_x}(-\frac{R_gx^2}{2T}+Ax+B)dx$$

$$S_{gi}=S_y\left[-\frac{R_gx^3}{6T}\Big|_0^{l_x}+\frac{Ax^2}{2}\Big|_0^{l_x}+Bx\Big|_0^{l_x}\right]=S_y\left[-\frac{R_gl_x^3}{6T}+\frac{Al_x^2}{2}+Bl_x\right]$$

$$S_{gi}=0.25\times\left[-\frac{0.012\dfrac{m}{month}\times(1100m)^3}{6\times550\dfrac{m^2}{month}}+\frac{0.0138\times(1100m)^2}{2}+10m\times1100m\right]$$

$$S_{gi}=3627.25m^3/m$$

After construction, the volume of water stored in the portion of the aquifer to the left of the excavation, S_1, is found after integrating equation (5.31) from $x=0$ to $x=450$ and multiplying by the specific yield. Following a similar procedure as above and substituting the constant values one obtains $S_1 = 608.63 m^3/m$. Similarly, the volume of water stored in the portion of the aquifer to the right of the excavation, S_2, is found after integrating equation (5.32) from $x'=0$ to $x'=600$ and multiplying by the specific yield. Thus, $S_2 = 1008.0 m^3/m$. Finally, the volume of water to remove is the difference between the volume before construction and that after it:

$$\Delta S_g = S_{gi} - S_1 - S_2 = (3627.25 - 608.63 - 1008.0) m^3/m = 2010.63 m^3/m$$

Thus over two thousand cubic meters of water per meter of aquifer need to be pumped. This is the volume to be removed initially. At this point we could use equations (5.31) and (5.32) in conjunction with Darcy's law to calculate the flux at $x=450$ and $x=600$, respectively. These values would be the pumping rates to be maintained to keep the construction site dry.

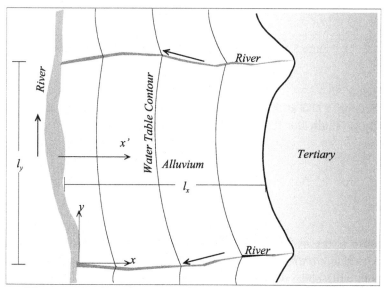

Figure 5.11: Plan View of Aquifer of Examples 5.4 through 5.8

Example 5.4: Effect of a Geologic Barrier on Regional Flow
Figure 5.11 shows a plan view of an unconfined alluvial aquifer underlain by a tertiary consolidated formation. Figure 5.12 shows a

profile section of the aquifer through axis x'. The hydraulic conductivity is 35*m/month*; the mean recharge rate is 10*mm/month;* the mean aquifer saturated thickness is 20*m*; the mean horizontal distance between the river and the tertiary formation is 860*m*; and the head at the river with respect to the mean sea level is 240*m*. Assuming that the tertiary formation is almost impervious, that the regional groundwater flow is almost one-dimensional (i.e., along x'), and that Dupuit assumptions are valid, (1) calculate the hydraulic heads along $□'$, and (2) estimate the aquifer discharge rate into the river.

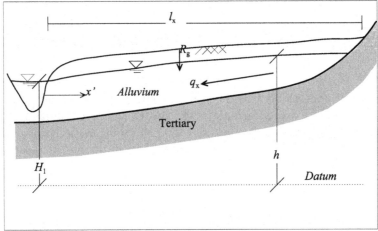

Figure 5.12: Profile Section of Aquifer of Example 5.4

Solution
(1) Setting $x'=0$ at the main river, the governing equation of regional steady groundwater flow is given by equation (5.14):

$$\frac{d^2h}{dx'^2} = -\frac{R_g}{T}, \quad 0 \le x' \le l_x$$

where h is the hydraulic head with respect to the mean sea level, and $T=\bar{K}b=35m/month \times 20m = 700 m^2/month$. This equation holds if the saturated thickness does not deviate too much with respect to the average value, b, and if the hydraulic gradients are small. At $x'=0$ the head corresponds to that at the left river. At $x'=l_x$, there is an abrupt change in the value of the hydraulic conductivity, from a value of K in the alluvium to a value of zero at the tertiary formation. This implies that there is a no flow condition in the x' direction at this point. This condition may be expressed mathematically by setting the hydraulic gradient in the x' direction equal to zero (i.e., the water table is horizontal). The boundary conditions imposed on the above equation are:

$$h(0)=H_1, \quad \frac{dh}{dx}(l_x)=0$$

Proceeding as in Example 5.2, the first integration of the flow equation yields equation (5.27) when replacing x by x'. This represents the hydraulic gradient as a function of distance. The second integration yields the hydraulic head, equation (5.28). On substituting the left boundary condition into this equation, one gets $B=H_1=240m$. On substituting the right boundary condition into equation (5.27), one gets

$$\frac{dh}{dx'}(l_x)=0=-\frac{R_g l_x}{T}+A \implies A=\frac{R_g l_x}{T}=\frac{0.01m/month\times860m}{700m^2/month}=0.0123$$

Therefore the expression for the hydraulic head is given by equation (5.23) with the above constant values. Plotting the head with respect to distance helps visualize the regional groundwater flow pattern (see problem 5).

(2) The specific discharge is given from Darcy's law, equation (4.13), using equation (5.27) as the hydraulic gradient:

$$q_x=-\bar{K}\frac{dh}{dx'}=\frac{R_g x'}{b}-\bar{K}A$$

This expression has a maximum value equal to $-\bar{K}A$ at $x'=0$ (see problem 5.5), and linearly decreases with distance to zero at $x'=l_x$. Therefore, the flow rate per unit aquifer length (in the y direction) at the main river is

$$Q_x=-\bar{K}A\times b\times 1=35m/month\times0.0123\times20m\times1m=-8.6m^3/month$$

where the negative sign implies that the direction of the flow is from the aquifer to the river.

Examples 5.2, 5.3, and 5.4 show that practical models of groundwater flow may be developed with simple analytical solutions to the one-dimensional groundwater flow equations. Models permit the calculation of hydraulic heads, hydraulic gradients, specific discharge, and seepage velocity and its direction at various locations in an aquifer. This is valuable information in hydrologic and environmental studies. For two-dimensional and three-dimensional aquifer domains, advanced mathematical methods for partial differential equations are needed. Even with the added complexity, traditional methods such as Fourier series and Laplace transform require regularly-shaped homogeneous aquifers and linearity in the equations. For these reasons, numerical methods are usually prescribed. These methods are involved, and require computational skills.

We introduce here applications of recent advances in mathematical research, which has produced the *method of decomposition* (Adomian 1994, 1983): an approximate analytical method that satisfies our demands for simplicity, while allowing the solution of (linear or nonlinear, steady or transient, one-dimensional or multidimensional) groundwater equations in (homogeneous or heterogeneous, regular or irregular) aquifers. Decomposition consists in deriving an infinite series, much like Fourier series, that in many cases converge to an exact solution. Many studies have reported new solutions to a wide class of equations (ordinary, partial, differential, integral, integro-differential, linear, nonlinear, deterministic or stochastic) in a variety of fields of mathematical physics and engineering (see Adomian, 1991 for a review). For nonlinear equations in particular, decomposition is one of the few *systematic* solution procedures available.

Example 5.5: Two-Dimensional Flow in an Unconfined Aquifer

Consider the more realistic two-dimensional regional groundwater flow of the aquifer of Example 5.4 depicted in Figures 5.11 and 5.12 and find an expression for the hydraulic head. The aquifer is limited by the main stream on one side, two tributaries on two sides, and the consolidated geologic formation on one side; assume that the planar dimensions of the aquifer are approximately rectangular in shape; locate the origin of the coordinates system at the confluence between one tributary and the main river (see Figure 5.11); the heads along the tributaries and the main stream are given according to previously surveyed functions. Assuming that Dupuit assumptions are valid and that the aquifer is homogeneous and isotropic, the governing flow equation is given by equation (5.16):

$$\frac{\partial^2 h}{\partial x^2} + \frac{\partial^2 h}{\partial y^2} = -\frac{R_g}{T}, \quad 0 \le x \le l_x, \ 0 \le y \le l_y \tag{5.33}$$

where $h(x, y)$ is the hydraulic head function of x and y, $l_x = 860m$, $l_y = 2000m$, $K = 35m/month$, $b = 20m$, so that $T = Kb = 35 \times 20 = 700 \, m^2/month$, and $R_g = 10mm/month$. For boundary conditions, we have a specified head at the rivers, and a no-flow boundary condition at the intersection of the aquifer with the tertiary formation. Thus the boundary conditions imposed on equation (5.33) are:

$$h(0, y) = f_1(y), \quad \frac{\partial h}{\partial x}(l_x, y) = 0, \quad h(x, 0) = f_2(x), \quad h(x, l_y) = f_3(x) \tag{5.34}$$

The head at the main river is obtained from data on its mean stage slope, $f_1(y) = 241 - 0.001y$. Assume that the head at the tributaries follow according to the functions $f_2(x) = Cx^2 + Ax + f_1(0)$, $f_3(x) = Ex^2 + Bx + f_1(l_y)$, $C = -R_g/(2T)$, and $A = -2Cl_x$, $B = -2El_x$, and $E = -R_g/T$. However, the functions f_1, f_2, and f_3 should be derived from field measurements of mean river stage.

Solution

Using the method of decomposition (Adomian, 1994), we define the operators $L_x = \partial^2/\partial x^2$ and $L_y = \partial^2/\partial y^2$. The inverse operators L_y^{-1} and L_x^{-1} are the corresponding two-fold indefinite integrals with respect to x and y, respectively. Write equation (5.33) as

$$L_x h + L_y h = -\frac{R_g}{T} \tag{5.35}$$

There are two partial decomposition expansions to equation (5.35): The x-partial solution and the y-partial solution. The x-partial solution, h_x, results from operating with L_x^{-1} on equation (5.35) and re-arranging. Multiplying by the inverse operator L_x^{-1},

$$h_x = -L_x^{-1}\frac{R_g}{T} - L_x^{-1}L_y h_x \tag{5.36}$$

Expanding h_x in the right side as an infinite series $h_x = h_{x0} + h_{x1} + h_{x2} + \dots$, equation (5.36) becomes

$$h_x = -L_x^{-1}\frac{R_g}{T} - L_x^{-1}L_y\left(h_{x0} + h_{x1} + h_{x2} + \dots\right) \tag{5.37}$$

The choice of h_{x0} often determines the level of difficulty in calculating subsequent decomposition terms and the rate of convergence (Adomian, 1994; Wazwaz, 2000). A simple choice is to set h_{x0} as equal to the first three terms in the right side of equation (5.37). Thus, the first approximation to the solutions is

$$h_{x0} = k_1(y) + k_2(y)x - L_x^{-1}\frac{R_g}{T} = k_1(y) + k_2(y)x - \frac{R_g x^2}{2T} \qquad (5.38)$$

where the integration "constants," k_1 and k_2, must be found from the x boundary conditions in equation (5.34):

$$h(0, y) = f_1(y) = h_{x0}(y) = k_1(y)$$

$$\frac{\partial h}{\partial x}(l_x, y) = 0 = \frac{\partial h_{x0}}{\partial x}(l_x, y) = k_2(y) - \frac{R_g l_x}{T} \quad \Rightarrow \quad k_2(y) = \frac{R_g l_x}{T}$$

Equation (5.38) becomes

$$h_{x0} = f_1(y) + \frac{R_g l_x x}{T} - \frac{R_g x^2}{2T} \qquad (5.39)$$

Equation (5.39) satisfies the governing equation (5.33) and the x boundary conditions in equation (5.34), but not necessarily the ones in the y direction. Now, to obtain, the y-partial solution to equation (5.33), h_y, operate with L_y^{-1} on equation (5.33) and rearrange:

$$h_y = -L_y^{-1}\frac{R_g}{T} - L_y^{-1}L_x h_y \qquad (5.40)$$

Expanding h_y in the right side as an infinite series $h_y = h_{y0} + h_{y1} + h_{y2} + \dots$, equation (5.40) becomes

$$h_y = -L_y^{-1}\frac{R_g}{T} - L_y^{-1}L_x\left(h_{y0} + h_{y1} + h_{y2} + \dots\right) \qquad (5.41)$$

Again, if we take h_{y0} as the first three terms in the right side of equation (5.41) we obtain the first approximation, that is

$$h_{y0} = k_3(x) + k_4(x)y - L_y^{-1}\frac{R_g}{T} = k_3(x) + k_4(x)y - \frac{R_g y^2}{2T} \qquad (5.42)$$

where the integration "constants," k_3 and k_4, are found from the y boundary conditions equation (5.34):

$$h_{y0} = f_2(x) + \left(\frac{f_3(x) - f_2(x)}{l_y} + \frac{R_g l_y}{2T} \right) y - \frac{R_g y^2}{2T} \tag{5.43}$$

The y-partial solution satisfies the differential equation (5.33) and the y boundary conditions in equations (5.34), but not necessarily those in the x direction. We now have two partial solutions to equation (5.33): the x-partial solution equation (5.39), and the y-partial solution equation (5.43). Since both are solutions to h, a combination of the two partial solutions yields

$$h_0(x, y) = \left(\frac{h_{x0}(x, y) + h_{y0}(x, y)}{2} \right) \tag{5.44}$$

To obtain the second term in the combined series, h_1, we need to re-derive a new x-partial solution, a new y-partial solution and combine them as above. Thus, the second term in the x-partial solution, h_{x1}, may be derived from the x-partial solution expansion equation (5.37):

$$h_{x1} = k_5(y) + k_6(y)x - L_x^{-1} L_y h_0 \tag{5.45}$$

where h_0 is given by equation (5.44), and k_5 and k_6 are such that equation (5.45) satisfies homogeneous (i.e., zero) x boundary conditions in equations (5.33). Similarly, the second term in the y-partial solution, h_{y1}, may be derived from y-partial solution expansion equation (5.41):

$$h_{y1} = k_7(x) + k_8(x)y - L_y^{-1} L_x h_0 \tag{5.46}$$

where h_0 is given by equation (5.44), and k_7 and k_8 are such that equation (5.46) satisfies homogeneous (i.e., zero) y boundary conditions in equations (5.33). Subsequently, h_1 is obtained by combining equations (5.45) and (5.46):

$$h_1(x, y) = \left(\frac{h_{x1}(x, y) + h_{y1}(x, y)}{2} \right) \tag{5.47}$$

Higher-order terms are derived similarly. The i-th order terms in the x-partial solution, h_{xi}, may be derived from equation (5.37):

$$h_{xi} = k_{4i+1}(y) + k_{4i+2}(y)x - L_x^{-1} L_y h_{i-1}$$

where h_{i-1} is the previous combined term in the decomposition series, and k_{4i+1} and k_{4i+2} are such that homogeneous (i.e., zero) x boundary conditions in equations (5.34) are satisfied. Similarly, the i-th order term in the y-partial solution, h_{yi}, may be derived from equation (5.41):

$$h_{yi} = k_{4i+3}(x) + k_{4i+4}(x)y - L_y^{-1}L_x h_{i-1}$$

where h_{i-1} is the previous combined term in the decomposition series, and k_{4i+3} and k_{4i+4} are such that homogeneous (i.e., zero) y boundary conditions in equations (5.34) are satisfied. Similarly to equation (5.47), the i-th combined term is given by

$$h_i(x, y) = \left(\frac{h_{xi}(x, y) + h_{yi}(x, y)}{2} \right) \tag{5.48}$$

Lastly, we approximate the final solution with N terms, $h \approx h_0 + h_1 + ... + h_N$, where each term in the series is a combination of two partial solutions, one in x and one in y. Due the high rate of convergence of decomposition solutions, the hydrologist often finds that one or two terms in the above iteration might be reasonably accurate in many practical applications.

The convergence of decomposition series has already been established in the mathematical community (Abbaoui and Cherruault, 1994, Cherruault, 1989, and Cherruault et al., 1992). It is also important to mention the rigorous mathematical framework for the convergence of decomposition series developed by Gabet (1994, 1993, 1992). He connected the method of decomposition to well-known formulations where classical theorems (e.g., fixed-point theorem, substituted series, etc.) could be used. In water resources, theorems on the convergence of decomposition series are shown in Serrano (2003c, 1998). In many complex linear and nonlinear problems an exact closed form solution is difficult to obtain. However, in these cases the usual fast convergence rate of decomposition series provides the modeler with a sufficiently accurate approximate solution. A convergent decomposition series made of the first few terms usually provides an effective model in practical applications. With the concepts of partial decomposition and of double decomposition (Adomian, 1994, 1991), the process of obtaining an approximate solution was further simplified. Also recent contributions suggest that the choice of the initial term greatly influences the rate of convergence and the complexity in the calculation of individual terms, especially for nonlinear equations (Wazwaz and Gorguiz, 2004; Wazwaz, 2000). Thus, as long as the initial term in a decomposition series, usually the forcing function or the initial condition, is described in analytic form, a partial decomposition procedure may offer a simplified approximate solution to many modeling problems.

In water resources, several fundamental works using decomposition have been published on groundwater flow (Serrano and Unny, 1987); contaminant transport (Adomian and Serrano, 1998; Serrano and Adomian, 1996; Serrano, 1988); special problems involving non-Fickian and scale-dependent contaminant transport (Serrano, 1997b, 1996, 1995b); stream-aquifer interaction (Serrano and Workman. 2008, 1998; Serrano et al., 2007; Srivastava et al., 2006); modeling in heterogeneous aquifers (Srivastava and Serrano, 2007; Serrano, 1995a); nonlinear moving boundaries in unconfined aquifers (Serrano, 2003a); infiltration in unsaturated and hysteretic soils (Serrano, 2004, 2003b, 2001b, 1998, 1990a); catchment hydrology and nonlinear flood propagation (Serrano, 2006; Sarino and Serrano, 1990); and nonlinear reactive contaminant transport (Serrano, 2003c).

Several fundamental problems that were considered tractable with numerical methods only have been easily approached with decomposition. Besides simplicity, an analytical solution offers a continuous spatio-temporal distribution in heads, gradients, velocities and fluxes, thus reducing instability. Combination of analytical decomposition with numerical methods offers an ideal modeling scenario that exhibits the advantages of both analytical and numerical procedures (Serrano, 1992).

Example 5.6: Two-Dimensional Distribution of Phreatic Surface

Use the solution obtained in Example 5.5 in a Maple program to graph the spatial distribution of the water table.

Solution

The following program illustrates the solution. Figure 5.13 shows the water table spatial distribution.

```
[ Initialize and enter the boundary conditions
[ > restart:
  A:=-2*C*lx: C:=-Rg/2/T: B:=-2*E*lx: E:=-Rg/T:
  f1:=y->241-0.001*y:
  f2:=x->C*x^2+A*x+f1(0):
  f3:=x->E*x^2+B*x+f1(ly):
[ Derive hx0 from equation (5.38).
[ > k1(y)+k2(y)*x-int(int(Rg,x),x)/T:
  hx0:=unapply(%,x,y):
  hx0(0,y)=f1(y):
  solve(%,k1(y)):
  k1:=unapply(%,y):
  diff(hx0(x,y),x):
  subs(x=lx,%)=0:
  solve(%,k2(y)):
  k2:=unapply(%,y):
```

Derive *hy*0 from equation (5.42).

```
> k3(x)+k4(x)*y-int(int(Rg,y),y)/T:
  hy0:=unapply(%,x,y):
  hy0(x,0)=f2(x):
  solve(%,k3(x)):
  k3:=unapply(%,x):
  hy0(x,ly)=f3(x):
  solve(%,k4(x)):
  k4:=unapply(%,x):
```

Derive *h*0 from equation (5.44)

```
> h0:=(x,y)->(hx0(x,y)+hy0(x,y))/2:
```

Derive *hx*1 from equation (5.45).

```
> k5(y)+k6(y)*x-int(int(diff(h0(x,y),y$2),x),x):
  hx1:=unapply(%,x,y):
  hx1(0,y)=0:
  solve(%,k5(y)):
  k5:=unapply(%,y):
  diff(hx1(x,y),x):
  subs(x=lx,%)=0:
  solve(%,k6(y)):
  k6:=unapply(%,y):
```

Derive *hy*1 from equation (5.46).

```
> k7(x)+k8(x)*y-int(int(diff(h0(x,y),x$2),y),y):
  hy1:=unapply(%,x,y):
  hy1(x,0)=0:
  solve(%,k7(x)):
  k7:=unapply(%,x):
  hy1(x,ly)=0:
  solve(%,k8(x)):
  k8:=unapply(%,x):
```

Derive *h*1 from equation (5.48).

```
> h1:=(x,y)->(hx1(x,y)+hy1(x,y))/2:
```

Derive *hx*2.

```
> k9(y)+k10(y)*x-int(int(diff(h1(x,y),y$2),x),x):
  hx2:=unapply(%,x,y):
  hx2(0,y)=0:
  solve(%,k9(y)):
  k9:=unapply(%,y):
  diff(hx2(x,y),x):
  subs(x=lx,%)=0:
  solve(%,k10(y)):
  k10:=unapply(%,y):
```

Derive *hy*2.

```
> k11(x)+k12(x)*y-int(int(diff(h1(x,y),x$2),y),y):
  hy2:=unapply(%,x,y):
  hy2(x,0)=0:
  solve(%,k11(x)):
  k11:=unapply(%,x):
  hy2(x,ly)=0:
  solve(%,k12(x)):
  k12:=unapply(%,x):
  h2:=(x,y)->(hx2(x,y)+hy2(x,y))/2:
```

Approximate *h=h*0+*h*1+*h*2.

```
> h:=(x,y)->h0(x,y)+h1(x,y)+h2(x,y):
```

Enter data, and check for convergence at one point in the middle of the domain.

```
> lx:=860: ly:=2000.0: T:=700: Rg:=0.01:
  h0(lx/2,ly/2), h1(lx/2,ly/2), h2(lx/2,ly/2);
```
$$248.5241071, -5.454821424, 2.131026784$$

Plot hydraulic head in 3D with suitable contours.

```
> plot3d(h(x,y),x=0..lx,y=0..ly,orientation=[-155,60],
         style=PATCHCONTOUR,color=gray,thickness=2):
  plots[display](%,axes=BOXED,labels=[`x(m)`,`y(m)`,`h(m)`],
         labeldirections=[HORIZONTAL,HORIZONTAL,VERTICAL],
         labelfont=[TIMES,ROMAN,16]);
```

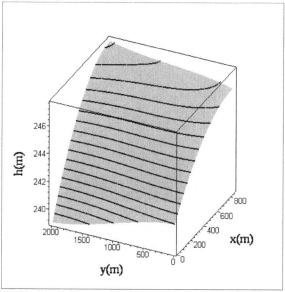

Figure 5.13: Water Table Distribution in Example 5.6

Having an analytical solution describing the hydraulic head, one can easily derive the specific discharge at any point with coordinates [x, y] by applying Darcy's law. Thus, from equations (4.11) and (4.13), the x-component of the specific discharge is given by

$$q_x = -K_x i_x = -K_x \frac{\partial h}{\partial x} \tag{5.49}$$

where
$\quad q_x$ = specific discharge in the x direction (volumetric flow rate per unit cross sectional area, including grains and voids (m/month))
$\quad K_x$ = hydraulic conductivity in the x direction (m/month)
$\quad i_x$ = hydraulic gradient in the x direction
Similarly, the y-component of the specific discharge is given by

$$q_y = -K_y i_y = -K_y \frac{\partial h}{\partial y} \tag{5.50}$$

where
$\quad q_y$ = specific discharge in the y direction (volumetric flow rate per unit cross sectional area, including grains and voids (m/month))
$\quad K_y$ = hydraulic conductivity in the y direction (m/month)

i_y = hydraulic gradient in the y direction

To obtain an estimate of the average macroscopic pore velocity (or filtration, or seepage velocity), one must divide by the porosity:

$$u_x = \frac{q_x}{n}, \qquad u_y = \frac{q_y}{n} \qquad (5.51)$$

where
u_x = mean pore velocity in the x direction (*m/month*)
u_y = mean pore velocity in the y direction (*m/month*)
n = soil porosity

From vector algebra, the resulting magnitude and direction of the specific discharge is given by

$$q(x,\ y) = \sqrt{q_x(x,\ y)^2 + q_y(x,\ y)^2}, \qquad \theta = \tan^{-1}(q_y / q_x) \qquad (5.52)$$

where
q = resultant magnitude of specific discharge (*m/month*)
θ = direction of q with respect to the x axis (*rad*)

Example 5.7: Groundwater Flow Velocity and Direction
Use the solution derived in Example 5.5 to calculate q_x, q_y, q and θ at a point with coordinates x=800 and y=1000m. Assume an average saturated thickness of b=243m and a porosity n=0.2.

Solution
The Maple program follows.

```
> restart:
  #Enter constants from Example 5.5
  A:=-2*C*lx:  C:=-Rg/2/T:  B:=-2*E*lx:  E:=-Rg/T:
  #Enter boundary conditions
  f1:=y->241-0.001*y:
  f2:=x->C*x^2+A*x+f1(0):
  f3:=x->E*x^2+B*x+f1(ly):
  #Enter partial solution hx from equation (5.39)
  hx:=(x,y)->f1(y)+Rg*lx*x/T-Rg*x^2/2/T:
  #Enter partial solution hy from equation (5.43)
  hy:=(x,y)->f2(x)+((f3(x)-f2(x))/ly
               +(Rg/2/T+C)*ly)*y-(Rg/2/T+C)*y^2:
  #Hydraulic head equation (5.44)
  h:=(x,y)->(hx(x,y)+hy(x,y))/2:
```

```
> #x-component of specific discharge equation (5.49)
  -T/b*diff(h(x,y),x):
  qx:=unapply(%,x,y):
  #y-component of specific discharge equation (5.50)
  -T/b*diff(h(x,y),y):
  qy:=unapply(%,x,y):
  #Magnitude and direction of specific discharge
  #equation (5.52)
  q:=(x,y)->sqrt(qx(x,y)^2+qy(x,y)^2):
  theta:=(x,y)->arctan(qy(x,y)/qx(x,y)):
  #pore velocity
  u:=(x,y)->q(x,y)/n:
> #data
  lx:=860: ly:=2000: T:=700: Rg:=0.010: b:=243.:
  X:=800: Y:=1000: n:=0.2:
> qx(X,Y); qy(X,Y); q(X,Y); u(X,Y);
  theta(X,Y); evalf(convert(%,degrees));
```

$$-0.003086419763$$
$$-0.0009053497933$$
$$0.003216464705$$
$$0.01608232352$$
$$0.2853294190$$
$$16.34817148 \; degrees$$

```
> #Plot at a scale q(X,Y) and its direction
  with(plots): arrow({[[X,Y],[qx(X,Y),qy(X,Y)]]},
     scaling=CONSTRAINED,shape=harpoon,axes=BOXED,
     labels=[`x(m)`,`y(m)`],labelfont=[TIMES,ROMAN,16])
```

Notice we used the Maple function diff(,) to find the derivative $\partial h/\partial x$ and $\partial h/\partial y$ to find the x and y directional components in the hydraulic gradient. Negative values in q_x and q_y indicate that the direction of the component is opposite to the corresponding coordinate axis. Notice that the angle with respect to the x axis is given in *radians* and in *degrees*. To plot the vector $q(x=X, y=Y)$, we used the function arrow(,) to produce a directional plot for a given vector-valued function; its first argument is the list $\{[[X, Y], [q_x(X, Y), q_y(X, Y)]]\}$, followed by plotting options.

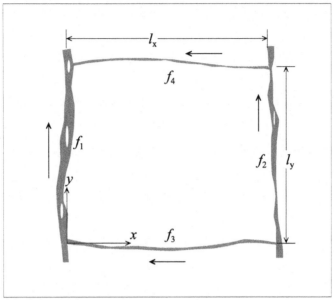

Figure 5.14: Top View of Aquifer of Example5.8

Example 5.8: Effect of Fixed Boundary Conditions

Consider a mildly sloping and thin aquifer bounded on all sides by streams, as depicted in Figure 5.14. The mean water elevation with respect to the sea level at the boundaries is $f_1(y)=100-0.2\times10^{-2}y$, $f_2(y)=103-0.1\times10^{-2}y$, $f_3(x)=100+0.8\times10^{-2}x-0.5\times10^{-5}x^2$, and $f_4(x)=99+0.883\times10^{-2}x-0.5\times10^{-5}x^2$. Assume $T=100m^2/month$, $R_g=10mm/month$, $l_x=600m$, $l_y=500m$, and $b=4m$. Develop a mathematical model to describe quantitatively the spatial distribution of the hydraulic head.

Solution

Assuming an approximately rectangular domain shape, that Dupuit assumptions are valid, and that the aquifer is homogeneous and isotropic, the governing flow equation is given by equation (5.16) as

$$\frac{\partial^2 h}{\partial x^2}+\frac{\partial^2 h}{\partial y^2}=-\frac{R_g}{T}, \quad 0\leq x\leq l_x,\ 0\leq y\leq l_y \qquad (5.53)$$

subject to the following boundary conditions:

$$h(0,\ y)=f_1(y),\ h(l_x,\ y)=f_2(y),\ h(x,\ 0)=f_3(x),\ h(x,\ l_y)=f_4(x) \qquad (5.54)$$

As in Example 5.5, We define the operators $L_x = \partial^2/\partial x^2$ and $L_y = \partial^2/\partial y^2$. The inverse operators L_y^{-1} and L_x^{-1} are the corresponding two-fold indefinite integrals with respect to x and y, respectively. Equations (5.53) reduces to

$$L_x h + L_y h = -\frac{R_g}{T} \tag{5.55}$$

The x-partial solution, h_x, results from operating with L_x^{-1} on equation (5.55) and re-arranging:

$$h_x = k_1(y) + k_2(y)x - L_x^{-1}\frac{R_g}{T} - L_x^{-1}L_y h_x \tag{5.56}$$

where the integration "constants" k_1 and k_2 are to be found from the x boundary conditions. Expanding h_x in the right side as an infinite series $h_x = h_{x0} + h_{x1} + h_{x2} + ...$, equation (5.56) becomes

$$h_x = k_1(y) + k_2(y)x - L_x^{-1}\frac{R_g}{T} - L_x^{-1}L_y\left(h_{x0} + h_{x1} + h_{x2} + ...\right) \tag{5.57}$$

Taking the first three terms on the right side as h_{x0},

$$h_{x0} = k_1(y) + k_2(y)x - L_x^{-1}\frac{R_g}{T} = k_1(y) + k_2(y)x - \frac{R_g x^2}{2T} \tag{5.58}$$

Applying the x boundary conditions from equations (5.54),

$$h_{x0} = f_1(y) + \left(\frac{f_2(y) - f_1(y)}{l_x} + \frac{R_g l_x}{2T}\right)x - \frac{R_g x^2}{2T} \tag{5.59}$$

Similarly, the y-partial solution to equation (5.53), h_y, results from operating with L_y^{-1} on equation (5.55) and rearranging:

$$h_y = k_3(x) + k_4(x)y - L_y^{-1}\frac{R_g}{T} - L_y^{-1}L_x h_y \tag{5.60}$$

where the integration "constants" k_3 and k_4 are to be found from the y boundary conditions. Expanding h in the right side as an infinite series $h_y = h_{y0} + h_{y1} + h_{y2} + ...$, equation (5.60) becomes

$$h_y = k_3(x) + k_4(x)y - L_y^{-1}\frac{R_g}{T} - L_y^{-1}L_x\left(h_{y0} + h_{y1} + h_{y2} + ...\right) \tag{5.61}$$

Again, if we take h_{y0} as the first three terms in the right side of equation (5.61) we obtain the first approximation to the solution, that is

$$h_{y0} = k_3(x) + k_4(x)y - L_y^{-1} \frac{R_g}{T} = k_3(x) + k_4(x)y - \frac{R_g y^2}{2T} \qquad (5.62)$$

Applying the y boundary conditions from equations (5.54),

$$h_{y0} \approx h_0 = f_3(x) + \left(\frac{f_4(x) - f_3(x)}{l_y} + \frac{R_g l_y}{2} \right) y - \frac{R_g y^2}{2T} \qquad (5.63)$$

We now have two partial solutions to equation (5.55): the x-partial solution equation (5.59), and the y-partial solution equation (5.6). Since both are approximations to h, a combination of the two partial solutions yields the improved first decomposition term, h_0, and the simplest solution to equation (5.55):

$$h(x, y) \approx h_0(x, y) = \left(\frac{h_x(x, y) + h_y(x, y)}{2} \right) \qquad (5.64)$$

Additional terms may be derived as described in Example 5.5. Patel and Serrano (2011) found that the first four terms of the decomposition solution in the center of the aquifer ($x = l_x/2$, and $y = l_y/2$) are respectively $h_0 = 105.162$, $h_1 = -1.984$, $h_2 = 1.009$, and $h_3 = -0.496\,m$. Adding the first four terms, we obtain $h \approx h_0 + h_1 + h_2 + h_3 = 103.691m$. In comparison, the exact solution obtained by traditional Fourier series at the same location yields $h = 103.527$, and the approximate solution gives an absolute error of $0.165\,m$. The decomposition solution satisfies the differential equation (5.53) with an error of -0.000083 ($month^{-1}$) in the center of the aquifer. It is also found that maximum relative errors of less than 1.2% occur in the center of the aquifer boundaries. The minimum error of about 0.16% occurs in the center of the aquifer. If we only use the first term in the decomposition series, that is if we set $h \approx h_0$ (equations (5.59), (5.63), and (5.64)), the maximum relative error increases to 1.99%. The simulations illustrate that the rate of convergence of the series solution is high, a typical feature of decomposition. Usually the first few terms are sufficient to assure an accurate solution; in the present case, by using the first term only the error is less than 2%. More importantly, the effort required to produce a decomposition solution is modest, as compared to that required to derive an exact analytical solution. A simple analytical expression of aquifer head is advantageous in the derivation of hydraulic gradients, seepage velocities, and groundwater fluxes.

Example 5.9: Modeling the Magnitude and Direction of Regional Groundwater Flow

Write a Maple program that uses the solution derived in Example 5.8 to plot a map of hydraulic head contours, and the magnitude and direction of the flow velocity field.

Solution

```
> restart:
  #Enter boundary conditions from Example 5.8
  f1:=y->100-0.2E-2*y:
  f2:=y->103-0.1E-2*y:
  f3:=x->100+0.8E-2*x-0.5E-5*x^2:
  f4:=x->99+0.883E-2*x-0.5E-5*x^2:
  #Enter x-partial solution hx from equation (5.59)
  hx:=(x,y)->f1(y)+((f2(y)-f1(y))/lx
                +Rg*lx/2/T)*x-Rg*x^2/2/T:
  #Enter y-partial solution hy from equation (5.63)
  hy:=(x,y)->f3(x)+((f4(x)-f3(x))/ly
                +Rg*ly/2/T)*y-Rg*y^2/2/T:
  #Hydraulic head equation (5.64)
  h:=(x,y)->(hx(x,y)+hy(x,y))/2:
  #x-component of specific discharge equation (5.49)
  -T/b*diff(h(x,y),x):
  qx:=unapply(%,x,y):
  #y-component of specific discharge equation (5.50)
  -T/b*diff(h(x,y),y):
  qy:=unapply(%,x,y):
  #Specific discharge,q(x,y), equation (5.52)
  q:=(x,y)->sqrt(qx(x,y)^2+qy(x,y)^2):
> #data from Figure (5.14)
  lx:=600: ly:=500: T:=100: Rg:=0.010: b:=4.:
> with(plots): dx:=50:
  #Produce a directional plot for vector q(x,y)
  g1:=arrow({seq(seq([[dx*i,dx*j],[qx(dx*i,dx*j),
     qy(dx*i,dx*j)]],i=1..(lx/dx-1)),j=1..(ly/dx-1))},
     length=40,scaling=CONSTRAINED):
Warning, the name changecoords has been redefined

> #Hydraulic head contours
  g2:=plots[contourplot](h(x,y),x=0..lx,y=0..ly,
     contours=[105.4,105,104.5,104,103.5,103,102.5,
     102,101.5,101,100.5,100],color=black,
     thickness=2,linestyle=1):
  #Lines of aquifer limits
  g3:=plot([[0,ly],[lx,ly]], color=black):
  g4:=plot([[lx,0],[lx,ly]],color=black):
  plots[display](g1,g2,g3,g4,labels=[`x (m)`,`y (m)`],
     labels=[`x (m)`,`y(m)`],
     labeldirections=[HORIZONTAL,VERTICAL],
     labelfont=[TIMES,ROMAN,16]);
```

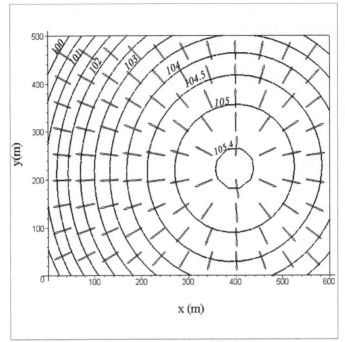

Figure 5.15: Plan View of Flow Field of Example 5.9

In this program we extend the commands of Example 5.7. To produce arrows representing the magnitude and direction of the vector $q(x, y)$, we sweep the aquifer domain and calculate q at specific locations separated a distance dx. To this end, we use a double sequence command, seq(,), similar to the double do loop in traditional programming. To generate the head contours at specified elevations, we use the command plots[contourplot]. In Figure 5.15 one can appreciate the spatial distribution of the water table and the direction of ground water flow from its recharge location at the highest elevation of the groundwater mound to the discharge areas on the rivers.

Most analytical solutions of *boundary-value initial-value problems* are restricted to rectangles, squares, circles and other regular domain shapes. However, with analytical decomposition, application of the above procedure to aquifer domains of irregular geometry is straight forward, as long as the aquifer boundaries are defined in a functional form.

Example 5.10: Modeling Flow in Irregular Aquifer Domain Shapes
    Build a mathematical model of regional groundwater flow for the aquifer depicted in Figure 5.14, described and solved in Examples 5.8 and

5.9. Assume that the boundary conditions are given by equations (5.54) in Example 5.8, except that the y aquifer dimension, $l_y(x)$, is now a function of x. In other words, $h(x, y)=f_4(x)$, on $y=l_y(x)$, with $l_y(x)=500+0.4x-0.1\times10^{-2}x^2$, after fitting a parabola to a few surveyed points on the river channel.

Solution

The solution procedure described in Examples 5.8 and 5.9 remains unchanged, except that in the y-partial solution the integration must now be done over a variable y domain, which is reflected in equation (5.63) with l_y now being a function of x. The following Maple program illustrates the basic changes. The graphing of arrows is now done in a do loop that accounts for a variable vertical dimension.

```
> restart:
  #Enter boundary conditions from Example 5.8
  f1:=y->100-0.2E-2*y:
  f2:=y->103-0.1E-2*y:
  f3:=x->100+0.8E-2*x-0.5E-5*x^2:
  f4:=x->99+0.883E-2*x-0.5E-5*x^2:
  ly:=x->500+0.4*x-0.1E-2*x^2:
  #Enter x-partial solution hx from equation (5.59)
  hx:=(x,y)->f1(y)+((f2(y)-f1(y))/lx
              +Rg*lx/2/T)*x-Rg*x^2/2/T:
  #Enter y-partial solution hy from equation (5.63)
  hy:=(x,y)->f3(x)+((f4(x)-f3(x))/ly(x)
              +Rg*ly(x)/2/T)*y-Rg*y^2/2/T:
  #Hydraulic head equation (5.64)
  h:=(x,y)->(hx(x,y)+hy(x,y))/2:
  #x-component of specific discharge equation (5.49)
  -T/b*diff(h(x,y),x):
  qx:=unapply(%,x,y):
  #y-component of specific discharge equation (5.50)
  -T/b*diff(h(x,y),y):
  qy:=unapply(%,x,y):
  #Specific discharge,q(x,y), equation (5.52)
  q:=(x,y)->sqrt(qx(x,y)^2+qy(x,y)^2):
> #data from Figure (5.14)
  lx:=600: T:=100: Rg:=0.010: b:=4.:
> with(plots): dx:=50:
  #Directional plot of q(x,y) for variable y
  X:=floor(lx/dx):
  for i from 1 to X do
    Y:=floor(ly(dx*i)/dx):
    g[i]:=arrow({seq([[dx*i,dx*j],[qx(dx*i,dx*j),
    qy(dx*i,dx*j)]],j=1..Y)},length=40,scaling=CONSTRAINED):
  end do:
  N:=i-1;
  Warning, the name changecoords has been redefined
```

$$N := 12$$

```
> #Hydraulic head contours
  g2:=plots[contourplot](h(x,y),x=0..lx,y=0..ly(x),
     contours=[105.4,105,104.5,104,103.5,103,102.5,
     102,101.5,101,100.5,100],color=black,
     thickness=2,linestyle=1):
  #Lines of aquifer limits
  g3:=plot(ly(x),x=0..lx, color=black):
  g4:=plot([[600,0],[600,ly(lx)]],color=black):
  plots[display](g[1],g[2],g[3],g[4],g[5],g[6],g[7],g[8],
     g[9],g[10],g[11],g[12],g2,g3,g4,labels=[`x (m)`,`y (m)`],
     labels=[`x (m)`,`y(m)`],
     labeldirections=[HORIZONTAL,VERTICAL],
     labelfont=[TIMES,ROMAN,16]);
```

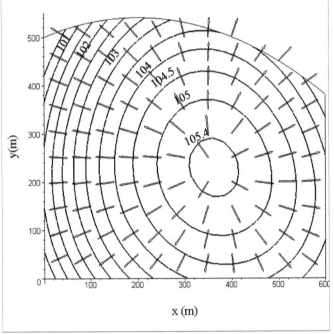

Figure 5.16: Plan View of Flow Field of Example 5.10

Most regional aquifers are not homogeneous in the hydraulic conductivity. A well-surveyed aquifer possessing a large number of values of conductivity calls for a numerical model that can account for a detailed variability in the aquifer parameters. However, in many cases the hydrologist has access to only a handful of values; this justifies the utilization of a simpler mathematical model. If the aquifer conductivity field can be described by a functional form fitted to the limited number of measurements, a simple analytical decomposition scheme may be applied to solve the equations in a heterogeneous aquifer (Serrano, 2011).

Example 5.11: Modeling Regional Flow in a Heterogeneous Aquifer
Build a mathematical model of regional groundwater flow for the aquifer in Figure 5.11 if the hydraulic conductivity gradually decreases with increasing x and y and the resulting transmissivity, fitted to a set of individual points, is given by $T(x, y) = a + cx + dy$; $a = 500$ $m^2/month$; $c = -0.2$ $m/month$; $d = -0.1$ $m/month$; $l_x = 860$ m; $l_y = 2000m$; and $R_g = 10mm/month$. The head at the rivers is given by $f_1(y) = 241 - 0.001y$; $f_2(x) = Cx^2 + Ax + f_1(0)$; $f_3(x) = Ex^2 + Bx + f_1(l_y)$; $C = -R_g/(2T)$; $A = -2Cl_x$; $B = -2El_x$; $E = -R_g/T$; and $T = 700m^2/month$.

Solution
From equation (5.16) the governing differential equation is

$$\frac{\partial}{\partial x}\left(T(x, y)\frac{\partial h}{\partial x}\right) + \frac{\partial}{\partial y}\left(T(x, y)\frac{\partial h}{\partial y}\right) = -R_g \quad 0 \leq x \leq l_x, \ 0 \leq y \leq l_y$$

(5.65)

$$h(0, y) = f_1(y), \ \frac{\partial h}{\partial x}(l_x, y) = 0, \ h(x, 0) = f_2(x), \ h(x, l_y) = f_3(x)$$

As in Example 5.4, We define the operators $L_x = \partial^2/\partial x^2$ and $L_y = \partial^2/\partial y^2$. Equation (5.65) becomes

$$L_x h + L_y h = -\frac{R_g}{T(x, y)} - \frac{1}{T(x, y)}\frac{\partial T}{\partial x}\frac{\partial h}{\partial x} - \frac{1}{T(x, y)}\frac{\partial T}{\partial y}\frac{\partial h}{\partial y}$$

(5.66)

The x-partial solution of equation (5.66) has new terms:

$$h_x = k_1(y) + k_2(y)x - L_x^{-1}\frac{R_g}{T(x, y)}$$

$$-L_x^{-1}L_y h_x - L_x^{-1}\frac{1}{T(x, y)}\frac{\partial T}{\partial x}\frac{\partial h_x}{\partial x} - L_x^{-1}\frac{1}{T(x, y)}\frac{\partial T}{\partial y}\frac{\partial h_x}{\partial y}$$

(5.67)

Expanding h_x in the right side as an infinite series $h_x = h_{x0} + h_{x1} + h_{x2} + ...$, equation (5.67) becomes

$$h_x = k_1(y) + k_2(y)x - L_x^{-1}\frac{R_g}{T(x, y)} - L_x^{-1}L_y\left(h_{x0} + h_{x1} + h_{x2} + ...\right)$$

$$-L_x^{-1}\frac{1}{T(x, y)}\frac{\partial T}{\partial x}\frac{\partial}{\partial x}\left(h_{x0} + h_{x1} + h_{x2} + ...\right)$$

(5.68)

$$-L_x^{-1}\frac{1}{T(x, y)}\frac{\partial T}{\partial y}\frac{\partial}{\partial y}\left(h_0 + h_1 + h_2 + ...\right)$$

As before, a simple choice for a first approximation gives

$$h_{x0}=k_1(y)+k_2(y)x-L_x^{-1}\frac{R_g}{T(x,\ y)} \tag{5.69}$$

where $k_1(y)$ and $k_2(y)$ are such that the x-boundary conditions in equation (5.65) are satisfied. A y-partial solution of (5.66) is given by

$$h_y=k_3(x)+k_4(x)y-L_y^{-1}\frac{R_g}{T(x,\ y)}-L_y^{-1}L_x\left(h_{y0}+h_{y1}+h_{y2}+...\right)$$

$$-L_y^{-1}\frac{1}{T(x,\ y)}\frac{\partial T}{\partial x}\frac{\partial}{\partial x}\left(h_{y0}+h_{y1}+h_{y2}+...\right) \tag{5.70}$$

$$-L_y^{-1}\frac{1}{T(x,\ y)}\frac{\partial T}{\partial y}\frac{\partial}{\partial y}\left(h_{y0}+h_{y1}+h_{y2}+...\right)$$

A first approximation to equation (5.70) is

$$h_{y0}=k_3(x)+k_4(x)y-L_y^{-1}\frac{R_g}{T(x,\ y)} \tag{5.71}$$

where $k_3(x)$ and $k_4(x)$ are such that the y boundary conditions in equation (5.64) are satisfied. Combining equations (5.69) and (5.71) we obtain a first approximation to equation (5.66) as

$$h_0(x,\ y)=\left(\frac{h_{x0}(x,\ y)+h_{y0}(x,\ y)}{2}\right) \tag{5.72}$$

Higher-order terms are obtained by successively combining x-partial solution terms

$$h_{xi}=k_{4i+1}(y)+k_{4i+2}(y)x-L_x^{-1}L_yh_{i-1}-L_x^{-1}\frac{1}{T(x,\ y)}\frac{\partial T}{\partial x}\frac{\partial h_{i-1}}{\partial x}$$

$$-L_x^{-1}\frac{1}{T(x,\ y)}\frac{\partial T}{\partial y}\frac{\partial h_{i-1}}{\partial y} \tag{5.73}$$

with y-partial solution terms

$$h_{yi}=k_{4i+3}(x)+k_{4i+4}(x)y-L_y^{-1}L_xh_{i-1}-L_y^{-1}\frac{1}{T(x,\ y)}\frac{\partial T}{\partial x}\frac{\partial h_{i-1}}{\partial x}$$

$$-L_y^{-1}\frac{1}{T(x,\ y)}\frac{\partial T}{\partial y}\frac{\partial h_{i-1}}{\partial y} \tag{5.74}$$

where h_{i-1} is he previous combined term. It is important to remark that several researchers (Adomian, 1994, 1983; Wazwaz, 2000) suggest there is considerable latitude in the choice of a decomposition term. For instance, in equations (5.73) or (5.74) h_1 may be composed of the first three terms in the right side only. In the above development, a key element is the analytical form for $K(x, y)$, such that the resulting integrals are calculable. Thus, from equation (5.69)

$$h_{x0} = k_1(y) + k_2(y)x - \frac{R_g}{c^2}I(x, y)$$

$$I(x, y) = T(x, y)\ln(T(x, y)) - T(x, y) \tag{5.75}$$

$$k_1(y) = f_1(y) + \frac{R_g}{c^2}I(0, y), \quad k_2(y) = \frac{R_g}{c}\ln(T(l_x, y))$$

and from equation (5.71),

$$h_{y0} = k_3(x) + k_4(x)y - \frac{R_g}{d^2}I(x, y)$$

$$k_3(x) = f_2(x) + \frac{R_g}{d^2}I(x, 0), \quad k4(x) = \left[f_3(x) - k_3(x) + \frac{R_g}{d^2}I(x, l_y)\right] / l_y \tag{5.76}$$

Substituting equations (5.75) and (5.76) into equation (5.72) we obtain the first approximation to equation (5.66). From equations (5.73) and (5.74) the calculation of higher-order terms suggests a fast convergence in the series. For example the first three decomposition terms at the center of the aquifer ($x = l_x/2$, and $y = l_y/2$) are $h_0 = 255.868$, and $h_1 = -7.426 \ m$.

Example 5.12: Visualizing the Flow in a Heterogeneous Aquifer
    Write a Maple program that uses the solution derived in Example 5.11 to plot a map of hydraulic head contours.

Solution
    The following Maple worksheet programs equations (5.72), (5.75), and (5.76) to calculate h_0. Equations (5.73) and (5.74) are also programmed to calculate h_1. The calculation of the integration constants for the latter is done algebraically, such that the homogeneous boundary conditions are satisfied (i.e., h_0 already satisfies them). Finally, the contour plotting command of the previous examples is applied.

```
> restart:
  T:=(x,y)->a+c*x+d*y:
  A:=-2*C*lx:  C:=-Rg/2/Tbar:  B:=-2*E*lx:  E:=-Rg/Tbar:
  f1:=y->241-0.001*y:
  f2:=x->C*x^2+A*x+f1(0):
  f3:=x->E*x^2+B*x+f1(ly):
  #Equations (5.75)
  Ix:=(x,y)->Rg/c^2*(T(x,y)*ln(T(x,y))-T(x,y)):
  hx0:=(x,y)->k1(y)+k2(y)*x-Ix(x,y):
  k1:=y->f1(y)+Ix(0,y):
  k2:=y->Rg/c*ln(T(lx,y)):
  #Equations (5.76)
  Iy:=(x,y)->Rg/d^2*(T(x,y)*ln(T(x,y))-T(x,y)):
  hy0:=(x,y)->k3(x)+k4(x)*y-Iy(x,y):
  k3:=x->f2(x)+Iy(x,0):
  k4:=x->(f3(x)-k3(x)+Iy(x,ly))/ly:
  #Equation (5.72)
  h0:=(x,y)->(hx0(x,y)+hy0(x,y))/2:
  #
  #Use Equation (5.73) and find integration constants
  #such that homogeneous B.C.'s are satisfied
  diff(h0(x,y),y$2):
  k5(y)+k6(y)*x-int(int(%,x),x):
  hx1:=unapply(%,x,y):
  hx1(0,y)=0:
  solve(%,k5(y)):
  k5:=unapply(%,y):
  diff(hx1(x,y),x):
  subs(x=lx,%)=0:
  solve(%,k6(y)):
  k6:=unapply(%,y):
  #
  #Use Equation (5.74) and find integration constants
  #such that homogeneous B.C.'s are satisfied
  diff(h0(x,y),x$2):
  k7(x)+k8(x)*y-int(int(%,y),y):
  hy1:=unapply(%,x,y):
  hy1(x,0)=0:
  solve(%,k7(x)):
  k7:=unapply(%,x):
  hy1(x,ly)=0:
  solve(%,k8(x)):
  k8:=unapply(%,x):
  h1:=(x,y)->(hx1(x,y)+hy1(x,y))/2:
  h:=(x,y)->h0(x,y)+h1(x,y):
> Rg:=0.01: lx:=860: ly:=2000: a:=500: c:=-0.2:
  d:=-0.1: Tbar:=700:
  g1:=plot3d(h(x,y),x=0..lx,y=0..ly,style=PATCHCONTOUR,
      orientation=[-135,60],color=gray,
      contours=[240,242,244,246,248,250,252,254,256]):
  plots[display](g1,axes=BOXED,labels=[`x (m)`,
      `y (m)`,`h (m)`],labeldirections=
      [HORIZONTAL,HORIZONTAL,VERTICAL],
      labelfont=[TIMES,ROMAN,16]);
```

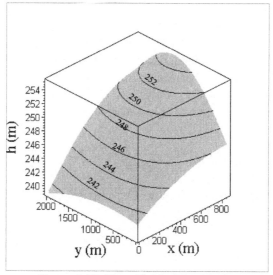

Figure 5.17: Flow Field of Aquifer in
Example 5.12

Heads are higher wherever transmissivity decreases. Other representations
in conductivity spatial variability are possible (Patel and Serrano, 2011).
Serrano (1997a; 1995a) used a statistical representation of aquifer
heterogeneity. The resulting equations are stochastic and decomposition
series is used to calculate statistical moments of head and velocity fields.

Example 5.13: Modeling Transient Flow
    The aquifer of Figure 5.12, the seasonal recharge from rainfall
follows a periodic function of the form

$$R_g(t) = \alpha + \beta \sin(\frac{\theta \pi t}{6})$$ (5.77)

where $\alpha = 3.14 \times 10^{-3}\, m/month$, $\beta = -3.128 \times 10^{-3}$, and $\theta = 1\, month^{-1}$. Assume
that $l_x = 100\, m$, $T = 100 m^2/month$, $S_y = 0.1$, and that the initial condition
(i.e., the head at $t=0$) is given by $V(x) = 100 + (R_g(0)l_x x)/T - (R_g(0)x^2)/(2T)$.
Build and solve a mathematical model that describes the hydraulic head
as a function of space and time.

Solution
    From equation (5.20), the governing equation is given by

$$\frac{\partial h}{\partial t} - \frac{T}{S_y}\frac{\partial^2 h}{\partial x^2} = \frac{R_g(t)}{S_y}, \qquad 0 \le x \le l_x,\ 0 < t$$ (5.78)

subject to the boundary and initial conditions given by

$$h(0,\ t)=V(0), \quad \frac{\partial h}{\partial x}(l_x,\ t)=0, \quad h(x,\ 0)=V(x) \tag{5.79}$$

There are two possible decomposition solutions to equation (5.78): the t-partial solution and the x-partial solution. The t-partial solution results after defining $L_t=\partial/\partial t$ and $L_x=\partial/\partial x^2$, multiplying equation (5.78) by L_t^{-1} (i.e., the integral from zero to t) and rearranging:

$$h_t=V(x)+L_t^{-1}\frac{R_g}{S_y}+\frac{T}{S_y}L_t^{-1}L_xh_t \tag{5.80}$$

where h_t is the t-partial solution. Decompose h_t in the right side of equation (5.80) $h_t=h_{t0}+h_{t1}+h_{t2}+...$, thus

$$h_t=V(x)+L_t^{-1}\frac{R_g}{S_y}+\frac{T}{S_y}L_t^{-1}L_x\left(h_{t0}+h_{t1}+h_{t2}+...\right) \tag{5.81}$$

The first term in the series, h_{t0}, is given by

$$\begin{aligned}h_{t0}&=V(x)+L_t^{-1}\frac{R_g(t)}{S_y}\\ &=100+\frac{R_g(0)l_xx}{T}-\frac{R_g(0)x^2}{2T}+\frac{1}{S_y}\left[\alpha t+\frac{6\beta}{S_y\theta\pi}\left(1-\cos(\frac{\theta\pi t}{6})\right)\right]\end{aligned} \tag{5.82}$$

Equation (5.82) satisfies the differential equation (5.78) and the initial condition, but not necessarily the x boundary conditions. Now the x-partial solution results after multiplying equation (5.78) by L_x^{-1} (or the two-fold x indefinite integral), and rearranging:

$$h_x=k_1(t)+k_2(t)x-L_x^{-1}\frac{R_g(t)}{T}+\frac{S_y}{T}L_x^{-1}L_th_x \tag{5.83}$$

where h_x is the x-partial solution. Decompose h in the right side as $h_x=h_{x0}+h_{x1}+h_{x2}+...$ Then,

$$h_x=k_1(t)+k_2(t)x-L_x^{-1}\frac{R_g(t)}{T}+\frac{S_y}{T}L_x^{-1}L_t\left(h_{x0}+h_{x1}+h_{x2}+...\right) \tag{5.84}$$

If we take h_{x0} as the first three terms in the right side of equation (5.84), we obtain the first approximation to the solution, that is

$$h_{x0}=k_1(t)+k_2(t)x-\frac{R_g(t)x^2}{2T} \tag{5.85}$$

where the constants k_1 and k_2 are found after applying the x boundary conditions in equation (5.79):

$$h_{x0}=100+\left(R_g(t)l_x x\right)/T-\left(R_g(t)x^2\right)/(2T) \qquad (5.86)$$

We now have two partial solutions to equation (5.78): The t-partial solution equation (5.82), and the x-partial solution equation (5.86). Since both are approximations to h, a combination of the two yields an improved first decomposition term h_0:

$$h_0(x,\ t)=\left(h_{t0}(x,\ t)+h_{x0}(x,\ t)\right)/2 \qquad (5.87)$$

In general, the combined i-th term, h_i, is obtained from the t-partial solution expansion, equation (5.81), as

$$h_{ti}=k_{3i}(x)+\frac{T}{S_y}L_t^{-1}L_x\ h_{i-1},\quad i>0 \qquad (5.88)$$

where k_{3i} is such that a homogeneous initial condition, equation (5.79), is satisfied, or from the x-partial solution expansion, equation (5.84), as

$$h_{xi}=k_{3i+1}(t)+k_{3i+2}(t)x+\frac{S_y}{T}L_x^{-1}L_t h_{i-1},\quad i>0 \qquad (5.89)$$

where k_{3i+1} and k_{3i+2} are such that homogeneous x-boundary conditions are satisfied. Combine equations (5.88) and (5.89) to get the next h_i.

Example 5.14: Visualization of Transient Hydraulic Head

Write a Maple program for the solution derived in Example 5.13, study the rate of convergence of the solution, and generate graphs of head versus time at fixed locations, and of head versus distance at fixed times.

Solution

The time integration of equation (5.82) is done with the int(,) command. More terms, are derived algebraically with the derivative command, diff (,) and the double integration int(,) commands.

```
> restart:
  V:=x->-Rg(0)/2/T*x^2+Rg(0)*lx/T*x+100:
  Rg:=t->alpha+beta*sin(theta*Pi*t/6):
  #Time integral in equation (5.82)
  1/Sy*int(Rg(xi),xi=0..t):
  It:=unapply(%,t):
  #Equation (5.82)
  ht0:=(x,t)->V(x)+It(t):
  #Equation (5.86)
  hx0:=(x,t)->V(0)+Rg(t)*lx*x/T-Rg(t)*x^2/2/T:
  #Equation (5.87)
  h0:=(x,t)->(ht0(x,t)+hx0(x,t))/2:
```

```
> #Equation (5.88)
  diff(h0(x,tau),x$2):
  k3(x)+T/Sy*int(%,tau=0..t):
  ht1:=unapply(%,x,t):
  ht1(x,0)=0:
  solve(%,k3(x)):
  k3:=unapply(%,x):
  #
  #Equation (5.89)
  diff(h0(x,t),t):
  k4(t)+k5(t)*x+Sy/T*int(int(%,x),x):
  hx1:=unapply(%,x,t):
  hx1(0,t)=0:
  solve(%,k4(t)):
  k4:=unapply(%,t):
  diff(hx1(x,t),x):
  subs(x=lx,%)=0:
  solve(%,k5(t)):
  k5:=unapply(%,t):
  h1:=(x,t)->(ht1(x,t)+hx1(x,t))/2:
  #
  #Equation (5.88)
  diff(h1(x,tau),x$2):
  k6(x)+T/Sy*int(%,tau=0..t):
  ht2:=unapply(%,x,t):
  ht2(x,0)=0:
  solve(%,k6(x)):
  k6:=unapply(%,x):
  #
  #Equation (5.89)
  diff(h1(x,t),t):
  k7(t)+k8(t)*x+Sy/T*int(int(%,x),x):
  hx2:=unapply(%,x,t):
  hx2(0,t)=0:
  solve(%,k7(t)):
  k7:=unapply(%,t):
  diff(hx2(x,t),x):
  subs(x=lx,%)=0:
  solve(%,k8(t)):
  k8:=unapply(%,t):
  h2:=(x,t)->(ht2(x,t)+hx2(x,t))/2:
  h:=(x,t)->h0(x,t)+h1(x,t):
> theta:=1: lx:=100: T:=100: Sy:=0.1: alpha:=0.00314:
  beta:=-0.003128:
> #Curves of h(x,.)
  G1:=plot(h(x,2),x=0..lx,color=black,
     legend=`t=2 months`):
  G2:=plot(h(x,4),x=0..lx,color=black,linestyle=3,
     legend=`t=4 months`):
  G3:=plot(h(x,6),x=0..lx,color=black,style=point,
     legend=`t=6 months`):
  G4:=plot(h(x,8),x=0..lx,color=black,style=point,
     symbol=cross,legend=`t=8 months`):
  plots[display](G1,G2,G3,G4,labeldirections=
     [HORIZONTAL,HORIZONTAL],
     labelfont=[TIMES,ROMAN,16],
     labels=[`x (m)`,`h (m)`]);
```

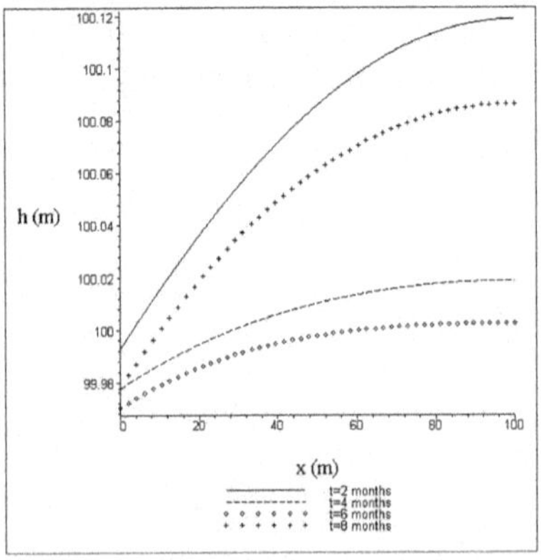

Figure 5.18: Head-Distance Profiles

```
> #Check convergence rate at x=1x, and t=6 m
  evalf(h0(1x,6)); evalf(h1(1x,6)); evalf(h2(1x,6));
                                        100.1914596
                                       -0.1888827675
                                        0.09051638374
> #Curves of h(., t)
  G5:=plot(h(20,t),t=0..36,color=black,linestyle=1,
     legend=`x=20 m`):
  G6:=plot(h(50,t),t=0..36,color=black,linestyle=3,
     legend=`x=50 m`):
  G7:=plot(h(70,t),t=0..36,color=black,style=point,
     legend=`x=70 m`):
  G8:=plot(h(100,t),t=0..36,color=black,style=point,
     symbol=cross,legend=`x=100 m`):
  plots[display](G5,G6,G7,G8,labeldirections=
     [HORIZONTAL,HORIZONTAL],
     labelfont=[TIMES,ROMAN,16],
     labels=[`x (m)`,`h (m)`]);
```

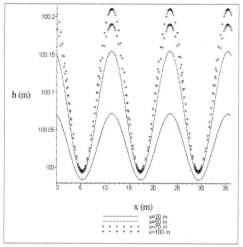

Figure 5.19: Head versus Time Profiles

For a fixed time, the curves $h(x, .)$ are smooth across the aquifer. For a fixed distance, the curves $h(., t)$ are periodic with time, and increase in amplitude as distance increases; this is so in this case because the head is not fixed at the right boundary. The convergence rate in this case is tested numerically by calculating terms h_0, h_1, and h_2 at $x=100m$ (in this case an adverse scenario) and $t=6months$. Clearly $|h_0| \gg |h_1| > |h_2|$ indicating a fast convergence rate. The form of the differential equation, the domain dimensions, and the values of the parameters affect the rate of convergence, at times producing a divergent series. Here we opt for approximating $h \approx h_0 + h_1$.

Transient flow may be generated in a groundwater system in a variety of ways. In Example, 5.14 unsteady behavior was produced by seasonal variability in the recharge. The case of time-dependent boundary conditions was discussed in Serrano (2008), Serrano et al. (2007), Serrano and Workman (2008, 1998), and Workman et al. (1997). Unconfined flow under significant vertical gradients renders the Dupuit assumptions invalid. The free surface then becomes a transient nonlinear differential equation by itself. A decomposition solution for this case is shown in Serrano (2003a). Extension of the above development to higher dimensional domains is straight forward. The only significant difference is that with higher dimensions there are as many partial decomposition expansions as problem dimensions, which can be combined to include information for all boundary conditions.

Example 5.15: Modeling Transient Flow in Higher Dimensions

Consider again the aquifer depicted in Figure 5.14. The mean hydraulic head at the boundaries are given by $f_1(y)=100-0.2\times10^{-2}y$, $f_2(y)=103-0.1\times10^{-2}y$, $f_3(x)=100+0.8\times10^{-2}x-0.5\times10^{-5}x^2$, and $f_4(x)=99+0.883\times10^{-2}x-0.5\times10^{-5}x^2$. The seasonal recharge from rainfall follows a periodic function of the form

$$R_g(t)=\alpha+\beta\sin(\frac{\theta\pi t}{6})\qquad(5.90)$$

where $\alpha=0.003m/month$, $\beta=-0.001\,m/month$, and $\theta=1\;month^{-1}$. Assume that $l_x=600m$, $l_y=500m$, $T=500m^2/month$, $S_y=0.01$, and that the initial condition, $h(x,\,y,\,0)=V(x,\,y)$, is given by the steady state solution derived in Example 5.8, that is by equations (5.59), (5.63), and (5.64). Develop a mathematical model to describe quantitatively the spatial and temporal distribution of the hydraulic head.

Solution

For a homogenous aquifer, the governing differential equation is given by equation (5.20) as

$$\frac{\partial h}{\partial t}-\frac{T}{S_y}\frac{\partial^2 h}{\partial x^2}-\frac{T}{S_y}\frac{\partial^2 h}{\partial y^2}=\frac{R_g}{S_y}\qquad 0\le x\le l_x,\;\; 0\le y\le l_y,\;\; 0<t \qquad(5.91)$$

subject to the boundary and initial conditions

$$h(0,\,y,\,t)=f_1(y),\;\; h(l_x,\,y,\,t)=f_2(y)$$

$$h(x,\,0,\,t)=f_3(x),\;\; h(x,\,l_y,\,t)=f_4(x)\;\; h(x,\,y,\,0)=V(x,\,y) \qquad(5.92)$$

The t-partial solution becomes

$$h_t = h(x, y, 0) + L_t^{-1} \frac{R_g}{S_y} + \frac{T}{S_y} L_t^{-1} L_x (h_{t0} + h_{t1} + ...) + \frac{T}{S_y} L_t^{-1} L_y (h_{t0} + h_{t1} + ...) \quad (5.93)$$

from which the first term is

$$h_{t0} = h(x,y,0) + L_t^{-1} \frac{R_g(t)}{S_y} = h(x,y,0) + \frac{1}{S_y} \left[\alpha t + \frac{6\beta}{S_y \theta \pi} \left(1 - \cos(\frac{\theta \pi t}{6}) \right) \right] \quad (5.94)$$

The x-partial solution of equation (5.91) is

$$h_x = k_1(y,\ t) + k_2(y,\ t)x - L_x^{-1} \frac{R_g(t)}{T} + \frac{S_y}{T} L_x^{-1} L_t (h_{x0} + h_{x1} + ...)$$

$$- L_x^{-1} L_y (h_{x0} + h_{x1} + ...) \quad (5.95)$$

where k_1 and k_2 are such that the x boundary conditions in equation (5.92) are satisfied. From equation (5.95) the first term is given by

$$h_{x0} = f_1(y) + \left(\frac{f_2(y) - f_1(y)}{l_x} + \frac{R_g(t)l_x}{2T} \right) x - \frac{R_g(t)x^2}{2T} \quad (5.96)$$

The y-partial solution of equation (5.91) is given by

$$h_y = k_3(x,\ t) + k_4(x,\ t)y - L_y^{-1} \frac{R_g(t)}{T} + \frac{S_y}{T} L_y^{-1} L_t (h_{y0} + h_{y1} + ...)$$

$$- L_y^{-1} L_x (h_{y0} + h_{y1} + ...) \quad (5.97)$$

where k_3 and k_4 are such that the y boundary conditions in equation (5.92) are satisfied. From equation (5.97) the first term is given by

$$h_{y0} = f_3(x) + \left(\frac{f_4(x) - f_3(x)}{l_y} + \frac{R_g(t)l_y}{2} \right) y - \frac{R_g(t)y^2}{2T} \quad (5.98)$$

From equations (5.94), (5.96), and (5.98), we have three versions of $h_0(x,\ y,\ t)$, respectively. Thus, a combination of them will yield the first decomposition term:

$$h_0(x,\ y,\ t) = \left(\frac{h_{t0}(x,\ y,\ t) + h_{x0}(x,\ y,\ y) + h_{y0}(x,\ y,\ t)}{3} \right) \quad (5.99)$$

In general of the combined *i-th* term, h_i, is obtained from the previous combined term, h_{i-1}, the *t*-partial solution expansion, equation (5.93), as

$$h_{ti}=k_{5i}(x,\ y)+\frac{T}{S_y}L_t^{-1}L_xh_{i-1}+\frac{T}{S_y}L_t^{-1}L_yh_{i-1},\quad i>0 \tag{5.100}$$

where k_{5i} is such that a homogeneous initial condition is satisfied, or from the *x*-partial solution expansion, equation (5.95), as

$$h_{xi}=k_{5i+1}(y,\ t)+k_{5i+2}(y,\ t)x+\frac{S_y}{T}L_x^{-1}L_th_{i-1}-L_x^{-1}L_yh_{i-1},\quad i>0 \tag{5.101}$$

where k_{5i+1} and k_{5i+2} are such that homogeneous *x*-boundary conditions in equations (5.92) are satisfied, or from the *y*-partial solution expansion, equation (5.97), as

$$h_{yi}=k_{5i+3}(x,\ t)+k_{5i+4}(x,\ t)y+\frac{S_y}{T}L_y^{-1}L_th_{i-1}-L_y^{-1}L_xh_{i-1} \tag{5.102}$$

where k_{5i+3} and k_{5i+4} are such that homogeneous *y*-boundary conditions in equations (5.92) are satisfied. A combination of the three versions of h_i, equations (5.100), (5.101), and (5.102) respectively, will yield the next term in the decomposition expansion.

Example 5.16: Visualizing Transient Flow in Higher Dimensions

Use the solution derived in Example 5.15 to write a Maple program that displays (1) a graph of the spatial distribution of the hydraulic head at *t*=12*months*, that is $h(x,\ y,\ 12)$; and (2) a graph of the temporal distribution of the hydraulic head at several fixed points, $h(200,\ 200,\ t)$, $h(250,\ 250,\ t)$, and $h(300,\ 300,\ t)$.

Solution

The following Maple worksheet illustrates the program. The time and space integrations, and the derivation of the integration constants are done analytically using the symbolic algebra features of Maple.   Three decomposition terms are derived, h_0, h_1, and h_2. Convergence rate is verified numerically by calculating these terms at a fixed point and a given time and assuring that $h_0>h_1>h_2$. In this case, three terms appear sufficiently accurate, although it seems that a transient problem would benefit from the inclusion of additional terms, since the magnitude of l_x, l_y, S_y, and the parameters in R_g greatly influence the rate of convergence.

```
> restart:
  #Boundary conditions and recharge
  f1:=y->100-0.002*y:
  f2:=y->103-0.001*y:
  f3:=x->100+0.008*x-0.000005*x^2:
  f4:=x->99+0.00883*x-0.000005*x^2:
  Rg:=t->alpha+beta*sin(theta*Pi*t/6):
  #Calculation of initial condition, V(x,t)
  #Steady x-partial solution Equation (5.59)
  k1(y)+k2(y)*x-int( int(Rg(0)/T,x), x):
  hx0:=unapply(%,x,y):
  hx0(0,y)=f1(y):
  solve(%,k1(y)):
  k1:=unapply(%,y):
  hx0(lx,y)=f2(y):
  solve(%,k2(y)):
  k2:=unapply(%,y):
  #Steady-sate y-partial solution Equation (5.62)
  k3(x)+k4(x)*y-int( int(Rg(0)/T,y), y):
  hy0:=unapply(%,x,y):
  hy0(x,0)=f3(x):
  solve(%,k3(x)):
  k3:=unapply(%,x):
  hy0(x,ly)=f4(x):
  solve(%,k4(x)):
  k4:=unapply(%,x):
  #Steady-state Equation (5.64) used as initial condition
  V:=(x,y)->(hx0(x,y)+hy0(x,y))/2:
  #
  #Time integral of recharge
  1/Sy*int(Rg(xi),xi=0..t):
  It:=unapply(%,t):
  #First t-partial solution equation (5.94)
  Ht0:=(x,y,t)->V(x,y)+It(t):
  #First x-partial solution equation (5.96)
  K1(y,t)+K2(y,t)*x-int( int(Rg(t)/T,x), x):
  Hx0:=unapply(%,x,y,t):
  Hx0(0,y,t)=f1(y):
  solve(%,K1(y,t)):
  K1:=unapply(%,y,t):
  Hx0(lx,y,t)=f2(y):
  solve(%,K2(y,t)):
  K2:=unapply(%,y,t):
  #First y-partial solution equation (5.98)
  K3(x,t)+K4(x,t)*y-int( int(Rg(t)/T,y), y):
  Hy0:=unapply(%,x,y,t):
  Hy0(x,0,t)=f3(x):
  solve(%,K3(x,t)):
  K3:=unapply(%,x,t):
  Hy0(x,ly,t)=f4(x):
  solve(%,K4(x,t)):
  K4:=unapply(%,x,t):
  #First combined term equation (5.99)
  h0:=(x,y,t)->(Ht0(x,y,t)+Hx0(x,y,t)+Hy0(x,y,t))/3:
  #
  #t-partial next term, equation (5.100)
  T/Sy*diff(h0(x,y,tau),x$2)+T/Sy*diff(h0(x,y,tau),y$2):
  K5(x,y)+int(%,tau=0..t):
  Ht1:=unapply(%,x,y,t):
  Ht1(x,y,0)=0:
  solve(%,K5(x,y)):
  K5:=unapply(%,x,y):
```

```
> #x-partial next term, equation (5.101)
  Sy/T*diff(h0(x,y,t),t)-diff(h0(x,y,t),y$2):
  K6(y,t)+K7(y,t)*x+int(int(%,x),x):
  Hx1:=unapply(%,x,y,t):
  Hx1(0,y,t)=0:
  solve(%,K6(y,t)):
  K6:=unapply(%,y,t):
  Hx1(lx,y,t)=0:
  solve(%,K7(y,t)):
  K7:=unapply(%,y,t):
  #y-partial next term equaiton (5.102)
  Sy/T*diff(h0(x,y,t),t)-diff(h0(x,y,t),x$2):
  K8(x,t)+K9(x,t)*y+int(int(%,y),y):
  Hy1:=unapply(%,x,y,t):
  Hy1(x,0,t)=0:
  solve(%,K8(x,t)):
  K8:=unapply(%,x,t):
  Hy1(x,ly,t)=0:
  solve(%,K9(x,t)):
  K9:=unapply(%,x,t):
  #equation (5.99)
  h1:=(x,y,t)->(Ht1(x,y,t)+Hx1(x,y,t)+Hy1(x,y,t))/3:
  #
  #t-partial next term, equation (5.100)
  T/Sy*diff(h1(x,y,tau),x$2)+T/Sy*diff(h1(x,y,tau),y$2):
  K10(x,y)+int(%,tau=0..t):
  Ht2:=unapply(%,x,y,t):
  Ht2(x,y,0)=0:
  solve(%,K10(x,y)):
  K10:=unapply(%,x,y):
  #x-partial next term, equation (5.101)
  Sy/T*diff(h1(x,y,t),t)-diff(h1(x,y,t),y$2):
  K11(y,t)+K12(y,t)*x+int(int(%,x),x):
  Hx2:=unapply(%,x,y,t):
  Hx2(0,y,t)=0:
  solve(%,K11(y,t)):
  K11:=unapply(%,y,t):
  Hx2(lx,y,t)=0:
  solve(%,K12(y,t)):
  K12:=unapply(%,y,t):
  #y-partial next term equaiton (5.102)
  Sy/T*diff(h1(x,y,t),t)-diff(h1(x,y,t),x$2):
  K13(x,t)+K14(x,t)*y+int(int(%,y),y):
  Hy2:=unapply(%,x,y,t):
  Hy2(x,0,t)=0:
  solve(%,K13(x,t)):
  K13:=unapply(%,x,t):
  Hy2(x,ly,t)=0:
  solve(%,K14(x,t)):
  K14:=unapply(%,x,t):
  #equation (5.99)
  h2:=(x,y,t)->(Ht2(x,y,t)+Hx2(x,y,t)+Hy2(x,y,t))/3:
  h:=(x,y,t)->h0(x,y,t)+h1(x,y,t)+h2(x,y,t):
> #Check convergence rate at a fixed point
  T:=500: lx:=600: ly:=500: Sy:=0.01: alpha:=0.003:
  beta:=-0.001: theta:=1: tt:=12:
  evalf(h0(lx/2,ly/2.,tt));
  evalf(h1(lx/2,ly/2.,tt));
  evalf(h2(lx/2,ly/2.,tt));

                              102.7785000

                              -2.366800888

                              1.146249512

> plot3d(h(x,y,12),x=0..lx,y=0..ly,orientation=[-135,60],
     shading=ZGRAYSCALE,style=PATCHNOGRID,axes=BOXED,
     labels=[`x (m)`,`y (m)`,`h(m)`],
     labeldirections=[HORIZONTAL,HORIZONTAL,VERTICAL],
     labelfont=[TIMES,ROMAN,16]);
```

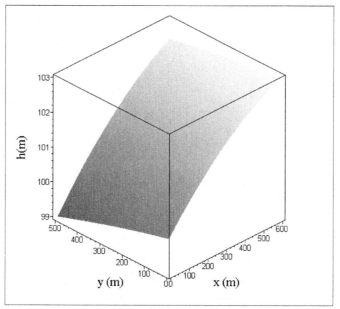

Figure 5.20: Head Spatial Distribution at *t*=12*months*

```
> g3:=plot(h(200,200,tau),tau=0..60,color=black,
      legend=`h(200,200,t)`):
  g4:=plot(h(250,250,tau),tau=0..60,color=black,
      style=point,legend=`h(250,250,t)`):
  g5:=plot(h(300,300,tau),tau=0..60,color=black,
      style=point,symbol=circle,legend=`h(300,300,t)`):
  plots[display](g3,g4,g5,axes=BOXED,labels=
      [`t (month)`,`h (m)`],labeldirections=
      [HORIZONTAL,VERTICAL],
      labelfont=[TIMES,ROMAN,16]);
```

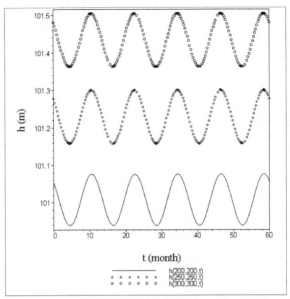

Figure 5.21: Head Time Distribution at Fixed Points

One of the most important features of decomposition is its ability to systematically derive solutions to nonlinear equations (Serrano, 2011). Many equations of groundwater flow and groundwater contaminant transport are nonlinear and their linearization may sometimes pose significant errors. In recent years, several works involving decomposition solutions to nonlinear groundwater flow and contaminant transport equations have been published. Serrano and Workman (2008, 1998) and Workman et al. (1997) investigated field applications of nonlinear one-dimensional models with Dupuit assumptions to the problem of stream-aquifer interaction. Verification with controlled laboratory experiments was reported by Serrano and Workman (2008) and Serrano et al. (2007). The effect of aquifer heterogeneity was investigated in Srivastava and Serrano (2007) and in Srivastava et al. (2006). When Dupuit assumptions are not adopted, the resulting unconfined groundwater equations exhibit a nonlinear free-surface and seepage boundary conditions. Groundwater flow subject to steady nonlinear free surface was investigated in Serrano (1995a). Moving nonlinear boundaries increase mathematical complexity. Decomposition models of transient nonlinear free surface with field verification were studied in Serrano (2003a). As discussed in Chapter 4, unsaturated flow models pose important mathematical challenges. Pressure-head-dependent soil-water diffusivities and hysteretic soil-water characteristic curves render the equations highly nonlinear. A new explicit solution to the Green and Ampt infiltration equation was presented in Serrano (2003b, 2001b). New solutions for vertical infiltration using the nonlinear Richard's equation were developed in Serrano (2004, 1998). A simple three-term decomposition solution was able to predict the experimentally-observed location of the wetting front with greater accuracy than the classical numerical solutions. Serrano (2004) also introduced simple physically-based hydrologic infiltration models that do not require the concept of infiltration rate capacity, that reflect a recovery in infiltration rate during periods of low rainfall, and that honor the soil-water functional relationships. Many contaminant transport models are inherently nonlinear. Non-symmetry in the plume spatial distribution, sharp front ends and long plume tails are natural responses of contaminant propagation subject to nonlinear chemical reactions. Serrano (2003c) studied several cases of nonlinear reactive contaminant transport. In surface hydrology, decomposition solutions of nonlinear wave propagation in rivers are beginning to appear in the literature (e.g., Serrano, 2006). The effect of nonlinearity in the differential equations is to produce the unsymmetric distribution in flood waves observed in nature.

Example 5.17: Modeling Nonlinear Groundwater Flow

In the aquifer depicted in Figure 5.14, the mean hydraulic head at the boundaries are given by $f_1(y)=100-0.2\times10^{-2}y$, $f_2(y)=103-0.1\times10^{-2}y$, $f_3(x)=100+0.8\times10^{-2}x-0.5\times10^{-5}x^2$, $f_4(x)=99+0.883\times10^{-2}x-0.5\times10^{-5}x^2$. Assume that $l_x=600m$, $l_y=500m$, a constant $K=1m/month$, $R_g=10mm/month$, and steady state conditions. Consider the nonlinearity in the differential equation and build a mathematical model to predict the spatial distribution in the hydraulic head.

Solution

From equation (5.16), the governing nonlinear differential equation with Dupuit assumptions in a homogeneous aquifer is given by

$$\frac{\partial}{\partial x}\left(Kh\frac{\partial h}{\partial x}\right)+\frac{\partial}{\partial y}\left(Kh\frac{\partial h}{\partial y}\right)=-R_g \quad 0\leq x\leq l_x,\ 0\leq y\leq l_y \quad (5.103)$$

subject to the boundary conditions given by

$$h(0,\ y)=f_1(y),\ h(l_x,\ y)=f_2(y),\ h(x,\ 0)=f_3(x),\ h(x,\ l_y)=f_4(x) \quad (5.104)$$

The x-partial solution of equation (5.103) is given by

$$h_x = k_1(y) + k_2(y)x - L_x^{-1}\frac{R_g}{Kh_x} - L_x^{-1}L_y h_x$$

$$-L_x^{-1}\frac{1}{h_x}\left(\frac{\partial h_x}{\partial x}\right)^2 - L_x^{-1}\frac{1}{h_x}\left(\frac{\partial h_x}{\partial y}\right)^2$$

(5.105)

which may be written as

$$h_x = k_1(y) + k_2(y)x - L_x^{-1}L_y h_x + L_x^{-1}N(h_x)$$

(5.106)

where k_1 and k_2 are such that the x boundary conditions in equations (5.104) are satisfied, and the nonlinear operator $\text{N}(h_x)$ is given by

$$N(h_x) = -\frac{1}{h_x}\left[\frac{R_g}{K} + \left(\frac{\partial h_x}{\partial x}\right)^2 + \left(\frac{\partial h_x}{\partial y}\right)^2\right]$$

(5.107)

Equation (5.106) may be expanded as (Adomian, 1994)

$$h_x = h_{x0} - L_x^{-1}L_y\sum_{i=0}^{\infty}h_{xi} + L_x^{-1}\sum_{i=0}^{\infty}A_{xi}$$

(5.108)

where the A_{xi} are the Adomian polynomials given as a generalized Taylor series expansion about an initial term h_{x0} :

$$A_{x0} = Nh_{x0}$$

$$A_{x1} = h_{x1}\frac{dNh_{x0}}{dh_{x0}}$$

$$A_{x2} = h_{x2}\frac{dNh_{x0}}{dh_{x0}} + \frac{h_{x0}^2}{2!}\frac{d^2Nh_{x0}}{dh_{x0}^2}$$

(5.109)

$$A_{x3} = h_{x3}\frac{dNh_{x0}}{dh_{x0}} + h_{x1}h_{x2}\frac{d^2Nh_{x0}}{dh_{x0}^2} + \frac{h_{x1}^3}{3!}\frac{d^3Nh_{x0}}{dh_{x0}^3}$$

$$\vdots$$

Alternate application of equations (5.108) and (5.109) sequentially yields the A_{xi} and the h_{xi}, respectively. In practice the number of terms one may calculate depends on the values of the parameters and the complexity in the functional form of $N(h_x)$. Usually the first few terms in a decomposition series are easily derivable if the initial term, h_{x0}, is simple. From equations (5.108) and (5.104), it is easy to see that a simple choice for the first term, h_{x0}, in the x-partial solution is given by

$$h_{x0}(x,\ y)=f_1(y)+\frac{f_2(y)-f_1(y)}{l_x}x \tag{5.110}$$

The y-partial solution of equation (5.103) is given by

$$h_y=k_3(x)+k_4(x)y-L_y^{-1}\frac{R_g}{Kh_y}-L_y^{-1}L_xh_y$$

$$-L_y^{-1}\frac{1}{h_y}\left(\frac{\partial h_y}{\partial x}\right)^2-L_y^{-1}\frac{1}{h_y}\left(\frac{\partial h_y}{\partial y}\right)^2 \tag{5.111}$$

which may be written as

$$h_y=k_3(x)+k_4(x)y-L_y^{-1}L_xh_y+L_y^{-1}N(h_y) \tag{5.112}$$

where k_3 and k_4 are such that the y boundary conditions in equation (5.104) are satisfied. Equation (5.112) may expanded as

$$h_y=h_{y0}-L_y^{-1}L_x\sum_{i=0}^{\infty}h_{yi}+L_y^{-1}\sum_{i=0}^{\infty}A_{yi} \tag{5.113}$$

where the A_{yi} are the Adomian polynomials given by equation (5.109) as a generalized Taylor series expansion about an initial term h_{y0}. From equations (5.112) and (5.104), a first term for the y-partial solution is

$$h_{y0}(x,\ y)=f_3(x)+\frac{f_4(x)-f_3(x)}{l_y}y \tag{5.114}$$

From equations (5.110) and (5.113), the first combined decomposition term is given by

$$h_0(x,\ y)=\frac{1}{2}\big(h_{x0}(x,\ y)+h_{y0}(x,\ y)\big)$$

The second term may be obtained from the x-partial expansion equation (5.108) as

$$h_{x1}=k_5(y)+k_6(y)x-L_x^{-1}L_yh_0-L_x^{-1}\frac{1}{h_0}\left[\frac{R_g}{K}+\left(\frac{\partial h_0}{\partial x}\right)^2+\left(\frac{\partial h_0}{\partial y}\right)^2\right] \tag{5.115}$$

where k_5 and k_6 are such that homogenous (i.e., zero) x boundary conditions in equation (5.104) are satisfied, or from the y-partial expansion equation (5.113) as

$$h_{y1}=k_7(x)+k_8(x)y-L_y^{-1}L_xh_0-L_y^{-1}\frac{1}{h_0}\left[\frac{R_g}{K}+\left(\frac{\partial h_0}{\partial x}\right)^2+\left(\frac{\partial h_0}{\partial y}\right)^2\right] \tag{5.116}$$

where k_7 and k_8 are such that homogeneous (i.e., zero) y boundary conditions in equation (5.104) are satisfied. Equations (5.114) and (5.116) may be combined to obtain the second decomposition term, h_1. In general, higher-order terms, h_i, are obtained from

$$h_i = \frac{1}{2}[k_{4i+1}(y) + k_{4i+2}(y)x - L_x^{-1}L_y h_{i-1} + L_x^{-1}A_{i-1}$$

$$(5.117)$$

$$+ k_{4i+3}(x) + k_{4i+4}(x)y - L_y^{-1}L_x h_{i-1} + L_y^{-1}A_{i-1}]$$

Example 5.18: Visualizing Spatial Distribution of Nonlinear Flow

Write a Maple program that utilizes the solution derived in Example 5.17 to describe the nonlinear spatial distribution of the hydraulic head.

Solution

The following Maple worksheet illustrates the program. Convergence rate was not checked and only two decomposition terms were used. Higher order terms may be easily added. The differences between linear and nonlinear solutions tend to be relatively small when an aquifer recharge is small and when hydraulic conductivity values are large. As recharge increases, or conductivity decreases, the errors incurred upon by linearization increase. In other words, linearization may be acceptable in sandy or coarsely-graded aquifers in dry regions. Clay or finely-graded aquifers in wet regions exhibit the highest errors due to linearization. The effect of linearization is to underestimate the magnitude of heads and gradients. This can be seen mathematically, as the linearized model omits several terms in the differential equations. Previous studies (Patel and Serrano, 2011; Serrano, 2003a, 1995a) further elaborate on these statements. In unsaturated soils the errors of linearization are dramatic, yielding situations where wetting fronts are completely missed by the linearized models (Serrano, 2004, 2003b).

```
> restart:
Rg:=0.01: K:=1: lx:=600: ly:=500:
#Boundary conditions
f1:=y->100-0.002*y:
f2:=y->103-0.001*y:
f3:=x->100+0.008*x-0.000005*x^2:
f4:=x->99+0.00883*x-0.000005*x^2:
#First x-partial solution Equation (5.110)
hx0:=(x,y)->f1(y)+(f2(y)-f1(y))/lx*x:
#First y-partial solution Equation (5.115)
hy0:=(x,y)->f3(x)+(f4(x)-f3(x))/ly*y:
#Combined first term
h0:=(x,y)->(hx0(x,y)+hy0(x,y))/2:
#
#Next x-partial term, equation (5.115)
#Note we use hx0 instead of h0 to simplify integrals
diff(hx0(x,y),y$2)+(Rg/K+diff(hx0(x,y),x)^2
    +diff(hx0(x,y),y)^2)/hx0(x,y):
```

```
>  Ix:=unapply(%,x,y):
   k5(y)+k6(y)*x-int( int(Ix(x,y),x), x):
   hx1:=unapply(%,x,y):
   hx1(0,y)=0:
   solve(%,k5(y)):
   k5:=unapply(%,y):
   hx1(lx,y)=0:
   solve(%,k6(y)):
   k6:=unapply(%,y):
   #
   #Next y-partial term, equation (5.116)
   #Note we use hy0 instead of h0 to simplify integrals
   diff(hy0(x,y),x$2)+(Rg/K+diff(hy0(x,y),x)^2
          +diff(hy0(x,y),y)^2)/hy0(x,y):
   Iy:=unapply(%,x,y):
   k7(x)+k8(x)*y-int( int(Iy(x,y),y), y):
   hy1:=unapply(%,x,y):
   hy1(x,0)=0:
   solve(%,k7(x)):
   k7:=unapply(%,x):
   hy1(x,ly)=0:
   solve(%,k8(x)):
   k8:=unapply(%,x):
   #Combined second term, equation (5.117)
   h1:=(x,y)->(hx1(x,y)+hy1(x,y))/2:
   #Approximate solution
   h:=(x,y)->h0(x,y)+h1(x,y):
>  plot3d(h(x,y),x=0..lx,y=0..ly,shading=ZGRAYSCALE,
       style=PATCHNOGRID,
       orientation=[-135,60],axes=BOXED,
       labels=[`x (m)`,`y (m)`,`h (m)`],
       labeldirections=[HORIZONTAL,HORIZONTAL,VERTICAL],
       labelfont=[TIMES,ROMAN,16]);
```

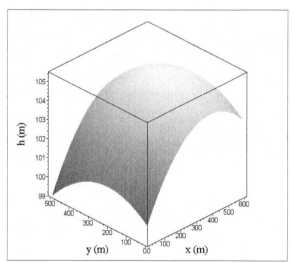

Figure 5.22: Head Spatial Distribution

5.3. EXPLOITATION OF GROUNDWATER RESOURCES

Aquifer Safe Yield

Groundwater is the primary source of water for municipal, industrial and agricultural uses in many localities. Groundwater is extracted through pumping wells. A water *well* is an excavation or structure created in the ground by digging, driving, boring or drilling to capture and extract water from productive layers of an aquifer. The well water is drawn by an electric submersible pump, a vertical turbine pump, a hand pump or a mechanical pump (e.g., from a water-pumping windmill). It can also be drawn up using containers, such as buckets, that are raised mechanically or by hand (see for example Figure 5.23). There are many kinds of water wells, depending on the purpose and prevailing field conditions (for detailed descriptions see Nielsen, 1991). Figure 5.24 illustrates a typical cross section of a drilled well.

Figure 5.23: A Hand-Drawn Water Well near Chinon, France

Groundwater is replenished naturally via recharge from rainfall, and seepage from streams and lakes. It can also be replenished artificially via injecting wells or infiltration galleries. The exploitation of groundwater should be balanced by an equal replenishment from natural or artificial means over long periods of time. When improper management of groundwater resources results in a long term exploitation rate that exceeds an aquifer natural replenishment, a gradual depletion of groundwater will occur. This causes a decrease in groundwater heads, which leaves many productive wells dry, and sometimes results in subsidence of the land surface.

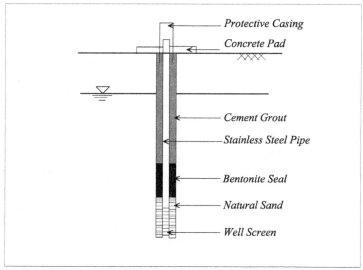

Figure 5.24: Cross Section of a Drilled Water Well

The water that can be safely extracted from an aquifer is an important hydrologic quantity in groundwater management. This rate is called the aquifer *safe yield*. The safe yield is the volume of water that can be extracted from an aquifer over a long period of time without adversely affecting the supply. This may be estimated from water balance calculations. The water balance equation written for the aquifer during a given year is (see Chapter 1):

$$R_g - Q_g - Q_p = \frac{\Delta S_g}{\Delta t} \tag{5.118}$$

where
R_g = groundwater recharge (*mm/year*)
Q_g = natural groundwater flow (discharge) (*mm/year*)
Q_p = groundwater exploitation (draft) (*mm/year*)
ΔS_g = change in groundwater storage (*mm/year*)

R_g may also represent seepage from rivers and lakes. The estimated volumes of seepage must be expressed in depth (*mm*) of water per unit aquifer, or unit watershed area. In equation (5.118) evapotranspiration and loss through the capillary fringe is neglected. The groundwater discharge, Q_g, may be estimated from streamflow records of the watershed by separating groundwater flow (see chapter 6 on *hydrograph* analysis). The change in groundwater storage, ΔS_g, may be estimated from a collection of observation wells across the aquifer or watershed. For an unconfined aquifer $\Delta S_g \approx S_y \Delta h$, where S_y is the aquifer specific yield and Δh is the mean change (i.e., averaged over all of the wells) in water table elevation during the period of analysis (*mm*). For a confined aquifer, the change in groundwater storage is the product of the aquifer storage coefficient times the mean change in *potentiometric head*.

Equation (5.118) describes the conditions for a particular year. Due to the natural fluctuation of hydrologic variables affecting natural replenishment, a sufficiently long period of analysis should be used (e.g., 20 years). During this period, mean annual recharge and mean annual groundwater discharge should be evaluated. Therefore, the safe yield is the amount of water that may be extracted from an aquifer such that the change in groundwater storage is zero over a long period of time. From equation (5.118),

$$\bar{Q}_p = \bar{R}_g - \bar{Q}_g \tag{5.119}$$

where
  $\bar{Q}_p$ = aquifer safe yield (*mm/year*)
  $\bar{R}_g$ = long-term mean annual recharge (*mm/year*)
  $\bar{Q}_g$ = long-term mean annual groundwater discharge (*mm/year*)

There are other methods that approximately estimate the safe yield of an aquifer in the absence of accurate recharge and groundwater flow data. They are based on the total annual precipitation, the total annual flow (i.e., surface and subsurface flow), and the average depth to the water table. The safe yield is estimated as the annual draft that makes the change in water table depth equal to zero (see McCuen, 1989, p. 268).

Example 5.19
Over a period of 20 years, the mean annual groundwater recharge to the main aquifer in a watershed is 150*mm/year*. Based on hydrograph analysis, it is estimated that, over the same 20-*year* period, the mean groundwater flow is 90*mm/year*. If the watershed has an area of 60 km^2, calculate the aquifer safe yield.

Solution
From equation (5.119), the safe yield is

$$\bar{Q}_p = \bar{R}_g - \bar{Q}_g = 150mm/year - 90mm/year = 60mm/year$$

To express this quantity in volume units, multiply by the drainage area:

$$\bar{Q}_p\frac{m^3}{year} = \bar{Q}_p\frac{mm}{year} \times A = 60\frac{mm}{year} \times \frac{m}{10^3mm} \times 60km^2 \times \frac{10^6m^2}{km^2} = 3.6 \times 10^6\frac{m^3}{year}$$

Thus, 3.6 millions cubic meters per year, or 9863 cubic meters per day, may be extracted from the main aquifer without affecting the long-term storage. For the groundwater manager, this number represents an average value that could be exceeded during a few dry years, as long as it is balanced by an equal amount of years where exploitation is less than the safe yield. It is important to remark that if the main aquifer extends beyond the watershed boundaries, then the safe yield could be different. The hydrologist should extend the analysis to a watershed that includes the entire aquifer. An understanding of the regional geology is vital here.

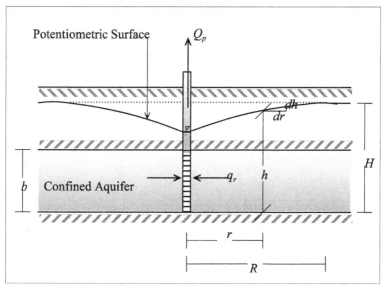

Figure 5.25 A Fully-Penetrating Well in a Confined Aquifer

Steady Flow to a Well in a Confined Aquifer

Consider the case of groundwater flow towards a fully-penetrating well in a homogeneous, isotropic, confined aquifer (Figure 5.25). A fully penetrating well is one whose screen, perforated pipe, or open well bore extends through the entire thickness of the aquifer. The aquifer has a uniform thickness, $b(m)$. The *potentiometric surface* prior to pumping, called the undisturbed head, $H(m)$, is represented by the dashed line in Figure 5.25. When the well starts pumping at a constant rate $Q_p(m^3/day)$, a *cone of depression* in the potentiometric surface centered at the well begins to form. This causes a hydraulic gradient that points radially towards the center of the well. Consequently, the flow in the aquifer is radially symmetric. The cone of depression continues to expand in the aquifer. When the cone of depression in the hydraulic head stops moving, a steady state condition is achieved. This condition is represented by the continuous line in the potentiometric surface. Because the flow in the aquifer is radially symmetric, it is appropriate to measure distances with respect to the center of the well.

Consider a point in the aquifer located at a distance $r(m)$ with respect to the center of the well. The hydraulic head with respect to a datum (i.e., the bottom of the aquifer, or the mean sea level) is $h(m)$. The hydraulic gradient at that point is dh/dr. The specific discharge $q_r = -K_r dh/dr$, where K_r is the bulk value of the radial hydraulic conductivity (*m/day* or *m/month*). The specific discharge points towards the center of the well. The flow cross-sectional area is the surface area of a cylinder of radius r, $2\pi rb$. Multiplying the specific discharge by the cross-sectional area and equating this to the pumping rate (i.e., applying continuity) we obtain

$$Q_p = 2\pi rbK_r \frac{dh}{dr} \qquad (5.120)$$

Placing on the left side of the equality terms of h, on the right side terms of r, and integrating,

$$\int_h^H dh = \frac{Q_p}{2\pi bK_r} \int_r^R \frac{dr}{r} \qquad (5.121)$$

The limits of integration are the current radius, r, where the head is h, and a large radius, R, called the well *radius of influence*, where the head is H (i.e., the undisturbed head). Solving,

$$H - h = \frac{Q_p}{2\pi bK_r} \ln\left(\frac{R}{r}\right) \qquad (5.122)$$

The difference between the undisturbed head and the head at a point is called the *drawdown*, $s = H - h$.

Knowing K_r and the head, H, at an observation well located at a distance r from the pumping well, one may use equation (5.122) to calculate the radius of influence, R, of a well at a given pumping rate. The observation well may be the pumping well itself having a radius r_w, usually taken to extend beyond the pipe radius to the outer gravel pack. Alternatively, equation (5.122) may be used to calculate the head versus distance from the pumping well, if the well radius of influence is known. Equation (5.122) could also be applied to two observation wells located at distances r_1 and r_2, having heads h_1 and h_2, respectively:

$$h_2 - h_1 = \frac{Q_p}{2\pi b K_r} \ln\left(\frac{r_2}{r_1}\right)$$

(5.123)

In this situation, equation (5.123) is used for the estimation of the aquifer transmissivity.

Example 5.20
    A fully penetrating well in a confined aquifer pumps at a constant rate of $2000\,m^3/day$ for a long time. Two observation wells located $20m$ and $160m$ from the well, show a difference in hydraulic head of $2.0m$. If the undisturbed head is $250m$ above the sea level, and the head in the farthest well is $249m$, (1) estimate the aquifer transmissivity, and (2) calculate the radius of influence of the well.

Solution
(1) From equation (5.123),

$$T = K_r b = \frac{Q_p}{2\pi(h_2 - h_1)} \ln\left(\frac{r_2}{r_1}\right) = \frac{2000 m^3/day}{2 \times \pi \times 2.0m} \times \ln\left(\frac{160m}{20m}\right) = 331.0 m^2/day$$

(2) From equation (5.122),

$$\frac{2\pi T(H - h_2)}{Q_p} = \ln\left(\frac{R}{r_2}\right) \quad \Rightarrow \quad R = r_2 . \exp\left(\frac{2\pi T(H - h_2)}{Q_p}\right)$$

$$R = 160m \times \exp\left(\frac{2 \times \pi \times 331.0 m^2/day \times (250m - 249m)}{2000 m^3/day}\right) = 452.5m$$

Hence, it is expected that the pumping well will not affect a region beyond $500m$ from its center. Alternatively, one could ask what would be the pumping rate that would reduce the radius of influence to a fixed value and with a given maximum drawdown at the well.

Steady Flow to a Well in an Unconfined Aquifer

Consider a pumping well in an unconfined aquifer (see Figure 5.26). As in confined aquifers, a radially symmetric cone of depression will form as a result of pumping. However, the cone of depression is formed by the water table. The saturated thickness of the aquifer is now a function of radius. If Dupuit assumptions are valid and the flow is approximately horizontal, the saturated thickness is equal to the hydraulic head, h, with respect to the bottom of the aquifer. This assumption is not valid in the vicinity of the well or if hydraulic gradients are strong. This is the case of well screens not penetrating the full saturated thickness of an aquifer. Proceeding as before, we use Darcy's law to write an expression for the radial specific discharge, multiply by the flow cross sectional area and equate it to the pumping rate:

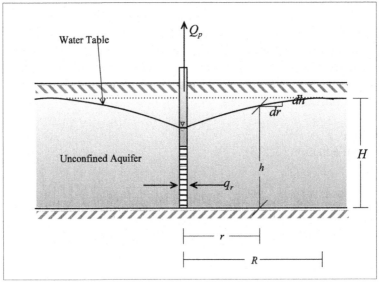

Figure 5.26: A Well in an Unconfined Aquifer

$$Q_p = 2\pi r h K_r \frac{dh}{dr} \qquad (5.124)$$

Placing on the left side of the equality terms of h, on the right side terms of r, and integrating,

$$\int_h^H h\,dh = \frac{Q_p}{2\pi K_r} \int_r^R \frac{dr}{r} \qquad (5.125)$$

Solving,

$$H^2 - h^2 = \frac{Q_p}{\pi K_r} \ln\left(\frac{R}{r}\right) \tag{5.126}$$

Wells in Aquifers with Natural Boundaries

Equations (5.120) through (5.126) assume that the wells are pumping aquifers of infinite extent. However, most aquifers are bounded by rivers, lakes, or impermeable boundaries such as buried rocks or tight faults. The presence of these boundaries affect the hydraulic heads generated by pumping wells. Nonetheless, the equations describing flow in infinite aquifers may be applied if one uses a combination of imaginary wells in such a manner that the physical conditions of the natural boundary are reproduced.

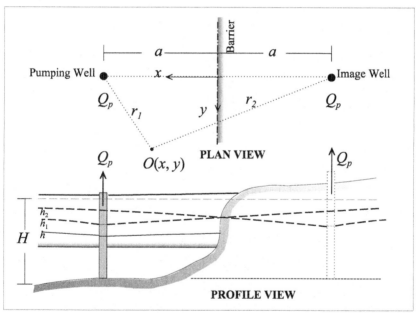

Figure 5.27: A Well Near a Geologic Barrier

Consider for example the case of a well in a confined aquifer located a distance a from a geological barrier that separates the aquifer from an impermeable unit (see Figure 5.27). The well is pumping at a constant flow rate Q_p for a long time. If the barrier were not present, the hydraulic head produced by the well would be h_1, or the drawdown s_1. However, the well is not receiving water from an infinite aquifer and the influence of this boundary creates an enhanced drawdown with a head h. To simulate this effect, let us introduce an imaginary well located a distance *a* on the opposite side of the barrier. The image well is pumping water at a rate Q_p. If the barrier were not present, the image well would create a cone of impression with a hydraulic head h_2, or a drawdown s_2. The resulting drawdown, s, is the summation of both effects, or $s = s_1 + s_2$.

Adopting a Cartesian coordinate system with origin at the barrier, an observation point O of coordinates (x, y) is located a distance $r_1 = \sqrt{(a-x)^2 + y^2}$ from the real well, and a distance $r_2 = \sqrt{(a+x)^2 + y^2}$ from the image well. The drawdown, s_1, caused by the real well at point O is given by equation (5.122) as

$$s_1 = \frac{Q_p}{2\pi b K_r} \ln\left(\frac{R}{r_1}\right)$$ (5.127)

where
   R = radius of influence of well (*m*)

The radius of influence is the distance from the well to a point in an infinite aquifer, assuming no barrier, where the head corresponds to the undisturbed head, H. Similarly, the drawdown, s_2, caused by the image well is given by equation (5.122) as

$$s_2 = \frac{Q_p}{2\pi b K_r} \ln\left(\frac{R}{r_2}\right)$$ (5.128)

Adding the drawdown effects caused by the real and the image well, the resulting drawdown at point O, s, is

$$s = H - h = \frac{Q_p}{2\pi b K_r} \ln\left(\frac{R^2}{r_1 r_2}\right)$$ (5.129)

Expressing r_1 and r_2 in terms of the coordinates of the observation point O, x and y,

$$s = H - h = \frac{Q_p}{2\pi b K_r} \ln\left(\frac{R^2}{\sqrt{[(a-x)^2 + y^2][(a+x)^2 + y^2]}}\right)$$ (5.130)

Equation (5.130) may be also applied to unconfined aquifers if the saturated thickness of the aquifer does not change substantially with distance. Therefore, if Dupuit assumptions are valid, the mean saturated thickness is b and equation (5.130) may be used for either confined or unconfined aquifers.

Consider now the case of a pumping well located a distance a from a stream of constant head. The recharging effect of the stream is to increase the hydraulic heads more than if the aquifer were infinite. To simulate this effect, let us introduce an imaginary well located a distance a on the opposite side of the stream. The image well is injecting water at a rate $-Q_p$, which would cause a cone of accretion. Repeating the procedure followed for the well near an impermeable boundary, and algebraically adding the drawdown effects of the real and the image wells, the resulting drawdown at an observation point O of coordinates x and y with respect to an origin located at the stream is

$$s=H-h=\frac{Q_p}{2\pi bK_r}\ln\left(\frac{r_2}{r_1}\right)=\frac{Q_p}{4\pi bK_r}\ln\left(\frac{(a+x)^2+y^2}{(a-x)^2+y^2}\right) \qquad (5.131)$$

Example 5.21

A well in an unconfined aquifer is pumping at a constant rate for a long period of time. The well is located at a distance of $100m$ from a river. The transmissivity of the aquifer is $50\,m^2/day$. An observation well located $40m$ from the well, in the line that marks the shortest distance between the well and the river, registers $0.5m$ of drawdown. Calculate the pumping rate.

Solution

With $x=60m$ and $y=0$, the pumping rate is, from equation (5.131),

$$Q_p=\frac{4\pi Ts}{\ln\left(\frac{y^2+(a+x)^2}{y^2+(a-x)^2}\right)}=\frac{4\times\pi\times50\frac{m^2}{day}\times0.5m}{\ln\left(\frac{(100m+60m)^2}{(100m-60m)^2}\right)}=113.31m^3/day$$

Unsteady Flow to a well in a Confined Aquifer

The time dependent groundwater flow equation in a confined, homogeneous, isotropic aquifer, equation (5.22), may be written in polar coordinates when a fully-penetrating pumping well generates axisymmetric flow conditions. The equation becomes (Bear, 1979)

$$\frac{S}{T}\frac{\partial h}{\partial t}-\frac{\partial^2 h}{\partial r^2}-\frac{1}{r}\frac{\partial h}{\partial r}=0 \qquad (5.132)$$

The solution to this equation was obtained by Theis (1935) as

$$s = \frac{Q_p}{4\pi T} W(u) \tag{5.133}$$

where

$$W(u) = \int_u^\infty \frac{e^{-u}}{u} du = -0.5772 - \ln u + u - \frac{u^2}{2.2!} + \frac{u^3}{3.3!} - ..., \quad u = \frac{r^2 S}{4Tt} \tag{5.134}$$

$W(u)$ is called the *well function*. Table 5.1 shows the well function magnitude for different values of u.

Table 5.1: Values of the Well Function $W(u)$

u	1.0	2.0	3.0	4.0	5.0	6.0	7.0	8.0	9.0
$\times 10^0$	0.219	0.049	0.013	0.0038	0.0011	0.00036	0.00012	0.000038	0.000012
$\times 10^{-1}$	1.82	1.22	0.91	0.70	0.56	0.45	0.37	0.31	0.26
$\times 10^{-2}$	4.04	3.35	2.96	2.68	2.47	2.30	2.15	2.03	1.92
$\times 10^{-3}$	6.33	5.64	5.23	4.95	4.73	4.54	4.39	4.26	4.14
$\times 10^{-4}$	8.63	7.94	7.53	7.25	7.02	6.84	6.69	6.55	6.44
$\times 10^{-5}$	10.94	10.24	9.84	9.55	9.33	9.14	8.99	8.86	8.74
$\times 10^{-6}$	13.24	12.55	12.14	11.85	11.63	11.45	11.29	11.16	11.04
$\times 10^{-7}$	15.54	14.85	14.44	14.15	13.93	13.75	13.60	13.46	13.34
$\times 10^{-8}$	17.84	17.15	16.74	16.46	16.23	16.05	15.90	15.76	15.65
$\times 10^{-9}$	20.15	19.45	19.05	18.76	18.54	18.35	18.20	18.07	17.95
$\times 10^{-10}$	22.45	21.76	21.35	21.06	20.84	20.66	20.50	20.37	20.25
$\times 10^{-11}$	24.75	24.06	23.65	23.36	23.14	22.96	22.81	22.67	22.55
$\times 10^{-12}$	27.05	26.36	25.96	25.67	25.44	25.26	25.11	24.96	24.86
$\times 10^{-13}$	29.36	28.66	28.26	27.97	27.75	27.56	27.41	27.28	27.16
$\times 10^{-14}$	31.66	30.97	30.56	30.27	30.05	29.87	29.71	29.58	29.46
$\times 10^{-15}$	33.96	33.27	32.86	32.58	32.35	32.17	32.02	31.88	31.76

Source: Wenzel (1942).

Knowing the aquifer transmissivity and the pumping rate, equation (5.133) may used to calculate the drawdown, s, at a given distance from the well, r, and a given time, t. More often, the Theis solution is used to estimate the aquifer parameters T and S in homogeneous aquifers, given the values of the drawdown with respect to time at observation wells (for heterogeneous aquifers see Serrano, 1997a). Data for this analysis are obtained from a pumping test in which discharge is kept constant. Drawdown may be measured at an observation well located a fixed distance, r, duringr different time intervals. Alternatively, drawdown can be measured at the same time in wells located at different distances. Taking logarithms on both sides of equation (5.133),

$$\log s = \left[\log\frac{Q_p}{4\pi T}\right] + \log W(u) \tag{5.135}$$

For a constant Q_p, the term in the square bracket is constant. Adding $\log W(u)$ to this constant, $\log s$ is obtained. On the other hand,

$$u = \frac{r^2 S}{4Tt} \quad \Rightarrow \quad \frac{t}{r^2} = \frac{S}{4T}\frac{1}{u} \tag{5.136}$$

On taking logarithms,

$$\log\frac{t}{r^2} = \left[\log\frac{S}{4T}\right] + \log\frac{1}{u} \tag{5.137}$$

The term in the square bracket is constant. Adding $\log(1/u)$ to this constant, $\log(t/r^2)$ is obtained. Thus, from equations (5.135) and (5.137), a graph between $\log W(u)$ and $\log(1/u)$ is similar to a graph between $\log s$ and $\log(t/r^2)$. This is the basis of the Theis' type curve method of aquifer parameter estimation. The procedure is described below.

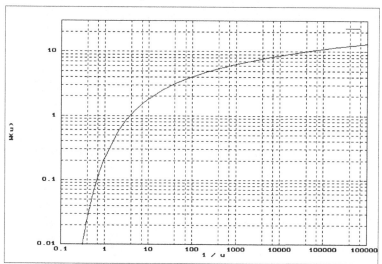

Figure 5.28: Theis Type Curve

(1) Plot $W(u)$ versus $1/u$ on double logarithmic paper. It is called the type curve (see Figure 5.28). It is a graphical representation of Table 5.1.

(2) From the pumping test data, plot s versus t/r^2 on transparent double logarithmic paper. This is called the data curve. The length of each cycle of this paper should be the same as that used in the type curve.

(3) Place the data curve over the type curve, moving the former up or down, left or right, while keeping the axis of the two plots parallel, until the data plot overlaps over a certain portion of the type curve (see Figure 5.29).

(4) Select any point from the overlapping part of the two graphs. This point need not be on the curves themselves. It is preferable to select a point on the type curve whose coordinates are a multiple of 10. Record $W(u)$ and $1/u$ coordinates, and the corresponding s and t/r^2 coordinates, of the matching point.

(5) From equation (5.133), the transmissivity is computed as

$$T=\frac{Q_p}{4\pi s}W(u) \tag{5.138}$$

Similarly, the storage coefficient is computed from

$$u=\frac{r^2 S}{4Tt} \quad \Rightarrow \quad S=\frac{4Ttu}{r^2} \tag{5.139}$$

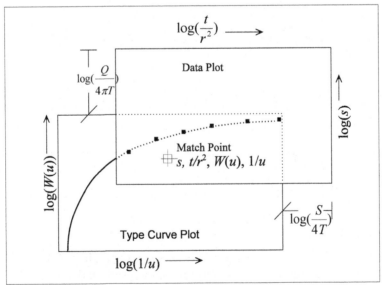

Figure 5.29 Matching the Data Curve to the Type Curve

Example 5.22: Estimation of Aquifer Parameters

A pumping test was performed in a confined aquifer. The aquifer was pumped at a constant rate of $2.0\,m^3/min$. An observation well located $60m$ from the pumping well recorded the drawdown data in Table 5.2. Following steps (1) through (5) above, estimate the aquifer transmissivity and storage coefficient.

Table 5.2: Drawdown Data for Example 5.22

$t(min)$	$s(m)$	$t(min)$	$s(m)$	$t(min)$	$s(m)$
1.0	0.201	10.0	0.567	80.0	0.927
1.5	0.265	14.0	0.634	100.0	0.963
2.0	0.302	18.0	0.671	120.0	1.000
2.5	0.338	24.0	0.719	150.0	1.042
3.0	0.369	30.0	0.759	180.0	1.070
4.0	0.415	40.0	0.808	210.0	1.100
5.0	0.454	50.0	0.847	240.0	1.119
8.0	0.533	60.0	0.878		

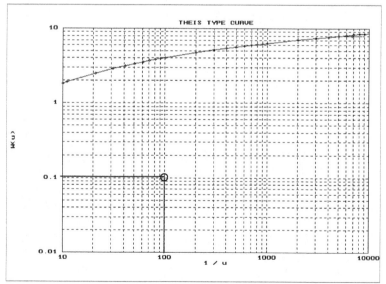

Figure 5.30 Type Curve for Example 5.22

Solution

(1) The type curve is plotted in double logarithmic paper with a range from 10 to 10000 for $1/u$, a range from 0.01 to 10 for $W(u)$, and three cycles on each axis. The resulting plot (Figure 5.30) has a shape

similar to that of the data plot obtained in item (2) below. The curves may be plotted by hand using Table 5.1, or with the aid of a spreadsheet or algebra software. In either case, make sure the length of each cycle is the same for the type curve and data plot.

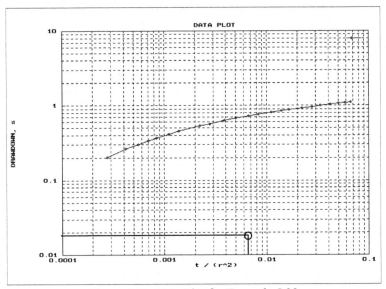

Figure 5.31: Data Plot for Example 5.22

(2) From Table 5.2, the time values are divided by $r^2 = 60^2 m^2$ and plotted with respect to drawdown (Figure 5.31). The data plot covers three cycles, each having the same length as that of the type curve in (1).

(3) Superimpose the data plot, Figure 5.31, on the type curve, Figure 5.30. Move the data plot up or down, while keeping the axis parallel to those of the type curve until the data curve overlaps over a certain portion of the type curve.

(4) After selecting an arbitrary point on the overlapping part of the two sheets, shown on the plots, the following coordinates are read: $W(u)=0.1$, $1/u=100$, $s=0.019$, and $t/r^2=0.0066$.

(5) From equation (5.138), the transmissivity is calculated as

$$T = \frac{Q_p}{4\pi s} W(u) = \frac{2.0 m^3/min}{4 \times \pi \times 0.019 m} \times 0.1 = 0.838 m^2/min = 1206 m^2/day$$

From equation (5.139), the storage coefficient is calculated as

$$S = \frac{t}{r^2} 4Tu = 0.0066 \frac{min}{m^2} \times 4 \times 0.838 \frac{m^2}{min} \times \frac{1}{100} = 2.212 \times 10^{-4}$$

Example 5.22 illustrates the traditional application of the Theis's method of aquifer parameter estimation. It relies on manual plotting, curve sliding, and subjective curve fitting. There are many software available to automate this and other inverse methods. The following example encourages the reader to write his or her own program of application.

Example 5.23: The Theis Method of Parameter Estimation
Write a simple Maple program to solve Example 5.22.

Solution
The following program is a preliminary version of the Theis' method. First, the well function is defined and used to produce the type curve for a range of values $1/u$ from 3 to 10,000, or $\log(1/u)$ from about 0.5 to 4 (see Example 5.22). The well function corresponds to the exponential integral function in Maple, $W(u) = E(1, u)$. A set of grid lines are also plotted to help reading the graph. Next, a vector with the time-drawdown data is created, $Data[[t_1, s_1], [t_2, s_2], ..., [t_N, s_N]]$. This vector is further processed to produce the data curve, by dividing time by r^2 and taking logarithms. The data curve is plotted on the type curve. The user now enters values of horizontal and vertical shifting values of the data curve that would make it closer to the type curve. This process of trial-and-error adjusting the shifting values and redrawing the curves, is interactively repeated until one judges the two curves coinciding over some of their lengths. The user then chooses and records the number of one of the points of the data curve, from left to right, as the matching point. In this example, we chose point number 1. The program then uses the coordinates in memory of the selected point and calculates $T = 1289 m^2/day$, and $S = 0.00023$. Notice the values obtained are slightly different from those derived manually in Example 5.22, which demonstrates the subjectivity of visually fitting curves. This program, and all programs in this book, was written as a classic Maple worksheet. It can be executed as part of the regular Maple workbench, which allows the possibility of sliding the data curve over the type curve with the mouse.

```
> restart: with(plottools):
  r:=60.: N:=23: Qp:=2.:
  W:=u->Ei(1,u):
  #Type curve
  g1:=plot(log10(W(1/10^u)),u=0.5..4,color=black):
  #Plot a grid of lines
  g2:=seq(line([0.5,-0.1+0.1*i],[4,-0.1+0.1*i]),i=0..12):
  g3:=seq(line([0.5+0.2*i,-0.1],[0.5+0.2*i,1.1]),i=0..18):
  Data:=[[1.,0.201],[1.5,0.265],[2.0,0.302],[2.5,0.338],
      [3.0,0.369],[4.0,0.415],[5.0,0.454],[8.0,0.533],
      [10.0,0.567],[14.0,0.634],[18.0,0.671],[24.0,0.719],
      [30.0,0.759],[40.0,0.808],[50.0,0.847],[60.0,0.878],
      [80.0,0.927],[100.0,0.963],[120.0,1.0],[150.0,1.042],
      [180.0,1.07],[210.0,1.1],[240.0,1.119]]:
  Data1:=[seq([Data[i,1]/r^2,Data[i,2]],i=1..N)]:
  #Data curve
  Datalog:=[seq([log10(Data1[i,1]),log10(Data1[i,2])],
      i=1..N)]:
  #Guess [x,y] shifting values for the data curve
  shift:=[4.2,0.75]:
  Shifted:=[seq(Datalog[i]+shift,i=1..N)]:
  g4:=plot(Shifted,style=point,color=black,symbol=box):
  plots[display](g1,g2,g3,g4,tickmarks=[4,8],axes=box,
      labels=[`log(1/u)`,`log(W(u))`],
      labeldirections=[HORIZONTAL,VERTICAL],
      labelfont=[TIMES,ROMAN,16]);
```

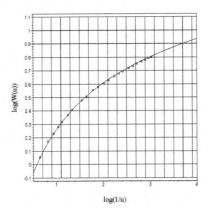

```
> #Select a data match point number from left to right
  PointNumber:=1:
  XCoordinate:=op(1,Shifted[PointNumber]);
  YCoordinate:=op(2,Shifted[PointNumber]);
  u1:=XCoordinate:
  w1:=YCoordinate:
  #Transmissivity in m^2/day
  T:=evalf(Qp*10^w1/(4*Pi*Data1[PointNumber,2])*60*24);
  #Storage coefficient
  S:=Data1[PointNumber,1]*4*T/10^u1/(60*24);
```

$$XCoordinate := 0.643697499$$
$$YCoordinate := 0.0531960574$$
$$T := 1288.791384$$
$$S := 0.0002258812194$$

A simplification of the Theis procedure was proposed by Jacob (1950), after noting that as t increases, u becomes small and most terms in equation (5.133) become negligible. For cases when $u<0.05$, the well function may be approximated by the first two terms in its series expansion. Thus equation (5.133) reduces to

$$s=\frac{Q_p}{4\pi T}(-0.5772-\ln u)=\frac{Q_p}{4\pi T}\left(\ln 0.562-\ln\frac{r^2 S}{4Tt}\right) \tag{5.140}$$

This may be written as

$$s=\frac{Q_p}{4\pi T}\ln\left(\frac{2.25Tt}{r^2 S}\right)=\frac{2.3Q_p}{4\pi T}\log\left(\frac{2.25Tt}{r^2 S}\right) \tag{5.141}$$

On semilog paper, equation (5.141) represents a straight line with a slope of $2.3Q_p/4\pi T$. Hence, the parameter estimation procedure is significantly simplified. For a *drawdown-time analysis*, the drawdown measurements are made in an observation well at various times. Thus, the distance, r, is constant. The procedure is as follows:

(1) Plot the drawdown versus time on semilogarithmic paper, with s on the vertical, ordinary, coordinate and t on the horizontal, logarithmic, coordinate.

(2) Fit a straight line through the points and calculate the slope, m, by selecting two points on the fitted line. Note: read the horizontal scale as the logarithm of time; if you use one cycle, it is 1.0; the slope must be positive.

(3) The transmissivity is estimated from equation (5.141) as

$$T=\frac{2.3Q_p}{4\pi m} \tag{5.142}$$

(4) Locate the time where the straight line intersects the time axis, $t=t_0$ and $s=0$. Substituting into equation (5.141) and solving, we obtain an expression to evaluate the storage coefficient:

$$S=\frac{2.25Tt_0}{r^2} \tag{5.143}$$

For a *drawdown-distance analysis*, drawdown measurements are made in various wells at a fixed time. Thus, time t is a constant. The procedure is as follows:

(1) Plot the drawdown versus distance on semilogarithmic paper, with s on the vertical, ordinary, coordinate, and r on the horizontal, logarithmic, coordinate.

(2) Fit a straight line through the points and calculate the slope, m. Again, t is read as a logarithm (interesting note: the slope m in a distance-drawdown analysis is exactly twice the slope of a time-drawdown analysis). The slope must be positive.

(3) The transmissivity is estimated from equation (5.142).

(4) Determine the intercept, r_0, on the radius axis ($r=r_0$, $s=0$). The storage coefficient is estimated from equation (5.143) as

$$S = \frac{2.25Tt}{r_0^2} \qquad (5.144)$$

Unsteady Flow to a Well in an Unconfined Aquifer

An analysis similar to that for confined aquifers may be done for axisymmetric flow in an unconfined homogeneous, isotropic, aquifer. Equation (5.22) may be written in polar coordinates and reduced to an equation mathematically identical to equation (5.132), except that the storage coefficient is substituted by the unconfined aquifer specific yield, S_y. Although the unconfined flow equation reduces to the same form as that for the confined flow, the Theis solution is not, in general, applicable to unconfined aquifers. The physical conditions of unconfined aquifers are behind this difficulty. Pumping an unconfined aquifer results in the dewatering of the aquifer. The saturated thickness of the unconfined aquifer is not constant, but rather a function of the hydraulic head. There is a vertical flow near the well, a condition that breaks the Dupuit assumptions. There is also a delayed yield due to gravitational drainage.

If the drawdown is small compared to the depth of the aquifer, the effect of dewatering and vertical flow may be neglected. In addition, if pumping is sustained for a prolonged period of time, the effect of delayed yield becomes negligible. In such situations, parameter estimation procedures for confined aquifers may be applicable to unconfined aquifers as well. According to Stallman (1971) and Hantush (1964), the pumping time restrictions are:

$$t > \frac{5bS_y}{K_z}, \quad t > \frac{10S_y s}{K_z} \qquad (5.145)$$

where
　　b=mean aquifer thickness (m)
　　K_z= vertical hydraulic conductivity (m^2/day)

and the rest of the terms as before. When the pumping time restrictions of inequalities (5.145) are satisfied, the parameter estimation procedures of confined aquifers may be applied to unconfined aquifers. In addition, the restriction $s<0.25H$, where H is the initial depth of saturation, must be satisfied. When these restrictions are satisfied, the observed values of the drawdown are corrected as follows:

$$s'=s-\frac{s^2}{2b}$$
(5.146)

where
　　s'=corrected drawdown (m)
　　s=measured drawdown (m)

The value of the storage coefficient obtained using a method for unconfined aquifers should be corrected as follows:

$$S_y=\frac{(b-\bar{s})S_y'}{b}$$
(5.147)

where
　　S_y= adjusted specific yield
　　S_y'= computed specific yield using a confined aquifer method
　　$\bar{s}$= drawdown at the geometric mean radius of all observation wells at the end of pumping (m)

Prior to using the Theis or Jacob method described in above, or any other method, the drawdown should be corrected according to equation (5.146). Once the calculations yield the transmissivity and the specific yield, the specific yield should be corrected according to equation (5.147). Finally, in order to check the validity of the calculations, the hydrologist should check the results with respect to restrictions (5.145).

For a more detailed description of the type-curve methods for confined and unconfined aquifers covering a variety of field conditions the hydrologist should consult Mariño and Luthin (1982), and Reed (1980). In addition to pumping tests, several laboratory and field procedures have been developed for the estimation of aquifer hydraulic properties. See Freeze and Cherry (1979) and Fetter (1994) for a more in depth description.

Modeling the Effect of Several Wells on Regional Groundwater Flow

Until now we considered a single well in an infinite aquifer, or that of a single well subject to special boundaries, and we took advantage of the resulting symmetry of flow with respect to the radius of the well. Let us study the general case of several pumping wells in an aquifer of finite dimensions with known boundary conditions (Patel and Serrano, 2011).

Example 5.24: Modeling the Effect of Wells

In Figure 5.14, $f_1(y)=100-0.2\times10^{-2}y$, $f_2(y)=103-0.1\times10^{-2}y$, $f_3(x)=100+0.8\times10^{-2}x-0.5\times10^{-5}x^2$, $f_4(x)=99+0.883\times10^{-2}x-0.5\times10^{-5}x^2$, $T=100m^2/month$, $R_g=10mm/month$, $l_x=600m$, $l_y=500m$, and $b=4m$. In addition, assume there are two wells pumping at a rate of $Q_1=Q_2=500\ m^3/month$, with a well-casing area $A_1=A_2=0.1\ m^2$, and located at the coordinates $x_1=400$, $y_1=200$, $x_2=100$, and $y_2=400\ m$. Develop a mathematical model to describe quantitatively the spatial distribution of the hydraulic head. Notice that Example 5.8 solved the same problem, but without pumping wells.

Solution

From equation (5.18), the governing differential equation is given by

$$L_xh+L_yh=-\frac{R_g}{T}+\sum_{i=1}^{N}\frac{Q_i}{A_iT}\delta(x-x_i)\delta(y-y_i)$$

(5.148)

$$h(0,\ y)=f_1(y),\ h(l_x,\ y)=f_2(y),\ h(x,\ 0)=f_3(x),\ h(x,\ l_y)=f_4(x)$$

where $N=2$, $L_x=\partial^2/\partial x^2$, and $L_y=\partial^2/\partial y^2$. Using the method of decomposition, the x-partial solution of equation (5.148) is given by

$$h_x=k_1(y)+k_2(y)x-L_x^{-1}\frac{R_g}{T}$$

(5.149)

$$+L_x^{-1}\sum_{i=1}^{N}\frac{Q_i}{A_iT}\delta(x-x_i)\delta(y-y_i)-L_x^{-1}L_y\big(h_0+h_1+h_2+...\big)$$

From the previous applications of decomposition, the pumping contribution from the i-th well, h_{ix}, to the first term, h_0, in equation (5.149) satisfies

$$L_xh_{ix}+L_yh_{ix}=\frac{Q_i\delta(x-x_i)\delta(y-y_i)}{A_iT},\quad h_{ix}(0,\ y)=h_{ix}(l_x,\ y)=0 \quad (5.150)$$

The solution of (21) may be written as (Myint-U and Debnath, 1987)

$$h_{ix} = F_i(x_i, y_i; x, y) + g_{ix}(x_i, y_i; x, y) \qquad (5.151)$$

where F_i is the free-space Green's function for Laplace's operator in equation (5.150),

$$F_i(x_i, y_i; x, y) = \frac{Q_i}{2\pi A_i T} \log\left[(x_i - x)^2 + (y_i - y)^2\right] \qquad (5.152)$$

and g_{ix} satisfies Laplace's equation subject to the homogeneous boundary conditions in equation (5.150).

$$g_{ix}(x_i, y_i; x, y) = \left(\frac{F_i(x_i, y_i; 0, y) - F_i(x_i, y_i; l_x, y)}{l_x} \right) x$$
$$\qquad (5.153)$$
$$- F_i(x_i, y_i; 0, y)$$

Analogous to equations (5.149)-(5.153), a y-partial expansion of equation (5.148) produces a pumping contribution from the i-th well, h_{iy}, given by

$$h_{iy} = F_i(x_i, y_i; x, y) + g_{iy}(x_i, y_i; x, y) \qquad (5.154)$$

with g_{iy} given by

$$g_{iy}(x_i, y_i; x, y) = \left(\frac{F_i(x_i, y_i; x, 0) - F_i(x_i, y_i; x, l_y)}{l_y} \right) y$$
$$\qquad (5.155)$$
$$- F_i(x_i, y_i; x, 0)$$

Thus, the first decomposition term in equation (5.148), and the first approximate solution, is given by

$$h_0(x, y) = \left(\frac{h_x(x, y) + h_y(x, y)}{2} \right) + \sum_{i=1}^{N} \left(\frac{h_{ix}(x, y) + h_{iy}(x, y)}{2} \right) \qquad (5.156)$$

where h_x is given by equation (5.59) in Example 5.8, h_y by equation (5.63), h_{ix} by equation (5.151), and h_{iy} by equation (5.154). If additional accuracy is desired, more decomposition terms may be easily generated from equations (5.57) and (5.61), Example 5.8, for the case without wells.

Example 5.25: Visualizing the Effect of Wells
   Write a Maple program that utilizes the solution derived in Example 5.23 to describe the effect of wells on the spatial distribution of regional hydraulic head.

Solution

The following Maple worksheet illustrates the program. Figure 5.32 shows the hydraulic head produced by the combined effect of recharge and the wells field.

```
> restart:
  #Boundary conditions
  f1:=y->100-0.002*y:
  f2:=y->103-0.001*y:
  f3:=x->100+0.008*x-0.000005*x^2:
  f4:=x->99+0.00883*x-0.000005*x^2:
  #Derivation of hx, equation (5.59)
  k1(y)+k2(y)*x-int( int(Rg/T,x), x):
  hx:=unapply(%,x,y):
  hx(0,y)=f1(y):
  solve(%,k1(y)):
  k1:=unapply(%,y):
  hx(lx,y)=f2(y):
  solve(%,k2(y)):
  k2:=unapply(%,y):
  #Derivation of hy, equation (5.63)
  k3(x)+k4(x)*y-int( int(Rg/T,y), y):
  hy:=unapply(%,x,y):
  hy(x,0)=f3(x):
  solve(%,k3(x)):
  k3:=unapply(%,x):
  hy(x,ly)=f4(x):
  solve(%,k4(x)):
  k4:=unapply(%,x):
  #Effect of recharge, equation (5.64)
  hxy:=(x,y)->(hx(x,y)+hy(x,y))/2:
  #
  #hx for well 1, equation (5.151)
  F1:=(x,y)->Q1/(2*Pi*A1*T)*log10(sqrt((x1-x)^2+(y1-y)^2)):
  gx1:=(x,y)->a1(y)*x+b1(y):
  gx1(0,y)=-F1(0,y):
  solve(%,b1(y)):
  b1:=unapply(%,y):
  gx1(lx,y)=-F1(lx,y):
  solve(%,a1(y)):
  a1:=unapply(%,y):
  hpx1:=(x,y)->F1(x,y)+gx1(x,y):

> #hy for well 1, equation (5.154)
  gy1:=(x,y)->c1(x)*y+d1(x):
  gy1(x,0)=-F1(x,0):
  solve(%,d1(x)):
  d1:=unapply(%,x):
  gy1(x,ly)=-F1(x,ly):
  solve(%,c1(x)):
  c1:=unapply(%,x):
  hpy1:=(x,y)->F1(x,y)+gy1(x,y):
  hp1:=(x,y)->(hpx1(x,y)+hpy1(x,y))/2:
  #
  #hx for well 2, equation (5.151)
  F2:=(x,y)->Q2/(2*Pi*A2*T)*log10(sqrt((x2-x)^2+(y2-y)^2)):
  gx2:=(x,y)->a2(y)*x+b2(y):
  gx2(0,y)=-F2(0,y):
  solve(%,b2(y)):
  b2:=unapply(%,y):
  gx2(lx,y)=-F2(lx,y):
  solve(%,a2(y)):
  a2:=unapply(%,y):
  hpx2:=(x,y)->F2(x,y)+gx2(x,y):
```

```
#hy for well 2, equation (1.54)
gy2:=(x,y)->c2(x)*y+d2(x):
gy2(x,0)=-F2(x,0):
solve(%,d2(x)):
d2:=unapply(%,x):
gy2(x,1y)=-F2(x,1y):
solve(%,c2(x)):
c2:=unapply(%,x):
hpy2:=(x,y)->F2(x,y)+gy2(x,y):
#Equation (1.156)
hp2:=(x,y)->(hpx2(x,y)+hpy2(x,y))/2:
h:=(x,y)->hxy(x,y)+hp1(x,y)+hp2(x,y):
> Rg:=0.01: T:=100: lx:=600:
Q1:=500.: A1:=0.1: 1y:=500: x1:=400: y1:=200:
Q2:=500.: A2:=0.1: x2:=100: y2:=400:
plot3d(h(x,y),x=0..1x,y=0..1y,numpoints=2500,
   shading=ZGRAYSCALE):
plots[display](%,axes=BOXED,
   labels=[`x (m)`,`y (m)`,`h(m)`],
   labeldirections=[HORIZONTAL,HORIZONTAL,VERTICAL],
   labelfont=[TIMES,ROMAN,16],orientation=[-135,60]);
```

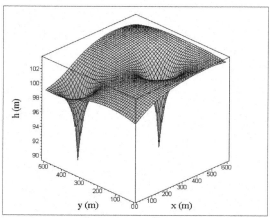

Figure 5.32: Output of Example 5.24

PROBLEMS

5.1 From top to bottom, an aquifer is composed of four layers with hydraulic conductivities of 25, 180, 48, and 110$m/month$. The soil-layer depths are 0.45, 2.2, 1.3, and 0.95m, respectively. Estimate the equivalent bulk horizontal and vertical hydraulic conductivities for the system.

5.2 An unconfined aquifer is bounded by two rivers running parallel to each other (see Figure 5.8). The average stage on the left river is $H_1 = 15m$ with respect to the bottom of the aquifer. The average stage on the right river is $H_2 = 13m$. The length of the aquifer is $l_x = 1000m$. The mean aquifer hydraulic conductivity is $\bar{K}=80m/month$. The aquifer receives a mean recharge from rainfall of $R_g=15mm/month$. (1) Calculate and plot the hydraulic heads across the aquifer. (2) Calculate the groundwater discharge rate at the left and right river boundaries. (3) Locate the position of the groundwater divide (i.e., distance, x, where the flow rate and hydraulic gradient is zero).

5.3 In Problem 5.2, (1) calculate the pore velocity of the aquifer assuming a porosity of 0.3. Plot the pore velocity with respect to distance. (2) How long is the mean travel time between the groundwater divide and the left river?

5.4 Assume that in the aquifer of Problem 5.2 a long mining excavation between the distances $x_1=400m$ and $x_2=500m$, respectively from the left river, is being planned. The excavation will eventually reach a level $H_0=3m$ with respect to the bottom of the aquifer. (1) Estimate the steady hydraulic heads across the aquifer after the excavation is completed, plot the head distribution before and after construction, and evaluate the impact of the construction on the groundwater levels. (2) Calculate the volume of groundwater to be removed to maintain a dry construction site. Assume a specific yield of 0.3.

5.5 In Example 5.4, (1) plot the head versus distance, and (2) plot the specific discharge versus distance.

5.6 Assume that in Example 5.4, Figure 5.12, the hydraulic conductivity is $55m/month$; the mean recharge is $2mm/month$; the mean saturated thickness is $20m$; the mean horizontal distance between the river and the tertiary formation is $600m$; and the head at the river with respect to the mean sea level is $110m$. (1) Calculate the hydraulic heads along x'. (2) Estimate the aquifer discharge rate at the river.

5.7 Example 5.6 uses the solution derived in Example 5.5 to plot a three-dimensional view of the hydraulic head. Modify the Maple program to produce (1) a single graph of h versus x at $y=0$, $y=1000$, and $y=2000m$, respectively; and (2) a two-dimensional, planar, view of the hydraulic head contours.

5.8 Example 5.7 uses the solution derived in Example 5.5 to calculate the components of the specific discharge q_x, and q_y; the resultant q, an its angle with respect to x, θ; and the seepage velocity u. Modify the Maple program in Example 5.7 to calculate these variables at a point with coordinates $x=100$ and $y=100m$. Assume an average saturated thickness of $b=243m$ and a porosity $n=0.2$.

5.9 Consider a again the aquifer bounded on all sides by streams, as depicted in Figure 5.14 and Example 5.8. The mean water elevation with respect to the sea level at the boundaries is $f_1(y)=100-0.2\times10^{-2}y$, $f_2(y)=103-0.1\times10^{-2}y$, $f_3(x)=100+0.8\times10^{-2}x-0.5\times10^{-5}x^2$, and $f_4(x)=99+0.883\times10^{-2}x-0.5\times10^{-5}x^2$. Assume $T=10m^2/month$, $R_g=15mm/month$, $l_x=600m$, $l_y=500m$, and $b=10m$. Re-derive, step by step, the mathematical model to describe quantitatively the spatial distribution of the hydraulic head.

5.10 Write a Maple program that uses the solution derived in Problem 5.9 to plot a map of hydraulic head contours, and the magnitude and direction of the flow velocity field. Plot contour with values reflecting the range of elevation in h. Plot q vectors every $\Delta x=\Delta y=25m$ with their length proportional to their magnitude. Hint: use the program in Example 5.9 as a model.

5.11 Problem 5.10 uses the solution derived in Problem 5.9 to plot hydraulic head contours. Modify the Maple program to produce (1) a single graph of h versus x at $y=0$, $y=100$, and $y=250m$, respectively.

5.12 The mean annual groundwater recharge of an aquifer in a watershed is $180mm/year$. The mean groundwater flow is $105mm/year$. If the watershed has an area of $110km^2$, calculate the aquifer safe yield in $m^3/year$.

5.13 In Example 5.20, what would be the pumping rate that would reduce the radius of influence to $200m$ with a maximum drawdown at the well of $2m$. Assume a well radius of $0.6m$.

5.14 A fully-penetrating well in a confined aquifer pumps at a constant rate of $1000m^3/day$ for a long time. In two observation wells located $10m$ and $40m$ from the well the difference in hydraulic head is $0.5m$. If the undisturbed head is $200m$ above the sea level, and the head in the farthest well is $198m$, (1) estimate the aquifer transmissivity, and (2) calculate the radius of influence of the well.

5.15 A fully penetrating well in an unconfined aquifer pumps at a constant rate of $2000m^3/day$ for a long time. Two observation wells located $20m$ and $160m$ from the well, show a difference in hydraulic head of $2.0m$. If the undisturbed head is $250m$ above the sea level, and the head in the farthest well is $249m$, (1) estimate the aquifer hydraulic conductivity, and (2) calculate the radius of influence of the well.

5.16 If in Problem 5.15 the bottom of the aquifer is at the sea level, (1) develop an expression to evaluate the aquifer transmissivity as a function of radius, r; and (2) plot T versus r.

5.17 A well is pumping at a constant rate in an unconfined aquifer for a long period of time. The well is located at a distance of 150m from a river. The transmissivity of the aquifer is $60\,m^2/day$. An observation well located 70m from the well, in the line that marks the shortest distance between the well and the river, registers 1.0m of drawdown. Calculate the pumping rate.

5.18 Repeat Problem 5.17 if instead of a river there is an impervious barrier, and the infinite-aquifer well radius of influence is 200m.

Table 5.3: Drawdown Data for Problem 5.19

$t(min)$	$s(m)$	$t(min)$	$s(m)$	$t(min)$	$s(m)$
1.0	0.101	10.0	0.467	80.0	0.827
1.5	0.165	14.0	0.534	100.0	0.863
2.0	0.202	18.0	0.571	120.0	0.900
2.5	0.238	24.0	0.619	150.0	0.942
3.0	0.269	30.0	0.659	180.0	0.970
4.0	0.315	40.0	0.708	210.0	1.000
5.0	0.354	50.0	0.747	240.0	1.019
8.0	0.433	60.0	0.778		

5.19 A pumping test was performed in a confined aquifer. The aquifer was pumped at a constant rate of $2.5\,m^3/min$. An observation well located 120m from the pumping well recorded the drawdown data in Table 5.3. Estimate the aquifer transmissivity and storage coefficient by Theis' method.

5.20 In a confined aquifer test, a drawdown of 1.45, 1.18. and 0.91m were measured at three observation wells located 140, 290 and 590m, respectively from the pumping well. If the drawdown data were simultaneously taken 24 hours after pumping began, and the pumping rate was $3100\,m^3/day$, estimate the transmissivity and storage coefficient of the aquifer using Jacob's method and a spreadsheet program.

5.21 Solve Example 5.22 by Jacob's method.

5.22 If in Example 5.24 there is a third well of area $A_3=0.1m^2$, located at $x_3=y_3=500m$, pumping at a rate of $Q_3=100m^3/month$, modify the program in Example 5.25 to produce a graph of the hydraulic head subject to the well field.

6 SURFACE RUNOFF AND STREAMFLOW

6.1 THE GENERATION OF STREAMFLOW

Surface runoff and *streamflow* in a watershed are generated after a complex interaction of several hydrologic processes. In previous chapters we discussed some of the functions that affect the eventual generation of overland flow, subsurface flow, and groundwater flow. In this chapter we introduce the basic concepts involved in streamflow generation and the quantitative methods for separation of the different components of streamflow of interest in applications.

As explained in Chapter 1, precipitation, P, that overcomes interception losses from the vegetation, I_n, reaches the ground surface, where it can follow a multitude of pathways (see Figures 1.1 and 6.1). If the soil moisture conditions are favorable (i.e., soil-water storage available, S_a, is greater than zero), water penetrates the unsaturated zone via infiltration, I, where it is subject to soil evaporation, E, and plant transpiration, T. Infiltration increases the value of the soil-water content, S_w. A portion of the soil water moves laterally in the unsaturated zone as subsurface flow, Q_s, where it discharges into springs and streams. Another portion of the soil water deep percolates due to gravitational forces and eventually produces recharge, R_g, to the regional aquifer. Recharge water increases the groundwater storage, S_g. Groundwater moves slowly until it discharges into streams, lakes, and eventually the ocean.

The increase in the soil moisture causes a decrease in the soil-water storage available and a consequent decrease in the infiltration rate. If rain continues, the decrease in the infiltration rate causes the excess of water to pond over natural depressions. The volume of this water, called depression storage, I_d, depends on the topographic characteristics of the watershed. With continued of rainfall, the excess of water over depression storage begins to move as *sheet flow* or *overland flow*, R_o. Overland flow discharges into small streams, where it moves as *channel flow* or streamflow. Small streams combine to form larger streams, which eventually grow into rivers. In time, rivers discharge into lakes and eventually into the ocean, thus completing the hydrologic cycle.

Figure 6.1 illustrates the three main components of streamflow: *overland flow*, *subsurface flow*, and *groundwater flow*. While the total flow rate in a stream may be expressed as the summation of these three components (see equation (1.3)), each one has a distinct hydrologic significance.

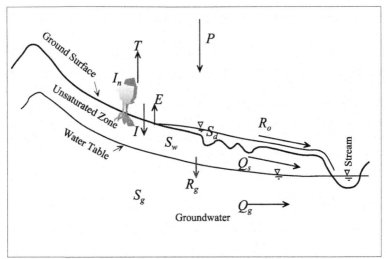

Figure 6.1: Main Components of Streamflow

Overland flow, R_o, refers to all the waters flowing on the surface of the earth as sheet flow. It results from the generation of effective precipitation throughout the watershed. The effective precipitation units (see chapter 4) are dynamically combined and routed over the ground surface. Among the streamflow components, overland flow is the one with the least hydraulic resistance, since it is governed by the laws of free-surface hydraulics. For this reason, overland flow is the fastest streamflow component: it appears earlier as streamflow in rivers and it recedes faster than other components.

Subsurface flow, Q_s, is the portion of infiltrated water that travels through the unsaturated zone. Due to the presence of the porous media, it faces considerable more hydraulic resistance than overland flow. For this reason, subsurface flow exhibits somewhat lower velocities than those of overland flow. In steeply sloping watersheds and in naturally vegetated areas, the presence of deep roots and natural macro-pores may substantially increase the subsurface flow velocities.

Groundwater flow, Q_g, is the portion of recharged water that becomes groundwater storage and flows through the saturated zone. Except in the presence of anomalous conditions, such as karst or large rock fractures, groundwater flow constitutes the slowest streamflow component. Flow through aquifer porous media is laminar with very low velocities. For this reason, groundwater continues to discharge into rivers and lakes for weeks and even months after the recharge-producing storm occurred.

The partition between overland flow and subsurface flow is determined by the infiltration rates. Therefore, many climatological, geological, and hydrologic factors intervene. The first one is precipitation intensity and its duration. High-intensity storms tend to generate relatively more overland flow, and less subsurface flow, than low-intensity storms. During high-intensity storms, infiltration rates are low and effective precipitation amounts are high. Conversely, low-intensity storms exhibit high infiltration rates, high subsurface flow, and low effective precipitation amounts.

Watershed soil characteristics, such as hydraulic conductivity, soil texture, and soil condition affect the overland flow versus subsurface flow proportion. The higher the value of the soil hydraulic conductivity, the higher the infiltration rates and the higher the subsurface flow volumes. Land use activities are equally important. Deforestation, agricultural development, and specially urbanization are known to substantially reduce infiltration rates and, correspondingly, increase the volumes of overland flow.

Watershed geology, geomorphology (i.e., watershed shape, drainage network pattern and drainage intensity), and topography (i.e., land slope) determine not only the partition between overland flow and subsurface flow, but also the occurrence and distribution of groundwater. Vegetation type and density control to a large extent the infiltration rates in a watershed. Plant roots accompanied by an increase in biological activity and organic matter in the root zone produce macro-pores and an increase in soil air content. This generates a substantial increase in infiltration rates and a corresponding increase in subsurface flow. It is known that naturally forested watersheds seldom produce appreciable quantities of overland flow. Subsurface flow appears to be the dominant component in all but the extreme rainfall events. Watersheds with high infiltration amounts, and correspondingly high subsurface flow amounts, tend to produce high recharge rates and high groundwater flow rates.

In summary, the magnitude of each of the three main components of streamflow is specially important in the following circumstances:

(1) Overland flow: in deforested and urbanized areas.
(2) Subsurface flow: in naturally-forested areas and steep watersheds.

(3) Groundwater flow: in karst areas and naturally-forested watersheds.

The primary input to overland flow is composed of the effective precipitation amounts generated across the land. In chapter 1 we introduced water balance models as fundamental tools to estimate effective precipitation as well as other components of the hydrologic cycle in a watershed. In chapter 4 we used infiltration models to estimate effective precipitation amounts generated during a storm. However, the analysis of the spatial distribution of overland flow is a difficult task, since it relates to the application of free-surface hydraulics laws to a complex pattern of three-dimensional topography affected by watershed soils and vegetation. Under special circumstances, such as flat urban areas, a watershed ground surface may be idealized as a combination of planes. This simplifies the overland flow regime to one-dimensional domains where the mass conservation and momentum equations may be solved analytically or numerically (see Ponce, 1989; Overton and Meadows, 1976).

The primary input to subsurface flow is infiltration. Redistribution of water in the unsaturated zone is governed by the laws of flow of water through unsaturated porous media (see chapter 4). The primary input to groundwater flow is recharge. Following the laws of flow of water through saturated porous media (see chapter 5), recharge eventually translates into groundwater flow discharge. For more detailed accounts on the generation of streamflow see Freeze and Cherry (1979).

Overland, subsurface, and groundwater flow, each with its typical volume and timing, move into discharge zones and eventually reach the main watershed stream. Thus, rivers are fed by a distributed source of water coming from different pathways along the stream length. The total flow rate, Q, passing through a fixed cross section of a river is composed of all the waters traveling via the surface and the subsurface environments of the watershed delineated by the particular streamflow station. In other words, the streamflow at a fixed river section is theoretically draining all the water that precipitates in the watershed marked by the stream location. For instance, the flow rate at the gage in Figure 1.4 is composed of waters initially precipitated everywhere on the watershed. This principle implies an ideal situation of homogeneous soils where the surface boundary of the watershed coincides with the groundwater divide. However, this statement is not accurate in cases of watersheds whose particular geology is such that a portion of its stream waters come from subsurface or groundwater flow infiltrated at an adjacent watershed. Similarly, part of infiltrated waters in a watershed may deep percolate to regional geological units that eventually discharge in other watersheds. This phenomenon is particularly important in small watersheds (i.e., less than $300\,km^2$ in surface area) with complex geological structures. In large watersheds, the amount of water coming from adjacent watersheds tends to balance that leaving it.

With the above provisions, the flow rate at a given cross section in a stream represents the hydrologic response of the watershed. Given the many measurement uncertainties pertaining the different hydrologic variables affecting streamflow, it is of utmost importance to study the resulting flow rate characteristics.

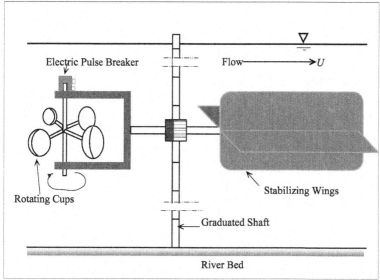

Figure 6.2: Illustration of a Current Meter

6.2 MEASUREMENT OF STREAMFLOW

Measurement Techniques

Discharge measurement through a river section, at a given time, has been approached by a multitude of techniques, each appropriate to particular river conditions (see Gupta, 1989 for a description of the various methods). For small mountain streams, the construction of hydraulic structures such as calibrated flumes equipped with stage meters and weirs is a viable solution to the problem of continuous streamflow monitoring. For short-term site investigations in small streams associated with highly turbulent flow, the injection of a known quantity of a tracer of given concentration at a given section, and the corresponding concentration monitoring at a downstream section offers accurate results. Other modern techniques such as ultrasonic electromagnetic measurements of velocity have been added to the available alternatives.

Figure 6.3: A USGS Type AA Current Meter (*Courtesy of Rickly Hydrological Company*)

Discharge Measurement with Current Meters

One of the most widely used techniques of streamflow measurement is based on the determination of the river cross-sectional area, and the average flow velocity. Flow velocities are measured with a *current meter*. A current meter is an instrument that transforms the fluid velocity at a point in a river into rotational velocity of a propeller placed against the water flow. There are many kinds of current meters available, each with features appropriate to the field conditions in question. A commonly used type for medium size rivers is the cup meter (see Figures 6.2 and 6.3). The propeller of this current meter is composed of a set of metal cups that rotate with an angular velocity, ω, proportional to the fluid velocity, U. The angular velocity is determined as the number of revolutions per minute. Each revolution closes an electrical circuit that is transmitted to a count meter. The current meter itself is supported by a graduated metal shaft that permits the measurement of the level of the water, b, with respect to the river bed, and the depth at which the velocity measure is desired.

In practice the observer locates the current meter at a particular depth and counts the number of revolutions in a one-minute interval. The angular velocity is transformed into the fluid velocity via the current meter calibration equation:

$$U=c_1\omega+c_2 \qquad\qquad (6.1)$$

where
U=flow velocity (*m/s*)

ω = angular velocity (*rev/min*)
c_1 = calibration constant (*m.min/(s.rev)*)
c_2 = calibration constant

The calibration constants are determined in a hydraulics laboratory, where the current meter is submerged into a rectangular canal filled with still water. The shaft of the current meter is attached to an electrically driven rating car mounted on rails extending through the entire length of the vertical walls of the canal. The rating car is operated at fixed velocities and the angular velocity is determined for each run. The calibration constants should be determined periodically (e.g., at least once a month), since they change due to mechanical wear and corrosion of the rotor assembly. Cleaning, lubrication, and regular maintenance of the current meter changes the magnitude of the calibration constants.

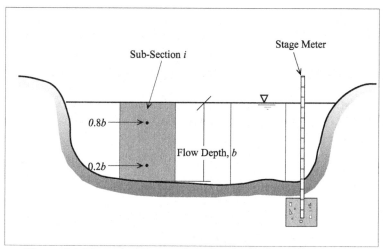

Figure 6.4: Numerical Integration of Velocity in a River Section

When the level of the water in the river exceeds one meter, an observer may not be able to stand on the river bed. The current meter is then suspended from a cable. A heavy weight is added to drive the current meter into the water. In this situation the observer stands on a bridge or a structure specifically built for discharge measurements. On the other hand, when the level of the water is less than 40 or 50*cm*, the size of the normal current meter generates extra turbulence and distorts the velocity measurement. In this situation a micro-current meter is necessary. This is a small current meter provided with a variety of replaceable propellers, each sensitive to a particular range of velocities.

The foregoing procedure yields the flow velocity at a particular point in a river (i.e., a fixed depth and location in the section). Since flow velocity changes with the depth of flow and with the location in the river cross section, an average value of the flow velocity must be determined and multiplied by the total cross-sectional area. To accomplish this, the river cross section is subdivided into several sub-sections (see Figure 6.4), where the velocity is measured using a current meter. The total flow rate is then obtained after a numerical integration of the various sub-section velocities times the corresponding sub-areas. Each sub-section velocity is obtained as an average between the velocity at 0.2 and at 0.8 of the depth of flow, b. In other words, the average velocity, $\bar{U}_i$, along the vertical at a particular subsection, i, is calculated as

$$\bar{U}_i = \frac{U_{0.2} + U_{0.8}}{2} \tag{6.2}$$

where
$\bar{U}_i$ = average velocity along vertical at a fixed sub-section i (m/s)
$U_{0.2}$ = velocity at 0.2 of the flow depth b (m/s)
$U_{0.8}$ = velocity at 0.8 of the flow depth b (m/s)

Equation (6.2) is an approximation of the actual average velocity over the depth. This process is repeated until all sub-sections have been measured. The flow rate is determined as

$$Q = \sum_{i=1}^{N} \bar{U}_i\, A_i \tag{6.3}$$

where
Q=total streamflow rate (m^3/s)
A_i= area of sub-section i (m^2)
N=number of sub-sections

In practice, the river width is subdivided into N sub-sections. The greater the number of sub-sections, the more accurate the flow rate measurement. One observer stands on one bank of the river. This person records the information obtained by a second observer and holds the end of a metallic tape meter. The second observer holds the other end of the tape meter and the current meter. At a fixed distance from the river edge, the latter introduces the shaft of the current meter and measures the depth of flow, b. He then places the current meter at a depth equal to $0.2b$ and takes the number of rotor revolutions over a one-minute interval. He then places the current meter at a depth equal to $0.8b$ and takes the number of revolutions in one minute. Next, the second observer moves into another sub-section (i.e., a greater distance from the edge) and repeats the measurement of the depth, then the velocity at 0.2 and at 0.8 of the depth. The area of the subsection, A_i, is calculated as the distance difference between two subsequent locations of the current meter with respect to the river edge. At each measurement point, the application of equation (6.1) yields the flow velocity. At each sub-section, the application of equation (6.2) yields the subsection velocity, U_i. Finally, the application of equation (6.3) yields the total flow rate Q.

Certain rules should be followed when selecting a section of the river as suitable for streamflow measurements. The streamflow station should be within a straight reach of the river for at least one kilometer. In a straight river reach the flow lines are approximately parallel, thus offering an accurate determination of velocity in a cross section. Meanders or curved portions of a river must be avoided. In a river meander the flow exhibits a complex three-dimensional pattern. Another important rule is to select a river section that is stable in shape and geographical location. In a straight river reach the possibilities for a stable section are higher than in a curved section. A river meander is dynamically active, moving over the years in a radial (outward) and downstream direction. A streamflow station with all its structures located in a river meander will be left dry when the meanders evolves. A comparison of aerial photographs of a prospect site taken at different times throughout several decades may help assess the potential instability of a river reach.

Continuous Monitoring of Streamflow Rate

The procedure described in the previous section may take between 30 minutes to two hours, depending on the size and characteristics of the river. In the end, a flow rate value representative of the day and time of observation is obtained. However, hydrologic analysis usually requires a long-term, continuous estimation of the flow rate in a river. To achieve this, a relationship between the surface water level, or river stage, h, and discharge flow rate, Q, is built.

The river stage is measured with a stage meter. The stage meter is a graduated metal bar anchored to the river bed (see Figure 6.4). The divisions in the stage meter are often given in meters with respect to the mean sea level. Normally, an observer visits the streamflow station twice or three times per day and records the stage in a record sheet. In more important regional streamflow stations in large watersheds a stilling well is built on the edge of the river (see Figure 6.5). The stilling well is hydraulically connected to the river with pipes. The water level in the stilling well is measured with a floater attached to a pen. The pen records the water level on a strip chart calibrated in meters above the mean sea level. A clockwork mechanism moves the chart longitudinally and permits the plotting of the stage with respect to the time of the day. See Figure 6.6 for an example of a stage versus time chart. An additional sophistication of these stage meters includes the telemetric transmission of stage versus time information to remote data bank sites.

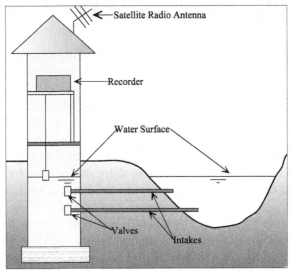

Figure 6.5: A Stilling Well at a Streamflow Station

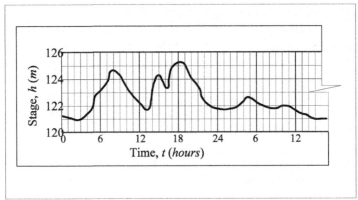

Figure 6.6: Example of a Stage versus Time Chart

To build a *h* versus *Q* relationship, a program of frequent discharge measurements must be conducted on at the streamflow station. This program should include several measurements during low-flow waters, medium waters, and high waters. Typically these include several visits to the station per year throughout at least five years. Each discharge measurement is conducted in a manner described in the previous section and includes the observation of the river stage at the time of measurement. After this program has been completed, several points with coordinates (Q, h) are obtained as a basis of the *stage-discharge relationship*. Fitting a smooth curve through the points will produce the required relationship. Figure 6.6 shows an example of a stage-discharge relationship for a streamflow station.

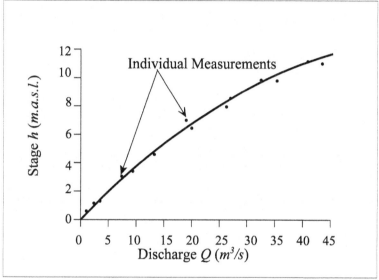

Figure 6.7: Stage versus Discharge Relationship in a River Section

Often a single relationship is not obtained for a streamflow station. In other words, different relationships are obtained for low waters (drought conditions), middle waters, and high waters (flooding conditions). This occurs because the shape of cross-sectional areas may be different during different flow regimes. For instance, during low waters sedimentation increases the level of the bottom of the river. On the other hand, during high waters the increased velocity causes erosion, and the consequent change in section shape, to the river bed. In addition to that, during extreme floods the water may overflow the river banks causing a collapse of the stage-discharge relationship. For these reasons, measurement of extreme flood conditions is difficult, since maximum levels in the stage meter may be surpassed and access to the site may be impossible or dangerous for discharge measurements. Clearly, the development of a reliable stage-discharge relationship may take several years of consistent work. After the relationship has been calibrated, periodic discharge monitoring should be done to verify its validity.

By combining a continuously-recorded stage versus time relationship with a well-calibrated stage versus discharge relationship (i.e., continuous digital recording of h versus t, Figure 6.6, and its transformation into values of Q via Figure 6.7 for fixed values of h), a relationship between flow rate versus time, Q versus t, is obtained. A plot of this relationship is called a *hydrograph*. The study of the hydrograph constitutes an important aspect of hydrologic analysis, since it represents the response of a watershed over time.

6.3 THE STREAMFLOW HYDROGRAPH AND ITS ANALYSIS

The Annual Hydrograph

As stated before, the study of the streamflow rate versus time at a particular river section is an important area of hydrologic analysis. The hydrograph is a vivid illustration of the hydrologic response of a watershed encompassed by the streamflow station. In previous chapters we discussed the hydrologic variables affecting the generation of streamflow in a watershed. Many of these variables depend on complex environmental quantities subject to spatial and temporal uncertainties. Yet, the combined effect of all intervening hydrologic processes is characterized by the resulting streamflow hydrograph.

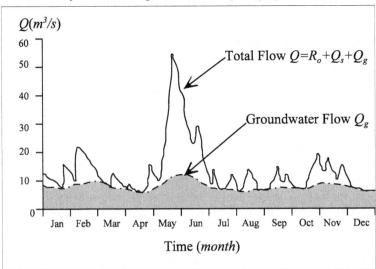

Figure 6.8: Streamflow Hydrograph with Sustained Groundwater

The annual hydrograph of a watershed is a graph of the total streamflow rate at the outlet of a watershed with respect to time. The time ranges from the beginning of the year to the end. Figure 6.8 shows a typical annual hydrograph of a watershed. As stated before, the total flow rate, Q is the summation of overland flow, R_o, subsurface flow, Q_s and groundwater flow, Q_g.

Several features may be noted by simply observing the hydrograph. For instance, the minimum flow rate throughout the year is represented by groundwater flow. In Figure 6.8 the groundwater flow rate is represented by a dashed line. This line is approximately drawn so as to coincide with the lowest magnitude in the flow rate. During periods of rainfall, the groundwater flow rate increases somewhat as a result of recharge. However, the exact amount of the increase is difficult to ascertain, unless field experiments are performed. Ordinarily the hydrologist assumes a nominal increase as shown in the graph. The difference between the total flow rate and the groundwater flow rate at a given time is composed of overland flow plus subsurface flow. In Figure 6.8, the groundwater flow rate is sustained throughout the year, indicating a watershed where groundwater flow is an important component in its hydrologic cycle. This characteristic may be associated with certain physical conditions in the catchment area. For example, the soils may be covered by a healthy variety of natural vegetation, which encourages infiltration and eventually groundwater recharge.

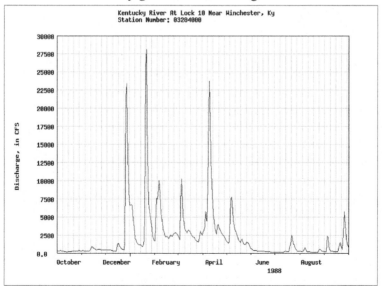

Figure 6.9: A Hydrograph where Groundwater Flow is Relatively less Important than Surface and Subsurface Flow

It is important to note that these features are relative. In other words, the observation of a sustained amount of groundwater flow rate is formulated in comparison to that of the total flow rate. For instance, Figure 6.9 shows a streamflow hydrograph of the Kentucky River at Lock 10 near Winchester. Notice the relatively low values of groundwater flow in comparison with those of surface runoff. In this watershed, surface and subsurface flow dominate the hydrologic response. This fact may be connected with physical watershed features, such as clay soils, extensive deforestation, or heavily urbanized areas within the watershed. These conditions limit the amount of infiltration and recharge, and encourage the production of overland flow.

Another important point to remember is that watersheds are dynamic entities. Physical watershed conditions change with time producing different hydrograph shapes for different years. The hydrologist should study annual hydrographs for typically wet, medium, and dry years. This gives an idea of the effect of climatic changes on the hydrologic response of the watershed. Besides natural climatological conditions, land use changes effected over long periods of time are usually reflected in gradual changes in the hydrograph. Massive deforestation, agricultural development, and urbanization have a significant impact on the hydrologic response and thus the streamflow hydrograph. Long term observation of the streamflow hydrograph provides important clues on the environmental impact of development projects.

The area under the total hydrograph for a given year represents the total streamflow volume over the year in question. The area under the groundwater hydrograph is the total groundwater flow volume for the year. These areas are calculated via numerical integration of the mean daily flow rates reported for the streamflow station, or by the use of a computer digitizer tracing the line of the hydrograph. Remember that the number obtained has the units of $(m^3/s) \times day$, which should be transformed into m^3 by multiplying by $86,400 s/day$. The resulting volume may be expressed as an equivalent depth of liquid water uniformly spread over the whole watershed by dividing by the watershed area (see Example 1.1, Chapter 1).

The total streamflow volume minus the total groundwater volume is equal to the volume of overland flow plus subsurface flow. Again, observing the magnitude of these quantities for typical wet, medium, and dry years gives an indication of the hydrologic regime of the watershed. Finally, observing these quantities over long periods of time (e.g., several decades) gives valuable information on environmental changes in the hydrologic response of the watershed.

Example 6.1: Calculating Water Yield from a Hydrograph

From the U.S. Geological Survey site you downloaded a text file containing two columns, discharge (m^3/s) and date (*days*), and 42 rows, each with data for each day. You named it Flow.txt and saved it in C:/Sergio/Hydrology_Second_Book/Chapter6/Q.txt. Fit the hydrograph data to a smooth analytical curve, integrate it, and express the flow volume in m^3.

Solution

The following worksheet uses the linear algebra commands in Maple. The data file is first read into the program and given an array named flowdata. Next the data is converted into a matrix and transposed twice to place the first column as time and the second as flow rate. Next, cubic splines are used to fit a nice curve, $Q(t)$, to the data and integrated to obtain volume in m^3. Finally the $Q(t)$ is plotted.

Read a list of flow versus time data from a text file called Flow.txt, which has 2 columns and 42 rows; column 1 is flow, column 2 is time: [[Q1, t=1], [Q2, t=2], . . . [QN,t=N]]

```
> Restart: readlib(readdata):
    flowdata:=readdata("C:/Sergio/Hydrology_Second_Book
    /Chapter6/Flow.txt",float,2):
```

To swap columns, so that time is in the first column, convert this list into a matrix.

```
> flowdata:=convert(flowdata,matrix):
```

Now, manipulate matrix so that time is the first column. First, transpose matrix.

```
> t1:=linalg[transpose](flowdata):
```

Next exchange the flow and time (1 and 2) rows.

```
> t2:=linalg[swaprow](t1,1,2):
```

Finally, transpose again to original form.

```
> t3:=linalg[transpose](t2):
```

Interpolate data with a cubic spline.

```
> readlib(spline):
    s:=spline(linalg[col](flowdata,2),
        linalg[col](flowdata,1),t,cubic):
```

Convert to a piecewise function for future use and calculations.

```
> Q:=unapply(s,t):
```

Intyerpolate to estimate flow rate at t=23.5 days

```
> Q(23.5);
```

$$709.9900496$$

Calculate water yield in m^3 by integrating the entire hydrograph

```
> S:=int(Q(t),t=1..42)*86400;
```

$$S := 0.2587170274\ 10^{10}$$

```
> plot(Q(t),t=0..42,labels=["Time(days)","Q(m^3/s)"],
    color=black,labeldirections=[HORIZONTAL,VERTICAL],
    labelfont=[TIMES,ROMAN,16]);
```

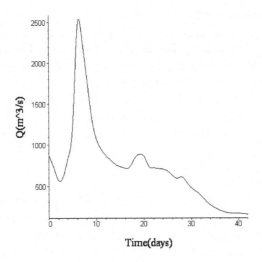

The Event Hydrograph

The annual, or multi-annual, streamflow hydrograph is useful in long term studies requiring an understanding of the hydrologic regime of a watershed. These studies include long term water resources evaluation, planning, and management. Many studies focus on short term analyses of the hydrologic response of a watershed. This is the case of projects requiring an evaluation of hydrologic quantities resulting from extreme events occurring during the lapse of a few hours to a few days, for example, analysis of high intensity rainfall events capable of generating flooding conditions in a watershed. These studies are needed in order to map *flood plain areas*, determine evacuation areas, plan and restrict urban development, and design hydraulic structures capable of controlling flooding waters. The basis of these studies is the streamflow hydrograph during a particular rainfall event (i.e., a storm). This is called the *storm hydrograph* (or *the event*, or the runoff hydrograph). Figure 6.10 shows an example of the rainfall hyetograph (i.e., rainfall intensity versus time) and the corresponding *event hydrograph* of a single storm, when plotted under the same time scale.

Let us study the details of Figure 6.10. First, the rainfall hyetograph. The total rainfall intensity, p, represents the time distribution of precipitation (see Chapter 2). An infiltration rate, f, separates the effective precipitation depth, R_o, from the cumulative (or total) infiltration depth, I (see Chapter 4).

Now the streamflow hydrograph is a plot of the total flow rate, Q, with respect to time, t, at the gaging station. In figure 6.10 an ideal, single peaked, hydrograph is shown. Although these types of storms are rare, it is instructive to study the basic components of a hydrograph in a single-peaked one. The main hydrograph portions are the *rising limb*, the *crest segment*, which includes the *peak flow rate*, Q_p, and the *recession limb*. These portions are marked by *inflection points* (IP). Only the most important inflection points are shown in Figure 6.10. The first inflection point, prior to the rising limb, actually marks the beginning of the storm. This point can be easily located by visual inspection. Note that it occurs some time after the beginning of effective precipitation in the rainfall hyetograph. Prior to the first inflection point, the hydrograph is receding from previous storms. In Figure 6.10 this corresponds to groundwater from previous rainfall events.

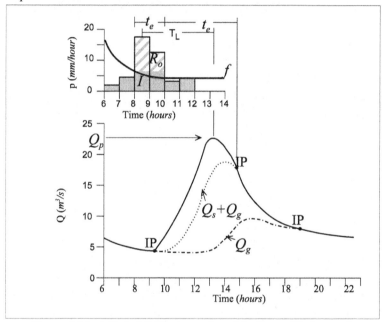

Figure 6.10: A Rainfall Hyetograph and its Storm Hydrograph

The second inflection point in the hydrograph of Figure 6.10 occurs in the recession limb after the peak. This point marks the end of *overland flow*. The third and last inflection point marks the end of *subsurface flow*. After this point the total flow rate is composed of *groundwater flow* only.

Between the first and the second inflection point there is a dashed line which theoretically represents the summation of subsurface flow, Q_s, plus groundwater flow, Q_g. Between the first and third inflection points there is another dashed line which theoretically represents groundwater. The actual shape of the subsurface and groundwater hydrographs is difficult to ascertain without the aid of field tracer tests. In principle, the subsurface and the groundwater flow rates take longer to appear as streamflow. The infiltration, recharge, and flow through porous media substantially retards their timing. As a result, the subsurface and groundwater flow components continue to recede for a period of time after the first inflection point, they reach a peak rate some time after the occurrence of the surface hydrograph peak rate, and they take a long time to recede (i.e., longer than that of the surface hydrograph).

Determination of the Inflection Points

As stated before, the inflection points in the streamflow hydrograph mark changes in the streamflow contributions. The first inflection point (see Figure 6.10), which is easily located by visual inspection, marks the beginning of the *storm runoff*. Of particular importance are the inflection points in the recession limb of the hydrograph (i.e., the portion of the hydrograph after the peak). These points may be found via an assumption on the particular analytical form of the recession limb. A common assumption states that two subsequent points in the recession limb of the hydrograph follow an exponentially decaying curve of the form

$$q_{t'} = q_o e^{-t'/k} \tag{6.4}$$

where

q_0 = a flow rate value in the recession limb (m^3/s)
$q_{t'}$ = recession flow rate t' units of time after the time of q_0 (m^3/s)
t' = time after q_0 (*hour*)
k = a recession constant typical of flow component
   (overland, subsurface, or groundwater) (*hour*)

This assumption is not entirely arbitrary since the recession of water outflowing from a tank follows an exponential law. If equation (6.4) is valid, then the recession limb should plot as a straight line on semi logarithmic paper. Figure 6.11 shows a graph of various points of the recession limb of a hydrograph plotted on semi logarithmic paper, with the logarithmic scale for the flow rate in the ordinates and the arithmetic scale for time in the abscissa. In this example one notes that at least three straight lines may be fitted to the resulting points. This implies that equation (6.4) would be valid for portions of the hydrograph within each straight line. Each straight line is characterized by a different value of the constant k.

One may further theorize that the first line immediately after the peak represents overland flow with a recession constant k_1, the second line represents subsurface flow with a recession constant k_2, and the third line represents groundwater with a recession constant k_3. Of course, this is an interpretation based on our analytical assumption of the form of the recession, since more (or less) than three lines may result. Interestingly, the intersection between two adjacent lines mark inflection points on the hydrograph. Of particular importance is the location of the last inflection point marking groundwater flow and the end of the *storm-runoff hydrograph*. Therefore this procedure may be used to locate the time when the last inflection point occurs.

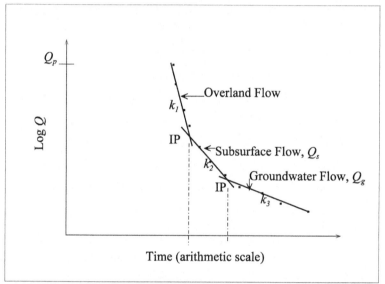

Figure 6.11: Location of Inflection Points in the Recession Limb

Let us write equation (6.4) as

$$\frac{q_{t'}}{q_0} = e^{-t'/k}$$

On taking logarithms,

$$\ln q_{t'} - \ln q_0 = -\frac{t'}{k}$$

Now set $t' = 1$ *hour*. The recession constant is given by

$$k = \frac{1}{\ln q_0 - \ln q_1} \qquad (6.5)$$

Thus, the estimation of the *recession constant, k*, valid for a particular component may be estimated by reading two subsequent flow rate values, separated one unit of time, corresponding to a particular straight line (i.e., a particular flow component) and using equation (6.5).

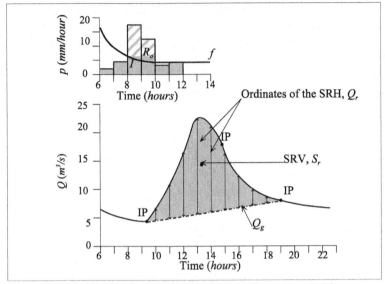

Figure 6.12: Approximate Separation of Groundwater Flow

Hydrograph Time Parameters

Returning to Figure 6.10, we note certain time measures that locate the rainfall hyetograph with respect to the produced runoff hydrograph. The *lag time*, T_L, is the time between the peak rainfall intensity and the peak of the hydrograph. More precisely, the lag time should be measured between the center of mass of the effective precipitation and the center of mass of the *storm-runoff hydrograph*, that is the hydrograph after the groundwater flow has been removed.

The *time of concentration*, t_c, is the time between the end of the effective precipitation and the second inflection in the hydrograph (i.e., the first inflection point after the peak flow rate). The time of concentration actually represents the time interval that effective precipitation water generated at the remotest part of the watershed takes to travel through the entire drainage system to the outlet of the watershed. In other words, the time of concentration is the longest travel time. In hydrograph analysis, it is determined as the time from the end of effective precipitation to the inflection point in the hydrograph. The inflection point used marks the end of overland flow. In urban watersheds composed mainly of overland flow, the inflection point used is the third, instead of the second. In other words, little infiltration through impervious surfaces causes little subsurface flow. Thus, the predominant component in the recession limb of the hydrograph is overland flow, which eventually meets groundwater flow at the last inflection point. The *time base*, T_b, of the hydrograph is the summation of the *duration of effective precipitation*, t_e, plus the time of concentration, t_c, or $T_b = t_e + t_c$. The duration of effective precipitation is less than or equal to the total duration of precipitation, t_d (see Chapter 2).

The above measures are determined from a comparison of the rainfall hyetograph of a particular storm with the corresponding runoff hydrograph. Since these measures are not constants, it is recommended to select several storms from the precipitation and streamflow records of the watershed. These storms should include low, medium and high intensity storms. From each storm the time parameters of the hydrograph are determined and average values are computed. The time parameters of the hydrograph constitute important input data for streamflow simulation programs.

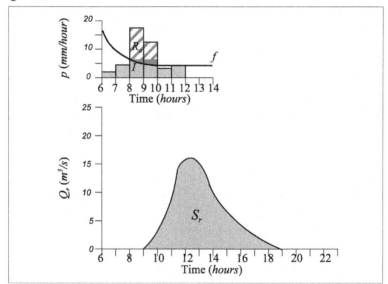

Figure 6.13: Storm-Runoff Hydrograph and Storm-Runoff Volume

Storm-Runoff Hydrograph and the Storm-Runoff Volume

In Chapter 4, we defined effective precipitation as the portion of the total precipitation that becomes overland flow, R_o, that is the portion of precipitation left after infiltration, I, is removed. However, it was noted that, except for urban watersheds, most storms are not sufficiently intense to generate overland flow. Therefore, the bulk of the storm hydrograph is generated by subsurface flow, that is water infiltrated in the watershed. For these reasons, we defined effective precipitation, R_o, as the portion of precipitation that becomes storm runoff. This is the part of the flow rate after the groundwater flow, Q_g, has been subtracted.

The theoretical shape of groundwater flow is depicted in Figure 6.10. However, its precise shape is difficult to define without field tests. For this reason, several approximations have been proposed. Figure 6.12 shows an idealization of the groundwater flow hydrograph as a straight line between the first and last inflection points. Although a straight line appears as a strong approximation, one should keep in mind that groundwater flow is a small portion of the total hydrograph, and a small error in the definition of groundwater should render smaller errors in the calculation of total storm volumes.

Differences between total flow rate and groundwater flow rate, $Q_r=Q-Q_g$, constitute the ordinates of the so-called *storm-runoff hydrograph* (SRH). Thus the SRH is simply the hydrograph resulting after groundwater has been removed (see Figure 6.13). Since groundwater is mainly composed of water recharged during past rainfall events, then the SRH represents the streamflow generated by the effective precipitation of the current storm. Therefore, the area under the SRH, called the *storm-runoff volume* (SRV), S_r, is actually the volume of effective precipitation depth, R_o, when expressed as uniform depth over the entire watershed. The SRV may be calculated as

$$S_r = c_1 \sum_{i=1}^{N} \left(Q_i - Q_{gi}\right)\Delta t = c_1 \sum_{i=1}^{N} Q_{ri}\, \Delta t \qquad (6.6)$$

where
$S_r = \text{SRV } (m^3)$
$Q_i = $ total flow rate at time interval i (m^3/s)
$Q_{gi} = $ groundwater flow rate at time interval i (m^3/s)
$Q_{ri} = $ SRH flow rate at time interval i (m^3/s)
$\Delta t = $ selected time interval (*hour*)
$N = $ number of ordinates used in calculation
$c_1 = 3600(s/hour)$, Δt in *hour*; or $c_1 = 86400(s/day)$, Δt in *day*

Equation (6.6) is simply a numerical integration using trapezoidal rule of the SRH. The SRV is related to R_o via the relationship

$$R_o = \frac{c_2 S_r}{A} \qquad (6.7)$$

where
  R_o = effective precipitation depth (mm)
  A = watershed area (km^2)
  $c_2 = 10^{-3}(mm.km^2/m^3)$

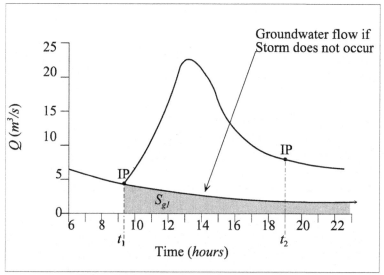

Figure 6.14: Groundwater Storage at Time t_1

Estimation of Groundwater Storage from the Hydrograph

The amount of groundwater storage volume in the regional aquifers of a watershed may estimated based on a streamflow hydrograph after the recession constant for groundwater has been evaluated. Figure 6.14 illustrates a storm hydrograph with their inflection points located at times t_1 and t_2, respectively. A procedure for locating inflection points was described earlier in this chapter (see Figure 6.11). In addition, a model for groundwater recession was proposed, equation (6.4), based on an exponentially decaying curve and a recession parameter, k. Once the parameter corresponding to groundwater recession flow has been estimated by reading two points in the line representing groundwater (i.e., beyond the last inflection point in Figure 6.11), then equation (6.4) may be used to synthesize groundwater flow rates in the absence of additional recharge from another storm.

Equation (6.4) may be used to calculate the amount of groundwater storage at a given time. For instance, Figure 6.14 shows the groundwater flow if the rainfall event does not occur. In such case, the streamflow rate from the previous storm would continue to recede as groundwater until eventually it reaches zero. The groundwater storage in the watershed at time t_1, S_{gl}, is the shaded area under the groundwater recession curve (i.e., the summation of all flow rate values from the current time, t_1, to the time when the flow rate becomes zero). Since the groundwater flow rate is given from equation (6.4), the above statement could be written mathematically as

$$S_{gl}=c_1\int_0^\infty q_{t'}\,dt'=c_1\int_0^\infty q_{t_1}e^{-t'/k}dt'=-c_1kq_{t_1}e^{-t'/k}\big|_0^\infty=S_{gl}=c_1kq_{t_1} \qquad (6.8)$$

where

S_{gl} = groundwater storage at time t_1 (m^3)
q_{t_1} = flow rate at time t_1 (m^3/s)
k = groundwater recession constant in equation (6.4) (*hour*)
t' = time after t_1 (*hour, day*)
c_1 = 3600s/*hour*, for k in *hour*; or c_1 = 86400s/*day*, for k in *day*

and the rest of the terms as before. This equation states that the groundwater storage in a watershed at a given time is simply the product of the groundwater recession constant times the flow rate at that time.

If the change in groundwater storage due to the storm is needed, one may calculate the storage at time t_2 from equation (6.8). Thus, the change in storage is given as

$$\Delta S_g=S_{t_2}-S_{t_1}=c_1k\left(q_{t_2}-q_{t_1}\right) \qquad (6.9)$$

where

ΔS_g = change in groundwater storage (m^3)
S_{t_2} = groundwater storage at time t_2 (m^3)
q_{t_2} = flow rate at time t_2 (m^3/s)

It is important to remark that the change in storage caused by a storm must be positive. In other words, there must be an increase in storage as a result of the rainfall event. If a negative value is obtained, it is likely that the last inflection point in the hydrograph was incorrectly located, either because of a mistake, or because the assumption of equation (6.4) is not applicable to the watershed. The correct inflection point should be at a time such that $q_{t_1} \leq q_{t_2}$.

If one wishes to express the change in storage in terms of uniform depth of water uniformly distributed over the entire watershed, equation (6.9) becomes

$$\Delta S_g = \frac{c_3 k \left(q_{t_2} - q_{t_1} \right)}{A} \qquad (6.10)$$

where
   ΔS= change in storage (mm)
   A=watershed area (km^2)
   c_3=3.6($mm.km^2.s/(m^3.hour)$) for k in hou
   c_3=86.4($mm.km^2.s/(m^3.day)$) for k in day

Estimation of Watershed Infiltration and Recharge from the Hydrograph

Hydrograph analysis may be used to estimate the watershed-wide infiltration effected during a storm. The hydrologic system being considered here is a whole watershed. Adopting a positive sign for any hydrologic quantity entering the system and a negative one for any quantity leaving the system, one may apply the water balance equation between the beginning of the storm and the end of the storm. It was previously stated that the first inflection point in the hydrograph is considered the beginning of the storm (i.e., at t_1 in Figure 6.14). The last inflection point in the hydrograph is considered the end of the storm (i.e., at t_2 in Figure 6.14). From equation (1.8) the water balance equation is:

$$P - ET - I - R_o = \Delta S_w \qquad (6.11)$$

where
   P=total precipitation depth during the storm (mm)
   ET=total evapotranspiration depth during the storm (mm)
   I=total infiltration depth during the storm (mm)
   R_o = effective precipitation depth (mm)
   ΔS_w = change in soil-water storage between t_1 and t_2 (mm)

Note that equation (6.11) neglects interception, I_n, and depression storage, I_d. All quantities are expressed in equivalent liquid water depth uniformly distributed over the whole watershed. Applying the water balance at the two hydrograph inflection points, t_1 and t_2, the change in storage is in fact a change in groundwater volume, ΔS_g. If we assume that all infiltrated water became groundwater recharge and $\Delta S_W = \Delta S_g$, then the change in storage is given by equation (6.9) as $\Delta S_w = \Delta S_g = S_{t_2} - S_{t_1}$. We remark again that ΔS_w should be positive (see previous section). Using equation (6.10), and neglecting the evapotranspiration, a reasonable assumption during the short term of a storm, the infiltration is obtained from equation (6.11) as

$$I = P - R_o - \frac{c_3 k \left(q_{t_2} - q_{t_1} \right)}{A} \qquad (6.12)$$

If all infiltration becomes recharge, an estimate of the change in the elevation of the groundwater table is

$$\Delta h = \frac{I}{S_y} \qquad (6.13)$$

where

Δh = change in water table elevation (mm)
S_y = aquifer specific yield

Example 6.2: Determination of Hydrograph Inflection Points

A watershed has a drainage area of $240\,km^2$. In August, 2009, a storm produced the rainfall-time distribution and the streamflow rate distribution given by Table 6.1. (1) Assuming that equation (6.4) is valid, find the inflection points on the recession limb of the hydrograph. (2) Calculate the groundwater recession constant, k. (3) Plot the streamflow hydrograph and locate the first and last inflection points.

Table 6.1: Rainfall and Runoff Data for Example 6.2

t (day)	p (mm/day)	Q (m^3/s)
7		2.14
8		1.91
9	0.0	1.68
10	15.0	1.45
11	18.0	4.60
12	14.0	9.75
13	5.0	13.00
14	0.0	10.30
15		7.70
16		5.90
17		4.70
18		3.80
19		3.02
20		2.58
21		2.22
22		1.92
23		1.66
24		1.44

Solution

(1) The recession flow rate values, Q, are plotted with respect to time, t, in semi-logarithmic paper, with Q in the logarithmic scale, and t in the linear scale (see figure 6.15). At least three straight lines may be fitted to the points. Intersections between the lines mark inflection points on the hydrograph. In particular, the intersection between the last two lines marks the last inflection point delimiting groundwater. It is located at a time $t_2 = 19.4 \approx 19.0 day$.

(2) Choose two discharge values, separated by one day, from the last line of Figure 6.15 corresponding to groundwater. For example, $q_0 = 1.92 m^3/s$ and $q_1 = 1.66 m^3/s$. Substituting into equation (6.5),

$$k = \frac{1}{\ln q_0 - \ln q_1} = \frac{1 day}{\ln 1.92 - \ln 1.66} = 6.87 day$$

(3) The linear hydrograph is plotted in Figure 6.16. The first inflection point is located by visual inspection at $t_1 = 10 day$.

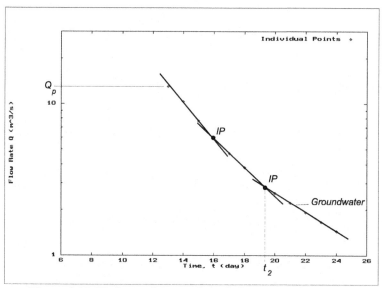

Figure 6.15: Hydrograph Recession Limb on Semi-Log Paper

Example 6.3: Calculation of Storm-Runoff Volume and Effective Precipitation Depth.

In Example 6.2, calculate (1) the SRV (m^3), and (2) the effective precipitation depth (*mm*).

Solution

(1) Assume that groundwater flow, Q_g, between the first and last inflection points is a straight line (see Figure 6.16). Starting at $t_1=10day$, apply equation (6.6) with $\Delta t=1day$:

$$S_r=c_1 \sum_{i=1}^{N} (Q_i-Q_{gi})\Delta t = \sum_{i=1}^{N} Q_{ri}\Delta t$$

$$S_r=86400\frac{s}{day} [(1.45-1.45)+(4.6-1.6)+(9.75-1.8)+(13.0-2.0)$$

$$+(10.3-2.2)+(7.7-2.35)+(5.9-2.55)+(4.7-2.7)$$

$$+(3.8-2.9)+(3.02-3.02)] \frac{m^3}{s}\times1day=3.599\times10^6 m^3$$

(2) From equation (6.7),

$$R_o=\frac{c_2 S_r}{A}=\frac{10^{-3}mm.km^2}{m^3}\times\frac{3.599\times10^6 m^3}{240km^2}=14.996mm$$

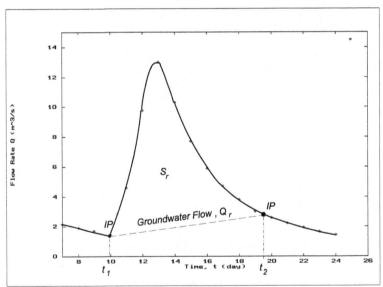

Figure 6.16: Hydrograph of Examples 6.2 and 6.3

Example 6.4: Calculation of Watershed Infiltration and Recharge

In Example 6.2, (1) calculate the watershed-wide infiltration depth due to the storm. (2) Assuming that all infiltration became groundwater recharge, and an average specific yield of 0.14, estimate the mean increase in water table elevation due to the storm.

Solution

(1) Apply a water balance equation between the beginning of the storm at time t_1 and the end of the storm at time t_2. From equation (6.12), and neglecting evapotranspiration, interception, and depression storage,

$$I = P - R_o - \frac{c_3 k\left(q_{t_2} - q_{t_1}\right)}{A}$$

$$I = (15 + 18 + 14 + 5)\frac{mm}{day} \times 1 day - 16.63 mm$$

$$-\frac{\dfrac{86.4 mm.km^2.s}{m^3.day} \times 6.87 days \times (3.02 - 1.45) \times \dfrac{m^3}{s}}{240 km^2} = 33.121 mm$$

(2) If all infiltration became recharge, then the average increase in water table elevation is given by equation (6.13) as

$$\Delta h = \frac{I}{S_y} = \frac{33.121 mm}{0.14} = 236.579 mm \approx 23.7 cm$$

This is a crude estimate. Clearly, there are areas of the watershed without an unconfined aquifer.

The Unit Hydrograph

An important contribution to the prediction of streamflow from rainfall was done by Sherman (1942, 1932). He introduced the concept of the *unit hydrograph* (UH). The unit hydrograph is defined as the storm-runoff hydrograph (SRH) generated by $1 mm$ of effective precipitation depth, R_o. Behind the unit hydrograph theory is the assumption that the effective precipitation depth is linearly related to the corresponding ordinates of the storm-runoff hydrograph. This implies that watersheds can be treated as linear systems that transform effective precipitation depths into storm-runoff hydrograph ordinates. This assumption is a crude approximation to the complexities behind the process of streamflow generation, since watersheds are not in general linear systems. Nevertheless, unit hydrographs are at the heart of the most commonly used computer simulation models in hydrology. The unit hydrograph method offers the hydrologist a powerful tool for streamflow forecasting during intense rainfall events. Many water resources applications today are based on the concept of the unit hydrograph. Flood wave forecasting; determination of the effect of development projects on streamflow; design of reservoirs, dam spillways, urban detention basins, and urban storm sewers are but a few of the hydrologic applications of unit hydrographs.

In the present text, we focus on the practical applications of unit hydrographs, rather than on the theoretical basis of linear systems. Those readers interested in an in depth treatment of linear systems, non-linear systems, and conceptual models in hydrology should consult Singh (1988).

Three types of unit hydrograph problems are of interest to the hydrologist, each type having a distinct objective: problem Type I seeks to derive a unit hydrograph from a rainfall hyetograph of a given duration, and its corresponding streamflow hydrograph; problem Type II seeks to change a unit hydrograph of a specific duration into another one of a different duration; and problem Type III seeks to predict the storm-runoff hydrograph caused by a rainfall hyetograph of a given duration using a unit hydrograph of the same duration. By *duration* we mean the time interval t_s of each *rainfall* intensity (see Figure 6.17). This is not necessarily the same as the duration of the effective precipitation, t_e (see Figure 6.10), or the total storm duration, t_d (see Figure 2.10). Therefore, a 1 *-hour* UH is one whose effective precipitation time t_s is one hour; a 3 *-hour* UH is attached to effective precipitation intervals given every three hours, etc. In the next three sections we discuss each of the three types of UH problems with examples. Since the three types of problems use the principle of superposition inherent to linear systems, and to avoid any confusion, the student must learn to recognize the distinct features of each problem type.

Derivation of a Unit Hydrograph (Problem Type I)

Problem Type I in unit hydrograph applications consists in the derivation of a unit hydrograph from a rainfall hyetograph of a specific duration, and its corresponding streamflow hydrograph. The rainfall hyetograph must be obtained from a rain gage representative of the watershed, if the watershed is small, or from a rain gage network, if the watershed is large. See Chapter 2 for the procedure to derive the time distribution of rainfall in a watershed. The streamflow hydrograph must be obtained from the historical records of the streamflow station at the outlet of the watershed.

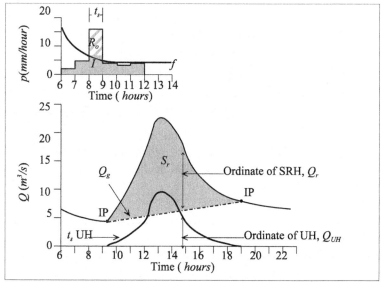

Figure 6.17: Derivation of a Unit Hydrograph

Referring to Figure 6.17, the procedure to derive a unit hydrograph from a simple storm may be summarized by the followings steps:

(1) Select a suitable storm. A suitable storm is one having a single peak of effective precipitation intensity (after infiltration and other losses have been subtracted), followed by a single-peak streamflow hydrograph. Take note of the *rainfall* duration, t_s.

(2) Separate the groundwater flow hydrograph, Q_g. This requires the location of the first and last inflection points of the hydrograph (e.g., see Example 6.1).

(3) Calculate the effective precipitation depth, R_o, in *mm*. The effective precipitation may be calculated in one of two ways: (a) from the rainfall hyetograph, after separating the infiltration via an infiltration model (e.g., see Example 4.9); or (b) from the streamflow hydrograph itself by deriving the SRH ($Q_r = Q - Q_g$), integrating the SRH to obtain the SRV, and dividing by the watershed area (e.g., see Example 6.2).

(4) Calculate each of the ordinates of the t_s UH by applying the principle

of superposition:

$$Q_{UH}(t) = \frac{(Q(t) - Q_g(t))}{R_o} = \frac{Q_r(t)}{R_o} \qquad (6.13)$$

where

$Q_{UH}(t)$ = UH flow rate (ordinate) at time t $((m^3/s)/mm)$
$Q(t)$ = total streamflow rate at time t (m^3/s)
$Q_g(t)$ = groundwater flow rate at time t (m^3/s)
$Q_r(t)$ = SRH flow rate at time t (m^3/s)

By applying equation (6.13) to several ordinates, at several times, the t_s UH is defined at several points. Note that equation (6.13) states that the magnitude (ordinate) of the UH at a given time is proportional to $1mm$ as the corresponding ordinate of the SRH at the same time $(Q-Q_g)$ is to R_o mm.

Table 6.2: Data and Calculations for Example 6.5

t (hour)	Q (m^3/s)	Q_g (m^3/s)	SRH Q_r (m^3/s)	2-hour UH Q_{UH} $(\frac{m^3/s}{mm})$
6	2.1	2.1	0.0	
7	1.9	1.9	0.0	
8	1.6	1.6	0.0	
9	1.4	1.4	0.0	0.0
10	4.6	1.6	3.0	0.4
11	9.7	1.8	7.9	1.0
12	13.0	1.9	11.1	1.5
13	10.3	2.1	8.2	1.1
14	7.7	2.3	5.4	0.7
15	5.9	2.5	3.4	0.4
16	4.7	2.6	2.1	0.3
17	3.8	2.8	1.0	0.1
18	3.0	3.0	0.0	0.0
19	2.5	2.5	0.0	
20	2.2	2.2	0.0	
21	1.9	1.9	0.0	
		Σ	42.1	

Example 6.5: Derivation of a Unit Hydrograph

The streamflow hydrograph of Table 6.2 was produced by a rainfall of an unknown intensity that lasted for a period of two hours. If the watershed area is $20\,km^2$, derive the 2-*hour* UH. Assume that the last inflection point occurred at $t_2 = 18hour$.

Solution

Following steps (1) through (4) for problem Type I, we proceed with the calculations as summarized in Table 6.2. The first inflection point is found by inspection to be at $t_1 = 9hour$. Prior to the first inflection point and after the last one, the flow rate is assumed to be groundwater flow. Between the first and last inflection points, we assume the groundwater flow, Q_g, to vary linearly as shown in the third column of Table 6.2, according to the equation

$$Q_g = q_{t_1} + \left(\frac{q_{t_2} - q_{t_1}}{t_2 - t_1} \right)(t - t_1), \qquad t_1 \le t \le t_2 \qquad (6.14)$$

where q_{t_1} and q_{t_2} are the flow rates at t_1 and t_2, respectively. The SRH in the fourth column is simply $Q_r = Q - Q_g$. Since the effective precipitation depth is not given, we need to calculate it from the SRV. The SRV, S_r is calculated by numerically integrating the SRH and applying equation (6.6) with $\Delta t = 1$ *hour*:

$$S_r = c_1 \sum_{i=1}^{N} Q_{ri} \Delta t = 3600 \frac{s}{hour} \times 42.1 \frac{m^3}{s} \times 1 hour = 151,560 m^3$$

The effective precipitation depth, R_o, is calculated from equation (6.7):

$$R_o = \frac{c_2 S_r}{A} = \frac{10^{-3} \frac{mm.km^2}{m^3} \times 151,560 m^3}{20 km^2} = 7.6mm$$

Finally the 2-*hour* UH ordinates, Q_{UH}, the last column in Table 6.2, are calculated from equation (6.13) as the SRH ordinates divided by R_o.

Example 6.6: Derivation of a Unit Hydrograph

The streamflow hydrograph of Table 6.3 was produced by a storm that started at 10:00 AM with a rainfall intensity of 8.5*mm/hour*. It continued with the same intensity until it abruptly ended at 3:00 PM. If the estimated φ index is 5.5*mm/hour*, derive the 5-*hour* UH. Assume that the last inflection point occurred at $t_2 = 70hour$.

Table 6.3: Streamflow Data and Calculations for Example 6.6

Clock Time	t (hour)	Q (m³/s)	Q_g (m³/s)	SRH Q_r (m³/s)	5-hour UH Q_{UH} ($\frac{m^3/s}{mm}$)
5:00 AM	0	11.4	11.4	0.0	
10:00 AM	5	11.3	11.3	0.0	
3:00 PM	10	11.1	11.1	0.0	0.0
8:00 PM	15	66.0	11.3	54.7	3.6
1:00 AM	20	72.0	11.6	60.4	4.0
6:00 AM	25	65.1	11.8	53.3	3.6
11:00 AM	30	57.2	12.0	45.2	3.0
4:00 PM	35	51.0	12.2	38.8	2.6
9:00 PM	40	43.5	12.5	31.0	2.1
2:00 AM	45	34.0	12.7	21.3	1.4
7:00 AM	50	26.8	12.9	13.9	0.0
12:00 Noon	55	21.0	13.1	7.9	
5:00 PM	60	18.5	14.3	4.2	
10:00 PM	65	15.1	13.6	1.5	
3:00 AM	70	13.8	13.8	0.0	
8:00 AM	75	13.0	13.0	0.0	
1:00 PM	80	11.2	11.2	0.0	
6:00 PM	85	11.0	11.0	0.0	
11:00 PM	90	10.6	10.6	0.0	

Solution

Following steps (1) through (4) for problem Type I, we proceed with the calculations as summarized in Table 6.3. The first inflection point is found by inspection to be at $t_1 = 10hour$. Prior to the first inflection point and after the last one, the flow rate is assumed to be groundwater. Between the first and last inflection points, we assume the groundwater flow, Q_g, to vary linearly as shown in the fourth column from the left in Table 6.3, according to equation (6.14). The SRH ordinates, the fifth column, are obtained by subtracting the fourth from the third column. Since the precipitation and infiltration intensities are given, and the watershed area is not, we calculate the effective precipitation as $R_o = (p - \varphi) \times t_s = (8.5 - 5.5)(mm/hour) \times 5hour = 15.0mm$. Finally the UH ordinates are calculated by dividing the SRH (the fifth column) by the effective precipitation depth, R_o.

In principle, a unit hydrograph of a specific duration is unique for a given watershed. In practice, one finds that unit hydrographs of a given duration derived from different storms are not the same. This is caused by inaccuracies in rainfall and streamflow procedures, and the departure of a watershed streamflow generation process from the linear system assumptions. It is advisable to select as many suitable storms from the streamflow records of a watershed as possible, each from a wide range of small, middle and large storms. Then derive a unit hydrograph of the same duration from each storm. Finally, an average unit hydrograph representative of the watershed should be calculated. If suitable storms are not available from the streamflow gage, storms with more complex rainfall and streamflow patterns may be used in conjunction with more elaborate matrix and numerical techniques (see Newton and Vinyard, 1967).

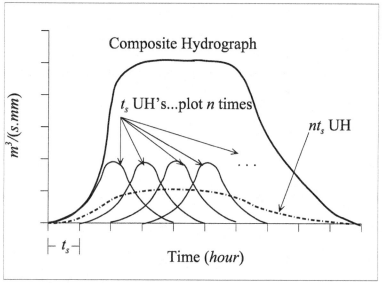

Figure 6.18: Changing the Duration of a Unit Hydrograph

Change the Duration of a Unit Hydrograph (Problem Type II)

Problem Type II seeks to change a unit hydrograph of a specific duration into another one of a different duration. For instance, convert a t_s UH into a nt_s UH. We remark again that the duration of a UH refers to the time interval of the rainfall that produced it, not that of the runoff. If the new duration is an integer multiple of the original duration (i.e. if n is an integer), the *lagging method* may be used. Referring to Figure 6.18, the following is the procedure to change a t_s UH into a nt_s UH, when the new duration is an integer multiple of the original duration:

(1) Plot the original t_s UH n times, each lagged t_s units of time from the previous one. If the calculations are done in tabular form, then instead of plotting write the ordinates of the t_s UH in n separate columns, each lagged t_s units of time from the previous one.

(2) Add the ordinates to produce a composite hydrograph.

(3) Divide each ordinate of the composite hydrograph by n. The resulting curve is the nt_s UH.

Example 6.7: Changing the Duration of a Unit Hydrograph
    Change the 5-*hour* UH derived in Example 6.6 into a 20-*hour* UH.

Solution
    In this case $n=20hour/5hour=4$. Since it is an integer, we use the lagging method. The calculations are summarized in Table 6.4. Following steps (1)-(3) above, the 5-*hour* UH ordinates are written in $n=4$ columns (columns two through five from left to right, respectively). Each 5-*hour* UH is lagged $t_s=5hour$ from the previous one. The composite hydrograph is obtained in column six by the horizontal summation of ordinates. Finally the 20-*hour* UH is obtained by dividing the ordinates of the composite hydrograph by $n=4$.

Table 6.4: Changing UH Duration of Example 6.7

t (hour)	5-*hour*UH $(m^3/(s.mm)$	5-*hour* UH $(m^3/(s.mm)$	5-*hour* UH $(m^3/(s.mm)$	5-*hour* UH $(m^3/(s.mm)$	Composite $(m^3/(s.mm)$	20-*hour* UH $(m^3/(s.mm)$
0	0.0				0.0	0.0
5	3.6	0.0			3.6	0.9
10	4.0	3.6	0.0		7.6	1.9
15	3.6	4.0	3.6	0.0	11.2	2.8
20	3.0	3.6	4.0	3.6	14.2	3.6
25	2.6	3.0	3.6	4.0	13.2	3.3
30	2.1	2.6	3.0	3.6	11.3	2.8
35	1.4	2.1	2.6	3.0	9.1	2.3
40	0.0	1.4	2.1	2.6	6.1	1.5
45		0.0	1.4	2.1	3.5	0.9
50			0.0	1.4	1.4	0.4
55				0.0	0.0	0.0

    If the new duration is not an integer multiple of the original duration (i.e., n is not an integer), the S *hydrograph* method may be used. This is also the case when the desired duration is less than the original duration.

The S hydrograph is a composite hydrograph resulting from plotting many times the UH. Referring to Figures 6.19 and 6.20 the following are the required steps:

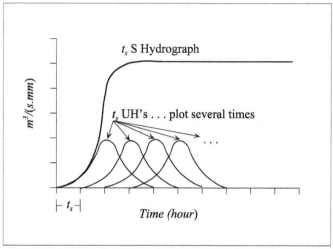

Figure 6.19: Derivation of an S Hydrograph

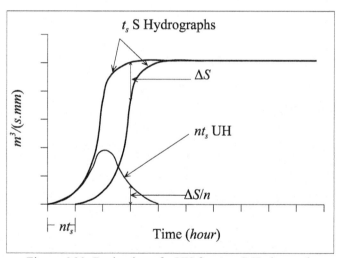

Figure 6.20: Derivation of a UH from an S Hydrograph

(1) Derive the t_s S hydrograph by plotting several times the original t_s UH several times, each lagged t_s units of time from the previous one, and adding ordinates (see Figure 6.19).

(2) Plot the S hydrograph derived from (1) a second time, but shifted nt_s

units of time (i.e., the desired new duration) from the first one (see Figure 6.20).

(3) Calculate ordinates of the new nt_s UH by dividing the differences between corresponding ordinates of the two S hydrographs, ΔS, by n (see Figure 6.20).

Example 6.8: The S-Hydrograph Method

Given a 1-*hour* UH as a set of [*t, q*] points [[0,0.0], [1,0.4], [2,1.0], [3,1.5], [4,1.1], [5,0.7], [6,0.45], [7,0.25], [8,0.1], [9,0.0]], with *t* in *hour* and *q* in $(m^3/s)/mm$, use the S-Hydrograph method to derive a 1/2-*hour* UH.

Solution

$t_s=1hour$, $nt_s=0.5hour$, $n=0.5$. The use the S-Hydrograph method suffers from instability issues; the UH, composite hydrographs, and S hydrograph need to be smoothed. The following Maple program implements the procedure described above and uses cubic splines to fit smooth analytic curves through the points on the various curves. It is a good idea to plot the points of a curve before fitting a smooth curve.

```
> restart: with(stats): ts:=1: nts:=0.5: n:=nts/ts:
  #enter 1-hour UH
  UH1:=[[0,0.0],[1,0.4],[2,1.0],[3,1.5],[4,1.1],
         [5,0.7],[6,0.45],[7,0.25],[8,0.1],[9,0.0]]:
  #peak time and time base
  tp:=3: Tb:=9:
> #using cubic splines fit a smooth curve
  with(CurveFitting):
  Spline(UH1,t):
  Q1:=unapply(%,t):
  QUH1:=t->piecewise(t<0,0,t<Tb,Q1(t),t>Tb,0):
> #derive the S hydrograph
  S1:=t->sum(QUH1(t-i*ts),i=0..20):
  UHp:=t->piecewise(t<Tb+10,(S1(t)-S1(t-nts))/n):
  #UH peak time
  eqn:=diff(UHp(t),t)=0:
  sols:=[solve(eqn,t)]:
  tpp:=sols[2]: t1:=floor(tpp): t2:=ceil(tpp):
  UHhalf:=[seq([j,UHp(j)],j=0..t1),[tpp,UHp(tpp)],
            seq([j,UHp(j)],j=t2..Tb)]:
  Spline(UHhalf,t):
  Qhalf:=unapply(%,t):
  #new UH time base
  sol1:=[solve(Qhalf(t)=0,t)]:
  Ns:=describe[count](sol1):
  for j from 1 to Ns do
       if(sol1[j]>0) and (sol1[j]<Tb) then Tbb:=sol1[j] end if:
  end do:
  QUHhalf:=t->piecewise(t<0,0,t<Tbb,Qhalf(t),t>Tbb,0):
> plot(QUHhalf(t),t=0..Tbb,color=black,legend=`1/2-hour UH`):
  plot(QUH1(t),t=0..Tb,color=black,legend=`1-hour UH`,linestyle=3):
  plots[display](%,%%,labels=[`Time (hours)`,`UH ((m^3/s)/mm)`],
       labeldirections=[HORIZONTAL,VERTICAL],
       labelfont=[TIMES,ROMAN,16]);
```

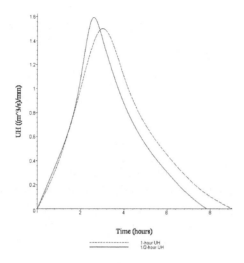

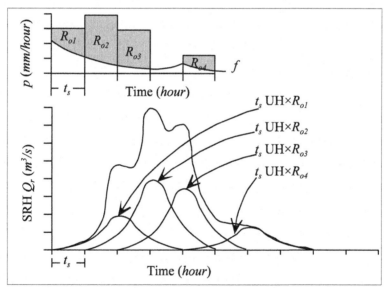

Figure 6.21: Predicting Streamflow with a Unit Hydrograph

Prediction of the Storm-Runoff Hydrograph (Problem Type III)

Problem Type III in unit hydrograph applications seeks to predict the storm-runoff hydrograph caused by a rainfall hyetograph of a given duration using a unit hydrograph of the same duration. This is the streamflow forecasting problem. A rainfall hyetograph, with rainfall intensities every t_s units of time, and a t_s UH (i.e. of the same duration) is needed. An infiltration rate curve, f, or a φ index model must also be available in order to estimate the effective precipitation depth, R_o (see Chapter 4). Referring to Figure 6.21, the procedure is as follows:

(1) Calculate the components of the effective precipitation depth from the rainfall hyetograph and the infiltration rate:

$$R_o = \sum_{i=1}^{N} R_{oi} = \sum_{i=1}^{N} (p_i - f_i)_s \qquad (6.15)$$

where

R_o = total effective precipitation depth (*mm*)
R_{oi} = effective precipitation depth component at time interval i (*mm*)
p_i = precipitation intensity at time interval i (*mm*)
f_i = infiltration (or loss) rate during time interval i (*mm*)
N = number of effective precipitation components in the storm

It is important to remark that, in this case, the magnitude of each individual effective precipitation depth, R_{oi}, is needed.

(2) Make sure that the duration of each effective precipitation component is the same as that of the given unit hydrograph. If the duration of the unit hydrograph is different, it needs to be changed to one that matches that of the given rainfall. In other words, problem Type II must be solved prior to solving problem Type III.

(3) Calculate the SRH produced by the effective precipitation component R_{oi}: Locate the first ordinate of the unit hydrograph (i.e., the zero) at the time when the R_{oi} began. Scale up the unit hydrograph by a factor of R_{oi} *mm* (i.e., multiply each UH ordinate, Q_{UH}, by R_{oi}).

(4) Repeat step (3) for all effective precipitation components in the storm.

(5) Add ordinates to obtain the combined SRH

(6) Add an estimated value of groundwater flow rate, Q_g, to obtain a more realistic representation of the total flow rate, Q.

Example 6.9: Predicting Streamflow Rate with a Unit Hydrograph
Using the 2-*hour* UH of Example 6.5 and the rainfall hyetograph given in Table 6.5, predict the total streamflow rate generated by the storm. Assume a φ index of 3.0 *mm/hour* and a nominal groundwater flow rate of 2.0 m^3/s.

Solution

Calculations are shown in Table 6.5. The first three columns (from left to right) are the time, the precipitation intensity, and the 2-*hour* UH, respectively. Following steps (1) through (6) above, we first calculate the effective precipitation depth components. There are three effective precipitation depth components, each lasting a time interval $t_s = 2 hour$. Thus from equation (6.15):

$$R_{o1} = (p_1 - \varphi)t_s = (15 - 3)\frac{mm}{hour} \times 2hour = 24mm$$

$$R_{o2} = (p_2 - \varphi)t_s = (25 - 3)\frac{mm}{hour} \times 2hour = 44mm$$

$$R_{o3} = (p_3 - \varphi)t_s = (10 - 3)\frac{mm}{hour} \times 2hour = 14mm$$

Table 6.5: Data and Calculations of Example 6.8

t (hour)	$p\ (\frac{mm}{hour})$	2-hour UH Q_{UH} $(m^3/(s.mm))$	$Q_{UH} \times R_{o1}$ (m^3/s)	$Q_{UH} \times R_{o2}$ (m^3/s)	$Q_{UH} \times R_{o3}$ (m^3/s)	SRH Q_r (m^3/s)	Q_g (m^3/s)	Q (m^3/s)
2:00 PM	0.0	0.0					2.0	2.0
3:00 PM	0.0	0.4					2.0	2.0
4:00 PM	15.0	1.0	0.0			0.0	2.0	2.0
5:00 PM	15.0	1.5	9.6			9.6	2.0	11.6
6:00 PM	25.0	1.1	24.0	0.0		24.0	2.0	26.0
7:00 PM	25.0	0.7	36.0	17.6		53.6	2.0	55.6
8:00 PM	0.0	0.4	26.4	44.0		70.4	2.0	72.4
9:00 PM	0.0	0.3	16.8	66.0		82.8	2.0	84.8
10:00 PM	10.0	0.1	9.6	48.4	0.0	58.0	2.0	60.0
11:00 PM	10.0	0.0	7.2	30.8	5.6	43.6	2.0	45.6
12:00 AM	0.0		2.4	17.6	14.0	34.0	2.0	36.0
1:00 AM	0.0		0.0	13.2	21.0	34.2	2.0	36.2
2:00 AM				4.4	15.4	19.8	2.0	21.8
3:00 AM				0.0	9.8	9.8	2.0	11.8
4:00 AM					5.6	5.6	2.0	7.6
5:00 AM					4.2	4.2	2.0	6.2
6:00 AM					1.4	1.4	2.0	3.4
7:00 AM					0.0	0.0	2.0	2.0
8:00 AM							2.0	2.0

Since the rainfall is given at $t_s = 2 - hour$ intervals (actually every hour, but the intensities change in magnitude every two hours), we may use the given 2-*hour* UH. The next three columns in Table 6.5 correspond to the SRH generated by each effective precipitation depth component. Thus, the column labeled $UH \times R_{o1}$ contains the ordinates of the 2-*hour* UH each multiplied by R_{o1}=24*mm*. Note that the first ordinate (i.e., the zero) is located at 4:00 PM, which is the time when R_{o1} began (with p_1=15*mm*).

The procedure is repeated for each effective precipitation depth component. Note that each SRH caused by an individual effective precipitation component begins at the time when such rainfall started. The SRH is the summation of the SRH ordinates produced by each of the N=3 precipitation components. The total flow rate is obtained by adding the combined SRH and groundwater.

Synthetic Methods of Unit Hydrograph

In the previous sections we have seen that the development of a UH for a watershed requires streamflow information at the watershed outlet. In many occasions a UH is needed for a watershed with no streamflow records are available. Several methods have been developed in the past to aid the hydrologist in the synthesis of an approximate UH based on certain topographic and physiographic characteristics (Gray, 1961; Bender and Robertson, 1961; Hickok et al., 1959; U.S. Soil Conservation Service, 1957; Taylor and Schwartz, 1952; Mitchell, 1948; Williams, 1945; Commons, 1942; Snyder, 1938). In this section we describe the popular Soil Conservation Service (SCS) method.

The SCS method employs an average UH developed from an analysis of a large number of UH's from field data of various-sized watersheds in different geographical locations. The *dimensionless UH* (see Table 6.6) has its ordinate values of discharge expressed as the dimensionless ratio with the peak discharge and its abscissa values of time as the dimensionless ratio with time to peak (time from the beginning of effective precipitation to the peak of the UH). The time to peak is given as

$$T_p = \frac{t_s}{2} + T_L \qquad (6.16)$$

where
  T_p = time from the start of effective rain to the UH peak (*hour*)
  t_s = desired UH duration (*hour*)
  T_L = UH lag time (from center of effective rain to the UH peak (*hour*)

The lag time may be computed as (Snyder, 1938)

$$T_L = c_4 (LL_c)^{0.3} \qquad (6.17)$$

where

c_4 = a land slope coefficient varying from 1.4 to 1.7 ($hour/km^{0.6}$)

L = length of the longest stream, from the outlet to the upstream limits of the watershed (km)

L_c = Length along the main stream in the watershed, from the outlet to a point opposite to the center of mass of the watershed (km)

The UH peak flow rate may be computed as

$$Q_p = \frac{c_5 A}{T_p} \qquad (6.18)$$

where

Q_p = UH peak flow rate ($(m^3/s)/mm$)

A = watershed area (km^2)

c_5 = 0.208($m^3.hour/(s.mm.km^2)$) (coefficient of storage capacity)

Table 6.6: The SCS Dimensionless UH

Dimensionless Time t/T_p	Dimensionless UH	Dimensionless Time t/T_p	Dimensionless UH Q_{UH}/Q_p
0.0	0.000	1.5	0.660
0.1	0.015	1.6	0.560
0.2	0.075	1.8	0.420
0.3	0.160	2.0	0.320
0.4	0.280	2.2	0.240
0.5	0.430	2.4	0.180
0.6	0.600	2.6	0.130
0.7	0.770	2.8	0.098
0.8	0.890	3.0	0.075
0.9	0.970	3.5	0.036
1.0	1.000	4.0	0.018
1.1	0.980	4.5	0.009
1.2	0.920	5.0	0.004
1.3	0.840	∞	0.000
1.4	0.750		

Source: Gray, D.M. (ed), 1973. *Handbook on the Principles of Hydrology.* Water Information Center Inc., New York, NY

Equations (6.16) through (6.18) may be used along with Table 6.6 to synthesize a UH for an ungaged watershed given information obtained from a topographic map. The UH obtained in this manner should be considered as an approximate UH along with any streamflow forecast predicted with it. For any detailed study, or a study related to the design of a large water resources facility, a streamflow station must be built for the watershed. The streamflow records obtained after a long period of time constitute the best evidence of the actual UH for a watershed. Even if only a few years of records are available, the data may be used to extrapolate in time the short term streamflow record, based on statistical correlation techniques with nearby watersheds (see Haan, 1977).

Example 6.10: Derivation of a Synthetic UH by the SCS Method

An ungaged watershed has a $300\,km^2$ of drainage area. From a topographic map, the length of the longest stream from the outlet to the watershed boundary upstream is 45km. Taking moments of area, the watershed centroid (or the center of mass) was located. The length along the main stream from the outlet to a point opposite to the watershed centroid was measured in the map as equal to 25km. Derive the 3-*hour* UH by the SCS method.

Solution

First estimate the UH lag time from equation (6.17) and adopting a conservative value for the c_4 coefficient (i.e., one which will produce a shorter lag time and thus a higher peak flow rate):

$$T_L = c_4\left(LL_c\right)^{0.3} = 1.4\frac{hour}{km^{0.6}}\times(45km\times25km)^{0.3} = 11.5\,hour$$

Next calculate the UH time to peak from equation (6.16):

$$T_p = \frac{t_s}{2} + T_L = \frac{3\,hour}{2} + 11.5\,hour = 13\,hour$$

The UH peak flow rate is given by equation (6.18) as

$$Q_p = \frac{c_5 A}{T_p} = \frac{\dfrac{0.208m^3.hour}{s.mm.km^2}\times300km^2}{13\,hour} = 4.80\frac{m^3/s}{mm}$$

To calculate individual UH points (i.e., pairs of t versus Q_{UH}), multiply the dimensionless time in Table 6.6 by T_p and the dimensionless flow rate by Q_p. Table 6.7 contains a few selected points that approximately depict the shape of the 3-*hour* UH.

Table 6.7: SCS 3-*hour* UH of Example 6.10

t (*hour*)	3-*hour* UH ($(m^3/s)/mm$)
0.0	0.00
6.5	2.06
13.0	4.80
19.5	3.17
26.0	1.54
39.0	0.36
52.0	0.09
65.0	0.02

Example 6.11: Changing Duration of a Synthetic UH (spreadsheet)
In Problem 6.10, use a spreadsheet to interpolate the 3-*hour* UH points to estimate values of the UH ordinates every hour. Next, derive the 12-*hour* UH for the same watershed in table format using the lagging method.

Solution
The following spreadsheet uses linear interpolation between the points in Table 6.7 to estimate values of the 3-*hour* UH every hour. The programming of the interpolation function is cumbersome but the table format is illustrative. Next, the lagging method (Problem Type II) is used to derive the required 12-*hour* UH.

t (*hour*)	SCS 3-*hour* UH ($(m^3/s)/mm$)	t (*hour*)	Fitted 3-*hour* UH ($(m^3/s)/mm$)	3-*hour* UH ($(m^3/s)/mm$)	3-*hour* UH ($(m^3/s)/mm$)	3-*hour* UH ($(m^3/s)/mm$)	Composite ($(m^3/s)/mm$)	12-*hour* UH ($(m^3/s)/mm$)
0	0	0	0.0000				0.0000	0.0000
6.5	2.06	1	0.3169				0.3169	0.0792
13	4.8	2	0.6338				0.6338	0.1585
19.5	3.17	3	0.9508	0.0000			0.9508	0.2377
26	1.54	4	1.2677	0.3169			1.5846	0.3962
39	0.36	5	1.5846	0.6338			2.2185	0.5546
52	0.09	6	1.9015	0.9508	0.0000		2.8523	0.7131
65	0.02	7	2.2708	1.2677	0.3169		3.8554	0.9638
		8	2.6923	1.5846	0.6338		4.9108	1.2277
		9	3.1138	1.9015	0.9508	0.0000	5.9662	1.4915
		10	3.5354	2.2708	1.2677	0.3169	7.3908	1.8477
		11	3.9569	2.6923	1.5846	0.6338	8.8677	2.2169
		12	4.3785	3.1138	1.9015	0.9508	10.3446	2.5862
		13	4.8000	3.5354	2.2708	1.2677	11.8738	2.9685
		14	4.5492	3.9569	2.6923	1.5846	12.7831	3.1958

t (hour)	SCS 3-hour UH ((m³/s)/mm)	t (hour)	Fitted 3-hour UH ((m³/s)/mm)	3-hour UH ((m³/s)/mm)	3-hour UH ((m³/s)/mm)	3-hour UH ((m³/s)/mm)	Composite ((m³/s)/mm)	12-hour UH ((m³/s)/mm)
		15	4.2985	4.3785	3.1138	1.9015	13.6923	3.4231
		16	4.0477	4.8000	3.5354	2.2708	14.6538	3.6635
		17	3.7969	4.5492	3.9569	2.6923	14.9954	3.7488
		18	4.0477	4.2985	4.3785	3.1138	15.8385	3.9596
		19	3.2954	4.0477	4.8000	3.5354	15.6785	3.9196
		20	3.0446	3.7969	4.5492	3.9569	15.3477	3.8369
		21	2.7938	4.0477	4.2985	4.3785	15.5185	3.8796
		22	2.5431	3.2954	4.0477	4.8000	14.6862	3.6715
		23	2.2923	3.0446	3.7969	4.5492	13.6831	3.4208
		24	2.0415	2.7938	4.0477	4.2985	13.1815	3.2954
		25	1.7908	2.5431	3.2954	4.0477	11.6769	2.9192
		26	1.5400	2.2923	3.0446	3.7969	10.6738	2.6685
		27	1.4492	2.0415	2.7938	4.0477	10.3323	2.5831
		28	1.3585	1.7908	2.5431	3.2954	8.9877	2.2469
		29	1.2677	1.5400	2.2923	3.0446	8.1446	2.0362
		30	1.1769	1.4492	2.0415	2.7938	7.4615	1.8654
		31	1.0862	1.3585	1.7908	2.5431	6.7785	1.6946
		32	0.9954	1.2677	1.5400	2.2923	6.0954	1.5238
		33	0.9046	1.1769	1.4492	2.0415	5.5723	1.3931
		34	0.8138	1.0862	1.3585	1.7908	5.0492	1.2623
		35	0.7231	0.9954	1.2677	1.5400	4.5262	1.1315
		36	0.6323	0.9046	1.1769	1.4492	4.1631	1.0408
		37	0.5415	0.8138	1.0862	1.3585	3.8000	0.9500
		38	0.4508	0.7231	0.9954	1.2677	3.4369	0.8592
		39	0.3600	0.6323	0.9046	1.1769	3.0738	0.7685
		40	0.3392	0.5415	0.8138	1.0862	2.7808	0.6952
		41	0.3185	0.4508	0.7231	0.9954	2.4877	0.6219
		42	0.2977	0.3600	0.6323	0.9046	2.1946	0.5487
		43	0.2769	0.3392	0.5415	0.8138	1.9715	0.4929
		44	0.2562	0.3185	0.4508	0.7231	1.7485	0.4371
		45	0.2354	0.2977	0.3600	0.6323	1.5254	0.3813
		46	0.2146	0.2769	0.3392	0.5415	1.3723	0.3431
		47	0.1938	0.2562	0.3185	0.4508	1.2192	0.3048
		48	0.1731	0.2354	0.2977	0.3600	1.0662	0.2665
		49	0.1523	0.2146	0.2769	0.3392	0.9831	0.2458
		50	0.1315	0.1938	0.2562	0.3185	0.9000	0.2250
		51	0.1108	0.1731	0.2354	0.2977	0.8169	0.2042
		52	0.0900	0.1523	0.2146	0.2769	0.7338	0.1835
		53	0.0846	0.1315	0.1938	0.2562	0.6662	0.1665
		53	0.0846	0.1108	0.1731	0.2354	0.6038	0.1510
		54	0.0792	0.0900	0.1523	0.2146	0.5362	0.1340
		55	0.0738	0.0846	0.1315	0.1938	0.4838	0.1210
		56	0.0685	0.0846	0.1108	0.1731	0.4369	0.1092
		57	0.0631	0.0792	0.0900	0.1523	0.3846	0.0962
		58	0.0577	0.0738	0.0846	0.1315	0.3477	0.0869
		59	0.0523	0.0685	0.0846	0.1108	0.3162	0.0790
		60	0.0469	0.0631	0.0792	0.0900	0.2792	0.0698
		61	0.0415	0.0577	0.0738	0.0846	0.2577	0.0644
		62	0.0362	0.0523	0.0685	0.0846	0.2415	0.0604
		63	0.0308	0.0469	0.0631	0.0792	0.2200	0.0550
		64	0.0254	0.0415	0.0577	0.0738	0.1985	0.0496

t	SCS 3-*hour* UH	t	Fitted 3-*hour* UH	3-*hour* UH	3-*hour* UH	3-*hour* UH	Composite	12-*hour* UH
(*hour*)	((m^3/s)/mm)	(*hour*)	((m^3/s)/mm)	((m^3/s)/mm)	((m^3/s)/mm)	((m^3/s)/mm)	((m^3/s)/mm)	((m^3/s)/mm)
		65	0.0200	0.0362	0.0523	0.0685	0.1769	0.0442
		66		0.0308	0.0469	0.0631	0.1408	0.0352
		67		0.0254	0.0415	0.0577	0.1246	0.0312
		68		0.0200	0.0362	0.0523	0.1085	0.0271
		69			0.0308	0.0469	0.0777	0.0194
		70			0.0254	0.0415	0.0669	0.0167
		71			0.0200	0.0362	0.0562	0.0140
		72				0.0308	0.0308	0.0077
		73				0.0254	0.0254	0.0063
		74				0.0200	0.0200	0.0050

Example 6.12: Changing the Duration of a Synthetic UH (Maple)

Write a Maple program that reads the 3-*hour* UH points derived in Example 6.10, Table 6.7, fits a smooth curve through the points, and derives a 12-*hour* UH. Plot both unit graphs.

Solution

The following Maple program takes advantage of the curve fitting routines available. First, the 3-*hour* UH is entered as an array of values $[[t_1, Q_{UH1}], [t_2, Q_{UH2}], ...]$. Using cubic splines a smooth analytic curve is fitted through the points. Then, the 12-*hour* UH is derived using the procedure previously described for Problem Type II.

```
> restart: with(stats): ts:=3: nts:=12: n:=nts/ts:
  #time to peak and time base
  Tp:=13.0: Tb:=66.0:
  #enter 3-hour UH
  UH3:=[[0.0,0.0],[6.5,2.06],[13.0,4.8],[19.5,3.17],
        [26.0,1.54],[39.0,0.36],[52.0,0.09],[65.0,0.02]]:
> #using cubic splines fit a smooth curve
  with(CurveFitting):
  Spline(UH3,t):
  Q3:=unapply(%,t):
  UH3:=t->piecewise(t<0,0,t<Tb,Q3(t),t>Tb,0):
> #the composite hydrograph (problem Type II)
  Comp:=t->sum(UH3(t-i*ts),i=0..n-1):
  #the 12-hour UH
  UH12:=t->piecewise(t<Tb+10,Comp(t)/n):
> plot(UH3(t),t=0..Tb,color=black,legend=`3-hour UH`):
  plot(UH12(t),t=0..Tb,color=black,legend=`12-hour
  UH`,linestyle=3):
  plots[display](%,%%,labels=[`Time (hours)`,`UH ((m^3/s)/mm)`],
        labeldirections=[HORIZONTAL,VERTICAL],
        labelfont=[TIMES,ROMAN,16]);
```

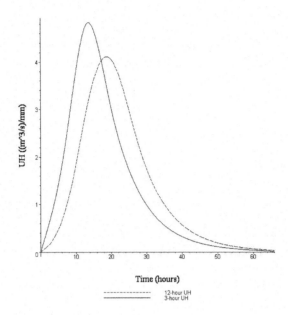

Time (hours)

- - - - - - - - - - -   12-hour UH
─────────   3-hour UH

Comparing Examples 6.11 and 6.12, it is easy to see that the results are similar. However, the spreadsheet provides values at discrete cells points only, whereas a computer algebra program, such as Maple, is comparatively simpler and it yields and analytical expression representing a smooth continuos curve in time, which may be useful in streamflow calculations.

Example 6.13: Analytical Streamflow Forecasting with a UH

Using the 12-*hour* UH of Example 6.12, write a Maple program to predict the total streamflow rate at the same watershed due to a storm with the following rainfall intensities in *mm/hour* given every 12 *hours*: [21.0, 35.0, 0.0, 14.0, 30.0, 0.0]. Assume a φ index of 3.0*mm/hour* and a nominal groundwater flow rate of 5.0m^3/s.

Solution

The following program reads the precipitation and other data, the SCS 3-*hour* UH from Example 3.10, which is converted into a 12-*hour* UH as in Example 6.12. Next, effective precipitation depths are calculated from equation (6.15). Finally, the total discharge ordinates are continuously calculated by applying the method described for Problem Type III of unit hydrographs. In other words, the shifted unit hydrographs are scaled and superimposed by the magnitude of each effective rainfall depth.

```
> restart: with(stats): ts:=3: nts:=12: n:=nts/ts:
  phi:=3: Qg:=5.0:
  #precipitation data every 12 hours
  P:=[0.0,21.0,35.0,0.0,14.0,30.0,0.0]:
  N:=describe[count](P):
  #time to peak and time base
  Tp:=13.0: Tb:=66.0:
  #enter the SCS 3-hour UH from Example 6.10
  UH3:=[[0.0,0.0],[6.5,2.06],[13.0,4.8],[19.5,3.17],
        [26.0,1.54],[39.0,0.36],[52.0,0.09],[65.0,0.02]]:
  #derivation of 12-hour UH, from Example 6.12
  with(CurveFitting):
  Spline(UH3,t):
  Q3:=unapply(%,t):
  UH3:=t->piecewise(t<0,0,t<Tb,Q3(t),t>Tb,0):
  Comp:=t->sum(UH3(t-i*ts),i=0..n-1):
  UH12:=t->piecewise(t<Tb+10,Comp(t)/n):
> #effective precipitation depths for Example 6.13
  Ro:=[seq( max( (P[i]-phi)*nts,0), i=1..N) ]:
> #streamflow forecasting (problem Type III)
  Q:=t->sum(UH12(t-(j-2)*nts)*Ro[j],j=1..N)+Qg:
  plot(Q(t),t=0..140,color=black,
       labels=[`Time (hours)`,`Q (m^3/s)`],
       labeldirections=[HORIZONTAL,VERTICAL],
       labelfont=[TIMES,ROMAN,16]);
```

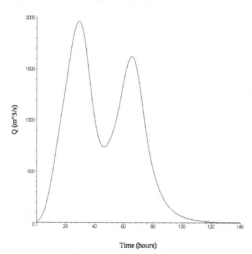

Time (hours)

Continuous Streamflow Simulation with the Unit Hydrograph

Once a UH of a given duration t_s is available, it can be used to forecast a streamflow hydrograph produced by effective precipitation depths of the same duration. For instance, assume that $t_s=1\,hour$, a 1-*hour* UH is given at discrete time intervals $t=0$, 1, 2, . . . , k as $Q_{UH}[0]$, $Q_{UH}[1]$,..., $Q_{UH}[k]$ ($(m^3)/mm$), respectively, and that effective precipitation depths are given every hour as $R_o[1]$, $R_0[2]$, ..., $R_o[k]$ (*mm*). To forecast the the SRH ordinates, each effective precipitation input is sampled with (i.e., multiplied by) all UH ordinates, as described in Problem Type III and Example 6.8 (see Figure 6.22):

$$Q_r[0]=R_o[0]Q_{UH}[0]$$

$$Q_r[1]= R_o[0]Q_{UH}[1]+R_o[1]Q_{UH}[0]$$

$$Q_r[2]=R_o[0]Q_{UH}[2]+R_o[1]Q_{UH}[1]+R_0[2]Q_{UH}[0]$$

$$Q_r[3]=R_o[0]Q_{UH}[3]+R_o[1]Q_{UH}[2]+R_o[2]Q_{UH}[1]+R_o[3]Q_{UH}[0]$$

$$\vdots$$

(6.19)

where

$Q_r[0]$, $Q_r[1]$,..., $Q_r[k]$ = SRH ordinates (m^3/s)

Equation (6.19) may be summarized as

$$Q_r[k]= R_o[0]Q_{UH}[k]+R_o[1]Q_{UH}[k-1]+ \cdots +R_o[k]Q_{UH}[0]$$

$$Q_r[k]=\sum_{i=0}^{k} R_o[i]Q_{UH}[k-i]=\sum_{i=0}^{k} R_o[k-i]Q_{UH}[i]$$

(6.20)

Equations (6.20) may be written in matrix form as

$$
\begin{matrix}
Q_r[0] \\
Q_r[1] \\
\vdots \\
Q_r[k]
\end{matrix}
=
\begin{matrix}
Q_{UH}[0] & 0 & 0 & \cdots & 0 \\
Q_{UH}[1] & Q_{UH}[0] & 0 & \cdots & 0 \\
\vdots \\
Q_{UH}[k] & Q_{UH}[k-1] & Q_{UH}[k-2] & \cdots & Q_{UH}[0]
\end{matrix}
\times
\begin{matrix}
R_o[0] \\
R_o[1] \\
\vdots \\
R_o[k]
\end{matrix}
$$

(6.21)

or in short as

$$Q_r=Q_{UH}\times R_o$$

(6.22)

where

Q_r = column vector of SRH ordinates (m^3/s)
Q_{UH} = matrix of UH ordinates ((m^3/s)/mm)
R_o = column vector of effective rain depths (mm)

As discussed before in Problem Type III, we remark again that the UH duration, t_s, must equal that of the effective precipitation pattern. In the above example, $t_s=1 hour$ and thus the effective precipitation is given at $t_s=1-hour$ intervals (see Figure 6.22). As the duration decreases the peak of the UH increases and the time base decreases. In the limit, as $t_s \to 0$, the discrete summation in equation (6.20) becomes a continuous integral of time:

$$Q_r(t)=\int_0^t R_o(\tau)Q_{IUH}(t-\tau)d\tau=\int_0^t R_o(t-\tau)Q_{IUH}(\tau)d\tau \qquad (6.23)$$

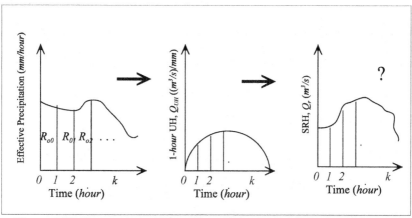

Figure 6.22: Forecasting a SRH with an Effective Precipitation and a UH

where

$Q_{IUH}(t)$ = the *instantaneous unit hydrograph*, IUH ($(m^3/s)/mm$)
$R_o(t)$ = continuous effective precipitation pattern (*mm*)
Equation (6.23) is called the *"convolution integral"* of an inflow effective precipitation hyetograph weighted by an IUH or or the system *"impulse response function."*

Example 6.14: Forecasting Streamflow with a UH

Beginning at midnight, a small watershed experienced a series of storms with intensities reported each hour in Table 6.8. Given a 1-*hour* UH in the same table, a constant loss rate given by the an index $\varphi=5mm/hour$ (see Chapter 4), and a groundwater flow rate $Q_g=5m^3/s$. Predict the streamflow hydrograph Q (m^3/s) produced by the rainfall pattern.

Solution

First, precipitation intensities and UH ordinates are stored in appropriate arrays. Effective rain depths at $t=i$, $i=1, 2, ..., 36$ *hours* after midnight are calculated as $R_{oi}=(p_i-\varphi)\times t_s$ (see Chapter 4). Next, equation (6.20) is applied to predict the SRH ordinates, Q_r. Finally, streamflow rates are calculated by adding groundwater flow as $Q_i=Q_r+Q_g$.

Table 6.8: Rainfall and UH Data for Example 6.14

t (hour)	1-hour UH $(m^3/s)/mm)$	p (mm/hour)	t (hour)	p (mm/hour)	t (hour)	p (mm/hour)
1	0.0	15	13	0	25	0
2	0.8	35	14	0	26	0
3	2.0	25	15	0	27	0
4	3.0	5	16	0	28	33
5	2.2	0	17	0	29	0
6	1.4	0	18	0	30	22
7	0.8	12	19	0	31	0
8	0.6	40	20	0	32	0
9	0.2	0	21	20	33	0
10	0.0	0	22	35	34	0
11		0	23	0	35	0
12		0	24	0	36	0

```
  Enter a 1-hour UH, and hourly rainfall intensity.
  Store them in arrays of equal size.
> with(stats): phi:=5: Qg:=10: ts:=1.0:
  Quh:=[0.,0.8,2.0,3.0,2.2,1.4,0.8,0.6,0.2,
          0.0,0,0,0,0,0,0,0,0,0,0,0,0,0,0,0,
          0,0,0,0,0,0,0,0,0,0,0]:
  p:=[15,35,25,5,0,0,12,40,0,0,0,0,0,0,0,0,
          0,0,0,0,20,35,0,0,0,0,0,33,0,22,0,0,
          0,0,0,0]:
  N:= describe[count](p):
  M:=describe[count](Quh):
  if(N<>M) then `Arrays size do not match`
                end if;
  #calculate effective precipitation depths
  Ro:=[seq(max((p[ii]-phi)*ts,0),ii=1..N)]:
  Apply Equation (6.20) to forecast the SRH ordinates.
> for i from 1 to N do Qr[i]:=sum(Ro[k]
                    *Quh[i-k+1],k=1..i) end do:
  #add groundwater flow
  Q:=[seq([t,Qr[t]+Qg],t=1..N)]:
  plot(Q,color=black,
        labels=[`Time (hours)`,`Q (m^3/s)`],
        labeldirections=[HORIZONTAL,VERTICAL],
        labelfont=[TIMES,ROMAN,16]);
```

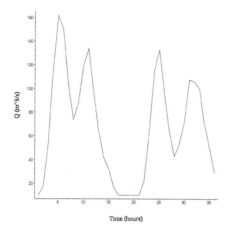

The Instantaneous Unit Hydrograph

The use of a UH with a rainfall hyetograph (problem Type III) requires that the duration, t_s, of the UH and that of the rainfall time interval be the same. Depending on how the rainfall is recorded by the various gages in the watershed, a collection of UH of different durations should be derived, each one to be used with a corresponding rainfall-time interval. An alternative approach attempts to derive a special UH from which all other UH's may be obtained. This unique function, called the *instantaneous unit hydrograph* (IUH), completely characterizes the streamflow response of a watershed.

The IUH is based on the fact that as the duration of the UH decreases, the peak of the UH increases and its time base decreases (i.e., recall that the area under a UH equals $1\,mm$). Applying the concepts of infinitesimal calculus, in the previous section we saw that as $t_s \to 0$, in the limit, the UH becomes an IUH. Theoretically, this zero-duration UH represents a streamflow response due to an effective rainfall of $1\,mm$ in depth uniformly distributed over the whole watershed and lasting for an infinitesimally short period of time (i.e., an instantaneous rainfall). Although such rainfall is unrealizable in practice, the concept of an IUH is useful. Having a IUH for a particular watershed permits the derivation of any finite-duration UH one may need in applications. With the advent of high-resolution train gages that now permit the measurement of rainfall intensities almost continuously, an IUH makes it possible the application of the convolution integral equation (6.23) to forecast streamflow almost in real time. The implementation of such an analytical approach is now straight forward with the use of modern symbolic mathematics software, such as Maple.

Many studies in the past have been conducted for the purpose of deriving an IUH. Most of these studies have focused on conceptual representations and abstract simplifications of the process of streamflow generation in a watershed. For instance, the separation of overland flow in a watershed as composed of two processes, pure translation followed by pure storage and detention, has produced the so-called *conceptual models* of rainfall-runoff in hydrology. The pure translation process may be simulated by drawing lines of equal travel time, or *isochrones*, in the watershed. The pure storage process may be simulated be a hypothetical linear reservoir located at the outlet. Many combinations of the above processes resulted in a multitude of schemes arranged to produce a IUH when the hypothetical systems are fed with an instantaneous unit of effective precipitation. For a detailed account with extensive references of conceptual models in hydrology the reader is referred to Singh (1988), Dooge (1973, 1959). Although conceptual models are mathematical and hypothetical abstractions of the actual streamflow generation process, they are nevertheless useful in hydrologic forecasting applications.

The parameters of conceptual models of the IUH of a watershed are estimated from measured streamflow hydrographs, and more specifically the SRH. In a general comparison of methods (Dooge et al., 1979) based on extensive numerical research (O'Kane and Dooge, 1977), Dooge showed that a simple two parameter model, such as the Nash (1957) model, gives better results than IUH obtained by the least squares method or by transform methods of solution. The Nash model conceived a watershed as composed of η equal linear reservoirs arranged in cascade one after the other. The first reservoir is instantaneously fed by a unit depth of effective precipitation. The outflow from the first reservoir becomes the inflow to the second reservoir. The outflow from the second becomes the inflow to the third, etc. The outflow from the η-th reservoir is the IUH of the watershed. Applying the continuity equation and solving, the IUH flow rate is given as

$$Q_{IUH}(t) = \frac{c_6 A t^{\eta-1} e^{-t/\kappa}}{\Gamma(\eta)\kappa^{\eta}} \tag{6.24}$$

where
   Q_{IUH} = IUH flow rate at time t $((m^3/s)/mm)$
   t = time from the start of effective precipitation (*hour*)
   η = number of hypothetical reservoirs
   κ = storage delay time in each reservoir (*hour*)

A=watershed area (km^2)

$\Gamma(\eta)=(\eta-1)!$, for η integer, or in general $\Gamma(\eta)=\int_0^\infty \xi^{\eta-1}e^{-\xi}d\xi$ is the two-parameter gamma function

$c_6=0.2778(m^3.hour)/(s.mm.km^2)$

The gamma function is found in mathematical tables or may be called from computer programs and spreadsheets. The computation of the IUH of a watershed based on recorded effective precipitation intensities and the corresponding SRH can be accomplished by the matching moments technique (O'Kane and Dooge, 1977). The sample first moment with respect to the time origin of an effective precipitation hyetograph is calculated from

$$M_{1p}'=\frac{1}{R_o}\sum_{i=1}^{N_p}R_{oi}t_i \qquad (6.25)$$

where

M_{1p}'= first moment with respect to the time origin of an effective precipitation hyetograph (*hour*)

R_{oi}= i-th component of effective rain depth (equation (6.15)) (*mm*)

R_o= total effective precipitation depth (equation (6.15)) (*mm*)

t_i= time interval from time origin to middle of effective precipitation component (*hour*)

N_p= number of effective precipitation depth components

The first moment about the time origin of a SRH is calculated from

$$M_{1r}'=\frac{\sum_{j=1}^{N_r}Q_{rj}t_j}{\sum_{j=1}^{N_r}Q_{rj}} \qquad (6.26)$$

where

M_{1r}'= first moment with respect to the time origin of a SRH (*hour*)

Q_{rj}= j-th ordinate of the SRH (m^3/s)

t_j= time interval from the time origin to Q_{rj} (*hour*)

N_r= number of SRH ordinates

The second moment about the center of area of an effective precipitation hyetograph can be evaluated as

$$M_{2p} = \frac{\sum_{i=1}^{N_p} R_{oi}\left(t_i - M'_{1p}\right)^2}{R_o} \tag{6.27}$$

where

M_{2p} = second moment about the center of area an effective precipitation hyetograph $(hour)^2$

The second moment about the center of area of a SRH is given as

$$M_{2r} = \frac{\sum_{j=1}^{N_r} Q_{rj}\left(t_j - M'_{1r}\right)^2}{\sum_{j=1}^{N_r} Q_{rj}} \tag{6.28}$$

where

M_{2r} = second moment about the center of area of a SRH $(hour)^2$

Based on a generalized expression between the moments of the IUH on the one hand, and the moments of the effective precipitation and SRH on the other (O'Kane and Dooge, 1977), it is possible to find the corresponding moments of the IUH. The first moment about the time origin of the IUH is given by

$$M'_{1U} = M'_{1r} - M'_{1p} \tag{6.29}$$

where

M'_{1U} = first moment about the time origin of the IUH $(hour)$

The second moment about the center of area of the IUH is given by

$$M_{2U} = M_{2r} - M_{2p} \tag{6.30}$$

where

M_{2U} = second moment about the center of area of the IUH $(hour)^2$

Finally, by substituting the analytical moments of the IUH equation (6.24) one arrives at expressions for the parameters of the Nash model:

$$\kappa = M_{2U} / M'_{1U} \tag{6.31}$$

$$\eta = M'_{1U}/\kappa \qquad (6.32)$$

Therefore, to fit a Nash model of the IUH, equation (6.24), of a watershed using the method of moments, one needs a recorded effective precipitation hyetograph and the corresponding SRH. The moments of the data are calculated using equations (6.25) through (6.28). The moments of the IUH are calculated from equations (6.29) and (6.30). Finally, the parameters κ and η are estimated form equations (6.31) and (6.32), respectively.

Example 6.15: Derivation of an IUH

Table 6.9 shows the effective precipitation components and the SRH ordinates (i.e., infiltration and groundwater flow have already been subtracted), respectively of a storm in a watershed of $21 km^2$ in drainage area. Derive the IUH using the Nash Model.

Table 6.9: Storm Data of Example 6.15

Clock Time	t (hour)	Effective Precipitation $(p\text{-}f)$ (mm/hour)	SRH, Q_r (m^3/s)
4:00 PM	0.0	12.0	0.0
5:00 PM	1.0	12.0	10.0
6:00 PM	2.0	22.0	25.0
7:00 PM	3.0	22.0	55.0
8:00 PM	4.0	0.0	70.0
9:00 PM	5.0	0.0	85.0
10:00 PM	6.0	7.0	60.0
11:00 PM	7.0	7.0	40.0
12:00 AM	8.0	0.0	36.0
1:00 AM	9.0		32.0
2:00 AM	10.0		20.0
3:00 AM	11.0		10.0
4:00 AM	12.0		5.0
5:00 AM	13.0		4.0
6:00 AM	14.0		1.0
7:00 AM	14.0		0.0

Solution

Begin by calculating the moments of the data. The first moment about the origin of the effective precipitation hyetograph is given by equation (6.25). Using equation (6.15), with a rainfall time interval $t_s = 2 hour$, and choosing the time origin at 4:00 PM, $R_o = 82.0 mm$, and $M'_{1p} = 3.1 hour$.

Note that the time interval t_i is between the origin and the middle of each $2-hour$ precipitation component. The first moment about the origin of the SRH is given from equation (6.26) as $M'_{1r}=5.7hour$. The second moment about the center of area of the effective precipitation hyetograph is given by equation (6.27) as $M_{2p}=4.1hour^2$. The second moment about the center of area of the SRH is given by equation (6.28) as $M_{2r}=6.5hour^2$.

The first moment about the origin of the IUH is given from equation (6.29) as $M'_{1U}=2.6hour$. The second moment about the center of area of the IUH is given from equation (6.30) as $M_{2U}=2.4hour^2$. Finally, the estimated parameters of the Nash model are given by equations (6.31) and (6.32), respectively as $\kappa=0.91hour$ and $\eta=2.86$. With these parameters, the form of the IUH for the watershed is completely defined by equation (6.24).

Some investigators have attempted to relate Nash's κ and η to watershed and storm characteristics using regression techniques (see for example Rao et. al, 1972).Once an IUH is available for a watershed, it may be used to derive any finite-duration UH for the same watershed. The procedure to derive a t_s UH from a IUH consists in dividing the time coordinate into t_s intervals. The value of the t_s UH at time t_i is simply the average of the IUH flow rate at times t_i and t_{i-1}. In other words,

$$Q_{UH}(t_i)=\frac{Q_{IUH}(t_{i-1})+Q_{IUH}(t_i)}{2}, \quad t_s=t_i-t_{i-1} \tag{6.33}$$

Besides being a tool to derive any finite-duration UH, the IUH has been used to detect the hydrologic effects of changes in land use. For instance, important changes in a watershed, such as gradual urbanization, agricultural development, improved artificial drainage, and mining activities may affect the characteristics of streamflow generation in a watershed. The partition between overland flow, subsurface flow and groundwater flow may also be affected by substantial changes in the watershed land use or the implementation of development projects. Since the IUH constitutes a unique function characterizing the streamflow response of a watershed, these changes in the watershed may be reflected in the features of the IUH. For instance, it is well known that urban development produces an increase in overland flow and a corresponding decrease in subsurface and groundwater flow in a watershed. This may be observed by a gradual change in the fundamental shape of the IUH of the watershed as derived from many storms prior, during, and after the development project. The IUH may exhibit an increase in the peak flow rate magnitude and a corresponding decrease in the time base. For an application of the IUH and other techniques to detect hydrologic effects of land use changes see Serrano et al. (1985).

The application of IUH to study environmental effects of development projects requires the detailed analysis of streamflow records in the watershed. Several storms selected from the pre-project and the post-project conditions should be used to account for the many uncertainties and approximations imbedded in data collection and model assumptions. Clear changes in the mean IUH derived from many storms should be observed. These changes should be distinguished from the normal variations in the IUH obtained after deriving it from storms of different characteristics. For applications of stochastic and statistical methods to characterize an IUH see Sarino and Serrano (1990).

Example 6.16: Deriving a Finite Duration UH from a IUH
A watershed with a drainage area of $21\,km^2$ and an IUH with parameters $\kappa = 0.72 hour$ and $\eta = 3.47$. Obtain ordinates of a 1-*hour* UH. Plot both functions on a single graph.

Solution
In the following Maple program the IUH is programmed and plotted as a continuous function. Equation (6.33) is used to obtain ordinates of a UH spaced by $t_s = 1 hour$. To calculate some points around the peak UH, we used calculus of maxima to locate the peak time of the IUH.

```
> restart:
  QIUH:=t->c6*A*t^(eta-1)*exp(-t/kappa)/(GAMMA(eta)*kappa ^eta):
  c6:=0.2778: kappa:=0.72: eta:=3.47: A:=21.:
  G1:=plot(QIUH(t),t=0..10,color=black):
  #Calculate ordinates of a ts=1hour UH
  QUH1:=[[0,0],seq([i,(QIUH(i-1)+QIUH(i))/2],i=1..10)]:
  G2:=plot(QUH1,color=black,style=point,symbol=circle):
  #Find the time of the peak IUH
  diff(QIUH(t),t)=0:
  tmax:=solve(%,t);
                         tmax := 1.778399999, 0.
> #Use the non-zero solution, tmax[1],
  #to estimate points around the peak UH
  PeakUH:=[[tmax[1],(QIUH(tmax[1]-1)+QIUH(tmax[1]))/2],
  [tmax[1]+1,(QIUH(tmax[1])+QIUH(tmax[1]+1))/2]]:
  G3:=plot(PeakUH,style=point,color=black, symbol=circle):
  plots[display](G1,G2,G3,color=black,
      labels=[`Time (hours)`,`IUH/UH (m^3/(s.mm))`],
      labeldirections=[HORIZONTAL,VERTICAL],
      labelfont=[TIMES,ROMAN,16]);
```

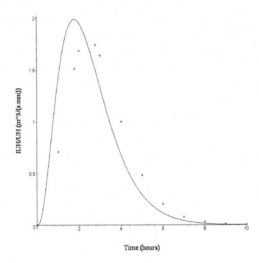

Example 6.17: Forecasting a SRH with an IUH

A watershed with a drainage area of $21\,km^2$ and an IUH with parameters $\kappa=0.72\,hour$ and $\eta=3.47$. Forecast the SRH generated by a design effective precipitation pattern given by $R_o(t)=100e^{(t-2.5)^2}$, where R_0 is given in *mm* (already adjusted for an infinitesimally small duration), and t is given in *hours*.

Solution

The following program takes advantage of the symbolic mathematics features in Maple. The design effective precipitation pattern is programmed as a continuous function of time, and the convolution integral equation (6.23) is used to forecast the SRH in real time.

```
> restart:
  QIUH:=t->c6*A*t^(eta-1)*exp(-t/kappa)/(GAMMA(eta)*kappa^eta):
  c6:=0.2778: kappa:=0.72: eta:=3.47: A:=21.:
  Ro:=t->100*exp(-(t-2.5)^2):
> Qr:=t->int(Ro(tau)*QIUH(t-tau),tau=0..t);
```

$$Qr := t \to \int_0^t Ro(\tau)\,QIUH(t-\tau)\,d\tau$$

```
> plot(Qr(t),t=0..12,color=black,
       labels=['Time (hours)','Qr (m^3/s)'],
       labeldirections=[HORIZONTAL,VERTICAL],
       labelfont=[TIMES,ROMAN,16]);
```

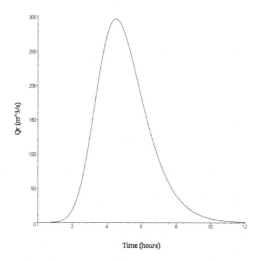

Time (hours)

6.4 HYDROLOGIC SIMULATION MODELS

In the previous sections we have discussed some of the most important techniques to simulate a streamflow hydrograph. UH techniques are empirical procedures that satisfy the continuity, but not the momentum equations. For a discussion on the theory of hydrodynamics in rivers the reader is referred to Martin and McCutcheon (1999). When UH or other techniques are included in a comprehensive watershed hydrologic program that involves the analysis of precipitation, the calculation of hydrologic abstractions, such as evapotranspiration and infiltration discussed in previous chapters, the result is a hydrologic simulation model capable of forecasting the streamflow hydrograph for a watershed, given a specified set of measured environmental conditions. Some of the first efforts in this arena included the Stanford Watershed Model (Crawford and Linsley, 1966) and the Hydrologic Simulation Program-Fortran (Johanson et al., 1980). From these early programs, many modeling approaches have been developed and applied to simulate storm water, flood plain hydrology, agricultural drainage, reservoir design, and river basin management. In 1971 the EPA developed the Storm Water Management Model (Metcalf and Eddy, 1971; Huber and Dickinson, 1988) to address the quantity and quality variations in urban runoff. The STORM model (Hydrologic Engineering Center HEC, 1975) and ILLUDAS (Tertstriep and Stall, 1974) received much attention thanks to its simplicity for simulating storm runoff and pipe systems.

Hydrologic simulation models may be classified according to various features: lumped parameter (e.g., Snyder UH, Nash IUH) versus distributed parameter models (e.g., kinematic wave; see Chapter 7); event models (e.g., HEC-1, SWMM, SCS TR-20) versus continuous simulation models (e.g., Stanford); deterministic (i.e., models with predictable parameters) versus stochastic models (e.g., synthetic flows and models using statistical techniques); analytical (e.g., Nash IUH) versus numerical models (e.g., models that use numerical solutions to solve the differential equations); physically based (e.g., HEC-1, SWWM that use the physical equations) versus empirical models that rely on certain suppositions.

Some of the most popular models include event simulation models such as HEC-1 Flood Hydrograph Package (HEC, 1981), HEC-HMS (HEC 1998), HEC-RAS to simulate flood plain hydraulics (HEC, 1995), the EPA SWMM (Huber and Dickinson, 1988), and the SCS TR-20 (SCS, 1984). They simulate single storm responses for a given rainfall and watershed data. UH methods are used to generate storm hydrographs, which are routed within stream channels (see Chapter 7). All of these models are now available for WINDOWS and come with a nice end-user graphical interface. Excellent reviews of models in hydrology have been published, including Kibler (1982), Stephenson and Meadows (1986), Maidment (1993), DeVries and Hromadka (1993), Hoggan (1997), James and James (1998), and McCuen (1998). One of the best introductions to HEC-HMS and HEC-RAS with illustrative application examples is given in Bedient and Huber (2002).

With the advent of Geographic Information Systems (GIS), the availability of digital terrain data has been added to several hydrologic simulation models. The lack of extensive data to field validate the output from complex simulation models has resulted in skepticism. The prevailing view now is to select the simplest simulation model that would satisfy the project objectives. Our approach in this book has been to provide the reader with the fundamental understanding and basic tools to develop his or her own small model. If the use of a specialized model is required, the literature cited in this section may be useful.

PROBLEMS

6.1 Go to the USGS site (http://water.usgs.gov), choose surface water data, select a streamflow station, choose tab-delimited data as an option, and display on your browser the daily streamflow in ft^3/s for the last year. Highlight a portion of the data, copy it, paste it in Notepad, and save it as a text file. Modify the Maple program in Example 6.1 to read the data, fit it to a smooth function and plot the hydrograph. Calculate the total annual water yield in ft^3.

Table 6.10: Rainfall and Runoff Data for Problem 6.3

t (hour)	p (mm/hour)	Q (m³/s)
7		4.24
8		4.01
9	0.0	3.78
10	10.0	3.55
11	17.0	6.70
12	15.0	11.85
13	8.0	15.10
14	0.0	12.40
15		9.80
16		8.00
17		6.80
18		5.90
19		5.12
20		4.68
21		4.32
22		4.02
23		3.76
24		3.54

6.2 Modify the program in problem 6.1 to enter time versus flow rate coordinates $[[t_1, Q_{g1}], [t_2, Q_{g2}],...]$ that define the groundwater hydrograph, fit them to a smooth curve, and plot it with the total hydrograph. Calculate the total groundwater flow volume for the year in ft^3. Write your observations on the relative importance of overland flow subsurface flow and groundwater flow in the watershed.

6.3 A watershed has a drainage area of $15\,km^2$. In May, 2009, a storm produced the rainfall-time distribution and the streamflow rate distribution given by Table 6.10. (1) Assuming that equation (6.4) is valid, find the inflection points on the recession limb of the hydrograph. (2) Calculate the groundwater recession constant, k. (3) Plot the streamflow hydrograph and locate the first and last inflection points.

6.4 In problem 6.3, (1) calculate the SRV (m^3), and (2) the effective precipitation depth (mm).

6.5 In problem 6.3, (1) calculate the watershed-wide infiltration depth due to the storm. (2) Assuming that all infiltration became groundwater recharge, and an average specific yield of 0.35, estimate the mean increase in water table elevation due to the storm.

Table 6.11: Streamflow Data for Problem 6.6

t (hour)	Q (m^3/s)
9	13.7
10	12.5
11	11.2
12	50.0
13	120.0
14	156.0
15	172.0
16	144.0
17	125.0
18	107.0
19	88.0
20	68.0
21	55.0
22	41.0
23	28.0
24	20.0
1	12.0
2	6.5
3	6.0

6.6 The streamflow hydrograph of Table 6.11. was produced by a rainfall of an unknown intensity that lasted for a period of three hours. If the Watershed area is $250\,km^2$, (1) the effective precipitation depth in *mm*, and (2) derive the 3-*hour* UH. Assume that the last inflection point occurs at $t_2 = 24 hour$

6.7 Assume that the streamflow data given in Example 6.6 (Table 6.3) was actually produced by a rainfall intensity of 7.5*mm/hour* lasting for the same five hours. Assume the same $\varphi = 5.5mm/hour$ index and that the last inflection point is at $t_2 = 75 hour$. Derive the 5-*hour* UH.

6.8 Change the 2-*hour* UH of Example 6.5 (Table 6.2) into a 6-*hour* UH.

6.9 Change the 5-*hour* UH of Example 6.6 (Table 6.3) into a 15-*hour* UH

6.10 Modify the program in Example 6.8 to produce a 15-*min* (0.25-*hour*) UH using the S-hydrograph method.

6.11 Modify the program in Example 6.8 to produce a 2-*hour* UH using the S-hydrograph method. Hint: now $nt_s > t_s$ and the 2-*hour* UH time base is greater than the original 1-*hour* UH. The corresponding "if" statements in the calculation of the new time base must be changed.

6.12 Using the UH of Example 6.6, Table 6.3, predict the total streamflow rate at the same watershed due to the following storm: at 3:00 PM it started to rain with an intensity of 8*mm/hour*; it continued raining with the same intensity until at 8:00 PM it abruptly increased to 20*mm/hour*; it continued raining with the same intensity until it abruptly ended at 1:00 AM of the following day. Then at 6:00 AM started to rain again with an intensity of 16*mm/hour*; it continued raining with the same intensity until it ended at 11:00 AM. Assume a φ index of 2*mm/hour* and a nominal groundwater flow rate of $1.8 m^3/s$.

6.13 An ungaged watershed has a $400 km^2$ of total drainage area. From a topographic map, the length of the longest stream from the outlet to the watershed boundary upstream is 48*km*. Taking moments of area, the watershed centroid (or the center of area) was located. The length along the main stream from the outlet to a point opposite to the watershed centroid was measured in the map as equal to 30*km*. Derive the 1-*hour* UH by the SCS method.

6.14 In Problem 6.13, use a spreadsheet to interpolate the 1-*hour* UH points to estimate values of the UH ordinates every hour. Next, derive the 4-*hour* UH for the same watershed in table format using the lagging method.

6.15 Write a Maple program that reads the 1-*hour* UH points derived in Problem 6.13, fits a smooth curve through the points using cubic splines, and derives a 4-*hour* UH. Plot both unit graphs.

6.16 Using the 4-*hour* UH of Problem 6.14 and a spreadsheet, predict the total streamflow rate at the same watershed due to a storm with the following rainfall intensities in *mm/hour* given every 4 *hours* starting at 1:00 PM: [11.0, 28.0, 0.0, 21.0] . Assume a φ index of 4*mm/hour* and a nominal groundwater flow rate of $3.0 m^3/s$.

6.17 Modify the Maple program in Problem 6.15 to use the 4-*hour* to predict the total streamflow rate at the same watershed due to a storm with the following rainfall intensities in *mm/hour* given every 4 *hours* starting at 1:00 PM:

[11.0, 28.0, 0.0, 21.0] . Assume a φ index of $4mm/hour$ and a nominal groundwater flow rate of $3.0m^3/s$. Note this is the Maple version of Problem 6.16.

6.18 Write a Maple program that verifies the calculations in Example 6.15. Show each moment equation with the individual values, and plot the IUH.

6.19 A watershed with a drainage area of $35\,km^2$ and an IUH with parameters $\kappa=1.72hour$ and $\eta=4.47$. Obtain ordinates of a 4-*hour* UH. Plot both functions on a single graph.

6.20 A watershed with a drainage area of $35\,km^2$ and an IUH with parameters $\kappa=1.72hour$ and $\eta=4.47$. Forecast the SRH generated by a design effective precipitation pattern given by $R_o(t)=100e^{(t-2.5)^2}$, where R_0 is given in *mm* (already adjusted for an infinitesimally small duration), and t is given in *hours*. Hint: use program in Example 6.17 as a model.

"And the weak shall defeat the strong
Nothing in the world is as weak and flexible as water
But when water attacks the hard and the strong, it proves its power
And the weak wins over the strong and the flexible wins over the hard"

Lao Tsu,Tao Te King, 600 B.C.

7 HYDROLOGY OF EXTREME EVENTS

Throughout the history of humanity, there has been a profound preoccupation for the understanding and prediction of natural catastrophes. Unable to control many natural hazards, such as hurricanes, tornados, earthquakes, floods, and droughts, humans have opted for studying the physical laws behind these phenomena with the purpose of predicting their occurrence. In hydrology, the analysis and prediction of floods and droughts has been the object of intense study. Understanding the characteristics of flood and drought periods in a watershed is the key to the design of preventive measures that ameliorate the adverse consequences of these events. For instance, knowing the range of values of extreme flood peaks is the basis for the design of flood control structures, such as dikes and reservoirs. The detection of an extreme flood wave early in the upstream areas of a watershed, and knowledge of the hydrology of flood wave propagation is at the heart of hydrological warning systems. Warning systems provide precious time to protect sensitive property and to evacuate flood plain areas. Understanding of the low flow regime in an important water-supply river provides the tools for the design of preventing measures, such as the construction of reservoirs and the implementation of water resources management policies.

In Chapter 2 we studied the principles of precipitation frequency analysis. In this chapter we extend some of those concepts to the analysis of floods and droughts, and introduce the fundamental concepts of flood wave propagation.

7.1 FLOOD WAVE PROPAGATION

In chapter 6 we studied the characteristics of event hydrographs formed as a result of the stream generation process in a small watershed. The streamflow hydrograph at the outlet of a watershed was the result of the combined overland flow, subsurface flow, and groundwater flow during a storm. In larger watersheds the streamflow rate at a particular cross section of a river is the result of the above process, in addition to the propagation of hydrographs generated upstream. Hydrographs generated on the upper portions of a watershed will travel through the river network according to the laws of wave propagation through open channel systems. The laws of mass conservation, momentum conservation, and energy dissipation in a natural river channel control the flow rate with respect to time at a given cross section of a river.

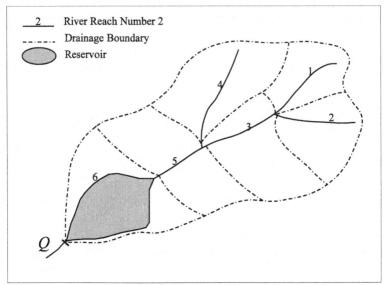

Figure 7.1: Division of a Large Watershed into Sub-Watersheds

The procedure for the streamflow analysis of a large watershed (i.e., larger than $300\,km^2$ in drainage area) consists in subdividing the drainage area into small sub-watersheds. Each sub-watershed is delineated to include the area draining towards one tributary, or in between tributaries along the main river. Each sub-watershed is studied for the four main components of streamflow within its smaller drainage area: overland flow, subsurface flow, groundwater flow, and *flood routing* from an upstream sub-watershed if any.

Figure 7.1 shows an example of a large watershed and its drainage system. The main stream has two tributaries and a reservoir prior to the watershed outlet where the streamflow gaging station is located. To study the streamflow variability in this large watershed, the river system has been divided into several segments or reaches, each identified with a number. The selection of reaches is done according to the physiographic characteristics of the watershed. Each *river reach* is either a tributary to the main stream, which defines a small watershed on its own, or a river segment between two subsequent tributary confluences.

In Figure 7.1, river reach 1 is the upper portion along the mean stream from its birth near the watershed boundary to the stream section immediately upstream the confluence of reach 2. Reach 2 is defined by tributary 2 from its birth to a stream section immediately upstream its confluence with reach 1. Reach 3 is defined by the main river from a point immediately downstream the confluence of reach 1 and reach 2 to a point immediately upstream the confluence of reach 4. Reach 4 is defined by tributary 4 from its birth to a point immediately upstream its confluence into the main river. Reach 5 is located along the main stream from a point downstream the junction of 3 and 4 to a point upstream the entrance to reservoir 6. Reach 6 is the portion of the main stream flooded by the reservoir from a point downstream the exit of reach 6 to the watershed outlet.

Using a detailed topographic map (not shown in Figure 7.1) the drainage boundaries corresponding to each reach may be drawn. The drainage area defined by each reach may be estimated using a polar planimeter, a computer digitizer, or GIS software. Thus, the drainage area defined by reach 1, called A_1, marks the streamflow generated at the outlet of reach 1 from overland flow, subsurface flow and groundwater flow inside its boundaries. Similarly, A_3 is the drainage area of reach 3 that marks the streamflow generated in its sub-watershed only. The total watershed area is simply

$$A = \sum_{i=1}^{N} A_i$$

where
  A=total watershed area (km^2)
  A_i= area of subwatershed i (km^2)
  N=number of subwatersheds

The flow rate, Q_i at the exit of reach i (or sub-watershed i) has two main components:

(1) The streamflow, q_{ri}, generated within its sub-watershed boundaries from overland flow, subsurface flow, and groundwater flow.

(2) Streamflow, q_{ui}, originated at upstream river reaches or tributaries, if any, and propagated through the river reach i .

q_{ri} may be estimated from rainfall gages located in sub-watershed i and using the hydrologic techniques described in previous chapters: starting from a given rainfall hyetograph, an effective precipitation is calculated using an infiltration model, and the flow rate at the outlet of the reach is estimated with an appropriate unit hydrograph. q_{ui}, on the other hand, requires the *hydrologic routing* of the inflow hydrograph entering the upstream limit of sub-watershed i to the outlet of the reach. This routing of the inflow hydrograph generated at upper reaches requires the application of the laws of *wave propagation* through open channel systems.

In Figure 7.1, q_{u1}, q_{u2}, and q_{u4} are all zero, since sub-watersheds 1, 2, and 4 do not have upstream hydrographs flowing into them. Therefore, $Q_1 = q_{r1}$, $Q_2 = q_{r2}$, and $Q_4 = q_{r4}$. On the other hand, $Q_3 = q_{r3} + q_{u3}$, where q_{r3} is the streamflow generated within sub-watershed 3 only, and q_{u3} is the hydrograph resulting after an inflow hydrograph, $(Q_1 + Q_2)$, has traveled through river reach 3. Similarly, $Q_5 = q_{r5} + q_{u5}$, where q_{u5} is the hydrograph resulting after the inflow hydrograph, $(Q_3 + Q_4)$, has been routed through river reach 5. Finally, the total watershed flow rate $Q = Q_6 = q_{r6} + q_{u6}$. q_{r6} is the overland flow, subsurface flow, groundwater flow produced in A_6, plus direct precipitation over the reservoir. q_{u6} is the hydrograph resulting after routing the inflow hydrograph, Q_5, through the reservoir flooding reach 6.

The above exercise demonstrates the important principle that streamflow hydrographs produced by different sub-watersheds may be added only after the spatial and temporal propagation features have been taken into account. The division of a large watershed into sub-watersheds must consider the number of tributaries and the travel of flood waves produced by each sub-watershed. The sequential routing and adding of individual hydrographs to produce the combined hydrograph of a watershed constitutes the inner process of hydrologic computer simulation models of today. With a friendly end-user interface, these software packages request information on the number of reaches, the order and sequence of their connection, sub-watershed areas, soil types, river characteristics, and rainfall time distribution. The model proceeds to execute the different facets of streamflow generation discussed in this book and graphs the resulting hydrograph. For information on models available to the hydrologist see Chapter 6. For more detailed information on algorithmic structure, and applications see Viessman and Lewis (1996); U.S. Army Corps of Engineers (1981); Hromadka et al. (1987); and Hoggan (1989).

Hydrologic River Routing: The Muskingum Method
In the previous section we emphasized that an important component of streamflow generation during an extreme flood event in a large watershed is the routing of an inflow hydrograph through a river reach. The inflow hydrograph entering a river reach at an upstream end moves through the river reach according to the laws of mass and momentum

conservation through a natural channel system. These laws result in the spatially varied unsteady flow equations in open channels. The simultaneous solution of these equations requires the application of numerical techniques that go beyond the scope of the present treatise (for more details see Martin and McCutcheon, 1999; Gunlach and Thomas, 1977; Viessman, 1996; Chow, 1959). In this section we present the Muskingum method, which introduces several simplifications that eliminate the complexities of *hydraulic routing* a hydrograph through a spatially varied river section. These simplifications imply a corresponding loss of accuracy in the calculations, but permit a simple estimation of the streamflow rate magnitude at a given section.

Consider a river reach being simultaneously monitored for streamflow rate at an upstream section and at a downstream section. The inflow hydrograph, or the hydrograph entering the upstream section is denoted as $I(t)$, and the outflow hydrograph, or the hydrograph leaving the downstream section is denoted as $O(t)$. If the inflow hydrograph represents the flow rate due to an extreme rainfall event produced at upstream portions of a watershed, then the outflow hydrograph will be the result of the inflow hydrograph traveling through the reach. As the flood wave travels through the reach, energy dissipation and propagation will occur from turbulence and from friction with the irregular shape of the river section and the tortuosity of the river. The energy dissipation will cause a decrease in the magnitude of the peak flow rate and a dispersion of the flood-wave front, forward and backward away from its center of mass. As a result, the time base of the observed hydrograph at the downstream end of the river reach will be greater than that at the upstream section. To simulate these effects, the Muskingum method combines the continuity equation with an empirical relationship between the storage in the river reach and the inflow and outflow hydrographs.

Neglecting evaporation and groundwater flow, the continuity equation applied to a river reach is, from equation (1.5),

$$I(t) - O(t) = \frac{dS(t)}{dt} \tag{7.1}$$

where
$I(t)$=inflow rate at time t (m^3/s)
$O(t)$=outflow rate at time t (m^3/s)
$S(t)$=river reach storage at time t (m^3)

Ordinarily, flow rates are given or calculated at fixed discrete intervals separated Δt units of time. A finite difference representation of equation (7.1) is

$$\frac{I_i + I_{i+1}}{2} - \frac{O_i + O_{i+1}}{2} = \frac{S_{i+1} - S_i}{\Delta t} \tag{7.2}$$

where
I_i = inflow rate at time step i (m^3/s)
O_i = outflow rate at time step i (m^3/s)
S_i = river storage at time step i (m^3)

To eliminate the storage from the continuity equation (7.2), we use the Muskingum equation, which conceives the river storage at a given time as a linear function of the weight between inflow and outflow rates:

$$S(t) = k[xI(t) + (1-x)O(t)] \tag{7.3}$$

where
k = storage constant (*hour, day*)
x = weighing factor

The storage constant in the Muskingum equation is approximately equal to the flood wave travel time within the reach. If a streamflow hydrograph simultaneously measured at the upstream and downstream sections is available, k may be estimated as the time interval between the peak time at the upstream section and that at the downstream one. The weighing factor varies from 0.0 to 0.5, with an average value of 0.2.

Writing the Muskingum equation (7.3) at discrete time intervals one obtains

$$S_{i+1} - S_i = k[x(I_{i+1} - I_i) + (1-x)(O_{i+1} - O_i)] \tag{7.4}$$

Substituting equation (7.4) into equation (7.2), one obtains an expression for the outflow rate forward in time:

$$O_{i+1} = c_0 I_{i+1} + c_1 I_i + c_2 O_i$$

$$c_0 = \frac{-kx + 0.5\Delta t}{k - kx + 0.5\Delta t}, \quad c_1 = \frac{kx + 0.5\Delta t}{k - kx + 0.5\Delta t}, \quad c_2 = \frac{k - kx - 0.5\Delta t}{k - kx + 0.5\Delta t} \tag{7.5}$$

Routing equation (7.5) is subject to $c_0 + c_1 + c_2 = 1$ (continuity restriction), and $k/3 \le \Delta t \le k$ (stability restriction).

The *direct problem*, or the forecasting problem, in hydrologic river routing may be formulated as follows: given $I(t)$, k, and x, predict $O(t)$. The procedure may be summarized as follows:

(1) Select a time interval, Δt, consistent with that at which the inflow hydrograph is given. Check for the stability requirement above.

(2) Calculate the routing constants c_0, c_1 and c_2 from equations (7.5). Check for the continuity restriction. Set iteration number $i=1$.

(3) For a given value of i, the current inflow rate, I_i, the future inflow rate Δt units of time later, I_{i+1}, and the current outflow rate, O_i, are known. These may be used to calculate the outflow rate forward in time, O_{i+1} from equation (7.5).

(4) Set $i=i+1$. Update the current and future values of the inflow rate. Set the current outflow rate to that computed in step (3).

(5) Repeat steps (3) and (4) for all time iterations i (i.e., until all values of the inflow hydrograph have been used).

Example 7.1: Hydrologic River Routing with Spreadsheets

Streamflow rate in the main river of a large watershed is being monitored. Prior to the passage of a flood wave, the flow rate at the monitoring station and at a station several kilometers downstream is 100 m^3/s. The flow rate at the upstream monitoring station is recorded in Table 7.1 at 6-*hour* intervals. Using the Muskingum method with $k=11 hour$ and $x=0.13$, predict the flow rate at the downstream station.

Table 7.1: Streamflow Data and Calculations for Example 7.1

Clock Time (hour)	i	$I_i(m^3/s)$	$c_0 I_{i+1}(m^3/s)$	$c_1 I_i(m^3/s)$	$c_2 O_i(m^3/s)$	$O_i(m^3/s)$
6:00 AM	1	100.0				100.0
12:00 PM	2	300.0	37.5	35.2	52.3	125.0
6:00 PM	3	680.0	85.0	105.6	65.4	256.0
12:00 AM	4	500.0	62.5	239.4	133.9	435.8
6:00 AM	5	400.0	50.0	176.0	227.9	453.9
12:00 PM	6	310.0	38.8	140.8	237.4	417.0
6:00 PM	7	230.0	28.8	109.1	218.1	356.0
12:00 AM	8	100.0	12.5	81.0	186.2	279.7

Solution

Following steps (1) through (5) above, select a time interval $\Delta t = 6 hour$, consistent with the recorded data. The stability requirement is satisfied since $k/3 \le \Delta t \le k$, or $11 hour/3 \le 6 hour \le 11 hour$. Routing constants are calculated from equations (7.5):

$$c_0 = \frac{-kx + 0.5\Delta t}{k - kx + 0.5\Delta t} = \frac{-11 hour \times 0.13 + 0.5 \times 6 hour}{11 hour - 11 hour \times 0.13 + 0.5 \times 6 hour} = 0.125$$

$$c_1 = \frac{kx + 0.5\Delta t}{k - kx + 0.5\Delta t} = \frac{11 hour \times 0.13 + 0.5 \times 6 hour}{12.570 hour} = 0.352$$

$$c_2 = \frac{k - kx - 0.5\Delta t}{k - kx + 0.5\Delta t} = \frac{11 hour - 11 hour \times 0.13 - 0.5 \times 6 hour}{12.570 hour} = 0.523$$

The continuity equation restriction is satisfied since $c_0 + c_1 + c_2$ $= 0.125 + 0.352 + 0.523 = 1.0$. Now set $i = 1$; $I_1 = 100 m^3/s$ and $I_2 = 300 m^3/s$. Applying equation (7.5), $O_2 = 125.0 m^3/s$. Each term in equation (7.5) is shown in a separate column on Table 7.1. Next, set $i = 2$; $I_2 = 300 m^3/s$ and $I_3 = 680 m^3/s$. Applying equation (7.5) again, $O_3 = 256 m^3/s$. Repeat the process until all values of the inflow hydrograph have been used. Note that the outflow hydrograph peak magnitude is less than that of the inflow. The time of the peak is also lagged by about 12 hours. This attenuation effect of a flood wave as it travels downstream is typical.

Example 7.2: Computer Programming of Hydrologic River Routing

The Kentucky river experienced a series of floods in 1991. Mean daily discharge rates (m^3/s) recorded at a station located at South Fork Licking are given by the following array: [385, 319, 266, 231, 202, 181, 167, 166, 165, 158, 154, 151, 156, 155, 153, 148, 133, 128, 126, 132, 143, 1130, 5490, 9370, 6660, 3130, 2200, 1720, 1430, 1400, 11300, 22400, 47400, 51400, 52700, 40800, 13900, 9650, 8560, 9760, 14000, 14000, 12900, 24500, 23500, 18100, 13500, 10600, 7990, 5680, 4730, 4240, 4440, 8030, 10800, 11300, 8860, 7560, 17300, 24400, 19700, 14300, 10700, 12500, 16200, 17400, 15100, 12000, 9190, 7050, 6070, 5240, 4550, 3990, 4120, 5280, 5770, 5540, 5030, 4460, 3890, 3310, 3140, 4120, 5670, 6930, 7460, 6640, 5390, 4820, 4130, 3740]. Prior to the storm, a downstream station recorded a flow rate of $400 m^3/s$. The portion of the river reach between South Fork Licking and the station downstream has Muskingum parameters given by $k = 5 hour$, $x = 0.2$. Write a Maple program that routes and plots the inflow hydrograph and predicts the corresponding one at the downstream station.

Solution

```
> #Enter Data.
  restart: with(stats):
  In:=[385,319,266,231,202,181,167,166,165,158,154,151,
      156,155,153,148,133,128,126,132,143,1130,5490,
      9370,6660,3130,2200,1720,1430,1400,11300,22400,
      47400,51400,52700,40800,13900,9650,8560,9760,
      14000,14000,12900,24500,23500,18100,13500,10600,
      7990,5680,4730,4240,4440,8030,10800,11300,8860,
      7560,17300,24400,19700,14300,10700,12500,16200,
      17400,15100,12000,9190,7050,6070,5240,4550,3990,
      4120,5280,5770,5540,5030,4460,3890,3310,3140,4120,
      5670,6930,7460,6640,5390,4820,4130,3740]:
  N:=describe[count](In): k:=3: x:=0.2:
  On[1]:=400: delta_t:=1:
  #Routing constants, equations (7.5)
  c0:=(-k*x+0.5*delta_t)/(k-k*x+0.5*delta_t):
  c1:=(k*x+0.5*delta_t)/(k-k*x+0.5*delta_t):
  c2:=(k-k*x-0.5*delta_t)/(k-k*x+0.5*delta_t):
  if (c1+c2+c3!=1.0) or (delta_t<k/3) or (delta_t>k)
      then `Stability restriction violated`
  end if;
```

Apply routing equation (7.5) iteratively. Store output in array of
coordinate [[t1, Q1], [t2, Q2]...] and plot.

```
> for i from 1 to N-1 do On[i+1]:=c0*In[i+1]
                     +c1*In[i]+c2*On[i] end do:
  Qin:=[seq([i,In[i]],i=1..N-1)]:
  Qout:=[seq([i,On[i]],i=1..N-1)]:
  plot(Qin,color=black,linestyle=3,
      legend=`Upstream Hydrograph`):
  plot(Qout,color=black,
       legend=`Downstream Hydrograph`):
  plots[display](%,%%,labels=[`t (days)`,`Q (m^3/s)`],
      labeldirections=[HORIZONTAL,VERTICAL],
      labelfont=[TIMES,ROMAN,16]);
```

Given the inflow and the outflow hydrographs simultaneously measured at an upstream and a downstream ends of a river reach, respectively, it is of interest to estimate the Muskingum parameters, k and x. This is *the inverse problem* in flood routing. Information on the value of these parameters may be later used to forecast an outflow hydrograph given an inflow one. To solve the inverse problem we use a "reverse" routing procedure. From equation (7.2),

$$S_{i+1}=(\overline{I}-\overline{O})\Delta t+S_i \qquad (7.6)$$

where
$\overline{I}=(I_i+I_{i+1})/2=$ average inflow rate (m^3/s)
$\overline{O}=(O_i+O_{i+1})/2=$ average outflow rate (m^3/s)

Since both the inflow and the outflow hydrographs are known, and given the storage at the previous times step, S_i, we may use equation (7.6) to calculate the storage at the next time step, S_{i+1}. Now, the Muskingum equation (7.3) for the storage at time $i+1$ is,

$$S_{i+1}=k[xI_{i+1}+(1-x)O_{i+1}] \qquad (7.7)$$

For the true value of x, the term in the square brackets in equation (7.7), $[xI_{i+1}+(1-x)O_{i+1}]$, is linearly related to the storage, S_{i+1}. This suggests that we may find the true value of x by plotting the term in the square brackets in equation (7.7) with respect to S_{i+1} for trial values of x. The value of x that yields the best linear relationship is the optimal or true one. From the slope of the latter curve, we obtain the value of k (see equation (7.7)).

The procedure for the estimation of the parameters of the Muskingum flood routing method is the following:

(1) Calculate S_{i+1} for every flow rate given (i.e., each i) from equation (7.6). For $i=1$ set $S_1=0$.

(2) Select a trial value of x. Plot S_{i+1} with respect to the term in the square brackets in equation (7.7), $[xI_{i+1}+(1-x)O_{i+1}]$, for each i (i.e., each given flow rate).

(3) Repeat step (2) until a straight line is obtained. This is the optimal value of x.

(4) Calculate the slope of the optimal x figure in step (3) by taking two

points. Substitute them into equation (7.7) to calculate the value of k.

Example 7.3: Estimation of Muskingum Routing Parameters

Assume that the inflow hydrograph and the calculated outflow hydrograph of Example 7.1 are given as measured data. Estimate the values of the Muskingum routing parameters x and k using a spreadsheet.

Solution

Table 7.2 contains the data and the calculations. The first columns from the left contain the time, the inflow and the outflow hydrographs. I is calculated as the average inflow during two subsequent time steps. O is calculated as the average outflow during two subsequent time steps. Now proceeding with step 1 in the method described above, calculate S_i from equation (7.6) as follows:

$$S_2 = (\bar{I} - \bar{O})\Delta t + S_1 = (200.0 - 112.5)\frac{m^3}{s} \times 6 hour \times \frac{3600s}{hour} = 1.89 \times 10^6 m^3$$

$$S_3 = (\bar{I} - \bar{O})\Delta t + S_2 = (490.0 - 190.5)\frac{m^3}{s} \times 6 hour \times \frac{3600s}{hour} + 1.89 \times 10^6 m^3$$

$$= 8.40 \times 10^6 m^3$$

$\vdots$

Table 7.2: Streamflow Data and Calculations for Example 7.3

Clock Time	i	I_i	O_i	$\bar{I}$	$\bar{O}$	S_{i+1}	$[xI_{i+1}+(1-x)O_{i+1}]$	$[xI_{i+1}+(1-x)O_{i+1}]$
(hour)		(m^3/s)	(m^3/s)	(m^3/s)	(m^3/s)	$(m^3 \times 10^6)$	$x=0.05$	$x=0.13$
6:00 AM	1	100.0	100.0					
12:00 PM	2	300.0	125.0	200.0	112.5	1.89	133.8	147.8
6:00 PM	3	680.0	256.0	490.0	190.5	8.40	277.2	311.1
12:00 AM	4	500.0	435.8	590.0	345.9	13.63	438.3	444.1
6:00 AM	5	400.0	453.9	450.0	444.9	13.74	451.2	446.9
12:00 PM	6	310.0	417.0	355.0	435.5	12.00	411.7	403.1
6:00 PM	7	230.0	356.0	270.0	386.5	9.49	349.7	339.6
12:00 AM	8	100.0	279.7	165.0	317.9	6.20	270.7	256.3

Next, set a trial value of $x=0.05$; calculate the term in the square brackets in equation (7.7)

$$[xI_2 + (1-x)O_2] = \left[0.05 \times 300.0\frac{m^3}{s} + 0.95 \times 125.0\frac{m^3}{s}\right] = 133.8\frac{m^3}{s}$$

Next, plot the values of S_{i+1} with respect to corresponding values of $[xI_{i+1}+(1-x)O_{i+1}]$ (see Figure 7.2). Repeat step (2) several times for different trial values of x (not shown in Table 7.2). The calculations corresponding to the optimal value of $x=0.13$ are shown in the last column of Table 7.2 and in Figure 7.2.

Finally, to estimate the value of k, apply equation (7.7) to two points in the plot with the optimal x (i.e., find the inverse of the slope):

$$k=\frac{(13.74-1.89)\times10^6 m^3/s}{(446.9-147.8)\dfrac{m^3}{s}\times\dfrac{3600s}{hour}}=11.0 hour$$

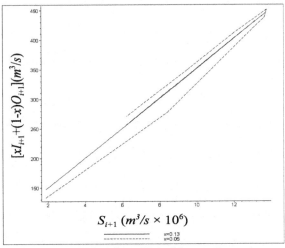

Figure 7.2: Estimation of Muskingum Parameters

Note that the estimated parameters coincide with the values given as data in Example 7.1.

Example 7.4: Computer Program for the Inverse Problem

A computer program for the inverse problem is indeed simple. Assume that the inflow and the calculated outflow hydrographs in Example 7.2 are the only data available, but the Muskingum routing parameters for the Kentucky river reach, k and x, are unknown. Write a Maple program to estimate the latter.

Solution

The following Maple commands are written at the end of the program in Example 7.2, unless the flows In[, , ,...] and On[, , ,...] are previously entered as data. First, the storage due to the various flow rates are computed. The user next enters a trial value of *x*, and a graph of the storage versus the term in the square bracket in equation (7.7) is produced. The user manually adjusts the value of *x* until a straight line is obtained. Once this is accomplished, the last portion of the program calculates the optimal value of *k*. The program below shows the last, optimal, values in this process.

```
[ Given a known inflow and outflow hydrographs, In and On, estimate x by trial and error
[ > S[1]:=0:
    for i from 1 to N-1 do
        Ibar[i+1]:=(In[i]+In[i+1])/2:
        Obar[i+1]:=(On[i]+On[i+1])/2:
        S[i+1]:=(Ibar[i+1]-Obar[i+1])*delta_t+S[i]:
    end do:
    #Guess a trial value of x
    x:=0.2:
    #Term in the square brackets in equation (7.7)
    for i from 1 to N-1 do
        Sq[i+1]:=(x*In[i+1]+(1-x)*On[i+1]):
    end do:
    Loop:=[seq([S[i],Sq[i]],i=2..N)]:
    plot(Loop,color=black,
        labels=[`S (m^3*10^6)`,`[x*I+(1-x)*O] (m^3/s)`],
        labeldirections=[HORIZONTAL,VERTICAL],
        labelfont=[TIMES,ROMAN,16]);
```

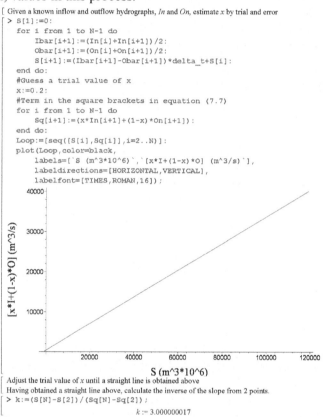

```
[ Adjust the trial value of x until a straight line is obtained above
[ Having obtained a straight line above, calculate the inverse of the slope from 2 points.
[ > k:=(S[N]-S[2])/(Sq[N]-Sq[2]);
```

$$k := 3.000000017$$

Hydraulic River Routing: Kinematic Wave Celerity

A *flood wave* consists in a variation in the flow conditions, such as an evolution in the discharge rate and water level. The *wave celerity* is the velocity with which this disturbance travels along a river channel. The wave celerity is, in general, different from that of the water velocity and it is a function of the type of wave under consideration. *Dynamic waves* govern the flow conditions when the inertial and pressure forces are important. This is the case of a large flood wave propagating through a wide river; the energy line and the water surface elevation are not parallel to the river bed profile. As the dynamic wave travels downstream, its crest attenuates and parts of the disturbance travel slower (i.e., backwards) than its center of mass, and parts of it faster (i.e., forward). Dynamic waves are described by the Saint-Venant Equations (Martin and McCutcheon, 1999; Chow et al., 1988). An important simplification is the case of a *kinematic wave*; here the gravity and friction forces are balanced and the flow does not accelerate significantly. The acceleration and pressure terms in the momentum equation are negligible, the energy line is parallel to the channel bottom, and the wave motion is essentially described by the continuity equation.

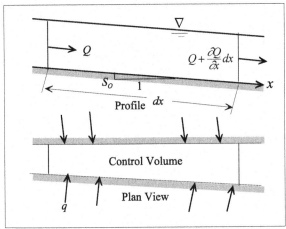

Figure 7.3: Control Volume in a River Reach

Figure 7.3 Shows a control volume in a river reach of length dx. Assuming constant water density, the flow rate entering the upstream end is $Q+qdx$, where Q is the upstream flow rate and q the lateral surface and groundwater inflow volume per unit channel length. The flow rate leaving the control volume may be expressed as that entering it plus the rate of change with respect to distance times the volume length, $Q+\partial Q/\partial x \cdot dx$. The net mass rate is that leaving the volume minus that entering it. The change in the water stored in the volume is $\partial(A dx)/dt$, where the cross-sectional area is $A(x)$. In words, the conservation of mass statement is

The net mass rate entering the volume minus the change in mass rate from sources or sinks = zero

Mathematically, the mass conservation equation is given by

$$\frac{\partial Q}{\partial x}dx + qdx + \frac{\partial A dx}{\partial t} = 0 \tag{7.8}$$

Dividing by dx and re-arranging,

$$\frac{\partial Q}{\partial x} + \frac{\partial A}{\partial t} = q \tag{7.9}$$

where
  Q=streamflow rate (m^3/s)
  A=average stream cross-sectional area (m^2)
  q=lateral inflow to the stream from overland and groundwater flow
     per unit length of channel (m^2)
  x=distance (m) from an upstream streamflow station with a known
     hydrograph, $Q_0(t)$, along the main channel parallel to the bottom
  t=time (*hour, day*)

With the assumptions of a kinematic wave, the slope of the energy
line is parallel to that of the bottom and the momentum equation reduces
to

$$S_o = S_f \tag{7.10}$$

where
  S_f=slope of the energy line
  S_o=slope of the channel bottom (see Figure 7.3)

The momentum equation can also be described in the form

$$A = \alpha Q^\beta \tag{7.11}$$

where
  α=a positive constant ($m^{2-3\beta}s^\beta$)
  β=a positive constant

Differentiating equation (7.11) with respect to t,

$$\frac{\partial A}{\partial t} = \alpha\beta Q^{\beta-1}\left(\frac{\partial Q}{\partial t}\right) \tag{7.12}$$

and substituting for $\partial A/\partial t$ in equation (7.9),

$$\frac{\partial Q}{\partial x} + \alpha\beta Q^{\beta-1}\left(\frac{\partial Q}{\partial t}\right) = q \qquad (7.13)$$

The *kinematic wave celerity* can be deduced from equation (7.13) as

$$c_k = \frac{dx}{dt} = \frac{dQ}{dA} = \frac{1}{\alpha\beta Q^{\beta-1}} \qquad (7.14)$$

where
  c_k=kinematic wave celerity (*m/hour*)

An observer moving along the channel with a velocity c_k would see the flow discharge increasing at a rate $dQ/dx=q$. If $q=0$, the observer would see a constant discharge. Both the dynamic and kinematic wave motion are present in natural flood waves. In many cases, the channel slope dominates the momentum equation and most of the flood propagates as a kinematic wave. Equation (7.13) is a nonlinear partial differential equation subject to the following boundary and initial conditions:

$$Q(0, t)=Q_0(t), \quad Q(x, 0)=f(x) \qquad (7.15)$$

where
  $f(x)$=the initial spatial flow rate distribution along the river channel (m^3/s), such that $f(0)=Q_0(0)$
  $Q_0(t)$=upstream flow rate at $x=0$

Several numerical solutions to the kinematic wave equation have ben proposed (Chow et al., 1988; Singh, 1996). A simple approximate analytical solution to the nonlinear kinematic wave equation was recently derived by combining an implicit solution obtained with the method of characteristics with analytical decomposition and successive approximation (Serrano, 2006). Thus, for the case of constant lateral flow, q, the solution to equation (7.13) subject to equation (7.15) is given by

$$Q=Q_0\left(t-\alpha\beta\left[Q_0(t)-qx\right]^{\beta-1}x\right)+qx \qquad (7.16)$$

Application of equation (7.16) in a river setting requires an inflow hydrograph, $Q_0(t)$, at an upstream station, the distance along the river channel, x, between the upstream and down stream station where the outflow hydrograph, $Q(t)$, is predicted, data to estimate the parameters α and β of a rating-curve relationship of the form $A=\alpha Q^\beta$ at a few cross sections in the river, and estimates of the base flow at the upstream and downstream stations. The implementation of equation (7.16) is nothing more than a simple formula for the temporal shifting of the upstream hydrograph, $Q_0(t)$, at hourly or daily times t, with an added lateral flow contribution, q.

Example 7.5: Flood Routing with the Nonlinear Kinematic Wave

Assume that at a given station a stream hydrograph is known and given by $Q_0(t) = 1 + e^{-(t-20)^2/50} (m^3/s)$. The rating curve is given by equation (7.11) with $\alpha = 0.2 (m^{2-3\beta} s^\beta)$. Assume that the lateral flow is $q = 0.001 \, m^2$. Predict the streamflow hydrograph at $x=500m$ downstream using the nonlinear kinematic wave equation (7.16) with various values of the parameter $\beta = 0.9$, $\beta = 1.0$ (the linear flood wave), and $\beta = 1.1$.

Solution

The following Maple program illustrates the calculations.

```
> #Data 1
  X:=500: alpha:=.2: beta:=.9: t1:=100: t2:=140: q:=0.001:
  Q0:=t->1+exp(-(t-20)^2/50):
  Q:=(x,t)->Q0(t-alpha*beta*(Q0(t)-q*x)^(beta-1)*x)+q*x:
  G1:=plot(Q(X,t),t=t1..t2,color=black,
      legend=`beta=0.9`,linestyle=1):
  G0:=plot(Q0(t),t=t1..t2,color=black,
      legend=`Qo(t)`,linestyle=1):
> #Data 2
  beta:=1:
  Q:=(x,t)->Q0(t-alpha*beta*(Q0(t)-q*x)^(beta-1)*x)+q*x:
  G2:=plot(Q(X,t),t=t1..t2,color=black,
      legend=`beta=1`,style=point, symbol=BOX):
> #Data 3
  beta:=1.1:
  Q:=(x,t)->Q0(t-alpha*beta*(Q0(t)-q*x)^(beta-1)*x)+q*x:
  G3:=plot(Q(X,t),t=t1..t2,color=black,
      legend=`beta=1.1`,linestyle=3):
> plots[display](G1,G2,G3,
      labels=[`Time (hours)`,`Q (m^3/s)`],
      labeldirections=[`horizontal`,`vertical`],
      font=[TIMES,ROMAN,16],labelfont=[TIMES,ROMAN,16]):
```

beta=0.9
beta=1
beta=1.1

The occurrence of the peak flow appears to be significantly sensitive to the magnitude of the nonlinear parameter β. For values of $\beta<1$, the peak flow occurs at a time earlier than that predicted by the linear hydrograph ($\beta=1$). For values of $\beta>1$, the peak flow occurs at a time later than that predicted by the linear hydrograph. This result is explained by the well known effects of lesser, or greater, river storage corresponding to various values of β. This suggests that, depending on the stream parameters, the simulation of flood propagation may not be appropriately described by a linear model. It is interesting to observe that the shape of the nonlinear hydrograph is not symmetric with respect to its center of mass. The reader may verify this by setting $\beta=1.5$, re-running the program and noting that the nonlinear hydrograph exhibits a sharper front end than that of the linear one. Sharp front ends and comparatively longer tail ends are typical of nonlinear waves. The above program may be easily adapted to read an hourly inflow hydrograph from a spreadsheet or a data file. The readdata( ) command is needed here (see Examples 2.6 and 3.11).

To account for variable lateral flow, while maintaining a simple, yet nonlinear, model, the lateral flow representation could be modified so as to account for the time variability of effective precipitation during high-intensity storms. For small sub-watersheds the lateral inflow may be given as (Serrano, 2006)

$$q(x,\ t)=q_0+\frac{cA_sP_e(t)}{L} \tag{7.17}$$

where
q_0 =constant lateral flow contribution from groundwater flow (m^2/s)
A_s =watershed area between the monitoring stations (m^2)
$P_e(t)$ =is the spatially-averaged effective precipitation rate in the sub-watershed($mm/hour$)
L =distance along the stream between the upstream and downstream stations (m)
$c=0.2778\times10^{-6}(m\ mm^{-1}hour\ s^{-1})$, a units conversion factor.

In equation (7.17), no consideration is given to overland flow storage or surface routing effects. The constant average lateral flow, q_0, may be easily estimated from the difference between average baseflow values at the downstream and the upstream stations, respectively. The effective precipitation, $P_e(t)$, may be obtained from hourly rainfall rate estimates after infiltration rate has been subtracted. The solution to the nonlinear kinematic flood wave now becomes (Serrano, 2006)

$$Q = Q_0 \left[t - \alpha \beta \left(Q_0(t) - q_0 x \right)^{\beta-1} x \right] + q_0 x + \frac{cA_s P_e(t)}{L} x \qquad (7.18)$$

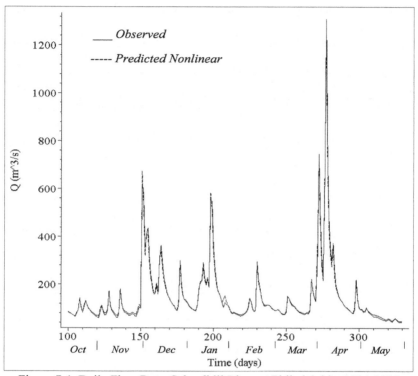

Figure 7.4: Daily Flow Rate, Schuylkill River at Philadelphia, 2004-2005

Figure 7.4 shows a comparison between the observed daily flow rates in the Schuylkill River at Philadelphia (Southeast Pennsylvania) and the predicted ones from equation (7.18) for the hydrologic year from September 2004 through May 2005. The inflow hydrograph, $Q_0(t)$ consisted of daily flow rates recorded by the U.S. Geological Survey at the Norristown station located $21 km$ upstream. Variable lateral flow was calculated from groundwater flow estimates and effective precipitation derived from rainfall data provided by the U.S. National Weather Service, after applying a simple infiltration model (Serrano, 2006). Figure 7.5 shows a detail of the simulations with the linear, the nonlinear, and the observed values. Clearly, the nonlinear model is significantly more accurate than the linear one. The linear kinematic wave model, on the other hand, appeared to significantly underestimate the flood-peak time.

The nonlinear kinematic wave equation is of simple application and permits the efficient forecast of nonlinear kinematic flood waves without the usual stability restrictions of numerical models. In circumstances when significant forward and backward hydrograph dispersion occurs, this model should not be applied in place of the full dynamic wave equations. The lateral flow correction in equation (7.18) is an adjustment for added flow in between stations. When the inflow hydrograph is significantly different in shape and magnitude from the resulting downstream one the correction will not be sufficient and this model should not be applied.

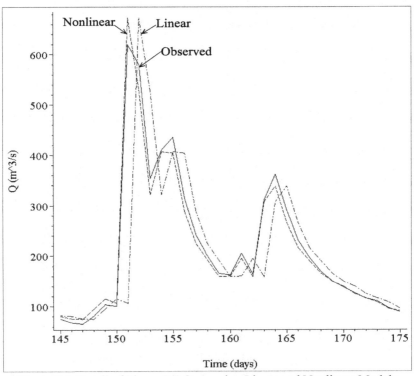

Figure 7.5: Detail of Figure 7.5 Comparing Linear and Nonlinear Models

Hydrologic Reservoir Routing: The Storage Indication Method (SIM)

Many watersheds have natural or artificial reservoirs within their drainage areas. Natural reservoirs, or lakes, occur when surface runoff waters fill large natural topographic depressions. The origins of these lakes may be associated with glacial formations or with natural embankments resulting from sediment deposition. Artificial reservoirs, on the other hand, are human made lakes constructed with the intend to store water for a specific purpose. By storing water over long periods of time the seasonal variability of rainfall and runoff is attenuated and a constant, average, output of water may be provided. During periods of intense upstream runoff, the excess waters fill the reservoir. The increased volume of water is used to supply a water resources demand during dry periods of the year. Reasons for the construction of a reservoir vary according to the needs in the region. A reservoir may be used to control flooding downstream; to provide water for artificial irrigation, domestic use in urban localities, or hydroelectric generation; to maintain minimum water levels for navigation; to create an ambiance for recreation and enhance the quality of life; or a combination of the above. It is also known that artificial reservoirs, especially large ones, may cause adverse environmental effects in the region by displacing human and animal settlements, increasing the groundwater levels in the region, creating soil drainage problems, altering the sediment and nutrient contents of the waters downstream, and creating a potential flooding hazard in cases of dam failure.

The design of a reservoir involves many hydrologic, hydraulic, geotechnical, environmental, economic, and social variables (see Linsley et al., 1992; Loucks et al., 1981). The choice of the dam type depends on considerations related to the geology of the foundation, the availability of materials, and the cost of labor. Earth dams appear to be more economical in regions where the cost of human labor is low and in locations where the quality of the rock foundation is dubious. Earth dams appear to adapt well to substantial subsiding. On the other hand, concrete dams are slimmer and require comparatively less amount of material than earth dams, but they must be built under a solid foundation.

The *emergency spillway* is an important component of a reservoir. It must be designed to withstand the passage of an adverse flood wave. The hydrograph describing the flow rate time distribution at the spillway constitutes the so called *design hydrograph*. The characteristics of the design hydrograph, such as peak flow rate, are conceived according to the size of the structure. In Chapter 2 it was explained that design rainfall events are conceived from an event return period commensurate with the size of the structure (i.e., the severity of the damage once it fails). Thus, the larger the structure, the higher the return period of the design rainfall to be used. Given a return period recommended (or mandated by regulations) for a particular water resources structure, and a local precipitation intensity, duration, and frequency relationship, the hydrologist can produce the characteristics of a design rainfall storm. With the rainfall storm and the techniques described in Chapter 6, the design hydrograph may be simulated at the inflow end of a reservoir. This is the design hydrograph obtained from precipitation analysis. Alternatively, a hydrologist may study the statistical properties of historical maximum flow rates in a watershed (later studied in this chapter). This analysis leads to an adverse maximum flow rate corresponding to a given return period. With the maximum flow rate a design hydrograph may deduced. This is the design hydrograph obtained from streamflow analysis.

Using an appropriate reservoir flood routing method, the passage of a design hydrograph is simulated. The result is the hydrograph downstream the reservoir. Besides the design of reservoirs, the procedure is used to forecast flow rate at locations downstream the reservoir. Flood forecasting is used for the delineation of the watershed flood plain areas, or the prediction in time of the flood peak magnitude of an actually measured upstream hydrograph. Flood plain delineation constitutes the bases for land use management and urbanization restrictions. On the other hand, if an extreme hydrograph is measured upstream in the watershed, hydrologic flood routing may be used to simulate the features of the downstream hydrograph and execute emergency evacuation procedures in a rational, objective, manner.

When a flood wave enters a reservoir it propagates and dissipates along the surface of the water. The energy dissipation effect is a function of the amount of water stored, the surface area, and the shape of the reservoir. Of interest to the hydrologist is the quantitative description of the flow rate at the outlet of the reservoir. As in the previous section, we focus here on a simplified *hydrologic reservoir routing* and leave the more complex *hydraulic reservoir routing* procedures to more in depth texts given in the references.

The first element to consider in the routing of an inflow hydrograph through a reservoir is the reservoir spillway. There are many kinds of spillways, such as the curved concrete type, the tubed "morning glory" type, and the earth dam spillway. Each kind is selected according to technical and economical considerations. In all cases, the function of the spillway is to evacuate a surcharge storage generated by the passage of an extreme flood wave. Figure 7.6 shows an example of a reservoir concrete spillway in profile. The curved shape of the downstream end of the spillway is designed according to energy loss minimization criteria (Chow, 1959). Upstream the spillway, we may distinguish some significant water threshold levels. The lowest possible water level is marked by the that of the reservoir draft intake. The normal level represents the mean water elevation averaged over seasonal fluctuations.

The spillway crest level marks the *normal maximum* elevation of the water. The maximum level is that produced by the design peak flow rate.

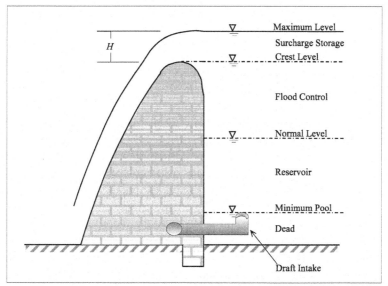

Figure 7.6: A Concrete Spillway with Various Storage Classes

The volume of water between the significant water levels constitute the allocations of water storage to particular purposes. For instance, between the minimum pool and the original ground surface we have the dead storage. This is the volume allotted to gradual sediment deposition throughout the service life of the reservoir. Between the minimum pool and the normal level we have part of the storage for irrigation, urban water supply, or hydroelectric generation. Between the normal level and the crest level we find the storage allotted to other purposes, such as flood control. Finally, between the crest level and the absolute maximum level we have the surcharge storage produced by the peak flow rate of the design hydrograph. These water volumes are slowly released through normal outlets such as pipes to turbines, or over the emergency spillway during extreme floods.

Thus, the first element in reservoir flood routing is a relationship between the water head above the crest of a spillway and the outflow rate downstream the spillway, or $O=f(H)$. According to the type and shape of the spillway, these relationships are found in hydraulics textbooks after considerations of continuity, energy, and momentum; or after experimentation in hydraulic reduced models. For an ungated concrete spillway the relationship is of the form

$$O=cwH^x \qquad (7.19)$$

where
  O=outflow rate (m^3/s)
  w=length of the spillway crest (m)
  H=head above spillway crest (m)
  c=a coefficient, theoretically 1.656 ($m^{0.5}/s$)
  x=exponent, theoretically 1.5

The second element in hydrologic reservoir routing is that related to the terrain and the shape of the reservoir. According to the physiographic configuration of the watershed, there corresponds a storage volume, S, to a given elevation of water above the spillway crest, H. This storage is found after a numerical integration of the volume of water marked by the topographic contour corresponding to the given elevation. A detailed topographic map of the part of the watershed covered by the reservoir is needed along with a device or method to calculate areas (i.e., polar planimeter, digitizer, digital terrain software, etc.). The volume of water under a given water level is estimated as the summation of sub-volumes comprised between subsequent contour levels, starting from the contour corresponding to the given water level down to the lowest contour at the bottom of the reservoir. The sub-volume of water between two subsequent contour levels is approximated as the watershed area covered by the line with an elevation half way between the two contours, times the elevation difference between the two contours.

For convenience, S is often defined as the "surcharge storage" or the storage above the emergency spillway crest. Normally the overflow rate is zero when S is zero. Thus, the second element necessary in hydrologic reservoir routing is a relationship between surcharge storage and the head above the crest of the spillway, or $S=f(H)$. This relationship is constructed by setting trial values of H, within the expected range of occurrence, and calculating the corresponding volume S as described above.

Since $O=f(H)$ and $S=f(H)$ (both depend on pool elevation), then both relations may be combined numerically to obtain a storage-outflow relationship, $S=f(O)$. This relationship may be plotted and if found to be linear, the slope of the graph is the storage constant, k, in a linear reservoir, or $S=kO$.

Routing an inflow hydrograph through a linear reservoir is a special case of the Muskingum river routing procedure discussed in the previous section. In this case, set $x=0$ in equations (7.5) and proceed as in Example

7.1. If the storage outflow relationship is nonlinear, we use continuity equation (7.2) to calculate the unknown terms at a given time. Let us re-write equation (7.2) as

$$I_i + I_{i+1} + \left(\frac{2S_i}{\Delta t} - O_i \right) = \frac{2S_{i+1}}{\Delta t} + O_{i+1} \qquad (7.20)$$

In equation (7.20) all the terms on the left side of the equality are known at a given iteration. Hence, we may calculate the value in the left side in m^3/s. What we need is a relationship between the terms on the right side of the equality and the outflow rate at the next time step. This relationship, called the *storage indication curve* (SIC), between $2S_{i+1}/\Delta t + O_{i+1}$ and O_{i+1} is provided by the function $S=f(O)$ previously derived from the spillway type and the reservoir configuration.

The procedure to route an inflow hydrograph through a reservoir using the *storage indication method* (SIM) is summarized in the following steps:

(1) *O=f(H) Relationship*. From the spillway type, obtain a hydraulic relationship between the head above the crest of the spillway, H, and the outflow rate, O.

(2) *S=f(H) Relationship*. Based on a detailed topographic map of the watershed area covered by the reservoir, obtain a numerical relationship (i.e., in table format) between the head above the crest of the spillway, H, and the surcharge storage in the reservoir, S. Begin by setting $S=0$ at $H=0$. Calculate S for several trial values of H within the expected range of occurrence.

(3) *SIC: O=f(2S/\Delta t+O)*. Combine the relationships obtained in steps (1) and (2) to obtain the SIC. In other words, create another column in the table with values of ($2S/\Delta t + O$). Set the time iteration $i=1$.

(4) *Continuity Equation*. For a given time iteration, i, the current value of the outflow rate, O_i, is known. Calculate the left side of equation (7.20), $I_i + I_{i+1} + (2S_i/\Delta t - O_i)$, using the current outflow rate and the known inflow rates. This is equal to the term $2S_{i+1}/\Delta t + O_{i+1}$ (i.e., the right side of equation (7.9).

(5) *SIC*: Enter the SIC with the value of $2S_{i+1}/\Delta t + O_{i+1}$ calculated in step (4), and read the corresponding outflow rate, O_{i+1}.

(6) *Update i*. Repeat steps (4) and (5) for all values of i (i.e., until all values of the inflow rate have been used).

Example 7.6: Hydrologic Reservoir Routing with the SIM

A reservoir has an average surface area of $5km^2$, and a concrete spillway with a crest width of 40.0 m. Prior to the passage of an extreme flood wave, the flow rate upstream and downstream the reservoir is 2.0 m^3/s. Route the inflow hydrograph given in the first three columns of Table 7.4, assuming that the surface area of the reservoir does not change significantly within the range of head values.

Solution

Following steps (1) through (6) above, we first obtain a relationship between head and outflow rate. Since the reservoir has a concrete spillway, we use equation (7.19):

$$O=cwH^x=1.656\frac{m^{0.5}}{s}\times40m\times(H\ m)^{1.5}=66.24H^{1.5}\frac{m^3}{s} \qquad (7.21)$$

Since the surface area of the reservoir does not change with head, the relationship between head and surcharge storage is simply the product of the average area times the head:

$$S=AH=5km^2\times\frac{10^6m^2}{km^2}\times H\ m=5\times10^6H\ m^3 \qquad (7.22)$$

Now applying equations (7.21) and (7.22) to typical values of the head, we create Table 7.3 with the values of the SIC. The first column from the left are trial values of H. The second column from the left is S as calculated from equation (7.22). The third column is O as calculated from equation (7.21). The fourth column in Table 7.3 is twice the second column divided by the time interval plus the third column. Since the inflow rate in Table 7.4 is given at daily time intervals, we use $\Delta t=1 day$. For instance for $H=0.1m$,

$$\frac{2S}{\Delta t}+O=\frac{2\times0.5\times10^6m^3}{1day\times\dfrac{86400s}{day}}+2.09\frac{m^3}{s}=13.66\frac{m^3}{s}$$

From Table 7.3, plot the SIC (Figure 7.7).

Table 7.3: Derivation of the SIC for Example 7.6

$H(m)$	$S\ (m^3 \times 10^6)$	$O(m^3/s)$	$2S/\Delta t + O(m^3/s)$
0.0	0.0	0.00	0.00
0.1	0.5	2.09	13.66
0.2	1.0	5.92	29.07
0.4	2.0	16.76	63.06
0.6	3.0	30.79	100.23
0.8	4.0	47.40	139.99
1.0	5.0	66.24	181.98

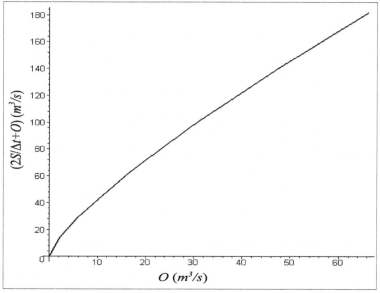

Figure 7.7: Storage Indication Curve for Example 7.5

We now have all the information to route the inflow hydrograph through the reservoir. The procedure follows a successive applications of steps (4) and (5). The calculations are summarized in Table 7.4. Column 1 in Table 7.4 is time, t. Column 2 is the iteration time step, i. Column 3 has the inflow rate values, I_i, of the inflow hydrograph. Column 4 has the summation of two subsequent flow rates, $I_i + I_{i+1}$, according to continuity equation (7.20). Column 5 contains the values of $2S_i/\Delta t - O_i$ (left side of equation (7.20). Column 6 contains the values of $2S_i/\Delta t + O_i$, or the right side of equation (7.20). Column 7 contains the outflow rate values, O_i. Values in columns 1, 2, and 3 are given from the data. Column 4 is calculated from column 3 as indicated. Values in columns 5 through 7 are to be filled on a row by row sequence as follows:

Table 7.4: Inflow and Calculated Outflow Hydrograph for Example 7.6

1	2	3	4	5	6	7
t (day)	i	I_i (m^3/s)	I_i+I_{i+1} (m^3/s)	$(2S_i/\Delta t-O_i)$ (m^3/s)	$(2S_i/\Delta t+O_i)$ (m^3/s)	O_{i+1} (m^3/s)
0	1	2.0	→ 17.0 →	→ 6.1 ↘	← 10.1 ←	← 2.0 ←
1	2	15.0	55.0	12.9	↘ 23.1 →	5.1
2	3	40.0	65.5	33.5	67.9	17.2
3	4	25.5	43.1	39.8	99.0	29.6
4	5	17.6	30.4	36.1	82.9	23.4
5	6	12.8	21.8	31.5	66.5	17.5
6	7	9.0	15.0	26.7	53.3	13.3
7	8	6.0	9.4	23.7	41.7	9.0
8	9	3.4	5.4	18.1	33.1	7.5
9	10	2.0			23.5	5.0

(a) starting with the given initial value of the outflow rate in column 7, $O_1=2.0$, enter this number on the SIC Figure 7.4, read the corresponding value of $2S_1/\Delta t+O_1=10.1$ and write it in column 6.

(b) To find the corresponding value in column 5, notice that the difference between column 6 and column 5 is $2\times O$. Thus, $2S_1/\Delta t-O_1=2S_1/\Delta t+O_1-2O_1$, or $6.1=10.1-2\times2.0$. Write this value in column 5.

(c) Next add $I_1+I_2+2S_1/\Delta t-O_1$ to obtain $2S_2/\Delta t+O_2$. In other words, add column 4 and 5 to obtain the new value (down) of column 6, $17.0 + 6.1 = 23.1$.

(d) Enter this number in the SIC Figure 7.4 and read the new outflow rate, $O_2=5.1$. This completes one loop in the calculations. The arrows in Table 7.4 indicate the order in the calculations.

(e) Repeat steps (b) through (d) sequentially until all values of the outflow rate are calculated.

Comparing the inflow and outflow hydrographs, notice the expected effect of the passage of the flood wave through the reservoir: an attenuation of the peak flow rate magnitude, a lagged peak time, and an increase in the time base of the outflow hydrograph. Mathematical simulations performed in this fashion with the aid of a computer help the hydrologist assess the performance of the existing, or proposed, water resources structures with respect to extreme events. These procedures constitute the fundamental tools of water resources management and design projects.

Example 7.7: Computer Program for the SIM

Assume that the inflow data of Example 7.4 constitutes a emergency design hydrograph to be routed through a future reservoir to be built at Fort Licking, Kentucky. Following steps (1)-(3) of the SIM, engineers fitted a SIC (similar to Figure 7.7) to an analytical function given by $S_p = O^a$, where $a = 1.3$ and $S_p = 2S/\Delta t + O(m^3/s)$. Using $\Delta t = 1\,day$ and $O_1 = 400\,m^3/s$ route the design hydrograph through the reservoir.

Solution

Using the data from Example 7.4, we modify the program by adapting it to execute steps (4)-(6) of the SIM. At the heart of calculations is a Maple procedure called "step(i)." For each iteration i, step(i) calculates continuity equation (7.20), and uses the inverse form of the SIC to estimate the future flow rate O_{i+1}. Inflow and outflow hydrographs are stored in arrays of coordinates $[[t_1,\ Q_1],\ [t_2,\ Q_2],\ ...]$ and plotted. The reservoir produces a substantial attenuation of the peaks in the inflow hydrograph, thus reducing the potentially adverse effect of flooding.

```
> restart: with(stats):
  #Enter data; calculatye initial storage constants
  In:=[385,319,266,231,202,181,167,166,165,158,154,
       151,156,155,153,148,133,128,126,132,143,1130,
       5490,9370,6660,3130,2200,1720,1430,1400,11300,
       22400,47400,51400,52700,40800,13900,9650,8560,
       9760,14000,14000,12900,24500,23500,18100,13500,
       10600,7990,5680,4730,4240,4440,8030,10800,
       11300,8860,7560,17300,24400,19700,14300,10700,
       12500,16200,17400,15100,12000,9190,7050,6070,
       5240,4550,3990,4120,5280,5770,5540,5030,4460,
       3890,3310,3140,4120,5670,6930,7460,6640,5390,
       4820,4130,3740]:
  N:=describe[count](In): On[1]:=400: dt:=1: a:=1.3:
  S:=q->q^(a):           #SIC
  Q:=s->s^(1/a):         #Inverse SIC
  Sp[1]:=S(On[1]):       #Initial 2S/dt+O
  Sm[1]:=Sp[1]-2*On[1]:  #Initial 2S/dt-O
> step:=proc(j)          #Basic iteration time step
      global Sm, Sp, S, Q, In, On;
      Sp[j+1]:=In[j]+In[j+1]+Sm[j]:
      On[j+1]:=Q(Sp[j+1]):
      Sm[j+1]:=Sp[j+1]-2*On[j+1]:
      On[j+1]:
  end:
[ Apply routing equation iteratively. Store output in array and plot.
> for i from 1 to N-1 do step(i) end do:
  Qin:=[seq([i,In[i]],i=1..N-1)]:
  Qout:=[seq([i,On[i]],i=1..N-1)]:
  plot(Qin,color=black,linestyle=3,thickness=2,
      legend=`Design Inflow Hydrograph`):
  plot(Qout,color=black,thickness=2,legend=`Outflow Hydrograph`):
  plots[display](%,%%,labels=[`t (days)`,`Q (m^3/s)`],
      labeldirections=[HORIZONTAL,VERTICAL],
      labelfont=[TIMES,ROMAN,16]);
```

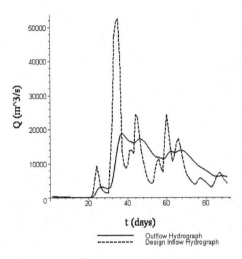

Hydrologic reservoir routing is at the heart of most methods to design flood control measures in urban hydrology. Regulations in many states and localities now require storage of water quantity or water quality in developing urban areas. New highways are now designed with roadside swales, or vegetated depressions for the amelioration of flood peaks and volumes. A *detention storage* involves slowing surface runoff in a temporary reservoir and then releasing it. In a *retention storage* the water is not released downstream, but removed through infiltration through a porous bottom or by evaporation. These are common solutions to mitigate flood waters, although designed retention becomes less practical as the size of the drainage area increases. The required storage volume should be based on an analysis of a design storm volume. A common method is to adopt a design rainfall hyetograph from the local IDF curves (see Chapter 2). The design rainfall storm is converted into an effective precipitation pattern after subtracting infiltration (see Chapter 4). The latter is converted into a design hydrograph at the watershed outlet using unit hydrograph methods (see Chapter 6). The area under the hydrograph yields the required storage volume.

A *detention basin* –also called *retarding basins or stormwater management ponds*– , is a temporary catchment built to delay the flooding waters. It usually has a low flow or underflow outlet and an emergency weir or spillway for high flows. Depending on the particular design and the hydraulic conditions, the underflow outlet can be treated as a hydraulic orifice on a nonlinear tank or a box culvert. Hydraulic texts list the storage versus outflow, or the head versus outflow, formulae for these devices. Using the flood routing techniques described in this section, a designed inflow hydrograph entering the detention basin can be transformed mathematically into an outflow hydrograph. By comparing the inflow peak rate with that of the outflow the engineer decides wether or not the attenuation effect is adequate. The size of the basin (i.e., its storage capacity) is increased or decreased according to its ability to meet a sufficiently small flood peak at the outlet. Many details and considerations in the design and operation of retention and detention basins are given in Bedient and Huber (2002), Mays 2001, Debo and Reese (1995), Horner et al. (1994), Urbonas and Stahre (1993), Water Environment Federation and the American Society of Civil Engineers (1992), Water Pollution Control Federation (1989), DeGroot (1982), Schueler (1987), and Poertner (1981).

7.2 FLOOD AND DROUGHT FREQUENCY ANALYSIS

Design Flood (Drought) of Water Resources Structures

The prediction of uncertain environmental variables is often a hydrologic problem of significance in water resources management and water resources design projects. Hydraulic structures acting as components of water resources projects are planned and built to withstand a specific input of water. The input of water corresponds to an extreme hydrologic event of a given severity.

Unable to predict future hydrologic events in an exact deterministic manner, hydrologists "predict" the occurrence of extreme events in a broad statistical sense. Based on statistical analyses of the best possible, and longest, historical streamflow record in the watershed, it is possible to predict the streamflow rate, or the volume magnitude, associated with a given *frequency*. In other words, instead of predicting the time of occurrence of a flood of certain magnitude, the hydrologist ascertains "how often" a flood of such magnitude occurs. For instance, a maximum annual flow rate of $Q=10,000 m^3/s$ occurs in a watershed, on an average, of once every 100 years. We say that such flow rate has *a return period*, T, of 100 years.

As the value of T increases, the possibility of encountering a higher value of Q increases. Thus, in the above example, the 200-*year* return period in the same watershed corresponds to a more severe flood (e.g., $Q=12,000 m^3/s$). Therefore, the given "severity" of the design hydrologic event mentioned before is provided by a specific value of the return period in years. Clearly, the larger the size of the structure to be built, and the greater the damage and losses once it fails, the greater the return period used in its design. This constitutes a statistically objective way to design a structure according to its size. For instance, a highway box culvert should be designed to withstand the flood associated with a low return period (e.g., $T=2year$) because the damage caused by its failure is considered small. On the other hand, the damage caused by the failure of a dam is, depending on its size, an accident of major proportions including the loss of human life. This implies that a return period of several hundreds of years should be used in its design.

The return period selected, or that required by regulations, for the design of a structure may reflect economic considerations. These include an evaluation of the cost of building a structure to protect against a certain event versus the damage, cleaning, and repair cost incurred by not protecting against such an event. Certain structures, such as large dams, must be built to withstand the worst possible event. In such cases it is considered that the loss of human life and the damage caused by the failure of the dam constitutes a catastrophe of major proportions and therefore they should be built as permanent structures designed to withstand the probable maximum precipitation event, PMP. In chapter 2 we introduced the basic concepts of return period, design rainfall, precipitation frequency analysis, and PMP. In this section we discuss the fundamental methodology for flood or drought frequency analysis.

The first point from the foregoing discussion is that the return period, T, to use in the design of a water resources system depends on the size of the structure to be built. T is usually provided to the hydrologists by governing regulations in the area, or provided as a recommendation by design manuals. For example, large flood-vulnerable hydraulic structures are designed for a $T=1000year$ or higher; for medium-sized hydraulic structures, such as navigable waterways, and river ports, a common value is $T=100year$; minor structures, such as highway culverts and railway bridges use a value of T between 10 and $50year$; the storm drainage in residential areas is designed using a value of T between 2.5 and $10year$. These are typical values recommended for various structures. In practice the hydrologist must consult the regulations applicable to the region of interest.

The second point from the foregoing discussion is the relationship between T and Q. Knowing the return period, the hydrologist needs to find the flow rate associated with it to design the structure. The relationship between return period and flow rate is derived from statistical analysis of historical records in a watershed.

Building a Flood Frequency Relationship

Given a specific return period to use in the design of a water resources structure, the hydrologist needs to find the corresponding design flow rate. To do this, a relationship between T and Q must be derived for the streamflow station under consideration. A fundamental requisite to the development of a reliable *flood frequency relationship* is the availability of long-term good-quality streamflow records. In chapter 2 we discussed some concepts on the quality of hydrologic data. We further remark that as a rule a flood frequency analysis should not be attempted if less than 20 years of record is available. No reliable statistical properties of the extreme streamflow regime of a site can be derived from a shorter record. Furthermore, consider the fact that such relationship would be used to design a structure that will last 50 or 100 years. The length of the record should be as long as possible, but in any case its length should be commensurate with the service life of the water resources system. If a sufficiently long record is not available, the use of longer records in nearby watersheds might be used in conjunction with more detailed statistical techniques (Serrano, 2001a; Kottegoda, 1980; Haan, 1977).

Another important requisite prior to deriving a reliable flood frequency relationship, is the assumption that the statistical properties of a historical streamflow record are *stationary*. This implies that the statistics do not vary over time, which occurs when land use changes in the watershed are not expected to be reflected in alterations in the streamflow regime of the watershed. It is important that the hydrologist investigates possible large scale development projects, such as agricultural development, urbanization, mining, and land drainage that might take place during the service life of the water resources project and alter the streamflow regime. If a substantial change in the streamflow characteristics is expected, then a flood frequency relationship built from historical records might not be valid.

Building of a flood frequency relationship is based on the concept of *probability of occurrence* associated with a given flow rate. The basic procedure involves collecting as many years of streamflow record as possible and selecting the maximum flow rate for every year. If a drought frequency is required, then the minimum flow rate per year is selected. Thus, if for example $N=60year$ of records are available, we would have 60 *sample* values of *annual maximum flow rate*, one per year of data. From the sample flows we observe the maximum during the entire series. This maximum, of the annual maximum flows, represents an estimate of the flow rate with a return period $T=N$. To continue with the same example of 60 years of record, the maximum of the 60 flow rate values, Q_{60} (m^3/s), is an estimate of the flow rate with a return period T=60$year$. We remark again that a return period of 60 years does not mean that once this flood occurs, one has to wait for 60 years until the next occurrence of a flood of this magnitude. It means that, if we had the longest possible record (e.g., 10,000 years, and impossibility in hydrology), the *average* interval between two subsequent occurrences is 60 years.

Understanding the implications of a return period, the next question relates to the calculation of flow rate values associated with different return periods. Based on the historical annual maximum (or *annual minimum* in drought analysis) flow rates, one may begin by constructing a *frequency histogram*. The frequency histogram is a diagram that summarizes the uncertainty features of the historical flows. To build a histogram, the range of values of the annual maximum flows are subdivided into class intervals, I.

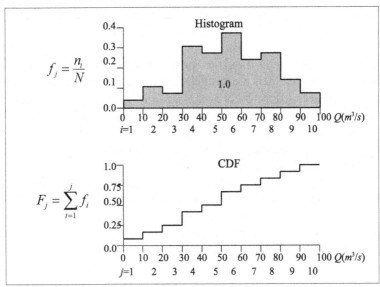

Figure 7.8: A Frequency Histogram and a CDF of Flow Rate

Referring to Figure 7.8, and continuing with the same example, let us assume that the range of values of the 60-year series of annual maximum flow rates is between 0.0 and 100.0 m^3/s, and that we wish to subdivide this range into 10 equal *class intervals* i=1, 2, . . . , 10, each with an discharge increment of ΔQ=10m^3/s. Starting with the first class interval, i=1, we count the number of years, n_1, the flow was between 0 and 10 m^3/s. The *relative frequency* of occurrence for the first class interval is

$f_1 = n_1/N$. For the second class interval, $i=2$, the number of years with a flow rate between 10 and 20 m^3/s is n_2, and its relative frequency is $f_2 = n_2/N$. Repeating this process for each class interval and plotting i versus f_i results in the frequency histogram for the series. This diagram summarizes, in one plot, the uncertainty picture of the series. Relatively speaking, one may observe the flow rate values that are more likely to occur, as opposed to the infrequent, or rare values. Obviously, the histogram shape depends on the specific choice of class intervals.

An alternative diagram, built from the frequency histogram, is the *cumulative distribution function* (CDF). In this graph the class intervals, j, have the same length as that of the histogram, but the ordinate F_j of a particular interval j is the summation of frequency values in the histogram from; the first class interval to the current value of j. In other words $F_j = \Sigma f_i$. This cumulative value is useful in the calculation of *probability of exceeding*, or not exceeding, a particular flow rate. For instance, in Figure 7.5, the sample probability that the flow rate in one year, any year, is less than or equal to $75\, m^3/s$ is $F_8 = 0.8 = 80\%$. Thus, the CDF gives an estimation of the *probability of not exceeding* that particular magnitude. The probability of exceeding such flow is $1 - F_8 = 1 - 0.8 = 0.2$. Note that the CDF varies from 0.0 (impossibility) to 1.0 (complete certainty). Now recall that by definition the return period is the inverse of the probability of exceeding. Thus, the return period associated with a flow rate of $75\, m^3/s$ is $T = 1/(1 - F_8) = 1/0.2 = 5 year$. On the average, such flow is expected to occur once every 5 years.

It is important to remark that the above analysis assumes that annual maximum flow rates are statistically independent of one another. This means that the fact that we had a very high flow rate one year has nothing to with whether or not we have a high maximum flow the next year or the year after that. This serial independence may be a reasonable assumption in small watersheds. In large watersheds, however, there is an inherent persistence, or memory, in the series. For this reason, we observe wet periods that last several years, followed by dry periods that last several years. For the analysis of time series exhibiting correlation other statistical techniques are available (Serrano, 2001a; Haan, 1977).

The frequency histogram and the CDF are discrete representations of an underlying continuous function, called the *probability density function* (PDF), describing the uncertainty behavior of flow rate in a streamflow station. Using statistical methods, a set of sample return periods, or the sample frequency histogram, is used to fit a theoretical continuous probability function. Referring to Figure 7.9, the continuous, theoretical function, describing flood frequency at the site is the probability density function. The continuous CDF is a smooth continuously increasing curve varying from 0 to 1. Once the analytical form of this curve is known, it can be used to calculate design flows associated with given return periods.

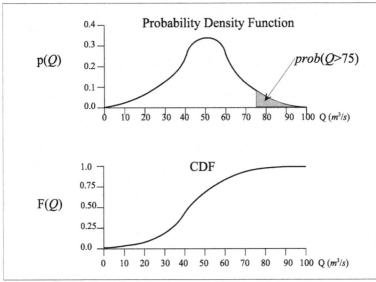

Figure 7.9: The Continuous Probability Density Function

Ordinates of the probability density function are related to the sample frequency histogram via the relationship

$$f_i = p(Q)\Delta Q$$

where
   $p(Q)$=ordinate of probability density function, PDF
   f_i= the expected relative frequency of class interval i
   ΔQ= width of class interval i (m^3/s)

Areas under the probability density function, or differences in ordinates in the continuous CDF, represent probabilities associated with given events. For instance, the probability of exceeding the flow $Q=75m^3/s$ may be estimated as

$$prob(Q>75)=\int_{75}^{\infty}p(Q)dQ=1-prob(Q\le75)=1-\int_{0}^{75}p(Q)dQ=1-F(75)$$

where:

$prob(Q>75)$=probability that $Q>75\,m^3/s$

$F(75)=prob(Q\le75)$= ordinate of the CDF evaluated at $Q=75\,m^3/s$

The return period, T, associated with this flow is

$$T=\frac{1}{prob(Q>75)}=\frac{1}{1-F(75)}$$

To fit a probability distribution to the sample flow rates two approaches are commonly used: the graphical and the analytical methods. The *graphical method* is based on the use of *probability paper*. Probability paper is a graph built for a specific probability distribution. The probability scale of this graph is adjusted such that the theoretical CDF plots as a straight line. In practice, the sample flow rates of the hydrologic series under study are plotted with respect to their estimated plotting position in the CDF. If the cloud of points may be fitted to a straight line, there is reason to believe that the series follows a probability distribution of the underlying probability paper.

Not all probability distributions may be arranged to produce probability paper. *Normal, Gumbel, Weibull*, and *Exponential* probability distributions are examples of some of the probability distributions for which probability paper may be produced. Therefore, the graphical procedure is limited in scope in that the sample flow historical series may be tested for only a few probability distributions. In addition, except for Normal paper the availability of graphical probability scales in spreadsheet software is limited. Often one has to use graphical and numerical methods to produce probability paper (Haan, 1977), or rely upon specialized statistical software. Nevertheless, the procedure is so simple in its application that it is worth the effort for preliminary studies.

The graphical procedure to derive a flood frequency relationship may be summarized by the following steps:

(1) From the historical streamflow records at the site, build the annual flood series by selecting the highest flood in a year. Do not omit any

year of record. You need to have at least 20 years of records (i.e., 20 flow rates). If there is more than one flood in some years, they may be included in the analysis provided that an adjustment is made in the calculation of the return period in step (3) below (see Haan, 1977 for details).

(2) Rank the flows in decreasing order of magnitude from the highest to the lowest and assign a rank, m, to each flow. Rank $m=1$ is given to the largest flow; $m=2$ to the second largest, etc. Rank $m=N$, with N the number of data points, is assigned to the lowest flow.

(3) Calculate the plotting position (i.e., the estimated return period) of each flow by a formula such as $T=(N+1)/m$.

(4) Select a probability paper for a candidate distribution.

(5) Plot the values of Q versus their estimated values of T.

(6) If a straight line may be fitted to the cloud of points, there is reason to believe that the extreme series follows the underlying distribution. If a straight line may not be fitted, or if some points (e.g., the highest flows) do not plot near the fitted line, then the candidate distribution is not a good model. In such case repeat steps (4) through (6) with a different probability paper.

It is recommended that the above procedure be repeated for several candidate distributions, even if a good model is found. Sometimes several distributions fit the flows reasonably well and the best one should be selected. Although statistical regression techniques could be used, most of the time the fitness to a straight line is a subjective decision. Note that in step (4) the estimated return period is calculated from an expression based on the relative magnitude of the flow in the ranked series. As the number of data points tends to infinity, this expression approaches the true return period (or the *population* inverse of the probability of exceeding). When N is small, the plotting position is a crude approximation of the true return period. For the above reasons, the graphical procedure of flood frequency must be used for preliminary studies only. For very large structures, the design flow should be estimated from precipitation records as described in chapter 2.

It is important to remark at this point that the Normal distribution, the common choice in statistical applications, is not, in general, a good model in extreme hydrology applications. However, many researches in the past have suggested that the log-Normal and the log-Pearson Type III distributions usually fit historical series of extreme flows. If the flows follow a log-Normal distribution, then the natural logarithm of the flows follow a Normal distribution. Thus, to test the log-Normal distribution as a model candidate, take the natural logarithm of the historical flows in step (1) above and follow the rest of the steps as before, except that in step (5) use normal probability paper.

Once a flood frequency relation is obtained, it can be used to estimate design flows associated with given return periods. Because of the limitations of the graphical procedure stated above, the hydrologist should not extrapolate the line beyond the fitted one supported by the historical record. Extrapolated values may be bound to have large errors.

Example 7.8: Developing a Graphical Flood Frequency Relation
   Table 7.5 lists the annual maximum flows of a river. (1) Using the graphical procedure, determine if the series follows a log-Normal probability distribution. (2) Assuming the log-Normal distribution is a good model, estimate the flow with a return period of 50 years.

Table 7.5: Flood Frequency Analysis of Example 7.8

Year	Q (m^3/s)	Ordered $Q(m^3/s)$	$\ln(Q)$	Rank m	$T=\frac{N+1}{m}$ (year)	Year	Q (m^3/s)	Ordered $Q(m^3/s)$	$\ln(Q)$	Rank m	$T=\frac{N+1}{m}$ (year)
1984	16200	28300	10.25	1	28.0	1997	17000	14400	9.57	14	2.0
1985	6500	24300	10.10	2	14.0	1998	10300	13600	9.52	15	1.9
1986	20300	20500	9.93	3	9.3	1999	19900	12100	9.40	16	1.8
1987	14700	20300	9.92	4	7.0	2000	13600	10900	9.30	17	1.7
1988	20500	20100	9.91	5	5.6	2001	5700	10400	9.25	18	1.6
1989	10100	19900	9.90	6	4.7	2002	8800	10300	9.24	19	1.5
1990	7200	19200	9.86	7	4.0	2003	9400	10100	9.22	20	1.4
1991	28300	18300	9.81	8	3.5	2004	19200	9400	9.15	21	1.3
1992	18300	17900	9.79	9	3.1	2005	6800	8800	9.08	22	1.3
1993	24300	17000	9.74	10	2.8	2006	14700	8400	9.04	23	1.2
1994	17900	16200	9.69	11	2.6	2007	8400	7200	8.88	24	1.2
1995	12100	14700	9.60	12	2.3	2008	20100	6800	8.82	25	1.1
1996	10900	14700	9.60	13	2.2	2009	10400	6500	8.78	26	1.1
						2010	14400	5700	8.27	27	1.0

Solution
(1) The first two columns from the left of Table 7.5 contain the year and the maximum flow rate. Following steps (1) through (6) above, the third column contains the re-arranged flow rate values in decreasing order of

magnitude. The fourth column has the natural logarithm of each re-arranged flow. In the fifth column a rank has been assigned to each flow. Finally, the seventh column has the return period associated with each flow as indicated.

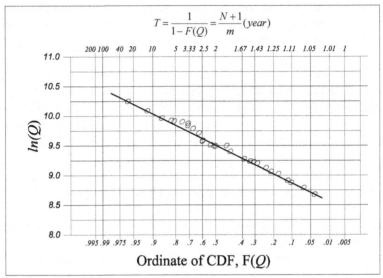

$$T = \frac{1}{1-F(Q)} = \frac{N+1}{m}(year)$$

Figure 7.10: Testing log-Normality on Normal Probability Paper

To test the suitability of the log-normal distribution using normal probability paper, one must plot $\ln(Q)$ versus T in Normal probability paper (see Figure 7.10). If log-Normal paper is available, then one must plot Q versus T. Note that Figure 7.7 is the CDF rotated 90° counter clock wise and with the probability scale altered so as to plot as a straight line (compare with Figure 7.9). Finally, a straight line is fitted through the points. In this case the log-Normal distribution appears to be a suitable model.

(2) Entering Figure 7.7 with $T=50year$, $\ln(Q)=10.31$, and $Q=30,000\,m^3/s$. Note that extrapolating the line may lead to large errors as small errors in logarithmic readings may translate into errors in flow rate of the order of thousands of m^3/s.

Example 7.9: Program to Plot Data on Normal Paper
    Historical annual water yield, Q $(m^3 \times 10^6)$, for a watershed is recorded in the following vector: Q:=[61.7, 44.4, 52.4, 35.6, 39.2, 49.8, 24.2, 45.6, 40.0, 49.7, 65.3, 44.0, 51.6, 56.5, 44.6, 71.4, 51.8, 43.8, 45.5, 58.2]. Write a Maple program that plots the data on Normal probability

paper and fits a linear regression line. State wether or not the data follows a Normal PDF.

Solution

The following program creates tick marks of the Normal CDF adjusted to plot as a straight line and fits a linear regression line and plots it along with the data.

```
> #Initialize; call statistics module; enter data
  restart: with(stats[statevalf]):
  Q:=[61.7, 44.4, 52.4, 35.6, 39.2, 49.8, 24.2, 45.6, 40.0,
      49.7, 65.3, 44.0, 51.6, 56.5, 44.6, 71.4, 51.8, 43.8,
      45.5, 58.2]:
  N:=describe[count](Q):      #Number of data points
  Qorden:=sort(Q):            #sort series in ascending order
  F:=[seq(j*100./(N+1),j=1..N)]:   #values of CDF
> #Create tickmarks of CDF 0.1% to 99.0%
  invF:=icdf[normald]:
  YTicks1:=[seq(evalf(invF(i/100))=convert(i,string),
           i=[.1,.5,1.0,5.0,10.0,50.0,90.0,95.0,99.0])]:
  YTicks2:=[seq(evalf(invF(i/100))="",
           i=[.2,.3,.4,2,3,4,20,30,40,60,70,80,96,97,98])]:
  YTicks:=[op(YTicks1),op(YTicks2)]:
> #Transform the F such that it plots as a straight line
  Fy:=map(invF,F/100.):
> #Organize data into coordinates [x,y]
  Data:=zip((x,y)->[x,y],Qorden,Fy)[]:
> #Fit a linear regression line to the data
  FIT:=unapply(rhs(fit[leastsquare[[x,y]]]([Qorden,Fy])),x):
  mu:=solve(FIT(x)=0);          #calculate the mean
  sigma:=solve(FIT(x)=1)-mu;    #standard deviation
```

$$\mu := 48.76500000$$
$$\sigma := 12.28761545$$

```
> #Plot data and fitted regression on Normal paper
  plots[display](
     plot(FIT,30..70,color=black,thickness=2),
     PLOT(POINTS(Data),AXESTICKS(DEFAULT,YTicks),AXESSTYLE(BOX)),
     symbol=circle,labels=[`Q (m^3 X 10^6)`,`F (%)`] );
```

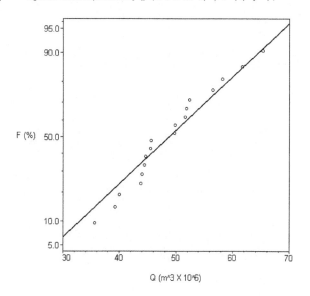

Q (m^3 X 10^6)

Since the data appears to follow a straight line, there is reason to believe that the Normal PDF is a good model to describe the random variable annual yield volume, Q. However, this decision is subjective, since there is no objective measure to ascertain how good is the fit. Further tests, such as the *Chi Squared goodness of fit test* should be performed on the data to evaluate the assumption of normality. See Serrano (2001a) for more details on the theory, examples, applications, and Maple programming.

Example 7.10: Program to Test Data for the log-Normal Distribution
Modify the program on Example 7.9 to test for log-Normality.

Solution
Minor changes to the program are needed. Essentially, the flow series is transformed into a logarithmic one, and tick marks for the horizontal, log-transformed, scale are created. Plotting data on probability paper helps with the estimation of parameters of probability distributions, the extrapolation or interpolation of data, the selection of possible distributions for further analysis, and the elimination of unsuitable ones.

```
> #Initialize; call statistics module; enter data
  restart: with(stats[statevalf]):
  Q1:=[61.7, 44.4, 52.4, 35.6, 39.2, 49.8, 24.2, 45.6, 40.0,
       49.7, 65.3, 44.0, 51.6, 56.5, 44.6, 71.4, 51.8, 43.8,
       45.5, 58.2]:
  Q:=map(ln,Q1):
  N:=describe[count](Q):     #Number of data points
  MinQ:=min(seq(Q[i],i=1..N)): MaxQ:=max(seq(Q[i],i=1..N)):
  Qorden:=sort(Q):           #sort series in ascending order
  F:=[seq(j*100./(N+1),j=1..N)]: #values of CDF
> #Create tickmarks of CDF 0.1% to 99.0%
  invF:=icdf[normald]:
  XTicks:=[seq(evalf(log(i))=convert(i,string),
           i=[10,20,30,40,50,60,70,80,90,100])]:
  YTicks1:=[seq(evalf(invF(i/100))=convert(i,string),
           i=[.1,.5,1.0,5.0,10.0,50.0,90.0,95.0,99.0])]:
  YTicks2:=[seq(evalf(invF(i/100))="",
           i=[.2,.3,.4,2,3,4,20,30,40,60,70,80,96,97,98])]:
  YTicks:=[op(YTicks1),op(YTicks2)]:
> #Transform the F such that it plots as a straight line
  Fy:=map(invF,F/100.):
> #Organize data into coordinates [x,y]
  Data:=zip((x,y)->[x,y],Qorden,Fy)[]:
> #Fit a linear regression line to the data
  FIT:=unapply(rhs(fit[leastsquare[[x,y]]]([Qorden,Fy])),x):
  solve(FIT(x)=0): mu:=exp(%);
  solve(FIT(x)=1): sigma:=exp(%)-mu;
```
$$\mu := 47.56087531$$
$$\sigma := 15.26092130$$
```
> #Plot data and fitted regression on Normal paper
  plots[display](
       plot(FIT,MinQ..MaxQ,color=black,thickness=2),
       PLOT(POINTS(Data),AXESTICKS(XTicks,YTicks),AXESSTYLE(BOX)),
       symbol=circle,labels=[`Q (m^3 X 10^6)`,`F (%)`] );
```

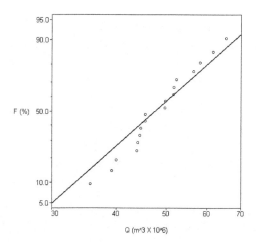

The data also appears to follow a log-Normal distribution. Again, further statistical tests would be required to evaluate which distribution would be more suitable. For comparison purposes, the reader should explore the various distributions available in Maple and modify the program to produce corresponding probability papers (see the chapter problems).

As an alternative to the graphical method of flood frequency, the analytical method is often employed. This method was introduced in chapter 2 in the section on Probable Maximum Precipitation. It assumes that the maximum annual flow rate, of a given return period, may be expressed as (see equation (2.6))

$$Q = \bar{Q} + K_T S_Q \qquad (7.23)$$

where

Q = maximum annual flow corresponding to a return period $T (m^3/s)$
$\bar{Q}$ = sample mean flow of historical series (m^3/s)
K_T = frequency factor
S_Q = sample standard deviation of historical series (m^3/s)

Equation (7.23) states that a particular realization of a maximum annual flow rate may be expressed as the mean flow rate plus (or minus) a factor of the standard deviation. This factor, K_T, depends on the probability distribution describing the flood series and the given return period. Table 7.6 has values of the frequency factor of the Normal distribution for various return periods. Table 7.7 has the values of the frequency factor of the *Gumbel distribution* as a function of the record length, N, and the return period. Table 7.8 has the values of the frequency factor for the *log-Pearson Type III distribution* as a function of the *skew coefficient* of the logarithm of the series, γ_Y, and the return period. Recall that if the flow rate follows a log-Normal distribution, then the logarithm of the flow rate follows a Normal distribution. The log-Normal, Gumbel, and log-Pearson Type III distributions have often been found to adequately describe hydrologic extreme series.

Table 7.6: Frequency Factors for the Normal Distribution

$T(year)$	K_T	$T(year)$	K_T	$T(year)$	K_T
200.00	2.576	2.86	0.385	1.25	-0.842
100.00	2.326	2.50	0.253	1.18	-1.036
40.00	1.960	2.22	0.126	1.11	-1.282
20.00	1.645	2.00	0.000	1.053	-1.645
10.00	1.282	1.82	-0.126	1.026	-1.960
6.67	1.036	1.67	-0.253	1.010	-2.326
5.00	0.842	1.54	-0.385	1.005	-2.576
4.00	0.674	1.43	-0.524	1.001	-3.090
3.33	0.524	1.33	-0.674		

Table 7.7: Frequency Factors for the Gumbel Distribution

N	\multicolumn{9}{c}{T (year)}								
	5	10	15	20	25	50	75	100	1000
15	0.967	1.703	2.117	2.410	2.632	3.321	3.721	4.005	6.265
20	0.919	1.625	2.023	2.301	2.517	3.179	3.563	3.836	6.006
25	0.888	1.575	1.963	2.235	2.444	3.088	3.463	3.729	5.842
30	0.866	1.541	1.922	2.188	2.393	3.026	3.393	3.653	5.727
35	0.851	1.516	1.891	2.152	2.354	2.979	3.341	3.598	
40	0.838	1.495	1.866	2.126	2.326	2.943	3.301	3.554	5.576
45	0.829	1.478	1.847	2.104	2.303	2.913	3.268	3.520	
50	0.820	1.466	1.831	2.086	2.283	2.889	3.241	3.491	5.478
55	0.813	1.455	1.818	2.071	2.267	2.869	3.219	3.467	
60	0.807	1.446	1.806	2.059	2.253	2.852	3.200	3.446	
65	0.801	1.437	1.796	2.048	2.241	2.837	3.183	3.429	
70	0.797	1.430	1.788	2.038	2.230	2.824	3.169	3.413	5.359
75	0.792	1.423	1.780	2.029	2.220	2.812	3.155	3.400	
80	0.788	1.417	1.773	2.020	2.212	2.802	3.145	3.387	
85	0.785	1.413	1.767	2.013	2.205	2.793	3.135	3.376	
90	0.782	1.409	1.762	2.007	2.198	2.785	3.125	3.367	
95	0.780	1.405	1.757	2.002	2.193	2.777	3.116	3.357	
100	0.779	1.401	1.752	1.998	2.187	2.770	3.109	3.349	5.261

Table 7.8: Frequency Factors for the Log-Pearson Type III Distribution

	T				(year)				
γ_Y	1.01	1.25	2	5	10	25	50	100	200
3.0	-0.667	-0.636	-0.396	0.420	1.180	2.278	3.152	4.051	4.970
2.8	-0.714	-0.666	-0.384	0.460	1.210	2.275	3.114	3.973	4.847
2.6	-0.769	-0.696	-0.368	0.499	1.238	2.267	3.071	3.889	4.718
2.4	-0.832	-0.725	-0.351	0.537	1.262	2.256	3.023	3.800	4.584
2.2	-0.905	-0.752	-0.330	0.574	1.284	2.240	2.970	3.705	4.444
2.0	-0.990	-0.777	-0.307	0.609	1.302	2.219	2.912	3.605	4.298
1.8	-1.087	-0.799	-0.282	0.643	1.318	2.193	2.848	3.499	4.147
1.6	-1.197	-0.817	-0.254	0.675	1.329	2.163	2.780	3.388	3.990
1.4	-1.318	-0.832	-0.225	0.705	1.337	2.128	2.706	3.271	3.828
1.2	-1.449	-0.844	-0.195	0.732	1.340	2.087	2.626	3.149	3.661
1.0	-1.588	-0.852	-0.164	0.758	1.340	2.043	2.542	3.022	3.489
0.8	-1.733	-0.856	-0.132	0.780	1.336	1.993	2.453	2.891	3.312
0.6	-1.880	-0.857	-0.099	0.800	1.328	1.939	2.359	2.755	3.132
0.4	-2.029	-0.855	-0.066	0.816	1.317	1.880	2.261	2.615	2.949
0.2	-2.178	-0.850	-0.033	0.830	1.301	1.818	2.159	2.472	2.763
0.0	-2.326	-0.842	0.000	0.842	1.282	1.751	2.054	2.326	2.576
-0.2	-2.472	-0.830	0.033	0.850	1.258	1.680	1.945	2.178	2.388
-0.4	-2.615	-0.816	0.066	0.855	1.231	1.606	1.834	2.029	2.201
-0.6	-2.755	-0.800	0.099	0.857	1.200	1.528	1.720	1.880	2.016
-0.8	-2.891	-0.780	0.132	0.856	1.166	1.448	1.606	1.733	1.837
-1.0	-3.022	-0.758	0.164	0.852	1.128	1.366	1.492	1.588	1.664
-1.2	-3.149	-0.732	0.195	0.844	1.086	1.282	1.379	1.449	1.501
-1.4	-3.271	-0.705	0.225	0.832	1.041	1.198	1.270	1.318	1.351
-1.6	-3.388	-0.675	0.254	0.817	0.994	1.116	1.166	1.197	1.216
-1.8	-3.499	-0.643	0.282	0.799	0.945	1.035	1.069	1.087	1.097
-2.0	-3.605	-0.609	0.307	0.777	0.895	0.959	0.980	0.990	0.995
-2.2	-3.705	-0.574	0.330	0.752	0.844	0.888	0.900	0.905	0.907
-2.4	-3.800	-0.537	0.351	0.725	0.795	0.823	0.830	0.832	0.833
-2.6	-3.889	-0.499	0.368	0.696	0.747	0.764	0.768	0.769	0.769
-2.8	-3.973	-0.460	0.384	0.666	0.702	0.712	0.714	0.714	0.714
-3.0	-4.051	-0.420	0.396	0.636	0.660	0.666	0.666	0.667	0.667

The analytical procedure for the estimation of a design flow rate associated with a given return period may be summarized by the following steps:

(1) Build the annual flood series as described before in step (1) of the graphical method. If you plan on using the log-Normal or the log-Pearson Type III distribution, take the natural logarithm of each flow to obtain the *transformed series* $Y=\ln(Q)$.

(2) Calculate the *sample statistics* (i.e., the mean, the standard deviation, and the skew coefficient) of the historical flows (or the transformed flows), by applying standard statistical formulae given below by equations (7.24)-(7.26). The *mean* defines the sample first moment with respect to the origin of the probability density function (i.e., locates its center of mass); the *standard deviation* is a measure of the second moment with respect to the mean, or the moment of inertia, and defines the spread of the data with respect to the mean (i.e., how much "uncertainty" there is amongst the flows); the *skew coefficient* is a measure of the third moment with respect to the mean and; it defines how symmetric with respect to the mean is the probability density function. Symmetric density functions (i.e., zero skewness) tend to follow a Normal distribution.

The sample statistics are calculated as follows:

$$\bar{Q} = \frac{1}{N}\sum_{i=1}^{N} Q_i \tag{7.24}$$

where
$\bar{Q}$ = sample mean (m^3/s)
Q_i = sample historical flows (m^3/s)
N = number of years of record

$$S_Q = \sqrt{\frac{1}{N-1}\sum_{i=1}^{N} (Q_i - \bar{Q})^2} \tag{7.25}$$

$$\gamma = \frac{N}{(N-1)(N-2)S_Q^3}\sum_{i=1}^{N} (Q_i - \bar{Q})^3 \tag{7.26}$$

where
γ = skewness coefficient

(3) Select a candidate probability distribution. Read the value of the frequency factor for the selected distribution, the given return period, and the sample statistics calculated in step (2).

(4) Compute the design flood from equation (7.23).

(5) Repeat steps (3) and (4) for other probability distributions and decide

which value is the most appropriate design flow. A conservative design would use the highest flow estimate. However, if the adopted number came from a probability distribution that poorly fits the data, errors might be large. It helps to know in advance whether or not the distribution used adequately describes the flood series. The use of probability paper helps eliminate poor models. Statistical goodness of fit tests provide an objective means to assess the quality of a model (see Serrano, 2001b).

Example 7.11: Flood Frequency Analysis by the Analytical Method
Using the historical series of Example 7.8 (Table 7.5), estimate the $100-year$ flood magnitude using the analytical method and assuming log-normality.

Solution
Following steps (1) through (4) above, we use the series reported in Table 7.5. Since we are using the log-Normal distribution, we use the natural logarithm of the flows (fourth column in Table 7.5). From equation (7.24) calculate the mean of the logarithmic series, $Q_Y=9.47$. From equation (7.25) calculate the standard deviation of the logarithmic series, $S_{Q_Y}=0.47$. From equation (7.26) calculate the coefficient of skew of the logarithmic series, $\gamma_Y=-0.60$. Although the coefficient of skew is not needed in the case of the normal distribution, it helps assess the validity of our assumption of normality of the logarithmic series. If normality is viable, $\gamma_Y \to 0$. However, our series exhibits a slight negative skewness and thus the assumption of normality of the logarithmic series (or log-normality of the regular flow series) is questionable.

From Table 7.6, the frequency factor for a return period of $T=100 year$ is $K_T=2.326$. From equation (7.23), the logarithm of the $100-year$ flow is

$$Q_Y = \overline{Q}_Y + K_T S_{Q_Y} = 9.47 + 2.326 \times 0.47 = 10.56$$

Thus, the $100\ year$ maximum annual flow rate assuming log-normality is

$$Q = e^{Q_Y} = e^{10.56} = 38,560 m^3$$

For the log-Normal and the log-Pearson Type III distributions, it is necessary to take the natural logarithm of each historical flow prior to the calculation of the sample statistics, as seen in Example 7.8. In addition to that, the frequency factor of the log-Pearson Type III is a function of the skew coefficient of the logarithmic series, γ_Y. The skew coefficient is biased if $N<100$, the usual case in hydrologic practice. The U.S. Water Resources Council (1981) recommends the use of a generalized weighted skew coefficient for the data of all nearby stations within a 150-km radius. In the absence of records, the adjusted skew coefficient is estimated as

$$\overline{\gamma}_Y = w\gamma_Y + (1-w)\gamma_r \qquad (7.27)$$

where
$\overline{\gamma}_Y$ = generalized skew coefficient of the logarithmic series
γ_Y = sample skew coefficient of the logarithmic historical series
γ_r = regional skew coefficient of logarithmic series in nearby stations
w = weighted factor

The weighted factor is obtained from the variances of the sample skew coefficients:

$$w = \frac{Var(\gamma_r)}{Var(\gamma_Y) + Var(\gamma_r)} = \frac{0.3025}{10^{A - B\log(N/10)} + 0.3025} \qquad (7.28)$$

where
$Var(\gamma_r)$ = variance of regional skew coefficient
$Var(\gamma_Y)$ = variance of the sample skew coefficient of historical series

$$A = \begin{cases} -0.33 + 0.08|\gamma_Y|, & |\gamma_Y| \le 0.9 \\ -0.52 + 0.30|\gamma_Y|, & |\gamma_Y| > 0.9 \end{cases}$$

$$B = \begin{cases} 0.94 - 0.26|\gamma_Y|, & |\gamma_Y| \le 1.5 \\ 0.55, & |\gamma_Y| > 1.5 \end{cases}$$

The right side of equation (7.28) is an approximation to the variances (square of the standard deviation) of the sample and regional skew coefficients in the U.S. For other locations, the variance of the regional skew coefficient, $Var(\gamma_Y)$, should be estimated from the variance of the skew coefficients of the logarithmic series of several nearby stations. Equations (7.27) and (7.28) provide the means to calculate an unbiased skew coefficient, $\overline{\gamma}_Y$. This value is entered in Table 7.8 to estimate the frequency factor, K_T. With the frequency factor, the sample mean, and sample standard deviation of the logarithm of the historical flows one proceeds as in Example 7.11 to estimate the design flood.

The above procedure of flood frequency analysis may be employed to drought frequency analysis. In such case the historical series is composed of the *minimum annual flow rate* for as many years as possible. The Gumbel distribution has been found to adequately describe drought series in the past.

7.3 THE HYDROLOGY OF DRAINAGE SYSTEMS

Natural watersheds have an inherent ability to evacuate runoff water produced as effective precipitation. In developed areas, however, this natural drainage of excess water produced during high-intensity rainfall events is altered. In urbanized areas, for example, the ground surface is impervious and the infiltration rates are substantially reduced, thus producing more overland flow volumes in the watershed than under natural conditions. To prevent damage from flooding, engineering aspects of urban development include the design of a sanitary and a storm sewer system. The purpose of these systems is to evacuate excess rainfall water from roofs, yards, streets and parking lots, and waste water from households, commercial establishments, and industries. In the past, urban drainage systems were designed to drain the combined excess waters from rainfall storms and sewage. This increases the risk of sewage overflow during extreme events. Today most drainage systems are separated, that is they are designed to dispose overland flow water only (i.e., storm water system), or waste water only (i.e., sanitary sewer system). Urban drainage systems substantially improve drainage efficiency; in other words, they increase overland flow volumes over short periods of time. These increased volumes may produce flooding in downstream areas. For this reason, detention ponds are built to temporary delay runoff water draining from urban areas.

Other drainage systems of developed areas, besides urban drainage systems, are the agriculture land drainage, road drainage, and airport drainage systems. To minimize crop damage and augment crop yield, agriculture drainage systems are designed to improve effective precipitation evacuation and maintain a water table elevation below the root zone. Temporary flooding caused by high-intensity storms may erode plants root system. Water table that periodically invades the root zone as a result of infiltration increases the chances of soil salinization. Thus, agricultural drainage systems combine soil grading, channel and ditch alignment, and installation of subsurface perforated tiles with good soil conservation practices.

Road drainage systems aim at the evacuation of overland waters away from the road surface and the control of subsurface waters from the road base. Water in the road base causes a decrease in the soil shear resistance and the erosion of the road foundation. In addition, flooding waters may cause damage in bridges and other structures.

The design of drainage systems involves two aspects: the first aspect consists in the determination of the design quantity of water; the second aspect consists in establishing the various structures capacity to conduct this quantity. The first aspect pertains to the peak rainfall intensity, or the peak flow rate, within the urban or rural area produced by a storm of a certain specified return period. This is the hydrologic aspect of the design. The second aspect involves the determination, location, dimensions and features of the hydraulic structures capable of evacuating the design flow rate. This is the water resources or hydraulic engineering aspect of the design.

In Chapter 2 (section 2.5; Example 2.9) we discussed the procedure to build a precipitation intensity-duration-frequency (IDF) relationship for a particular area. Once an IDF relationship is available, the design rainfall intensity, p, of a specified critical duration, t_s, and a specified return period, T, may be estimated. As stated before, the design return period is usually given by local regulations. The critical duration is normally taken as the time from the beginning of the storm when the entire watershed is contributing with surface runoff at the outlet. As defined in Chapter 6, this time corresponds to the watershed time of concentration, or $t_s = t_c$. The time of concentration may be estimated from hydrograph analysis (see chapter 6, Figure 6.10), or in the absence of streamflow records it may estimated from empirical formulae (Gupta, 1989; McCuen et al., 1984; Overton and Meadows, 1976).

The design flow rate is estimated from various methods that consider adverse rainfall conditions. There are two common procedures of computing peak stormwater flow rate in small urban watersheds (i.e., less than $50\,km^2$). The U.S. Soil Conservation service has evolved a procedure to determine the peak discharge by making use of the *soil cover complex curves* and extended it to apply to urban watersheds. The *rational method* is still very popular due to its simplicity, although a wide latitude of subjective knowledge is involved in its application (McPherson, 1969).

The equation of maximum flow rate for the rational method is

$$Q_p = c_f CAp \qquad (7.29)$$

where

Q_p = storm peak flow rate (m^3/s)
c_f = frequency factor
C = runoff coefficient ($m.hour/(mm.s)$)
A = drainage area (m^2)
p = rainfall intensity *($mm/hour$) for a duration equal to the time of concentration, t_c, and a return period, T

In a common application of equation (7.29), c_f is taken as unity which applies to design storms with a return period of 2 to 10 years, a representative frequency for residential sewers. For storms of higher return periods the coefficients are higher because of smaller infiltration and other losses. For values of T=25, 50 and 100 years, c_f is equal to 1.1, 1.2, and 1.25, respectively. Table 7.9 shows recommended values of the runoff coefficient, C for use with metric units in equation (7.18).

Table 7.9: Average Values of Runoff Coefficient, C, in Equation (7.29)

Description	$C(\frac{m.hour}{mm.s} \times 10^{-7})$	Description	$C(\frac{m.hour}{mm.s} \times 10^{-7})$
City	1.65	Roofs	2.20
Suburban Business	1.65	Lawn Heavy Soil	0.83
Industrial	1.93	Lawn Sandy Soil	0.50
Residential Multi-units	1.79	Rural Watersheds	
Housing Estates	1.38	Bare Surface	1.10
Bungalows	1.10	Grassland	0.96
Parks, Cemeteries	0.55	Cultivated Land	0.83
Asphalt Paving	2.20	Timber	0.50

A *storm drainage system* consists of many segments of sewer drains. Each segment is built between inspection boxes or manholes. The network of segments is buried under access roads or streets and the whole network of segments approximately follows the existing or re-graded topography of the urban area. Inlets to storm sewers are usually constructed at low elevation portions of streets. The tributary area and the flow rate entering each drain is different. To determine the peak flow rate, not only at the outlet but at interim points of entry to each drain, a step by step application of equation (7.29) is made. Each contributing area or component may have a different runoff coefficient according to the type of cover or the kind of buildings. Thus, equation (7.29) applied to areas with mixed covers becomes

$$Q_p = c_f \, p \sum_{i=1}^{N} C_i A_i \qquad (7.30)$$

where

Q_p = peak flow rate at a point in a sewer line (m^3/s)

p = design rainfall intensity corresponding to the time of concentration (overland plus sewer transit time) to the desired point ($mm/hour$)

C_i = runoff coefficient of component from Table 7.9 ($m.hour/(mm.s)$)

A_i = surface area of component (m^2)

N = number of components contributing until desired point

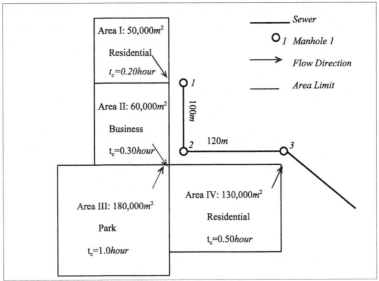

Figure 7.11: Illustration of a Simple Storm Sewer System

Consider the simple storm drainage system illustrated in Figure 7.11. There are four drainage areas or components, each with a specific runoff coefficient determined by the type of land cover. Area I drains toward manhole 1. The peak flow rate from Area I entering the sewer line occurs when all area is contributing with overland flow. Thus, the design rainfall is estimated from the IDF relationship with a given design return period and a duration equal to the time of concentration for of Area I. The time of concentration is estimated from empirical formulae derived after the assumption that overland flow occurs as sheet flow over a plane (Overton and Meadows, 1976). With the estimated design rainfall, the area of component I, an the component runoff coefficient, the peak flow rate at manhole 1 is calculated from equation (7.19).

Areas I, II and III contribute toward manhole 2. To determine the peak flow rate at manhole 2, one has to add the products of $C_i A_i$ for areas I, II, and III, according to equation (7.30), and multiply it by the design rainfall. The design rainfall applicable to manhole 2 corresponds to a time of concentration at such point. The time of concentration at manhole 2 is the longest travel time to manhole 2: either the travel time in Area I plus the inlet travel time through the sewer between manholes 1 and 2, or the travel time in Area II, or the travel time in Area III. The inlet travel time through a sewer line is calculated from an estimation of the average flow velocity divided by the sewer length. The storm sewers are designed for just flowing full at the grade of ground surface slope by applying Manning's equation (see any text on open channel hydraulics). A minimum velocity of 0.9m/s is maintained when flowing full in order to produce a minimum non-depositing slope for silt and grit particles that are heavier than the sewage solids. For this purpose the slope at times is increased in excess of the surface grade. The upper limit on velocity is about 5m/s from scour considerations.

From above, a careful consideration must be given to the direction of flow and the areas contributing to a particular point in a sewer line. Proceeding as before, to estimate the design peak flow rate at manhole 3 in Figure 7.11, the summation of each component's runoff coefficient times its area is multiplied by the design rainfall intensity corresponding to the total time of concentration at manhole 3.

Several formulae have been proposed for the estimation of the time of concentration, t_c, in small areas affected by overland flow (see Chow et al., 1988, page 500 for a summary). A simple equation adapted to overland flow is given by (Kirpich, 1940)

$$t_c = gL^{0.477}S^{-0.385} \qquad (7.30)$$

where
t_c = time of concentration (*hour*)
L = length of overland flow from head water to outlet (*m*)
S = average land slope (*m/m*)
$g = 1.2981 \times 10^{-4}(hour/m^{0.77})$ for concrete or asphalt surfaces
$g = 3.2453 \times 10^{-4}(hour/m^{0.77})$ for bare soil

The procedure for the estimation of the design flow rate of different sections of a storm sewer system using the rational method may be summarized in the following steps:

(1) Obtain a topographic map of the area and delineate the limits of each contributing area, the surface area of each component, the runoff coefficient according to each component's cover type or construction type (Table 7.9), the direction of the flow, the time of concentration of each component (equation (7.31)), and the storm sewer network with the individual manholes.

(2) Derive or obtain a precipitation IDF relationship valid for the location of the watershed.

(3) Estimate the flow rate at the highest manhole in the network by applying equation (7.30) and taken into consideration the different areas, each with a different runoff coefficient, contributing to the manhole. The design rainfall corresponds to the time of concentration at that manhole.

(4) Apply the calculations of step (3) to each manhole in the sewer line. Work sequentially downstream. The design rainfall at a manhole corresponds to the time of concentration, or the longest travel time of either sewer line or component area contributing to the manhole.

Example 7.12: Design Flow Rate of a Storm Sewer System

Estimate the design flow rate at manholes 1, 2, and 3 of the storm sewer system illustrated in Figure 7.11 for a return period of 10 years. Assume that the system is being planned for a community in Miami, Florida, and that rainfall frequency relationships developed by the U.S. National Weather Service (Chapter 2) are applicable. Assume that the average flow velocity in any sewer line is $1.3m/s$.

Solution

Following steps (1) through (4) above, we use the sewer layout in Figure 7.11. For a precipitation IDF relationship we use the curves developed by the U.S. National Weather Service (Chapter 2, Equation (2.5), Figure 2.20, and Table 2.6). Miami, Florida, is located in Area 1 in Figure 2.20. For Area 1, with a return period of 10 years, the IDF constants are $a=127.0mm$ and $b=0.60hour$. Thus, equation (2.5) with a duration $t_s=t_c$ becomes

$$p = \frac{127mm}{t_c + 0.6hour} \qquad (7.32)$$

where

　p=design rainfall intensity for T=10 years ($mm/hour$)
　t_c=time of concentration ($hour$)

Calculations are summarized in Table 7.10. Column 1 contains the area number or the sewer segment when appropriate. Column 2 contains the manhole number where the design flow rate is desired. Column 3 has the runoff coefficient of each contributing area as read in Table 7.9. Column 4 has the drainage area of each contributing area. Column 5 has the product of the runoff coefficient times the drainage area of each component for application of the rational formula. Column 6 has the summation of values in column 5 for all contributing areas up to the desired point (areas not contributing to the flow in the desired point must not be included). Column 7 contains the values of overland flow time for each area or sewer segment. The runoff time of a sewer segment is calculated as the ratio of the length of the segment to the average velocity of flow. For instance the flow time from manholes 1 to 2 is equal to $(100m)/(1.3m/s)=76.92s=0.02hour$.

Table 7.10: Design Flow Rate for Example 7.12

1	2	3	4	5	6	7	8	9	10
Area or Segment	Manhole	C_i ($\frac{m.hour}{mm.s}\times10^{-7}$)	A_i (m^2)	C_iA_i ($\frac{m.hour}{mm.s}\times10^{-7}$)	ΣC_iA_i ($\frac{m^3.hour}{mm.s}\times10^{-7}$)	t ($hour$)	t_c ($hour$)	p ($\frac{mm}{hour}$)	Q_p ($\frac{m^3}{s}$)
I	1	1.79	50,000	89,500	89,500	0.20	0.20	158.75	1.42
II		1.65	60,000	99,000		0.30			
1 - 2						0.02			
III		0.55	180,000	99,000		1.00			
	2				287,500		1.0	79.38	2.28
IV		1.79	130,000	232,700		0.50			
2 - 3						0.03			
	3				520,200		1.03	77.91	4.05

Column 8 contains the time of concentration at the manhole where the design flow is desired. The time of concentration corresponds to the longest travel time among all possible pathways to such manhole. For instance, the only drainage area to manhole 1 is Area I with a flow time of 0.20 hours. Thus, in this case the time of concentration is 0.20 hours. However, for manhole 2 water may flow from Area 1 to manhole 1 and then from manhole 1 to manhole 2 through the sewer line with a total flow time of 0.22 hours; a second possibility is from Area II to manhole 2 with a flow time of 0.30 hours; a third possibility is from Area III to manhole 2 with a flow time 1.0 hours. Therefore, the time of concentration, the longest travel time from among all the possibilities is 1.0 hour. A similar analysis for manhole 3 leads to the conclusion that the time of concentration for manhole 3 is 1.03 hour, that is the time of concentration at manhole 2 plus the flow time through segment 2-3.

Column 9 has the values of the design rainfall intensity at each manhole obtained from equation (7.32) with the value of the time of concentration in column 7. Finally, Column 10 contains the design flow rate valid for each manhole as calculated from equation (7.30), or simply the product of columns 6 times 9. With the design flow rates at different manholes in the system, the engineer proceeds to obtain the appropriate dimensions of a pipe capable of carrying such discharge by using standard hydraulics formulae (see Gupta, 1989 for detailed examples).

The foregoing example illustrates the basic procedure of engineering design of a storm sewer system using the concepts of extreme event hydrology. It is important to remark that the use of the rational formula adopts questionable assumptions on the occurrence of the peak flow rate that tends to over design the capacity of the sewers (see Gray, 1973). It appears that the use of unit hydrograph methods (see Chapter 6) offer a methodology more in agreement with the natural watershed time distribution of surface runoff.

Generally urban storm sewers are composed of hundreds of line segments arranged in a complex pattern. The procedure in such cases lends itself to the application of computational methods. Several computer software are available to the user for this purpose (see Viessman, 1996 for a summary). In 1964 the U.S. Soil Conservation Service (SCS) developed a computerized watershed model known as the TR-20 (SCS, 1975a). It is a very versatile model that has the capability of solving many hydrologic problems comprising the formulation of runoff hydrographs; routing hydrographs through channels and reservoirs, thus providing flow rates at selected locations of the system; combining or separating hydrographs at confluences; and determining peak discharges and their time of occurrences at individual storm events. The model is widely used in small watershed projects and floodplain studies. When the purpose is to assess the peak discharge or peak flow hydrograph for a drainage design, a method simplified from TR-20 is used. This is referred to as TR-55 (SCS, 1975b, 1986). For practical design considerations and computer software see Haestad Methods (2002) and Debo and Reese (1995).

PROBLEMS

7.1 In the same graph, plot the inflow and the outflow hydrographs of Example 7.1. Estimate the percentage in flood peak reduction and the time phase between flood peaks.

7.2 If $k=24hour$ and $x=0.2$, route the following inflow hydrograph through a river reach using the Muskingum method. Starting at 0 hours, the inflow rates are given in m^3/s every 12 hours are as follows: 1.0, 3.3, 15.5, 29.4, 32.8, 30.7, 26.3, 21.4, 17.3, 13.6, 10.3, 7.7, 6.0, 5.1, 4.6. Assume $O_1=1.0m^3/s$.

7.3 Modify the Maple program in Example 7.2 to solve Problem 7.2. Plot the inflow and the outflow hydrographs.

7.4 Using the given inflow and calculated outflow hydrographs of Problem 7.2, estimate the Muskingum routing parameters.

7.5 Assume that the inflow and the calculated outflow hydrographs in Problem 7.2 are the only data available, but the Muskingum routing parameters for the river reach, k and x, are unknown. Modify the Maple program in Example 7.4 to estimate the latter.

7.6 Rerun the program in Example 7.5 after setting $\beta=1.5$. State your observations about the effect of this parameter on the shape of the nonlinear hydrograph.

7.7 In the same graph, plot the inflow and the outflow hydrographs of Example 7.6. Estimate the percentage in flood peak reduction and the time phase between flood peaks.

7.8 A reservoir has an average surface area of $10km^2$, and a concrete spill way with a crest width of $30.0m$. Prior to the passage of an extreme flood wave, the flow rate upstream and downstream the reservoir is $100.0m^3/s$. Route the inflow hydrograph of Table 7.2 assuming that the surface area of the reservoir does not change significantly within the range of head values.

7.9 Assume that in Example 7.7 the exponent in the SIC is in fact $a=1.4$ and that the inflow hydrograph receded to a constant value of $400m^3/s$ after the flood ended. Modify the program in Example 7.7 to simulate the outflow hydrograph for a period of 2 months beyond flood. *Hint*: Besides changing the value of a, the inflow vector, I_n, needs to be altered by adding a sequence command (seq(,)) at the last slot that inserts 2 months (60 values) equal to 400.

7.10 Solve Example 7.6 using Maple and plot the inflow and the outflow hydrographs. *Suggestion*: Modify the program in Example 7.7; use the inflow data in Table 7.4; add a statement for $O(H)$ and solve for H using the solve command (solve(,)); add a statement for $S(H)$ and eliminate H, thus defining the SIC function $2S/\Delta t + O$ versus O. This function needs to be solved for O numerically each time step inside the step( ) procedure by using the fsolve (,) command.

7.11 Using the flow rate series of Example 7.8 and the graphical procedure, (1) determine if the series follows a Normal probability distribution. (2) Assuming the Normal distribution is a good model. Estimate the flow with a return period of $T=50$ years. Compare your estimate with that obtained in Example 7.8. Which one would you adopt and why?

7.12 Solve Problem 7.11 with Maple. For this purpose, modify the program in Example 7.9.

7.13 Solve Example 7.8 (Table 7.5) with Maple. For this purpose, modify the program in Example 7.10 to plot the log-transformed data of Table 7.5 on Normal paper.

7.14 Table 7.11. shows the maximum annual flow rates at a river station. (1) Modify the program in Example 7.10 to investigate the suitability of the log-Normal distribution as a model of flood frequency for the data in Table 7.11. (2) Assuming log-Normality, estimate the flow with a return period of 25 years.

Table 7.11: Annual Maximum Flow Rate Data for Problem 7.14

Year	$Q(m^3/s)$	Year	$Q(m^3/s)$	Year	$Q(m^3/s)$
1980	225	1989	455	1998	220
1981	300	1990	1340	1999	222
1982	212	1991	350	2000	190
1983	330	1992	455	2001	260
1984	503	1993	302	2002	292
1985	100	1994	405	2003	480
1986	290	1995	202	2004	800
1987	369	1996	699	2005	498
1988	215	1997	411		

7.15 Using the flow data in Table 7.11, investigate the suitability of the Weibull distribution as a model of flood frequency, and estimate the flow with a return period of 25 years. To this end, modify the program in Example 7.10 to plot the $\log(Q)$ versus $-\log(-\log(m/N+1))$, where m is the rank and N is the number of data points.

7.16 Using the flow data in Table 7.11, investigate the suitability of the Exponential distribution as a model of flood frequency, and estimate the flow with a return period of 25 years. To this end, modify the program in Example 7.10 to plot the values of Q versus $-\log(1-m/(N+1))$, where m is the rank and N is the number of data points.

7.17 Solve Example 7.11 using the analytical method and assuming that the flow series follows a Gumbel Distribution. Which design flood would you adopt and why?

7.18 Solve Example 7.11, using the analytical method and assuming that the flow series follows a log-Pearson Type III distribution and that the regional skew coefficient of the logarithmic series in nearby stations is -0.85. Which design flood would you adopt and why?

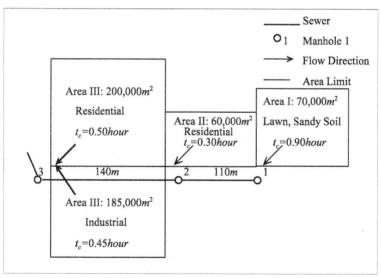

Figure 7.12: Storm Sewer System of Problem 7.19

7.19 Estimate the design flow rate at manholes 1, 2, and 3 of the storm sewer system illustrated in Figure 7.12 for a return period of 5 years. Assume that the system is being planned for a community in Washington, DC, and that rainfall frequency relationships developed by the U.S. National Weather

Service (Chapter 2, equation (2.5)) are applicable. Assume that the average flow velocity in any sewer line is $1.2 m/s$.

"If your opponent strikes with fire, counter with water, becoming completely fluid and free flowing. Water, by its nature, never collides with or breaks against anything. On the contrary, it swallows up any attack harmlessly. . . Study how water flows in a valley stream, smoothly and freely between the rocks. Everything – mountains, rivers, plants, and trees should be your teacher."

Morihei Ueshiba.

8 HYDROLOGY AND WATER QUALITY

8.1 HYDROLOGICAL ASPECTS OF WATER QUALITY

During its slow movement towards the ocean, natural waters experience not only the physical processes described in the previous chapters, but also complex chemical and biological interactions with natural and human-generated constituents. Water rarely exists as a pure chemical in nature. It usually contains mixed and dissolved chemicals, solid particles, and active biological organisms in suspension. Water quality is the term associated with the chemical characteristics of water. The physical hydrologic processes of precipitation, infiltration, overland flow, subsurface flow, groundwater flow, and stream flow facilitate the dissolution, chemical precipitation and movement of atmospheric, land and water chemicals. Hydrogeologists study the characteristics of natural waters and their interaction with the surrounded geologic media.

Of particular interest to modern hydrologists, is the effect of physical hydrologic processes on the propagation of unnatural or abnormal chemical contaminants generated by human activities. The discharge of harmful chemicals or other constituents in concentrations above naturally occurring background levels is called water pollution. Any condition caused by human activity that adversely affects the quality of a stream, lake, ocean or source of groundwater, or that adversely affects the use of natural water for human consumption, is also water pollution. The levels of water pollution have reached such point that water should be considered as an endangered natural resource today. Water is a precious resource that must be protected by current technologies, government organizations, private industries, and the public in general.

Today's industry and agricultural processes generate a variety of chemical byproducts that one way or another may reach streams, lakes, or the groundwaters. Some of these compounds are toxic to humans even in low concentrations. The quality of water that we ingest, as well as the quality of water in lakes, streams, rivers, aquifers, and oceans is critical to our health and the environment. Polluted water is not only a threat to human health but also to aquatic life. An unpolluted natural stream enables a wide diversity of aquatic organisms to thrive. It contains enough dissolved oxygen to support life and is free of abnormally high concentrations of organic and inorganic pollutants, suspended matter and toxins. A polluted water, on the other hand, inhibits the growth of many organisms, and only the undesirable types of organisms that do not require oxygen will flourish.

In the past, water contamination was primarily due to microbiological agents. Although many advances in public health have been made, incidences of water borne diseases still occur in many parts of the world. Typical disease agents present in polluted waters are the parasite Giardia lamblia, viral agents, the bacterium E. coli, and cyanobacteria. Although an effective water treatment process will remove these and other agents, many people in rural areas of the world drink untreated water from rivers and wells.

Pollution of surface water frequently results in a situation where the contamination can be seen or smelled. However, contamination of groundwater most often results in a situation that can not be detected by human senses.

8.2 MEASURES OF WATER QUALITY

To objectively examine water quality, a quantitative assessment of several characteristics must be done. The following is a summary of the most important water quality parameters. For a more complete description, as well as exact methods for measuring them see Environmental Protection Agency (1979), Water Pollution Control Federation (1989a), and Sawyer and McCarty (1978). For an in depth treatment of potential environmental contaminants and their properties see Shineldecker (1992).

Dissolved Oxygen
Dissolved oxygen (DO) is the amount of molecular oxygen dissolved in water. *DO* is an important measure of natural water fitness to support aquatic life. Natural water habitats are sensitive to *DO*. This parameter may be measured in the laboratory or in the field with a special meter in concentration units $[ML^{-1}]$ such as *mg/L*. *DO* decreases with temperature. For example the saturation DO at 5^oC is $13mg/L$, whereas at 20^oC is $9mg/L$. Therefore, cool water may contain much more dissolved oxygen than warm water. As a result, aquatic life in streams and lakes endures more oxygen stress during summer months than during other seasons.

Biochemical Oxygen Demand
Biochemical oxygen demand (BOD) is the amount of oxygen required to oxidize any organic matter present in the water biochemically. *BOD* is an indirect measure of the level of organic contamination present in water. The more organic matter present, the greater the amount of oxygen that

microorganisms may consume in oxidizing the wastes to CO_2 and H_2O (waste stabilization). *BOD* is measured in the laboratory at 20^oC, under darkness (to prevent algae from producing oxygen), and an excess of nutrients for microorganisms. The test takes five days (BOD_5), or 20 to 30 days for an ultimate test (BOD_u).

Microorganisms present in natural waters are usually acclimated to metabolize the organic wastes contained in a water sample. Water polluted with industrial chemicals may require the addition of microbial "seed" to assure oxidation. If ammonia is present in the water, an inhibitor must be added to prevent an enhanced reading caused by the oxidation of ammonia to nitrate. *BOD* is determined as the change in *DO* per unit dilution volume registered during the time of the experiment:

$$BOD_t = \frac{DO_i - DO_f}{\left(V_s/V_b\right)}$$

(8.1)

where
BOD_t=biochemical oxygen demand at t days (mg/L)
DO_i=initial dissolved oxygen in the sample bottle (mg/L)
DO_f=final dissolved oxygen in the sample bottle (mg/L)
V_b= sample bottle volume (mL)
V_s= sample volume (mL)

Example 8.1
A 10-mL water sample is collected in a 250-mL BOD bottle. The bottle is then filled with dilution water. The initial *DO* of the mixture is 10mL. The *DO* after five days of incubation is 4mL. What is the BOD_5 of the sample?

Solution
From equation (8.1),

$$BOD_5 = \frac{DO_i - DO_f}{\left(V_s/V_b\right)} = \frac{10mg/L - 4mg/L}{10mL/250mL} = 150mg/L$$

Chemical Oxygen Demand
The equivalent amount of oxygen required to oxidize any organic matter in a water sample by means of a strong chemical oxidizing agent is called *chemical oxygen demand* (*COD*). The *COD* is measured in the

laboratory as the difference between the initial amount of the strong oxidizing agent added to the sample (usually chromic acid) and the one remaining after a process of digestion of two hours. Although a *COD* test is relatively simple and fast to perform, as compared to a *BOD* test, its procedure does not replicate natural existing conditions.

Total Organic Carbon

Total organic carbon (*TOC*) is the amount of organic carbon in a sample. It provides an estimate of the organic contamination present in the water. This is important because organic pollutants will consume oxygen, and because some organic compounds are toxic. *TOC* measurement instruments automatically oxidize organic matter to carbon dioxide and then measure CO_2 content.

Oil and Grease

Oil and grease is a measure of the amount of oily or greasy substances without the specific determination of the chemical constituents present. This is accomplished by estimating the amount of organic compounds soluble in the solvent trichlorotrifluoroethane. Oil and grease is only measured in waste waters, since its abnormal presence could have a detrimental effect on treatment processes.

Total Solids

Total solids (*TS*) is the amount of organic and inorganic matter in the water. It is a gross indicator of water contaminants. *TS* is determined in the laboratory by evaporating a known sample of water in a previously weighted crucible dish at $103^\circ C$, and then weighing the crucible again. Thus, *TS* is the mass of residue remaining per unit sample volume, or

$$TS = \frac{m_{cf} - m_{ci}}{V} \tag{8.2}$$

where
 TS = total solids (*mg/L*)
 m_{ci} = initial crucible mass (*mg*)
 m_{cf} = crucible mass after drying (*mg*)
 V = sample volume (*L*)

Volatile Solids

Volatile solids (*VS*) is the amount of matter that volatilizes when heated at $550^\circ C$. It is an approximation of the amount of organic matter present in the water. This test is usually performed after the completion of the *TS* test. The crucible containing the total solids mass is heated at the above temperature until all volatile matter has been ignited or burned. The *VS* is given by

$$VS = \frac{m_{cf} - m_{cx}}{V}$$ (8.3)

where
$\quad VS =$ the volatile solids (mg/L)
$\quad m_{cx} =$ crucible mass after ignition (mg)

Fixed Solids
$\quad$ *Fixed solids* (*FS*) represent the amount of mineral matter, that is the solids that do not volatilize. *FS* is the difference between *TS* and *VS*:

$$FS = TS - VS$$ (8.4)

Example 8.2
$\quad$ A 25-*mL* water sample is placed in a crucible dish that weights 50.0*g*. After evaporation drying at $103^{o}C$, and cooling in a desiccator, the crucible weights 50.020*g*. Then the crucible is fired at $550^{o}C$ for one hour, after which it weights 50.005*g*. Estimate the *TS*, the *VS* and the *FS* of the sample.

Solution
$\quad$ From equations (8.2)-(8.4),

$$TS = \frac{m_{cf} - m_{ci}}{V} = \frac{50.020g - 50.000g}{25mL} \times \frac{10^3 mg}{g} \times \frac{10^3 mL}{L} = 800.0 mg/L$$

$$VS = \frac{m_{cf} - m_{cx}}{V} = \frac{50.020g - 50.005g}{25mL} \times \frac{10^3 mg}{g} \times \frac{10^3 mL}{L} = 600.0 mg/L$$

$$FS = TS - VS = 800.0 mg/L - 600.0 mg/L = 200.0 mg/L$$

Total Suspended Solids
$\quad$ *Total suspended solids* (TSS) is the amount of matter suspended in the water. *TSS* is determined in the laboratory by passing a known volume of water in a previously weighted glass microfiber filter of effective retention $1.5\,\mu m$, then drying the filter at $103^{o}C$, and then weighing the

filter again. *TSS* is the mass of the material remaining in the filter per unit volume of the sample:

$$TSS = \frac{m_{ff} - m_{fi}}{V} \qquad (8.5)$$

where
  TSS=total solids (*mg/L*)
  m_{fi}= initial filter mass (*mg*)
  m_{ff}= filter mass after drying (*mg*)

Volatile Suspended Solids
  After the TSS test, the solids residue may be burned at 550°C and the filter weighted again. The mass difference will yield the *volatile suspended solids* (*VSS*):

$$VSS = \frac{m_{ff} - m_{fx}}{V} \qquad (8.6)$$

where
  VSS=volatile suspended solids (*mg/L*)
  m_{fx}= filter mass after ignition (*mg*)

Fixed Suspended Solids
  Fixed suspended solids (*FSS*) is the matter remaining from the *VSS* analysis, that is the unburnable matter or the inorganic matter in the sample:

$$FSS = TSS - VSS \qquad (8.7)$$

Total Dissolved Solids
  The *total dissolved solids* (*TDS*) is the amount of matter dissolved in water. Water naturally contains a number of different dissolved inorganic constituents. The major cations are calcium, magnesium, sodium, and potassium. The major anions are chloride, sulfate, carbonate, and bicarbonate. Although not in ionic form, silica can also be a major constituent. They might also be some minor constituents, such as iron, manganese, fluoride, nitrate, strontium, and boron. Trace elements such as arsenic, lead, cadmium, and chromium may be present in amounts of only a few micrograms per liter, but they are very important from the water quality point of view. Dissolved organic matter may also be present in the water. Dissolved gases are found in both surface and groundwater.

These may include oxygen and carbon dioxide. Nitrogen, which is more or less inert is also present. Minor gases of concern in water quality are hydrogen sulfide, which is toxic and produces odors, and methane. These are usually present in polluted waters.

Rain water may dissolve chemicals present in the atmosphere. The processes of infiltration and groundwater flow may dissolve minerals naturally present in the soil or rock, or contaminants propagating thorough the unsaturated zone and the aquifer, such as pesticides, herbicides, gasoline components, and other chemicals. The quality of groundwater varies substantially from place to place. It can range from a TDS of $100mg/L$ or less for some fresh groundwater to more than $100,000mg/L$ for some brines found in deep aquifers. Surface runoff may dissolve minerals and other chemicals present in the near surface of the soil.

Water use by humans is translated in an increase in the TDS. Even the treatment of potable and waste waters increases the amount of TDS. The effects of a TDS greater than $500mg/L$ in potable water are various. Dissolved solids may corrode water distribution systems, and have a detrimental effect on industrial processes. There is also the belief that a water rich in dissolved minerals is detrimental for human health, particularly water rich in inorganic minerals that are difficult to assimilate by the human body, even though in principle some of the minerals are necessary for human growth and general health. TDS is measured indirectly as the difference between the total solids and the total suspended solids:

$$TDS = TS - TSS \qquad (8.8)$$

TABLE 8.1: Classification of Water Based on TDS

Type	TDS (mg/L)
Fresh	0-1,000
Brackish	1,000-10,000
Saline	10,000-100,000
Brine	>100,000

From the above relationships, we deduce that TS is the sum of the volatile plus the fixed solids. The TS can also be estimated as the sum of the TSS plus the TDS. Since the TSS is the sum of FSS plus the VSS (see eq.(8.7)), then the TDS is the sum of the fixed dissolved solids (FDS) plus the volatile dissolved solids (VDS). Table 8.1 illustrates a classification of water based on TDS.

Nitrogen

Nitrogen is an important parameter because it can act as a nutrient stimulating algae growth (*eutrophication*) and because oxidation of reduced nitrogen forms can consume considerable amounts of oxygen. Nitrogen may occur in several forms, including organic ammonia, nitrite, nitrate and molecular. Microorganisms present in the water may convert among all of these forms of nitrogen.

Phosphorus

Phosphorus present in the water stimulates the growth of algae (eutrophication). It exists in water as phosphates and organophosphates. Often household detergents are a major source of phosphates.

Metals

Metals are present in natural and polluted waters. Sodium, potassium, calcium, chromium, mercury, zinc, lead, and copper may be present in the water due to industrial pollution. Many of them are toxic. They are measured in water samples by an atomic absorption spectrophotometer.

Turbidity

Turbidity is an indirect measurement of suspended matter in the water, and it affects its clarity. Clouded water is caused by suspended particles scattering or absorbing light. Since microorganisms attach to the surface of suspended particles, turbidity is important in potable water. Turbidity is measured with an instrument that gauges the amount of light scattered at an angle of 90° from a source light.

Hardness

Hardness is the concentration of multivalent cations measured as calcium carbonate ($CaCO_3$). The cations responsible for hardness are calcium, magnesium, ferric iron, ferrous iron, strontium, and manganese. Hard water tends to form a scale on pipes, cooking containers, boilers, heat exchangers, etc. Hard water also requires a substantially greater amount of soap for bathing or clothes washing.

Alkalinity

Alkalinity is defined as the capacity of water to neutralize acids. Alkalinity in water is caused by the presence of salts of weak acids and strong bases. In natural water this condition is usually caused by the presence of bicarbonate, although it could also be produced by the presence of carbonate, hydroxide, phosphate, borate, and other ions.

pH

pH is the negative log of the hydrogen ion concentration. The *pH* magnitude affects biological and chemical reactions, controls the solubility of metallic ions, and interferes with natural aquatic life. It is measured with a *pH* meter.

8.3 SOURCES OF WATER CONTAMINATION

Pollution in natural waters comes from many sources. Municipal and industrial waste water are the most commonly reported forms. Publicly owned treatment works receive waste water from the sewer pipes of homes, businesses, and industries. Typically, waste water exhibits a BOD_5 of 150 to 300mg/L, *TSS* of 150 to 300mg/L, *COD* of 400 to 600mg/L, *DO* of about 0mg/L, ammonium and nitrogen concentrations of 15 to 40mg/L, and a *pH* of 6 to 8. After treatment to remove contaminants, the water must meet certain requirements. For example the U.S. Environmental Protection Agency requirements for discharge into natural waters are: a maximum BOD_5 of 30mg/L, a maximum *TSS* of 30mg/L, and a *pH* between 6 and 9. It is desirable that communities and industries that discharge into lakes or pristine streams reduce the above values by a factor of 3 to protect the natural aquatic life and reduce the risk of eutrophication.

Industries use and then discharge vast quantities of water each day. A large portion of it is used for cooling purposes only. However, much unwanted and dangerous materials are also present in many industrial waste waters. Some industries treat their waters and then discharge them into rivers, lakes, or marine waters. Others pretreat their waters for dangerous chemicals, or for chemicals not sensitive to normal municipal treatment, prior to discharging them into publicly own treatment plants. Unfortunately, many industries in the world manage to discharge their waste waters into natural streams without any form of treatment. Given the enormous volumes of waste water produced daily, the damage to the natural environment is incalculable.

Environmental regulations set for industrial waste waters are more detailed than those for publicly owned treatment works because of the large variety of constituents contained in industrial waste water. Many different categories of industrial wastes are recognized. For example, automobile manufacturing waste water contains soluble and insoluble oils, cyanides, acids, bases, metals, paints and other species. Petroleum refining produces water with high *BOD*, phenols, organic sulfur, organic nitrogen, naphthenic acids, inorganic acids, alkalis, and inorganic salts. Metal finishing and plating produces waste water with oil, grease, cyanides, acids, bases, and metals. Dairy production produces waste water high in *BOD*, and organic nitrogen. Pulp and paper making produces waste water rich in sulfites, organics, chlorinated organics, acids, fibers, and solids. Many of these compounds are highly toxic, non biodegradable, difficult to treat, and remain in the water even after treatment.

There are many other sources of chemical and microbiological agents that are adversely impacting the quality of surface and groundwater. These include the deposition of atmospheric contaminants from rained water, animal feedlot runoff, irrigation excess flow, drainage from intensive agriculture (fertilizers, insecticides, nematicides, herbicides, fungicides, etc.), construction site runoff, combined sewer overflow, drainage or leakage from septic tanks, sewage treatment lagoons, municipal landfills, toxic and hazardous waste landfills, underground storage tanks, and chemical and petroleum product accidental spills. For example, effluents from septic tanks typically have a BOD_5 of 100 to $300mg/L$, a *TSS* of 50 to $100mg/L$, a *COD* of 300 to $600mg/L$, a *DO* of about $0mg/L$, and ammonium and nitrogen concentrations of 15 to $60mg/L$. Landfill leachates may also contain abnormally high levels of metals, and organic compounds.

Groundwater contamination is a widespread problem in industrialized, suburban, and rural areas. The sources of groundwater pollution are many and the contaminants are numerous. Industrial solvents, such as trichloroethylene, 1,1,1-trichloroethane, tetrachloroethane, benzene, and carbon tetrachloride have been found in many areas. Suburban waters have high levels of nitrate due to the use of lawn fertilizers as well as septic tank discharges. Groundwater in agricultural areas have high levels of fertilizers, and synthetic organic agricultural chemicals. Landfills in urban and rural areas are important sources of contamination. Underground storage tanks holding petroleum products and synthetic organic chemicals leak and cause extensive groundwater pollution. Extraction and processing of metallic ore and coal have been the source of groundwater contamination. Groundwater moving through mineralized rock zones may contain excessive amounts of heavy metals. Mining and milling expose overburden and waste rock to oxidation. Oxidation of pyrite can produce sulfuric acid. Finally accidental chemical spills from industrial storage or industrial facilities have been the cause of significant contamination of the groundwaters. A large percentage of today's vast chemical production is transported on board of motor vehicles. These surface vehicles are subject to the normal highway accident statistics that sometimes result in high concentration chemical spills, which propagate through the soil and the groundwater.

Surface and groundwater contaminants will naturally tend to travel and propagate along the many paths of the hydrologic cycle described in previous chapters. This causes the contamination of soils, aquifers, streams, and lakes. Pollution is not an irreversible process. There are natural conditions that act to remove contaminants. Attenuation mechanisms include dilution, dispersion, mechanical dispersion (in soils and aquifers), volatilization, biological activity, ion exchange and adsorption on soil particle surfaces, chemical reactions, and radioactive decay. Finally, many techniques have been developed for restoring the quality of surface and ground water that has been contaminated. See for example Metcalf and Eddy, Inc. (1991); Water Pollution Control Federation (1977); Devinny et al. (1990).

The health effects of exposure to abnormally high concentrations of chemical contaminants are various. For example arsenic causes skin and nervous system disorders; barium causes circulatory problems; cadmium causes kidney problems; chromium causes liver or kidney malfunction; lead is highly toxic to pregnant women and infants, and it is usually associated with kidney and nervous system disorders; mercury causes kidney and nervous system problems; nitrate causes methemoglobinemia; selenium has adverse gastrointestinal effects; silver causes skin discoloration; fluoride produces skeletal damage and hardening of the arteries. As toxicology research evolves, a variety of health effects associated with exposure to organic compounds have been found. For example high concentrations of total trihalomethanes and benzene significantly increase the risk of cancer.

8.4 WATER QUALITY STANDARDS

Water quality standards represent regulations imposed by environmental and government organizations on the quality of water that may be applied to a specific use. Based on the analytical capability to detect a contaminant in drinking water, the potential health risk, and the occurrence or potential for occurrence in drinking water, there are some maximum concentration levels specified for a wide variety of chemical substances. These values represent maximum levels with an adequate margin of safety, taking into consideration the available water treatment technologies and cost. Maximum concentrations for compounds that are

Table 8.2: U.S. Environmental Protection Agency Drinking Water Standards

Chemical	MCL ($\mu g/L$)	Chemical	MCL ($\mu g/L$)	Chemical	MCL ($\mu g/L$)
Synthetic organic chemicals		**Synthetic organic chemicals (continued)**		**Inorganic chemicals (continued)**	
Acrylamide	0.0	Hexachlorobenzene	1.0	Mercury	2.0
Adipates	500.0	Hexachlorocyclopentadiene (HEX)	50.0	Nickel	100.0
Alachlor	2.0	Indenopyrene	0.4	Nitrate (as N)	10,000.0
Aldicarb	3.0	Lidane	0.2	Nitrite (as N)	1,000.0
Aldicarb sulfoxide	4.0	Methoxychlor	40.0	Selenium	50.0
Aldicarb sulfone	2.0	Methylene chloride	5.0	Silver	100.0
Atrazine	3.0	Monochlorobenzene	100.0	Sulfate	4×10^5
Benzene	5.0	Oxamyl (vydate)	200.0	Thallium	5.0
Benzo[a]anthracene	0.1	PCBs as decachlorobiphenol	0.5		
Benzo[a]pyrene	0.2	Pentachlorophenol	1.0	**Microbiological parameters**	
Benzo[b]fluoranthene	0.2	Picloram	500.0	Giardia lamblia	0 organisms
Benzo[k]fluoranthene	0.2	Simaze	4.0	Legionella	0 organisms
Butylbenzyl phthalate	100.0	Styrene	100.0	Heterotrophic bacteria	0 organisms
Carbofuran	40.0	2,3,7,8-TCDD (dioxin)	3×10^{-8}	Viruses	0 organisms
Carbontetrachloride	5.0	Tetrachloroethylene	5.0		
Chlorodane	2.0	1,2,4-Trichlorobenzene	70.0	**Radionuclides**	
Chrysene	0.2	1,1,2-Trichloroethane	5.0	Radium 226	20.0 pCi/L
Dalapon	200.0	Trichloroethylene (TCE)	5.0	Radium 228	20.0 pCi/L
Dibenz[a,h]anthracene	0.3	1,1,1-Trichloroethane	200.0	Radon 222	300.0 pCi/L
Dibromochloropropane (DBCP)	0.2	Toluene	1000.0	Uranium	30 pCi/L
o-Dichlorobenzene	600.0	Toxaphene	3.0		
p-Dichlorobenzene	75.0	2-(2,4,5-Trichlorophenoxy)-			
1,2-Dichloroethane	5.0	propionic acid (2,4,5,-TP, or Silvex)	50.0		
1,1-Dichloroethylene	7.0	Vinyl chloride	2.0		
cis-1,2-Dichloroethylene	70.0	Xylenes (total)	10,000.0		
trans-1,2-Dichloroethylene	100.0				
1,2-Dichloropropan	5.0	**Inorganic chemicals**			
2,4-Dichlorophenoxyacetic acid (2,4-D)	70.0	Aluminum	50.0		
Di(ethylhexyl)phthalate	6.0	Antimony	6.0		
Diguat	20.0	Arsenic	50.0		
Dinoseb	7.0	Asbestos (fibers per liter)	7×10^6		
Endothall	100.0	Barium	2000.0		
Endrin	2.0	Beryllium	4.0		
Epichlorohydrin	0.0	Cadmium	5.0		
Ethylbenzene	700.0	Chromium	100.0		
Ethylene dibromide (EDB)	0.05	Copper	1,300.0		
Glyphosate	700.0	Cyanide	200.0		
Heptachlor	0.4	Fluoride	4,000.0		
Heptachlor epoxide	0.2	Lead	15.0		

carcinogenic, or chronically toxic, are set as close to zero as possible based on the treatment costs, and the health risks associated with an acceptable daily intake from drinking water. Risks from carcinogenic compounds is expressed in terms of additional cancer risk over a life time of exposure at a given level. A cancer risk of 10^{-6} implies that there would be an additional cancer-related death in a population of 1,000,000 people.

Table 8.2 illustrates the current drinking water standards as stipulated by the U.S. Environmental Protection Agency. Some of these values may change, as they are based on continuing toxicological research. As new knowledge accumulates on the potential health risks of a contaminant, and as new treatment technologies become available, stricter standards and new contaminants may be added to the list.

QUESTIONS AND PROBLEMS

8.1 Write a one-page essay describing your own thoughts about the effect of hydrologic phenomena (i.e., precipitation, infiltration, depression storage, surface runoff, groundwater flow, stream flow) on pollution of natural waters. Discriminate between natural pollution and human-based pollution.

8.2 In your own words, define each of the following terms without writing equations: Turbidity; alkalinity; hardness; biochemical oxygen demand; dissolved oxygen; water pollution; volatile suspended solids; fixed suspended solids; total dissolved solids; chemical oxygen demand.

8.3 Explain what natural processes exist that make water pollution a reversible phenomenon.

8.4 What are the possible adverse effects of nitrogen and phosphorus pollution in water?

8.5 Why is it important to maintain a minimum amount of dissolved oxygen in natural waters?

8.6 What are the possible adverse effects of an elevated amount of organic carbon in water?

8.7 What kind of contaminants might be present in suburban lawn pesticides and fertilizers? Using your knowledge of hydrology, hypothesize the possible paths these contaminants may take.

8.8 Using library or Internet resources, investigate an industry and describe in one page the types of wastes that would be released to its waste waters.

8.9 If the *TSS* of a water sample is 250*mg/L*, and the *FSS* is 101*mg/L*, what is the *VSS*?

8.10 A sample of 10*mL* of water from a river is collected in a 300*mL* *BOD* bottle. The bottle is filled with dilution water. The initial *DO* of the mixture is 8.5*mg/L*. The final *DO* is 3*mg/L*. Estimate the BOD_u.

8.11 A waste water sample of 20*mL* is placed in a 49-*g* crucible dish. After evaporation at a 103°*C*, the crucible weights 49.014*g*. The crucible is then fired at **550°*C*** for one hour. After cooling, the crucible weights 49.004*g*. Calculate the *TS*, the *VS*, and the *FS*.

8.12 If the *VDS* is 29% of the *TS*, the *FDS* is 38%, the *VSS* is 25%, and the *FSS* is 8%, estimate the ratios of *TDS* and *TSS*.

13. If in problem 12 the *VSS* is 240*mg/L*, estimate the *FSS*, the *FDS*, *VDS*, *TDS*, *TSS*, and *TS* in *mg/L*.

9 THE HYDROLOGY
OF RIVER POLLUTION

9.1 MODELING WATER QUALITY IN RIVERS AND STREAMS

A collection of mathematical equations describing the hydrologic physical, chemical, and biological characteristics of water quality, or the transformation and propagation suffered by different contaminants in a river, constitutes a mathematical model. With an appropriate numerical algorithm implemented in a computer, the model offers a simplified qualitative and quantitative representation of the complex processes occurring in nature. Mathematical models are useful in the assessment of water quality conditions in a river, the prediction of the effect of new contaminant discharges, or the forecasting of the movement of a contaminant through a river system after an accidental chemical spill. Hydrologic consultants and water resources managers often use water quality models as fundamental tools for prevention, management, and remediation strategies. Building a mathematical model of water quality requires the consideration of a river system from the physical, chemical, and biological perspectives. The objective is to recognize and quantify the various interactions between river hydrology, chemistry, and biology.

The principal physical characteristics of interest in water quality modeling in rivers include: geometry (width and depth), river slope, bed roughness, tortuosity, velocity, flow rate, mixing characteristics (dispersion in the river), water temperature, suspended solids, and sediment transport. These characteristics have been discussed in chapters 6 and 7. Flow rate, velocity, and geometry appear to be the most important ones affecting water quality. In particular, low flow characteristics (drought conditions) represent a critical condition of river water quality. From the intuitive notion of dilution, the most adverse situation occurs at times when there is less water in the channel.

The principal chemical features of interest in water quality include: *DO* variations (including the effects of oxidizable nitrogen, and temperature variation), *pH*, alkalinity, *TS*, *TDS* (*VDS*, *FDS*), *TSS* (*VSS*, *FSS*), and concentrations of inorganic and organic chemicals that are potentially toxic. These have been discussed in chapter 8.

The principal biological characteristics include: viruses and bacteria type and count, fish populations, rooted aquatic plants, and biological slimes (sphaerotilus).

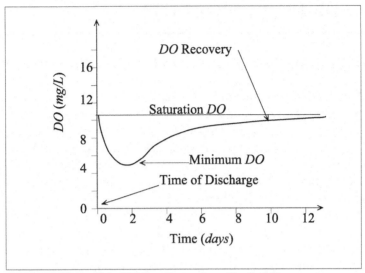

Figure 9.1: *DO* Sag Curve for a Typical Stream

9.2 THE IMPACT OF POLLUTION ON DISSOLVED OXYGEN

The discharge of waste water in rivers produces a slow decrease in *DO*. This is caused by the consumption of oxygen by the various organisms as they oxidize materials of the waste water in a stream. This process is called *deoxygenation*. Another set of reactions is the dissolving of molecular oxygen from the atmosphere into the water. This process is called *reaeration*. It depends on the water temperature, flow velocity, stream depth, flow turbulence, and oxygen deficit. Deoxygenation and reaeration have opposite effects in the stream *DO* level. As soon as waste water is discharged, deoxygenation will cause a slow decrease in the *DO* with time up to a minimum level, after which reaeration will cause a slow recovery in the *DO* with time up to levels close to the saturation *DO*. The time evolution of the *DO* at a point in a stream moving with the average flow velocity is called the *DO sag curve*. Figure 9.1 shows a typical *DO* sag curve.

The saturation *DO* depends on the water temperature and on the *TDS*. However, the effect of the *TDS* is less important in most fresh water systems. Table 9.1 shows the saturation *DO* with respect to temperature.

The oxygen deficit at a point moving with the average flow velocity in a stream, at a given time, and a given water temperature, is the difference between the potential saturated oxygen level and the actual dissolved oxygen level:

$$D=DO_{sat}-DO_{act} \qquad (9.1)$$

where

D=oxygen deficit (mg/L)
DO_{sat}= saturation DO (mg/L)
DO_{act}= actual DO for stream (mg/L)

TABLE 9.1: Saturation DO in Distilled Water.

Temperature ($^{\circ}C$)	DO (mg/L)	Temperature ($^{\circ}C$)	DO (mg/L)
0	14.6	16	9.9
1	14.2	17	9.7
2	13.9	18	9.5
3	13.5	19	9.3
4	13.1	20	9.1
5	12.8	21	8.9
6	12.5	22	8.7
7	12.1	23	8.6
8	11.8	24	8.4
9	11.6	25	8.3
10	11.3	26	8.1
11	11.0	27	8.0
12	10.8	28	7.8
13	10.5	29	7.7
14	10.3	30	7.6
15	10.1		

Example 9.1

A water sample is taken from a river. The water temperature is $20^{\circ}C$, and the DO is 8.0mg/L . Calculate the oxygen deficit.

Solution

From Table 9.1, the DO_{sat} corresponding to $20^{\circ}C$ is 9.1mg/L. Now from equation (9.1),

$$D=DO_{sat}-DO_{act}=9.1mg/L-8.0mg/L=1.1mg/L$$

Starting from the premise that the rate of oxygen consumed is proportional to the amount of organic matter present in the stream, we can develop an elementary model that describes the time variability of oxygen deficit at a moving point in a stream. The amount of organic matter in the stream may be expressed in terms of the BOD_u (see chapter 8). The consumption of organic matter depends on the types and numbers of micro-organisms present, the temperature, the current level of DO, and other factors. The rate of oxidation of organic matter (the rate reduction of BOD) can be assumed to be proportional to the current level of BOD:

$$\frac{dL}{dt} = -kL \tag{9.2}$$

where
    $k = BOD$ rate constant ($days^{-1}$)
    $L = BOD$ at time t (mg/L)

Separating variables, noting that at $t=0$, $L=L_0$, and integrating, we obtain

$$\int_0^{L_t} \frac{dL}{L} = -\int_0^t kdt$$

$$\Rightarrow \ln\left(\frac{L_t}{L_0}\right) = -kt \tag{9.3}$$

where
    L_0 = initial BOD, or BOD_u (mg/L)
    L_t = BOD at time t (mg/L)

On taking exponentials,

$$L_t = L_0 e^{-kt} \tag{9.4}$$

The oxygen consumed at time t may be estimated as the difference between the initial BOD and the BOD at time t:

$$y_t = L_0 - L_t = L_0 - L_0 e^{-kt} = L_0\left(1 - e^{-kt}\right) \tag{9.5}$$

where
    y_t = oxygen (BOD) consumed at time t (mg/L)

Example 9.2
A water sample from a river receiving pollution has a BOD_5 of

$180mg/L$. If the *BOD* rate constant is $0.10/day$, estimate the BOD_u and the BOD_2.

Solution

From equation (9.5),

$$L_0 = BOD_u = \frac{y_t}{(1-e^{-kt})} = \frac{180mg/L}{\left(1-e^{-\frac{0.10}{day} \times 5day}\right)} = 458mg/L$$

Similarly,

$$y_2 = L_0(1-e^{-kt}) = (458mg/L)\left(1-e^{-\frac{0.10}{day} \times 2day}\right) = 83mg/L$$

Equations (9.4) and (9.5) may be used to build a graph showing the time evolution of the *BOD* and the oxygen consumed, respectively, at a point in a stream moving with the mean flow velocity. Moreover, these relationships may help us build a mathematical model of oxygen deficit. As stated before, the rate of oxygen consumed may be assumed to be proportional to the amount of organic matter present in the stream, which we express as BOD_u. If we further assume that the rate of oxygen entering the stream from the atmosphere is proportional to the dissolved oxygen deficit in a stream, then we can express the rate of change in the stream oxygen deficit as:

$$\frac{dD}{dt} = k_1 L - k_2 D \tag{9.6}$$

where

t = time (*days*)
L = ultimate stream BOD (*mg/L*)
k_1 = deoxygenation constant ($days^{-1}$)
k_2 = reaeration constant ($days^{-1}$)

Substituting equation (9.4) into (9.6),

$$\frac{dD}{dt} = k_1 L_0 e^{-k_1 t} - k_2 D \tag{9.7}$$

This is a first order linear differential equation with constant coefficients. Its solution is easily obtained by using the integrating factor. With an initial condition $D(t=0)=D_0$, then

$$D(t)=\frac{k_1 L_0}{k_2-k_1}\left(e^{-k_1 t}-e^{-k_2 t}\right)+D_0 e^{-k_2 t} \tag{9.8}$$

where
   D=stream oxygen deficit at time t (mg/L)
   D_0= initial oxygen deficit at $t=0$ (mg/L)

This relationship, called the Streeter Phelps equation, implies that the waste water discharging into a stream mixes completely in a relatively short period of time, as compared to that of the simulation time. Equation (9.8) could be used to estimate the oxygen deficit as a function of time, and the DO after equation (9.1).

After the waste water is released into the river, the most adverse situation occurs when the oxygen deficit D is maximum. The critical time when this happens may be obtained by differentiating equation (9.8) with respect to t, equating to zero, and solving for t:

$$t_{crit}=\frac{1}{k_2-k_1}\ln\left[\frac{k_2}{k_1}\left(1-\frac{D_0(k_2-k_1)}{k_1 L_0}\right)\right] \tag{9.9}$$

where
   t_{crit}= time to maximum D (minimum DO) $(days)$

The deoxygenation rate for the above equations may be estimated from a series of experiments similar to those performed for a BOD evaluation. The reaeration rate is usually determined from empirical formulae based on stream characteristics such as flow velocity, channel slope, and average water depth. If sufficient information is available, the coefficients are estimated by calibration of the DO sag curve from measured values of the DO and BOD at various points along the stream. These measurements are usually performed during drought periods to reflect the most adverse condition, and at night to avoid the effect of algal oxygen production.

Example 9.3
   A waste water treatment plant is discharging into a river. The

upstream water (i.e., before the discharge), and the waste water conditions are summarized in Table 9.2. If the mean river flow velocity below the plant during late summer is $15km/day$, the deoxygenation coefficient is $0.5/day$, and the reaeration rate is $3.0/day$, determine the minimum DO and its distance from the plant.

Table 9.2: Data for Example 9.3

	BOD, y (mg/L)	Flow Rate, Q (m^3/day)	DO (mg/L)	Temperature $T(°C)$
Upstream Water	10	200,000	2	20
Waste Water	60	600,000	1	22

Solution

Using the subscripts u, w, and r to denote upstream, waste water, and resulting conditions after mixing in the river, respectively, we first calculate the resulting river flow rate:

$$Q_r = Q_u + Q_w = 200,000 \ m^3/day + 600,000 m^3/day = 800,000 m^3/day$$

Next, we calculate the resulting water temperature, T_r, by using an energy balance equation:

$$T_r Q_r = T_u Q_u + T_w Q_w$$

$$T_r = \frac{20°C \times 200,000 m^3/day + 22°C \times 600,000 m^3/day}{800,000 m^3/day}$$

$$T_r = 21.5°C$$

Now we calculate the resulting BOD, L_r, by using a mass balance equation:

$$L_r Q_r = L_u Q_u + L_w Q_w$$

$$L_r = \frac{10mg/L \times 200,000 m^3/day + 60mg/L \times 600,000 m^3/day}{800,000 m^3/day}$$

$$L_r = 47.5mg/L$$

Similarly, calculate the resulting dissolved oxygen, DO_r:

$$DO_r Q_r = DO_u Q_u + DO_w Q_w$$

$$DO_r = \frac{2.0mg/L \times 200,000m^3/day + 1.0 \times 600,000m^3/day}{800,000m^3/day} = 1.25mg/L$$

With a resulting water temperature of $21.5°C$, the saturation dissolved oxygen, DO_{sat}, is (from Table 9.1), $8.8mg/L$. Thus, the stream oxygen deficit is, from equation (9.1),

$$D_r = DO_{sat} - DO_{act} = 8.8mg/L - 1.25mg/L = 7.55mg/L$$

The time at which the minimum DO, and the maximum D, occurs is given from equation (9.9) as

$$t_{crit} = \frac{1}{k_2 - k_1} \ln \left[\frac{k_2}{k_1} \left(1 - \frac{D_r(k_2 - k_1)}{k_1 L_r} \right) \right]$$

$$t_{crit} = \frac{1}{3.0/day - 0.5/day} \ln \left[\frac{3.0/day}{0.5/day} \left(1 - \frac{7.55mg/L \times (3.0/day - 0.5/day)}{0.5/day \times 47.5mg/L} \right) \right]$$

$$t_{crit} = 0.083 days = 2.0 hour$$

Assuming a constant uniform velocity during low flow conditions in the river, we estimate the critical distance X_{crit} below the plant where the minimum DO occurs:

$$X_{crit} = 0.083 days \times 15.0 \ km/day = 1.25km$$

Thus, the maximum deficit occurs 0.083 days after the water is discharged into the river, or approximately $1.25km$ downstream. Using equations (9.8) and (9.1), we finally estimate the maximum deficit, D_{crit}, and the minimum dissolved oxygen, DO_{crit}, respectively in the stream:

$$D_{crit} = D(t_{crit}) = \frac{k_1 L_r}{k_2 - k_1} \left(e^{-k_1 t_{crit}} - e^{-k_2 t_{crit}} \right) + D_r e^{-k_2 t_{crit}}$$

$$D_{crit} = \frac{0.5/day \times 47.5mg/L}{3.0/day - 0.5/day} \left(e^{-0.5/day \times 0.28day} - e^{-3.0/day \times 0.28day} \right)$$

$$+ 6.3mg/L \times e^{-3.0/day \times 0.28day} = 7.59mg/L$$

$$DO_{crit} = DO_{sat} - D_{crit} = 8.8mg/L - 7.59mg/L = 1.30mg/L$$

This value is far below the required minimum of 4.0mg/L for the survival of fish populations.

9.3 EFFECT OF WASTE SOURCES ON WATER QUALITY

Conservative Substances
In the previous section we investigated the effect of the discharge of waste water on dissolved oxygen in the stream. In this section we will study its effects on the concentration of various chemicals downstream a waste source.

We have applied the concept of mixing of waste water with river water, and that related to mass balance at a discharge point (see Example 9.3). A common assumption in water quality models is that of *complete mixing* between the waste water and the resident river water at the discharge point. Normally this is not the actual case, since a contaminant plume develops from the discharge point along the river, gradually spreading across the river. This plume will eventually cover the whole depth and width of the river at a distance L_m from the source. The distance to complete mixing depends on several factors, including the mean flow velocity, flow turbulence, the dimensions of the river, and the dispersion properties of the contaminants present in the waste water. An approximate estimate of the distance to complete mixing is given by the Yotsukura equation:

$$L_m = \frac{C_m U B^2}{H} \qquad (9.10)$$

where
L_m = distance from the source to complete mixing (m)
U = mean flow velocity (m/s)
B = mean stream width (m)
H = average stream depth (m)
C_m = mixing coefficient equal to 4.265 for a midstream discharge, or 8.530 for a side bank discharge (s/m)

The stream flow velocity may be measured using conventional hydrometric techniques, or it may be estimated using approximate formulae for uniform flow as applied to low flow conditions in the stream. These formulae use information on the cross-section dimensions, and longitudinal slope of the river.

Assuming that the a complete mixing exists immediately downstream from a discharge point, the mass balance concept implies the application of the conservation of mass to a particular chemical constituent:

Mass rate of chemical upstream + mass rate added by waste water
= mass rate of chemical immediately downstream

Since the substance mass rate is the product of the flow rate and substance concentration,

$$Q_u C_u + Q_w C_w = Q_r C_r \qquad (9.11)$$

where
    Q_u = upstream flow rate (m^3/s)
    Q_w = waste water flow rate (m^3/s)
    Q_r = resulting flow rate downstream the source (m^3/s)
    C_u = upstream substance concentration (mg/L)
    C_w = substance concentration in the waste water (mg/L)
    C_r = resulting substance concentration downstream (mg/L)

The term $W = Q_w C_w$ is the input waste load (mg/s, or kg/day) to the river. The water mass balance may be expressed as

$$Q_u + Q_w = Q_r \qquad (9.12)$$

Upstream conditions are usually known or measured, and waste water characteristics are provided by design, if the problem in question is a proposed waste water facility. In such a case, equations (9.11) and (9.12) may be used to estimate the concentration of a typical contaminant in the river after mixing. If the upstream concentration is zero, then from equation (9.11)

$$C_r = \left(\frac{Q_w}{Q_r} \right) C_w = \frac{W}{Q_r} \qquad (9.13)$$

which indicates that the downstream concentration is equal to that of the waste water reduced by the ratio of the waste water flow rate to the total river flow rate. This is the effect of dilution. By increasing the river flow, the resulting concentration is correspondingly decreased.

Assuming complete mixing at tributary points in a river system, and steady flow conditions between tributary points (i.e., flow rate remains constant, and the effect of groundwater is neglected), the above basic equations may be used to depict concentration of *conservative substances* at several river reaches. Conservative substances are those that do not experience losses due to chemical reactions or biological degradations during its transport through the river system. Such substances may include *TDS*, chlorides, and certain metals during times of the year where transport is in dissolved form.

Example 9.4

Figure 9.2 shows a river system with one waste water discharge point, one tributary, and one water intake along its course. The flow rate and bromide concentrations (a conservative substance) are also provided. In order to maintain a desired bromide concentration of $200mg/L$ at the water intake, determine the required waste water reduction, or the required increase in the tributary flow Q_T.

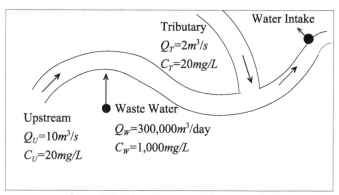

Figure 9.2: River System of Example 9.4

Solution

The total flow at the water intake is

$$Q_r = Q_u + Q_T + Q_w$$

$$Q_r = \left(10m^3/s + 2m^3/s\right) \times 86,400s/day + 300,000m^3/day = 1,336,800m^3/day$$

The waste loads are calculated as follows:

$$W_u = Q_u C_u = \frac{10m^3/s \times 20mg/L \times 1,000\ L/m^3 \times 86,400s/day}{1,000,000mg/kg} = 17,280\frac{kg}{day}$$

$$W_w = Q_w C_w = \frac{300,000m^3/day \times 1,000mg/L \times 1,000L/m^3}{1,000,000mg/kg} = 300,000\frac{kg}{day}$$

$$W_T = Q_T C_T = \frac{2m^3/s \times 20mg/L \times 1,000L/m^3 \times 86,400s/day}{1,000,000mg/kg} = 3,456\frac{kg}{day}$$

$$W_r = Q_r C_r = \frac{1,336,800m^3/day \times 200mg/L \times 1,000L/m^3}{1,000,000mg/kg} = 267,360\frac{kg}{day}$$

From equation (9.11), and defining W_w' as the industrial waste load, with a concentration C_w', required to maintain a maximum bromide concentration $C_r = 200mg/L$, then

$$Q_u C_u + Q_w C_w' + Q_T C_T = Q_r C_r$$

$$\therefore\ W_u + W_w' + W_T = W_r\ \Rightarrow\ W_w' = W_r - W_u - W_T$$

$$W_w' = 267,360kg/day - 17,280\ kg/day - 3,456kg/day = 249,744kg/day$$

The relative difference between the actual and the required waste load is

$$\Delta W = \frac{W_w - W_w'}{W_w} = \frac{300,000kg/day - 249,744kg/day}{300,000kg/day} = 0.17$$

or 17% reduction. This may be accomplished by reducing the effluent bromide, C_w', concentration to

$$C_w' = C_w \times (1 - \Delta W) = 1,000mg/L \times (1 - 0.17) = 833mg/L$$

If the industrial concentration is not reduced, the tributary flow must be increased to dilute the upstream concentration. Thus, defining Q_T' the required tributary flow, and noting that the flow at the water intake is correspondingly increased, equation 9.11 becomes

$$Q_u C_u + Q_w C_w + Q_T' C_T = (Q_u + Q_w + Q_T')C_r$$

$$\Rightarrow Q_T' = \frac{Q_w(C_w - C_r) - Q_u(C_r - C_u)}{C_r - C_T}$$

$$Q_T' = \frac{300,000 \frac{m^3}{day}}{86,400 \frac{s}{day}} \times (1,000 - 200)\frac{mg}{L} - 10\frac{m^3}{s} \times (200 - 20)\frac{mg}{L}}{(200 - 20)\frac{mg}{L}} = 5.43\frac{m^3}{s}$$

Thus, it is required an additional tributary flow rate release of $\Delta Q_T = Q_T' - Q_T = 5.43 m^3/s - 2.0 m^3/s = 3.43 m^3/s$.

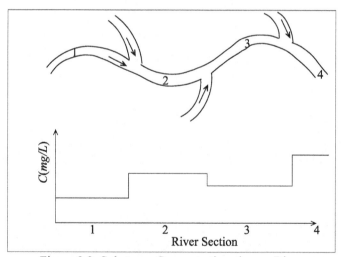

Figure 9.3: Substance Concentration along a River

The above analysis may be used to investigate the variations of a substance concentration along a river system composed of different tributaries, each with distinct flow rate and concentration characteristics. Figure 9.3 illustrates the case of a river reach receiving three tributaries. Section 1 of the river, upstream from the first tributary, carries a background concentration and a waste load of a particular contaminant. Section 2, downstream from the first tributary, exhibits an increased value of concentration due to high waste loads from the tributary. Section 3, downstream from the second tributary, exhibits a decreased concentration value due to a high flow rate coupled with a low concentration provided by the tributary. Section 4, downstream from the third tributary, exhibits a high concentration magnitude due to a high one coming from the tributary. The chart in figure 9.3 offers a schematic representation of the variability of solute concentration with distance and the effect of dilution. Similar graphs may be constructed for the flow rate, and the waste load along the river.

Non-Conservative Substances

Until now, we have considered conservative substances. Conservative substances do not experience any transformation in the stream. However, certain substances decay with time due to chemical reactions, bacterial degradation, radioactive decay (for radioactive contaminants), or deposition of solid particles out of the water column. Oxidizable organic matter, organic nutrients, volatile chemicals and bacteria are examples of *non-conservative substances*. When a transformation, reaction, or set of reactions, take place, the contaminant concentration decreases with time according to a specific functional relationship. In this cases it is useful to study the corresponding mass conservation equation.

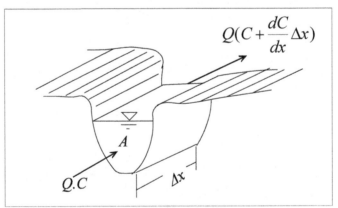

Figure 9.4: Mass Balance in a River Reach

Consider a river reach element of length Δx (Figure 9.4), with a cross sectional area A. Assume that the average area and the flow rate, Q, remain approximately constant along the element (i.e., assume uniform area, and neglect groundwater flow). We further assume that the river system is at a steady state, which implies that the variables are constant with respect to time. The mass conservation statement could be written as:

Mass rate of chemical downstream - mass rate of chemical
upstream = mass rate loss due to transformation

Defining the *concentration gradient* as the change of concentration per unit distance, the mass rate downstream may be expressed as that upstream plus the concentration gradient times distance. Referring to Figure 9.4, the mass conservation equation is

$$Q\left(C + \frac{dC}{dx}\Delta x\right) - QC = I \tag{9.14}$$

where
I=mass rate loss due to transformation (kg/day)

Since $Q=UA$, where U is the flow velocity, equation (9.14) becomes

$$UA\Delta x \frac{dC}{dx} = I$$

$$U\frac{dC}{dx} = \frac{I}{V} \tag{9.15}$$

where
V=element volume (m^3)

A common representation of I/V (loss rate per unit volume) conceives that the substance decays according to a *first-order reaction*. In other words, the mass rate of loss of the substance is proportional to the substance concentration, and $I/V=-KC$. Thus, equation (9.15) reduces to

$$U\frac{dC}{dx} = -KC \tag{9.16}$$

where
K=the decay rate of the substance (day^{-1})

If the upstream concentration is C_0, the solution to equation (9.16) is

$$C(x) = C_0 e^{-\frac{Kx}{U}} \tag{9.17}$$

Since $x/U=t$, the time to travel a distance x at a mean velocity U, then

$$C(x) = C_0 e^{-Kt} \tag{9.18}$$

These equations imply that a non-conservative substance decaying at a rate K, will experience an exponential decrease in concentration downstream. The conservative substance, on the other hand, will experience changes in concentration only at points of entrance of new load and flows.

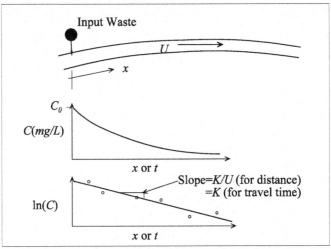

Figure 9.5: Decay of Non-Conservative Substances

Now taking natural logarithms on both sides of equation (9.18),

$$\ln C = \ln C_0 - Kt \tag{9.19}$$

This equation plots as a straight line with a slope $-K$ (for travel time), or $-K/U$ (for distance). Figure 9.5 shows a river receiving an input load with a concentration C_0 upstream, and the corresponding downstream concentration distribution according to equations (9.17), or (9.18), and (9.19). This provides an opportunity to estimate the decay rate constant of a substance in a stream from measurements of the concentration C at various downstream locations. Plotting the natural logarithm of the concentration sample points against travel time, and fitting a straight line, one can estimate K from the slope of the line.

Example 9.5

A stream with an average flow velocity of $6 m/s$ is sampled for total coliform count per Liter (N/L) at different distances downstream a sewage treatment plant. The results are shown in Table 9.3. Estimate the total coliform decay rate, K ($days^{-1}$).

Table 9.3: Data for Example 9.5

x (km)	10	20	30	40
C (N/L)	52,000	23,000	8,000	5,000

Solution

The following Maple program plots the survey data on semi-log paper, fits a least-squares straight line through the sample points, derives the line slope, and applies equation (9.19) to estimate K as the negative of the slope times U.

```
> restart: with(stats):
  X:=[10,20,30,40]:                    #distance, x data
  Cdata:=[52000.,23000.,8000.,5000.]: #Concentration, C
  n:=describe[count](X):                #number of points
  U:=6*86.4:                            #velocity in km/day
  Clog:=[seq(log(Cdata[i]),i=1..n)]:   #take the log of C
  #fit a least square line to semi-log data
  fit[leastsquare[[x,y], y=a*x+b, {a,b}]]([X,Clog]):
  C:=unapply(rhs(%),x):       # define as a function C(x)
  slope:=op(1,C(x))/x:
  K:=-U*slope;
  #define the tick marks for the log scale
  YTicks:=[seq(evalf(log(i))=convert(i,string),
          i=[1000,2000,3000,4000,5000,6000,7000,8000,
             9000,10000,20000,30000,40000,50000,60000,
             70000,80000,90000,100000])]:
  #Define [x,y] data for plotting
  Data:=zip((x,y)->[x,y],X,Clog)[]:
  plot(C(x),x=0..50,color=black,thickness=2):
  PLOT(POINTS(Data),AXESTICKS(DEFAULT,YTicks),AXESSTYLE(BOX)):
  plots[display](%,%%,labeldirections=[HORIZONTAL,VERTICAL],
      symbol=box,labels=[`X (m)`,`Coliform Count (N/L)`],
      labelfont=[TIMES,ROMAN,16]);
```
$$K := 41.89434100$$

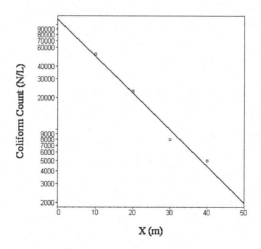

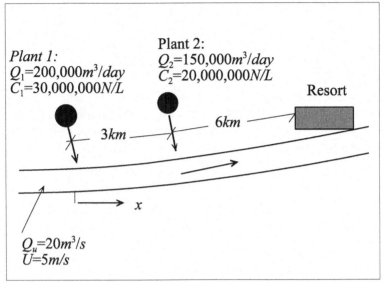

Figure 9.6: River Reach of Example 9.6

Example 9.6

Figure 9.6 shows a river reach receiving waste loads from two waste water treatment plants, and having a recreational resort downstream the plants. Based on the total coliform count and flow information given in the figure, and assuming a coliform decay rate $K=2/day$, estimate the concentration at the resort. If the required maximum concentration at the resort is $5,000 N/L$, determine whether or not disinfection at the plants is necessary.

Solution

The concentration C_{01} immediately downstream Plant 1 is, from equation (9.13),

$$C_{01} = \left(\frac{Q_1}{Q_u + Q_1} \right) C_1 = \frac{200,000 \frac{m^3}{day} \times 30,000,000 \frac{N}{L}}{20 \frac{m^3}{s} \times 86,400 \frac{s}{day} + 200,000 \frac{m^3}{day}} = 3.112 \times 10^6 \frac{N}{L}$$

Similarly, the concentration C_{02} due to Plant 2 is

$$C_{02} = \left(\frac{Q_2}{Q_u + Q_1 + Q_2} \right) C_2$$

$$C_{02} = \frac{150,000 \frac{m^3}{day} \times 20,000,000 \frac{N}{L}}{20 \frac{m^3}{s} \times 86,400 \frac{s}{day} + 200,000 \frac{m^3}{day} + 150,000 \frac{m^3}{day}} = 1.444 \times 10^6 \frac{N}{L}$$

The flow velocity may expressed as

$$U = \frac{5 m/s \times 86,400 s/day}{1,000 m/km} = 432 km/day$$

Thus, the resulting C_r concentration downstream the waste water treatment plants is the summation of the effects caused by each plant. From equation (9.17),

$$C_r(x) = C_{01} e^{-Kx/U} + C_{02} e^{-K(x-3)/U}, \qquad x > 3km$$

$$C_r(9) = 3.112 \times 10^6 \frac{N}{L} \exp\left[-\frac{\frac{2}{day} \times 9km}{432 \frac{km}{day}} \right] + 1.444 \times 10^6 \frac{N}{L} \exp\left[-\frac{\frac{2}{day} \times 6km}{432 \frac{km}{day}} \right]$$

$$C_r(9) = 4.389 \times 10^6 \frac{N}{L} > 5,000 \frac{N}{L}$$

Thus, disinfection at each plant is necessary.

Longitudinal Dispersion of Contaminants in Rivers

In the preceding sections, we have assumed that contaminants experience complete mixing from side to side and top to bottom of a river section as soon as released in the stream. We also assumed there is no longitudinal mixing as contaminants travel along the stream. In reality, however, there is considerable longitudinal mixing caused by the horizontal and vertical velocity gradients, local turbulence caused by irregular sections and meanders, and contaminant diffusion effects inherent to each substance when propagating in aquatic media.

This phenomenon is called *longitudinal dispersion*. It causes the propagation of a contaminant away from its center of mass. In other words, certain portions of a contaminant will travel at speeds lower than that of the mean water velocity, and certain portions at higher speeds. The result is a *contaminant plume* of growing size. This effect is particularly important in instantaneous point spills. A highly concentrated contaminant that initially occupies a small area will gradually disperse and cover a long portion of the stream.

Thus, if *contaminant particles* travel at a velocity, U_p, different from than of the fluid velocity, U, and the system is not at a steady state, such as in the case of a short term accidental spill, then the continuity equation (9.11) needs to be modified. Referring to a control volume in a river reach (Figure 9.4), let us define the substance mass rate as the product U_pC (i.e., $(m/day) \times (kg/m^3) = kg/(m^2day)$, or mass per unit cross-sectional area per day). The net mass rate is the difference between the output mass rate minus the one. The mass conservation statement is:

Net mass rate of substance + change of mass within reach per unit time = mass rate loss due to transformation

Assuming a first order reaction as before, the above statement could be written mathematically as

$$\frac{\partial(U_pC)}{\partial x} + \frac{\partial C}{\partial t} = -KC \tag{9.20}$$

Note that the substance particle velocity is not constant, and thus remains inside the derivative. An independent relationship is needed to transform the substance particle velocity into simpler measurable variables. This relationship is the *Fick's law of diffusion*:

$$\left(U_p - U\right)C = -D_x \frac{\partial C}{\partial x} \;\Rightarrow\; U_p = U - \frac{D_x}{C}\frac{\partial C}{\partial x} \tag{9.21}$$

where
  D_x = longitudinal *dispersion coefficient* (km^2/day)

This equation states that the pollutant particles move relative to the fluid particles in a direction of decreasing concentration. In other words, pollutant particles propagate from regions of high concentration to those of low concentration. Substituting equation (9.21) into (9.20), and assuming the dispersion coefficient and the flow velocity as constants, we obtain the *convection dispersion differential equation*:

$$\frac{\partial C}{\partial t} - D_x \frac{\partial^2 C}{\partial x^2} + U \frac{\partial C}{\partial x} + KC = 0 \tag{9.22}$$

Boundary conditions imposed on this equation assume that the stream is very long and the substance concentration is zero at locations far from the area of interest. Solutions to the convection dispersion equation depend on the form in which the contaminant is introduced into the stream. For example, if an instantaneous spill of a substance of mass M occurs, the solution to equation (9.22) is

$$C(x, \ t) = \frac{M}{A\sqrt{4\pi D_x t}} e^{-\frac{(x-Ut)^2}{4D_x t} - Kt} \tag{9.23}$$

This equation may be recognized as a normal probability distribution with mean Ut and a variance $4D_x t$. Knowing the initial mass, stream velocity, the cross-sectional area, and the dispersion coefficient, equation (9.23) could be used to estimate the substance concentration at a distance x downstream the spill and t units of time after the spill. Furthermore, it could be used to simulate concentration *breakthrough curves*. A concentration versus distance breakthrough curve is created by calculating the concentration magnitude for several locations along the stream, while keeping the time constant. This produces a picture of the shape of the contaminant plume at a fixed time after the spill. Alternatively, a concentration versus time breakthrough curve is created by calculating the concentration magnitude for several times, while keeping the distance fixed. This will simulate the time evolution of a contaminant concentration as detected by an observer at a fixed location in the river.

Equation (9.23) also illustrates the main dispersion and dissipation properties of contaminants in rivers. By plotting two concentration versus distance curves, one at time $t=t_1$, and one at time $t=t_2$, with $t_2>t_1$, one can easily observe that the center of mass of the first plume is located a distance Ut_1 from the injection point, and the center of mass of the second plume is located a distance Ut_2 from the injection point (Figure 9.7). This means that the contaminant plume travels at a mean velocity U. Similarly , one may plot two concentration versus time curves, one at a distance x_1 from the injection point, and one at a distance x_2, with $x_2>x_1$

(Figure 9.7). Note that the peak concentration decreases in magnitude as it travels downstream, while the "spread" (the dispersion, or the plume variance) simultaneously increases.

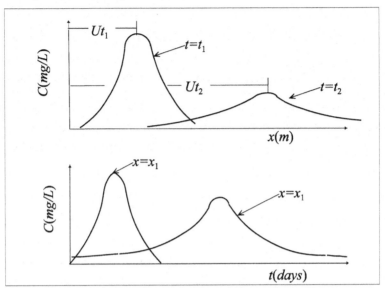

Figure 9.7: Dispersion Properties of Contaminant Plumes

Example 9.7

An accident of a truck tank transporting trichloroethylene (TCE) occurred near a stream. It is estimated that about $20\,m^3$ of a solution containing a TCE concentration of $800\,mg/L$ reached the stream. If the average stream velocity and flow rate are $2\,m/s$ and $1.5\,m^3/s$, respectively, estimate the maximum TCE concentration at a drinking water intake located $5\,km$ downstream. Assume decay is negligible and a river dispersion coefficient of $1\,km^2/day$.

Solution

From equation (9.23), the maximum concentration at $x=5\,km$ occurs at $x=Ut_p$, where t_p is the mean travel time (i.e., the one that makes the exponent zero, and the exponential equal to one). Therefore,

$$t_p = \frac{x}{U} = \frac{5km \times 1,000m/km}{2m/s \times 86,400s/day} = 0.0289\,days$$

and the maximum concentration $C(x=5km,\ t_p)=C_{max}$

$$C_{max} = \frac{M}{A\sqrt{4\pi D_x t_p}} = \frac{20m^3 \times 800\frac{mg}{L}}{1.5\frac{m^3}{s}\sqrt{4\pi 1\frac{km^2}{day} \times 10^6 \frac{m^2}{km^2} \times 0.0289 days}} = 35.4\frac{mg}{L}$$

This value is clearly greater than the EPA allowable concentration for TCE (see Table 8.2). Therefore, the water treatment plant will have to be shut down during the passage of the plume, or special technologies will have to be employed to treat the TCE in the water.

Example 9.8

$2,000\,m^3$ of a solution with a concentration of $800mg$ of ethylbenzene were accidentally discharged into a river with an average flow rate of $1.5\,m^3/s$ and a mean fluid velocity of $0.5m/s$. If the dispersion coefficient is $100\,km^2/day$ and there is no decay, (1) calculate the maximum contaminant concentration, and the time of its occurrence, at a drinking water plant located $300km$ donwstream the spill; (2) estimate the time interval, (t_1, t_2), after the spill when the contaminant concentration at the plant exceeds maximum drinking water standards; (2) plot the time breakthrough curve at the plant indicating the non-compliant times.

Solution

Table 7.2 indicates a maximum allowable concentration of $0.7mg/L$ for ethylbenzene. The following Maple program applies equation (9.23).

```
> restart: with(plottools):
  Dx:=100:          #disp. coeff. in km^2/day
  dx:=Dx*10^6:      #disp coeff. in m^2/day
  V:=2000:          #volume in m^3
  C0:=800:          #initial conc. in mg/L
  M:=V*C0:          #initial mass in m^3*mg/L
  Q:=1.5:           #flow rate in m^3/s
  U:=0.5:           #flow velocity in m/s
  u:=U*86.4:        #flow velocity in km/day
  A:=Q/U:           #area in m^2
  X:=300:           #plant distance in km
  K:=0:             #decay rate in 1/day
  C:=(x,t)->M/(A*sqrt(4*Pi*dx*t))
           *exp(-(x-u*t)^2/(4*Dx*t)-K*t):
  #(1)
  tp:=X/u;          #time of Cmax in days
  Cmax:=evalf(C(X,tp));
```
$$tp := 6.944444444$$
$$Cmax := 5.709197170$$

```
> #(2)
  eqn:=C(X,t)=0.7:
  t1:=fsolve(eqn,t,0..tp);
  t2:=fsolve(eqn,t,tp..infinity);
                                    t1 := 5.346093032
                                    t2 := 8.883988487
> #(3)
  g1:=plot(C(X,t),t=0..t2+3, color=black):
  l1:=line([t1,0],[t1,C(X,t1)],color=black,thickness=2):
  l2:=line([t2,0],[t2,C(X,t1)],color=black,thickness=2):
  plots[display](g1,l1,l2,labeldirections=[HORIZONTAL,VERTICAL],
         labels=[`t (days)`,`Ethylbenzene Concentragtion (mg/L)`],
         labelfont=[TIMES,ROMAN,16]);
```

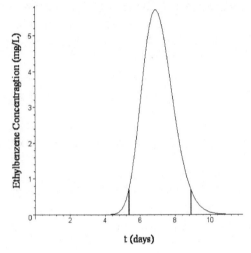

In part (1) we find that the maximum concentration at the plant is 8.9*mg/L*, and that it occurs about 5.4*days* after the spill. In part (2), we set $C(300, t)=0.7$ and solve for t. t_1 is the time in the rising limb of the plume when this condition occurs, and t_2 is that in the falling limb. Thus, between 5.3 and 8.8 days after the spill, the concentrations exceed the norm. In part (3) the time breakthrough curve of the plume at the plant $C(300, t)$ is plotted along with lines marking the interval (t_1, t_2).

Example 9.9

In Example 9.8, (1) in one graph plot the space breakthrough curves 1, 4, 8 days, respectively, after the spill; and (2) repeat step (1) if the contaminant decay rate 0.25/*day*.

Solution

Modify the program in Example 9.8 to plot C versus x for various fixed times. This shows the shape of the plume along the river channel and the extent of pollution at the various times. Note that when $K \neq 0$ the concentrations are significantly lower.

```
> restart:
  Dx:=100:          #disp. coeff. in km^2/day
  dx:=Dx*10^6:      #disp coeff. in m^2/day
  V:=2000:          #volume in m^3
  C0:=800:          #initial conc. in mg/L
  M:=V*C0:          #initial mass in m^3*mg/L
  Q:=1.5:           #flow rate in m^3/s
  U:=0.5:           #flow velocity in m/s
  u:=U*86.4:        #flow velocity in km/day
  A:=Q/U:           #area in m^2
  X:=300:           #plant distance in km
  K:=0:             #decay rate in 1/day
  C:=(x,t)->M/(A*sqrt(4*Pi*dx*t))
          *exp(-(x-u*t)^2/(4*Dx*t)-K*t):
  #(1)
  g1:=plot(C(x,1),x=0..500,color=black,legend="t=1 day"):
  g2:=plot(C(x,4),x=0..500,color=black,linestyle=3,legend="t=4
  days"):
  g3:=plot(C(x,8),x=0..500,color=black,linestyle=4,legend="t=8
  days"):
  plots[display](g1,g2,g3,labeldirections=[HORIZONTAL,VERTICAL],
        labels=[`x (km)`,`Ethylbenzene Concentragtion (mg/L)`],
        labelfont=[TIMES,ROMAN,16]);
```

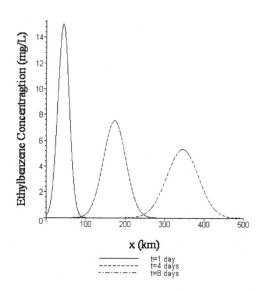

```
> #(2)
  K:=0.25:
  g4:=plot(C(x,1),x=0..500,color=black,legend="t=1 day"):
  g5:=plot(C(x,4),x=0..500,color=black,linestyle=3,legend="t=4
  days"):
  g6:=plot(C(x,8),x=0..500,color=black,linestyle=4,legend="t=8
  days"):
  plots[display](g4,g5,g6,labeldirections=[HORIZONTAL,VERTICAL],
        labels=[`x (km)`,`Ethylbenzene Concentragtion (mg/L)`],
        labelfont=[TIMES,ROMAN,16]);
```

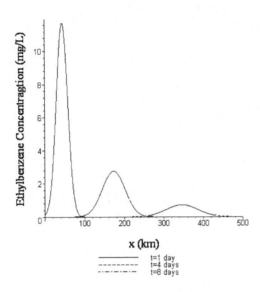

Mathematical models of river pollution, such as equation (9.23), may be used in the estimation of a river dispersion coefficient. By injecting a tracer of known mass at an upstream section of a river, and then monitoring the concentration with time at fixed locations downstream, information necessary for the evaluation of the dispersion coefficient is gathered. At each location the maximum concentration C_{max} and time to peak t_p is recorded. Then equation (9.23) is used to estimate D_x at different locations, and an average value is calculated. More accurate values of the dispersion coefficient may be obtained from an evaluation of the plume variance, which requires the utilization of the entire breakthrough curves (Fischer, 1968). A third category of estimation methods are based on empirical equations fitted to a set of dispersion coefficients in various rivers. One of those equations is (McQuivey and Keefer, 1974):

$$D_x = \frac{mQ}{S_0 B} \tag{9.24}$$

where
D_x = dispersion coefficient (km^2/day)
Q = steady state base flow rate (m^3/s)
S_0 = river bed slope (m/m)
B = mean river width (m)

$m = 5.02 \times 10^{-3} (km^2.s/(day.m^2))$

A more in depth studies of river pollution models are found in Thomann and Mueller (1987), Fischer et al. (1979). Guidelines for the planning of tracer studies are given in U.S. Geological Survey (1970).

PROBLEMS

9.1 A waste water treatment plant is discharging into a river. The upstream water (i.e., before the discharge), and the waste water conditions are summarized in Table 9.4. If the mean river flow velocity below the plant during late summer is $20km/day$, the deoxygenation coefficient is $0.45/day$, and the re-aeration rate is $2.5/day$, determine the minimum DO and its distance from the plant.

Table 9.4: Data for Problem 9.1

	BOD, y (mg/L)	Flow Rate, Q (m^3/day)	DO (mg/L)	Temp., $T(°C)$
Upstream Water	15	250,000	1.5	17
Waste Water	65	560,000	0.5	20

9.2 Using the data from problem 9.1, plot the DO sag curve. Describe your procedure.

9.3 If in problem 9.1, the waste water is poorly treated and it discharges an effluent with a BOD of $250mg/L$. Find the minimum DO and its location downstream the plant.

9.4 Plot the DO sag curve for problem 9.3. Describe your procedure.

9.5 If in Example 9.4 the chloride concentrations in the system are $C_u=30mg/L$, $C_w=920mg/L$, and $C_T=25mg/L$, and the required chloride concentration at the intake is $150mg/L$, determine the required waste water reduction, or the required increase in the tributary flow Q_T.

9.6 A stream with an average flow velocity of $5m/s$ is sampled for total coliform count at different distances downstream a sewage treatment plant. The results are shown in Table 9.5. Estimate the total coliform decay rate, K.

Table 9.5: Data for Problem 9.6

x (km)	10	20	30	40
C (N/L)	48,000	24,100	12,200	3,100

9.7 If in Example 9.6, $K=0.1/day$, and $Q_2=130,000m^3/day$, determine whether or not disinfection in the plants is necessary.

9.8 Redo Example 9.8 if the river flow velocity is 0.4m/s and the initial contaminant volume is $500m^3/s$.

9.9 In Problem 9.8, (1) in one graph plot the space breakthrough curves 1, 4, 8 days, respectively, after the spill; and (2) repeat step (1) if the contaminant decay rate $0.25/day$. *Hint*: Modify the program of Example 9.9 with the new data in Problem 9.8.

9.10 A river receives a discharge of $400,000m^3/day$ at a concentration of 150mg/L. The flow rate upstream is $800,000m^3/day$ at zero concentration. For 15km downstream, the velocity is 10km/day. A region of slow moving water is then encountered for the next 20km, where the velocity drops to 2km/day. If the decay rate of the substance is $0.2/day$, what is the concentration at a point 35km from the out fall?

10 THE HYDROLOGY
OF LAKE POLLUTION

10.1 MODELING WATER QUALITY IN LAKES

Lakes and reservoirs vary from small ponds and dams to the monumental large and deep lakes of the world. They present significantly different hydrologic characteristics from streams and rivers. Distinguishing physical features include relatively low flow-through velocities and the existence of important vertical gradients in water temperature and other water quality variables. For these reasons, lakes often become permanent sinks for chemicals, nutrients, and other substances in incoming rivers. Thus, *eutrophication* constitutes a water quality problem in lakes (see Chapter 8). In previous chapters we discussed some of the hydrologic characteristics of lakes that affect water quality: Water balance, evaporation, area-depth and volume-depth relationships, and average detention time.

An important distinguishing feature of lakes is *temperature stratification*. Lakes in general are not well mixed systems. *Temperature gradients* usually develop along shore and with depth. During the summer heating, lakes develop a warm surface layer of water overlying a colder, deeper, layer. This phenomenon is less important in tropical lakes. Temperature stratification is an important ecological consideration when projecting power generation plants, and studying the effects of temperature variability on sensitive ecosystems. Thermal stratification may indirectly cause the "trapping" of chemicals in regions of reduced water interaction and exchange. It also affects the vertical profiles of *DO*. Often low *DO* exists in the lower layer due to minimal exchange with aerated water in the top layer.

The vertical temperature profile at the end of the winter is often homogeneous from top to bottom (see Figure 10.1). With the onset of the Spring warming, the surface layer begins to heat and stratify as a distinct layer of lower density from the one beneath it. This stratification is mainly caused by heat absorption by the first few meters and the corresponding low vertical conductivity of heat. By the end of the Summer, a strong stratification exists and at least three distinct layers may have formed. The *epilimnion* is the surface layer, generally having a constant temperature with depth due to well mixing caused by winds. Below the epilimnion, there is a second region called the *metalimnion*, which exhibits strong vertical temperature gradients (the "*thermocline*").

Below the metalimnion there is a third colder region called the *hypolimnion* which extends to the bottom of the lake. For preliminary water quality modeling of stratified lakes, only two layers are often considered: the epilimnion and the hypolimnion.

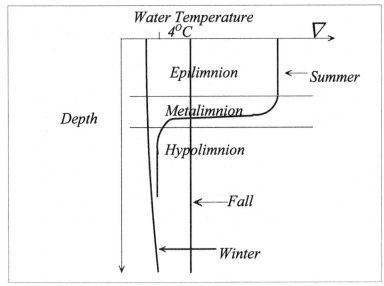

Figure 10.1: Lake Water Temperature Profile

During the Fall, surface temperatures begin to cool and the thermocline penetrates deeper into the lake causing the fall mixing until isothermal conditions are achieved late in the Fall. A Winter inversion may occur as surface layers continue to cool below the temperature of maximum water density ($4^{o}C$). This would make the deep layers to remain at a temperature slightly above $4^{o}C$, while the upper layers could reach the freezing point.

Lakes as Completely Mixed Systems

Recall that a simplified assumption to river pollution conditions conceived the river as a completely mixed system. A similar assumption could be adopted for lakes in order to develop preliminary lakewide water quality response models. Complete horizontal and vertical mixing is reasonable only when the time scale of the problem is so long, that seasonal blending processes result in a completely mixed lake over the years. This is a crude approximation to the actual spatial distribution of certain substances in a lake. However, it permits a basic understanding of the mass balance relationships. Referring to Figure 10.2, the water continuity equation for a lake is given by

$$P.A + Q_u + Q_T + Q_w - E.A = \frac{dS}{dt} \qquad (10.1)$$

where

P=annual precipitation (*m/year*)
A=mean lake surface area (m^2)
Q_u=(upstream) main river inflow rate ($m^3/year$)
Q_T=net tributary inflow rate, including groundwater ($m^3/year$)
Q_w=waste water inflow rate ($m^3/year$)
Q_r=(resulting) main river outflow rate ($m^3/year$)
E=annual evaporation rate (*m/year*)
S=mean lake volume, or storage (m^3)
t=time (*year*)

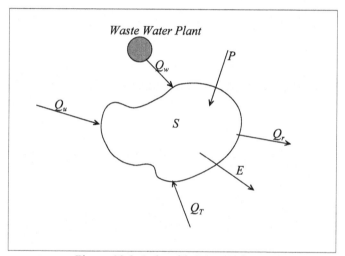

Figure 10.2: Lakewide Mass Balance

The solid waste load entering the lake may come from various sources: Pollution from the main river, from the tributaries, municipal waste, deposition from precipitation, or from internal sources such as the release of substances from bottom sediments. The total waste load input is

$$W = Q_u C_u + Q_w C_w + Q_T C_T + P.A.C_p + S.C_s \qquad (10.2)$$

where

W=total mass input (*kg/year*)
C_u= main river (upstream) concentration (kg/m^3)
C_w= concentration in waste water (kg/m^3)

C_T = substance concentration in tributaries (kg/m^3)
C_p = substance concentration in precipitation (kg/m^3)
C_s = substance rate released from lake sediments ((kg/m^3)/year)

Thus, the mass conservation statement for the lake could be stated

Net mass rate of substance + change of mass in lake per unit time
= mass rate loss due to transformation

If we further assume that the substance decays with a first order decay coefficient as we did for rivers, and recalling that the net mass rate is equal to the mass rate downstream minus the input waste load, the mass conservation statement could be written as

$$Q_r C - W(t) + \frac{d(S.C)}{dt} = -K.S.C \tag{10.3}$$

where
C = mean substance concentration in lake (kg/m^3)
K = substance decay coefficient ($year^{-1}$)

If Q_r, K, and the mean volume of the lake assumed constants, equation (10.3) reduces to

$$S\frac{dC}{dt} + (Q_r + K.S)C = W(t), \qquad C(0) = C_0 \tag{10.4}$$

where
C_0 = initial concentration (kg/m^3)

When the input load $W(t)$ is zero, equation (10.4) describes the time of decay of the average substance concentration $C = C_1$ in the lake due to a given initial concentration C_0. The solution of this first order linear differential equation is

$$C_1(t) = C_0 e^{-(\frac{Q_r}{S} + K)t} = C_0 e^{-(\frac{1}{t_d} + K)t} \tag{10.5}$$

Thus, the time for the concentration decrease to a given level depends on the inverse of the *detention time*, t_d (i.e., the "hydraulic flushing of the lake"), and the decay rate, K, of the substance. Figure 10.3 shows the relative effect of these two parameters on the time decay of substance concentration.

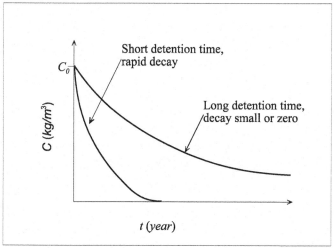

Figure 10.3: Time Decay of Concentration

If the input waste load, $W(t)$, is not zero, the substance concentration in the lake is the resultant of two opposite effects: the decrease in concentration, C_1, caused by lake flushing and substance decay, and the increase in concentration, C_2, caused by the input waste load, $W(t)$. If the waste load $W(t)=W$ is constant, then C_2 satisfies equation (10.4) subject to a zero initial condition and a constant waste load. Its solution is

$$C_2 = \frac{W\left(1 - e^{-(\frac{1}{t_d} + K)t}\right)}{Q_r(1 + Kt_d)} \qquad (10.6)$$

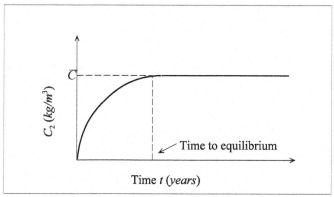

Figure 10.4: Concentration Increase Due to Constant Waste Load

Equation (10.6) indicates that after a sufficiently long time, the concentration in a lake due to a constant waste load reaches a constant value $\overline{C}=W/[Q_r(1+Kt_d)]$. The time elapsed before this equilibrium condition is reached depends on the detention time and the substance decay rate (see Figure 10.4). If the equilibrium conditions are achieved under no substance decay (i.e., conservative substances), $\overline{C}=W/Q_r$. It is interesting to compare this results with equation (9.13) obtained for rivers. Thus, the ratio of the waste load to the flow rate appears to be an upper-bound first estimate of the steady state water quality response of a river or a lake system to a conservative input load.

The total water quality response is the summation of the initial condition and the waste load effects, $C(t)=C_1(t)+C_2(t)$, or the summation of equations (10.5) and (10.6), respectively. Figure 10.5 illustrates the relative effect of the initial condition and the waste load on the overall concentration. An initial concentration C_0 which is lower than the equilibrium concentration due to the waste load alone, $\overline{C}$, will result in an increasing concentration with respect to time up to a steady condition. On the other hand, an initial concentration which is greater than the equilibrium concentration due to the waste load alone will result in a decreasing concentration with time until a steady condition is reached.

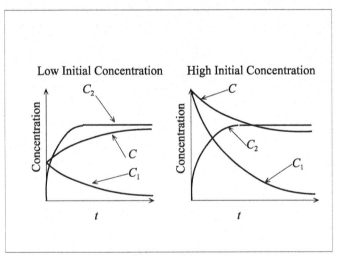

Figure 10.5: Effect of Initial Condition and Waste Input on overall Lake Concentration

Equations (10.5) and (10.6) may be used to study the concentration time evolution of a substance in a lake when the waste loads are not constants over time, but could be approximated as piece-wise constants over finite time intervals. Figure 10.6 illustrates two such cases. The left portion of the figure shows a single waste step of magnitude W_1 starting at time zero, and ending at time t_1. Below appears the resulting concentration as calculated from equation (10.6), with $0 \le t \le t_1$, and then from equation (10.5), with the time set to $t-t_1$, $t > t_1$ and $C_0 = C_2(t_1)$ from the previous step. The right portion of Figure 10.6 shows the general case of a time variable waste load as approximated by constant steps W_1, W_2, ..., at finite intervals $\Delta t = t_1 = t_2 - t_1 = ...$, etc. Below appears the substance concentration successively calculated by adding equations (10.5) and (10.6) each time step. Starting from time zero with a known initial concentration, C_0, the concentration in the interval $(0, t_1)$ is calculated as $C = C_1 + C_2$. The magnitude of the concentration at the end of the period, $C(t_1)$, becomes the initial concentration for the next time step, and the process is repeated for every interval.

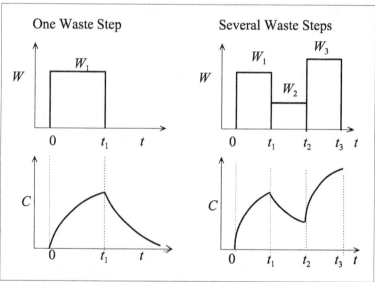

Figure 10.6: Lake Concentration Subject to Variable Input

Thus, in general, if is specified as a series of steps of magnitude W_i, $i = 1, 2, ..., n$ given at times $0, t_1, t_2, ..., t_n$ respectively, then the concentration load is given by

$$W(t) = \sum_{i=1}^{n-1} W_i H(t-t_i) H(t_{i+1}-t) + W_n H(t-t_n) \qquad (10.7)$$

where
    $W(t)$=time-variable waste load expressed as a step function (*kg/year*)
    W_i=constant waste load at time interval (t_{i-1}, t_i) (*kg/year*)

$H(t-t_i)$=*Heaviside unit step function*, defined as

$$H(t-t_i)=\begin{cases} 0, & t<t_i \\ 1, & t\geq t_i \end{cases} \qquad (10.8)$$

To obtain a recursive expression of lakewide concentration, let us define the following functions from equations (10.5) and 10.6):

$$f_1(t)=e^{-(\frac{1}{t_d}+K)t}, \qquad f_2(t)=\frac{1-f_1(t)}{Q_r(1+Kt_d)} \qquad (10.9)$$

The general expression for the contaminant concentration is then

$$C(t)=\sum_{i=1}^{n-1} C_{0_i} f_1(t-t_i)+W_i f_2(t-t_i)H(t-t_i)H(t_{i+1}-t) \qquad (10.10)$$

where

C_{0_i}=initial condition at $t=t_i$ (*kg/year*) from the previous time step:

$$C_{0_i}=C_{0_{i-1}} f_1(t_i-t_{i-1})+W_{i-1} f_2(t_i-t_{i-1}) \qquad (10.11)$$

See Example 10.4 for a recursive application of equations (10.9)-(10.11).

Example 10.1
    A lake has been receiving an average load of a conservative substance of 28,000*kg/day* for a long time. If the mean lake volume is $2.5\times10^{12}m^3$, and the average outflow rate is $4,200\,m^3/s$, compute the lakewide equilibrium concentration (*mg/L*) if the initial concentration is zero.

Solution
The lakewide detention time is

$$t_d=\frac{S}{Q_r}=\frac{2.5\times10^{12}m^3}{4,200m^3/s\times86,400s/day\times30day/month}=229.64month$$

The equilibrium concentration is

$$\bar{C}=\frac{W}{Q_r(1+Kt_d)}=\frac{28,000kg/day}{4,200m^3/s\times86,400s/day}\times\frac{10^6mg}{kg}\times\frac{m^3}{10^3L}=0.0772mg/L$$

Example 10.2

In Example 10.1, the contaminant load stopped at $t_1 = 500month$. Calculate and plot the concentration from 0 to $t_2 = 1000month$.

Solution

For the time interval $(0, t_2)$, the concentration is given by equation (10.6) as

$$C_2 = \frac{W\left(1 - e^{-\left(\frac{1}{t_d} + K\right)t}\right)}{Q_r(1 + Kt_d)}, \qquad 0 \le t \le t_1$$

For the time interval (t_1, t_2), the concentration is given by equation (10.5) with an initial condition $C_0 = C_2(t = t_1)$:

$$C_1(t) = C_0 e^{-\left(\frac{1}{t_d} + K\right)(t - t_1)}, \qquad C_0 = C_2(t_1), \quad t_1 < t \le t_2$$

Note the time shifting $(t - t_1)$ for the latter curve. The following Maple program shows the simulations.

```
> restart: S:=2.5E12: Qr:=4200: W:=28000: K:=0:
  td:=S/Qr/86400/30: t1:=500: t2:=1000:
  C2:=t->W*(1-exp(-(1/td+K)*t))/(Qr*(1+K*td))/86.4:
  C0:=C2(t1):
  C1:=t->C0*exp(-(1/td+K)*t):
  g1:=plot(C2(t),t=0..t1,color=black,thickness=2):
  g2:=plot(C1(t-t1),t=t1..t2,color=black,thickness=2):
  plots[display](g1,g2,labeldirections=[HORIZONTAL,VERTICAL],
       symbol=box,labels=[`t (months)`,`C (mg/L)`],
       labelfont=[TIMES,ROMAN,16]);
```

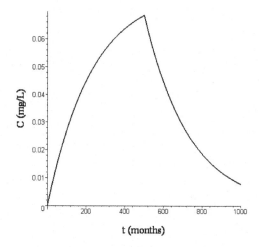

t (months)

Example 10.3

Since the 1960's a lake had been receiving an average load of phosphorous of 35,000kg/day. Early in 2002, the load is drastically decreased to 20,000kg/day. If the mean lake volume is $1.5 \times 10^{12} m^3$, and the average outflow rate is $6,500 \, m^3/s$, derive an expression of lakewide phosphorous concentration, $C(mg/L)$, versus time after 2002, t, assuming that phosphorus is a conservative substance.

Solution

The lakewide concentration in 2002 is the result of long-term application of phosphorous. From equation (10.6), the initial condition, C_0, for further simulations is given by

$$C_0 = \frac{W}{Q_r + Kt_d} = \frac{35,000 \frac{kg}{day} \times 10^6 \frac{mg}{kg} \times 10^{-3} \frac{m^3}{L}}{6,500 \frac{m^3}{s} \times 86,400 \frac{s}{day}} = 0.062 \frac{mg}{L}$$

After 2002, The resulting concentration is the summation of that due to the initial condition plus that due to the reduced loading. From equations (10.5) and (10.6),

$$C(t) = C_0 e^{-\frac{Q_r}{S}t} + \frac{W}{Q_r}\left(1 - e^{-\frac{Q_r}{S}t}\right) = \frac{W}{Q_r} + \left(C_0 - \frac{W}{Q_r}\right)e^{-\frac{Q_r}{S}t}$$

$$C(t) = \frac{20,000 \times 10^6 \times 10^{-3}}{6,500 \times 86,400} + \left(0.062 - \frac{20,000 \times 10^6 \times 10^{-3}}{6,500 \times 86,400}\right) \times e^{-\frac{6,500 \times 86,400 \times 30}{1.5 \times 10^{12}}t}$$

$$C(t) = 0.036 + 0.026 e^{-0.011t}$$

where C is given in mg/L and t is given in days after 2002.

Example 10.4: Simulation of Lakewide Concentration under Variable Loading

A lake has a volume of $1.5 \times 10^{12} m^3$, an average outflow rate of $6,500 \, m^3/s$, and a variable loading $W=[35000, 0, 45000, 30000, 0]$ (kg/day) at time steps $T=[0, 36, 60, 84, 120]$ *months*, respectively. If the initial concentration is $0.015 mg/L$ and the contaminant has a decay rate of $0.001/month$, plot the variable waste load and the lakewide concentration versus time in months.

Solution

The following Maple program implements equations (10.7)-(10.11).

```
> restart: with(stats):
  S:=1.5E12: Qr:=6500: K:=0.001: c0:=0.015:
  td:=S/Qr/86400/30:
  T:=[0,36,60,84,120]:
  w:=[35000,0,45000,30000,0]:
  N:=describe[count](T):
  #equation (10.7):
  W:=t->sum(w[k]*Heaviside(t-T[k])*Heaviside(T[k+1]-t),
      k=1..N-1)+w[N]*Heaviside(t-T[N]):
  Equation (10.9):
  f1:=t->exp(-(1/td+K)*t):
  f2:=t->(1-f1(t))/(Qr*(1+K*td))/86.4:
  C0[1]:=c0:
  #loop to calculate step IC's from equation (10.11):
  for i from 2 to N do
      C0[i]:=C0[i-1]*f1(T[i]-T[i-1])+w[i-1]*f2(T[i]-T[i-1]);
  end do:
  #definition of C(t) as a piecewise function, equation (10.10):
  C:=t->sum((C0[j]*f1(t-T[j])+w[j]*f2(t-T[j]))
      *Heaviside(t-T[j])*Heaviside(T[j+1]-t),j=1..N-1):
> plot(W(t),t=0..T[N],color=black,thickness=2,
      labeldirections=[HORIZONTAL,VERTICAL],
      symbol=box,labels=[`t (months)`,`W (kg/day)`],
      labelfont=[TIMES,ROMAN,16]);
  plot(C(t),t=0..T[N],color=black,thickness=2,
      labeldirections=[HORIZONTAL,VERTICAL],
      symbol=box,labels=[`t (months)`,`C (mg/L)`],
      labelfont=[TIMES,ROMAN,16]);
```

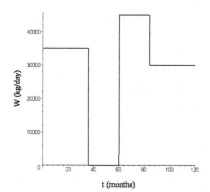

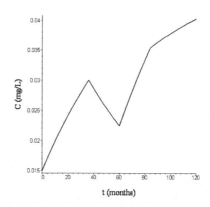

Example 10.5

A lake in a rural agricultural community has an average storage volume of $86.5 \times 10^6 m^3$, and an average flow rate of $6 m^3/s$. Land application of the insecticide Ethion in the watershed for the last six months has resulted in contaminated surface runoff and groundwater flow to the lake. It is estimated that the average annual loading of the insecticide is about 2,600kg/day. Assuming a decay rate of 0.096/$month$, and that the use of Ethion has been eliminated in the area, calculate the equilibrium concentration in the lake, the maximum concentration, and the time after pesticide termination to reach a level of $0.1 mg/L$.

Solution

From equation (10.6), the equilibrium concentration after prolonged time is

$$\bar{C}=\frac{W}{Q_r+KS}=\frac{2,600\frac{kg}{day}\times10^6\frac{mg}{kg}\times10^{-3}\frac{m^3}{L}}{6\frac{m^3}{s}\times86,400\frac{s}{day}+\frac{0.096/month}{30day/month}\times86.5\times10^6m^3}=3.27\frac{mg}{L}$$

The maximum concentration occurs at $t=0.5year$. Thus, from equation (10.6)

$$C=\frac{W\left(1-e^{-(\frac{Q_r}{S}+K)t}\right)}{Q_r+KS}=\bar{C}\times\left(1-e^{-(\frac{Q_r}{S}+K)t}\right)$$

$$C=3.27\frac{mg}{L}$$

$$\times\left(1-\exp\left[-\left\{\frac{6\frac{m^3}{s}\times86,400\frac{s}{day}+\frac{0.096}{month}}{86.5\times10^6m^3}\times0.5year\times365\frac{day}{year}\right\}\right]\right)$$

$$C=2.66\frac{mg}{L}$$

After termination of loading, the time t' required to reach a concentration of $0.1mg/L$ is given by equation (10.5), taking natural logarithms, solving for the time, and using $C_0=C(t=0.5year)=2.66mg/L$:

$$C(t')=C_0e^{-(\frac{Q_r}{S}+K)t'}$$

$$\Rightarrow \ln\left(\frac{C}{C_0}\right)=-\left(\frac{Q_r}{S}+K\right)t' \Rightarrow t'=-\frac{\ln\left(\frac{C}{C_0}\right)}{\left(\frac{Q_r}{S}+K\right)}$$

$$t' = - \frac{\ln\left(\dfrac{0.1\dfrac{mg}{L}}{2.66\dfrac{mg}{L}} \right)}{\left(\dfrac{6\dfrac{m^3}{s} \times 86{,}400\dfrac{s}{day}}{86.5 \times 10^6 m^3} + \dfrac{0.096/month}{30 day/month} \right) \times 30\dfrac{day}{month}} = 11.90 month$$

Thus, it takes almost one year to reach the desired concentration after the termination of the loading, or $t=6month+11.9month=16.9month$ from the beginning of loading. Figure 10.7 illustrates the lakewide concentration versus time curve for this example.

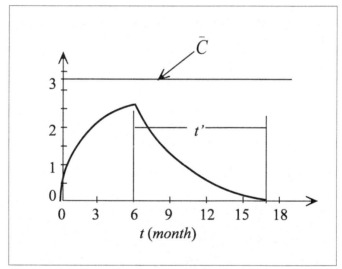

Figure 10.7: Concentration Time Evolution for Example 10.1

Lakewide Response to Suspended Sediments

The above development may be extended to study the effect of suspended solids, particulate forms of nutrients, and toxicants entering a lake. If it is assumed that these substances do not experience chemical or biological transformation, then the only mechanism of sediment loss from the water column is via the settling to the bottom of a lake. Denoting C

as the sediment concentration, the mass balance equation (10.3) becomes

$$Q_r C - W(t) + \frac{d(SC)}{dt} = -v_n AC \qquad (10.12)$$

where
v_n = net sediment loss velocity from the water column (m/day)
A = surface lake area (m^2)

The solution to equation (10.12) is similar to that of equations (10.5) and (10.6), except that the loss due to transformation is now due to the settling of particles out of the water column with a decay constant K_s given by

$$K_s = \frac{v_n A}{S} = \frac{v_n}{H} \qquad (10.13)$$

where
H = ratio of the area to the volume (i.e., mean lake depth) (m)
K_s = loss rate due to settling (day^{-1})

The average flux or mass rate of deposition out of the water column is

$$F_s = v_n AC \qquad (10.14)$$

where
F_s = particle deposition mass rate (kg/day)

The particles deposited will become part of the stationary bed sediment of the lake and will play an important role in the building of bed toxicants or nutrients. Substituting equation (10.14) into equation (10.12), and assuming steady state conditions, we obtain an average estimate of this mass input to the sediment:

$$F_s = W - Q_r C \qquad (10.15)$$

This equation implies that the average mass loss rate out of the water column is the difference between the input sediment load and the mass leaving the lake. The mass loss rate may be measured directly by the installation of sediment traps that collect the sediment precipitation at a specific location on the bottom of the lake.

For comparative purposes with other lakes, sometimes it is useful to express the mass flux as an aerially normalized function. Dividing equation (10.12) by A, and assuming steady state, the aerially normalized flux ($kg/(m^2 day)$) to the bottom of a lake or a reservoir is

$$v_n C = \frac{W}{A} - \frac{Q_r}{A} C \qquad (10.16)$$

Note that $Q_r/A = H/t_d$.

Lakewide Response to an Instantaneous Spill

The lakewide response to an impulse or accidental dump or spill of a substance over a short period of time may be estimated as a especial case of the continuous load studied in the previous sections. Two points should be noted in extending this theory. First, the assumption of complete mixing of the substance may not be reasonable in a large lake or in the case of a near-shore spill. In such cases, an analysis of the contaminant dispersion inside the lake is needed. The theory and techniques behind this analysis is beyond the scope of the present treatment. Second, the concept of "instantaneous" implies the introduction of a substance during an infinitesimally short period of time. This mathematical concept may approach a real spill introduced during a relatively short period of time if the simulation time after the spill is significantly greater than that of the spill. For example, a substance spill that lasted a few days may be assumed approximately "instantaneous" for modeling purposes if the simulation time is of the order of months.

Aware of these limitations, if we assume that there is complete mixing of the substance in a relatively short period of time, and that the spill duration is approximately instantaneous, then the lakewide concentration after the spill is governed by equation (10.4) subject to a zero initial concentration, and a loading W expressed as a single contaminant pulse of mass $M(kg)$. It can be shown that the solution to the differential equation is

$$C(t) = \frac{M}{S} e^{-(\frac{Q_r}{S} + K)t} = \frac{M}{S} e^{-(\frac{1}{t_d} + K)t} \qquad (10.17)$$

This equation states that there is an "instantaneous" increase in lakewide concentration to a value equal to M/S after which the concentration decays exponentially (see Figure 10.8).

In this chapter we have introduced some fundamental hydrologic models of pollution in lakes. More in depth references should be consulted for the analysis of contaminant dispersion when the assumptions of complete mixing are not reasonable (Thomann and Mueller, 1986; Reckhow and Chapra, 1983; Chapra and Reckhow, 1983; Pinder and Gray, 1977). Additional references in limnology and lake physical, chemical and biological processes include Lerman (1978), Wetzel (1975), and the classical works of Hutchinson (1967, 1957).

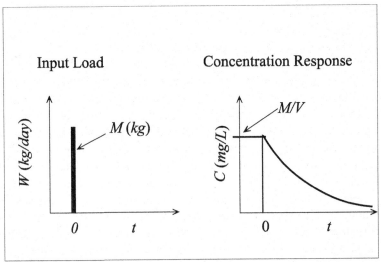

Figure 10.8: An Instantaneous Spill and its Temporal Response

PROBLEMS

10.1 A lake has been receiving an average load of a conservative substance of 32,000 kg/day for a long time. If the mean lake volume is $0.5 \times 10^{12} m^3$, and the average outflow rate is $3,200 m^3/s$, compute the lakewide equilibrium concentration (mg/L).

10.2 Solve Example 10.2 if the substance decay rate is $0.01/month$.

10.3 Solve Example 10.3 if the phosphorous decay rate is $0.001/month$.

10.4 In one graph plot $C(t)$ from: (1) Example 10.3 when phosphorous is assumed a conservative substance, and (2) Problem 10.3 when the phosphorous decay rate is $0.001/month$.

10.5 Since the 1960's a lake had been receiving an average load of phosphorous of 35,000kg/day. Early in 2002, the load increased to an unknown value. At that time the lakewide average concentration was 0.015mg/L. Early in 2004 the concentration was 0.025mg/L. If the decay rate is 0.001/day, the mean lake volume is $1.5 \times 10^{12} m^3$, and the average outflow rate is 6,500m^3/s, calculate the new input load to the lake back in 2002 in kg/day.

10.6 A lake has a volume of $1.5 \times 10^{11} m^3$, an average outflow rate of 4,500 m^3/s, and a variable loading W=[150000, 0, 450000, 300000, 500000,0] (kg/day) at time steps T=[0, 36, 60, 84, 120, 240] *months*, respectively. If the initial concentration is 0.2mg/L and the contaminant has a decay rate of 0.01/*month*, plot the variable waste load and the lakewide concentration versus time in months.

10.7 A lake in a rural agricultural community has an average storage volume of $10^8 m^3$, and an average flow rate of 6.5 m^3/s. Land application of a herbicide in the watershed for the last six months has resulted in contaminated surface runoff and groundwater flow to the lake. It is estimated that the average annual loading of the insecticide is about 2,800kg/day. Assuming a decay rate of 0.08/*month*, and that the herbicide has been replaced by one that biodegrades fast, calculate the equilibrium concentration in the lake, the maximum concentration, and the time after pesticide termination to reach a level of 0.01mg/L. Plot the concentration versus time.

10.8 Repeat Problem 10.5, except that the lake volume is only $32.0 \times 10^6 m^3$, and the load is 2,000kg/day.

10.9 A lake is receiving an average sediment load of about 22,000kg/day from its tributaries. If the principal outflow rate is 3.8m^3/s and the lake has an average suspended solids concentration of 0.25mg/L, estimate the rate of particle deposition out of the column of water (kg/day).

10.10 If in Problem 10.9 the net solids loss velocity is 0.38m/day, estimate the lake surface area.

10.11 A lake has an average volume of $2.35 \times 10^{12} m^3$, and the average outflow rate is 3,900 m^3/s. An accidental spill of about 50,000kg of trichloroethene occurred one day. Compute and plot the lakewide concentration response (mg/L) versus time assuming (1) trichloroethene is a conservative substance, and (2) the decay rate is 0.002/day.

10.12 In Problem 10.11, part (1), how long do we have to wait before the concentration decays below 0.01 $\mu g/L$?

10.13 A lake has an average volume of $1.98 \times 10^{12} m^3$, and the average outflow rate is $4,750 \, m^3/s$. An accidental spill of a conservative substance occurred two months ago. If the average concentration today is $25 mg/L$, estimate the initial mass of the spill. Assume a decay rate constant of $0.002/day$.

"All around us we see the bridges of life collapsing, those capillaries which create all organic life. This dreadful disintegration has been caused by the mindless and mechanical work of man, who has wrenched the living soul from the Earth's blood –water."

Viktor Schauberger (1885 - 1958)

11 SOIL AND GROUNDWATER POLLUTION

11.1 PROPAGATION OF CONTAMINANTS IN THE SUBSURFACE

In chapter 8 we discussed the fundamental aspects of water quality of interest to the hydrologist. We studied various measures of water quality, the basic types of chemicals that may be found in natural waters, and the possible sources of contamination. The purpose of this chapter is to provide some insight into the hydrologic and chemical factors that influence the subsurface migration of contaminants.

Land Disposal of Solid Waste

An important source of subsurface contamination is the land disposal of solid wastes. Much of the solid waste (or refuse) that is now disposed of on land is situated in engineering disposal systems called *sanitary landfills*. The solid waste is compacted, applied on the land, and then covered with a layer of earth. A sanitary landfill is usually composed of several layers of compacted waste and soil. A properly designed landfill is located according to local hydrologic and geologic conditions, and founded over a set of synthetic liners and natural layers of soil with low permeability. The objective is to minimize the risk of soil and groundwater contamination. Unfortunately many old landfills are poorly planned and poorly operated open dumps.

Improperly designed landfills are subject to leaching by percolated water from rain or snowmelt. Water from precipitation may dissolve chemicals present in the waste and eventually scape from the landfill. The liquid derived from this process, called *leachate*, will propagate through the bottom of the landfill, the unsaturated zone, and the saturated zone. The infiltrated water may cause a groundwater mound within or below a landfill. Water table mounding causes leachate to flow vertically and radially from the landfill (see Figure 11.1). Radial flow may cause leachate springs at the edge of a landfill or seepage into streams and other surface water bodies. Vertical flow may contaminate the groundwater and eventually other discharge zones in contact with the regional aquifer, such as rivers, lakes, springs, and drinking water wells.

Another source of subsurface contamination is sewage disposal on land. The widespread use of septic tanks and drains in rural, recreational, and suburban areas delivers filtered sewage directly to the subsurface. This is a frequently reported source of groundwater contamination.

Municipal sewage in industrialized countries is being processed in primary and secondary waste water treatment plants. This significantly decreases the substance concentrations discharged into rivers, but produces large volumes of solid residual materials known as *sewage sludge*. The sludge contains a number of potential contaminants and it is usually spread in agricultural or forested lands. Although this practice increases the contents of nutrients in the soil, and therefore increases the productivity of agricultural fields, the groundwater may be adversely affected by the subsurface migration of some contaminant byproducts, including pathogenic bacteria and viruses.

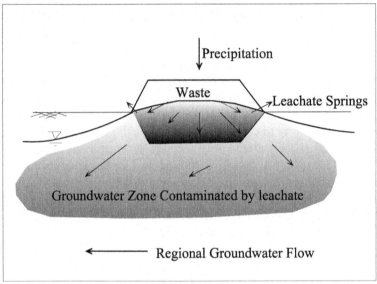

Figure 11.1: Contamination from Sanitary Landfills

Chemical Spills

In chapter 8 we mentioned other sources of groundwater contamination, including the effects of agricultural activities, especially the application of herbicides and pesticides, the deep well disposal of liquid wastes, the disposal of radioactive waste, and accidental chemical spills. It is instructive to observe the general features of contaminant propagation after an accidental chemical spill. Figure 11.2 shows the soil and the groundwater *contaminant plume* generated after the release of a conservative substance. Recall that a conservative substance is one capable of traveling through the soil and the aquifer without undergoing chemical reactions or decay.

For a short term release, the chemicals will penetrate the unsaturated zone, and may also flow onto the land surface in the regions where the spill flow intensity is greater than the soil infiltration capacity. Due to gravitational flow, the chemicals will travel to a certain depth below the ground surface. The initial depth will depend on the volume of contaminated fluid, the density of the contaminant, soil porosity, temperature, soil hydraulic conductivity, soil field capacity, and other physical properties. After the initial penetration, the contaminant will tend to propagate vertically due to downward hydraulic gradients caused by infiltration from precipitation, and radially due to contaminant dispersion.

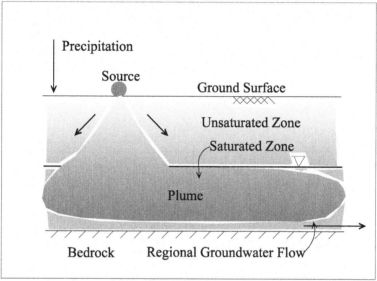

Figure 11.2: Contaminant Plume Caused by an Accidental Spill

For a continuous chemical release, the contaminant will slowly propagate through the unsaturated zone aided by infiltration from precipitation and horizontal radial dispersion in the soil. Eventually the contaminant plume may cross the water table and begin to propagate through the saturated zone following the regional groundwater flow. Once in the aquifer, the contaminants may eventually reach discharge zones, or drinking water wells.

Classical methods of groundwater pollution control of conservative substances include the artificial manipulation of hydraulic gradients, and the construction of physical barriers. Hydraulic control methods include the construction of pumping wells to capture the contaminant, and passive controls such as the construction of ditches to lower the water table and cause the contaminated water to flow in a desired direction. The water is treated to remove contaminants and then re-injected into the aquifer. Physical barriers and membranes attempt to prevent the plume from migrating through the aquifer, or to divert infiltrated water and regional groundwater to mix and move the plume. For more information on the engineering aspects of aquifer *remediation* see Fetter (1993), Devinny et al. (1990), and Boutwell et al. (1986).

Non-Aqueous Phase Liquids

The above simplified picture of contaminant migration in the subsurface is significantly complicated when the contaminants consist of halogenated solvents or hydrocarbons. Due to the massive production and use of industrial solvents and synthetic organic chemicals in the world today, the number and magnitude of sites contaminated with these products has increased dramatically in the last decades. These compounds behave and propagate differently in the subsurface.

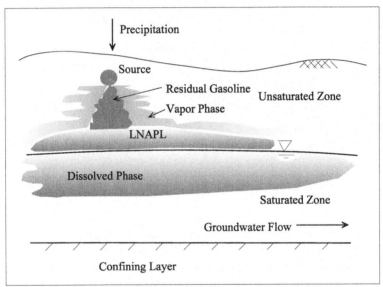

Figure 11.3: Spill of a Light Non-Aqueous Phase Liquid

Consider for example the case of a gasoline leak from an underground storage tank (Figure 11.3). Initially the spilled gasoline will travel vertically in the unsaturated zone until it finds the water table. This is not necessarily true if the spilled volume is small. In such a case the free product will remain absorbed by the soil in the unsaturated zone. Recall that a portion of infiltrated water remains absorbed in the unsaturated zone when the suction forces are greater than the gravitational forces. This occurs when the soil-water content is below the field capacity. When the infiltration intensity is high and the water content exceeds the field capacity, the gravitational forces will cause deep percolation of part of the water. A similar phenomenon occurs with a spilled liquid, except that gasoline is less dense and less viscous than water, and thus the flow rates are different. Volatile substances present in gasoline will vaporize and slowly propagate horizontally and vertically in the unsaturated zone.

If the spill is large, gasoline will reach the water table and will remain floating on it as a light non-aqueous phase liquid (LNAPL). The low density of gasoline, the adsorption by the soil particles, especially clays and soils with organic matter, and the low solubility of gasoline products in water, cause the free product to float on the water table. The hydraulic gradient at the water table will cause a slow move of the LNAPL, but essentially it will stabilize after a few months. If not removed, the floating LNAPL will become a long term source of contamination to the saturated zone. Due to deep percolation from rainfall and water table fluctuations, the LNAPL will dissolve small amounts of gasoline, which penetrate the saturated zone. The solubility of gasoline in water is very small. However, even small solubility levels cause concentrations significantly greater than the maximum allowable. The dissolved phase of gasoline will travel in the aquifer according to the regional groundwater flow and the laws of dispersion in porous media. However, many of the components of gasoline will suffer a rapid biological degradation, depending on the *DO* level present in the groundwater.

Thus, it can be seen that the subsurface contamination scenario of non-aqueous phase liquids consists of several *contaminant phases*, each with distinct propagation properties: the *residual product*, the *vapor phase*, and the LNAPL in the unsaturated zone, and the *dissolved phase* in the saturated zone. Non-aqueous phase liquids with higher density than that of water will behave similarly. A layer of dense non-aqueous phase liquid (DNAPL) will form on the water table. If the spilled volume is large, a portion of the contaminant will propagate vertically to the bottom of the aquifer, where it will form another layer of DNAPL. The latter will slowly move laterally because of gravity along the slope of the bottom of the aquifer. Each layer of DNAPL constitutes a long-term source of dissolved phase contaminant to the aquifer.

In the case of subsurface contamination by LNAPL and DNAPL, traditional groundwater pollution forecasting models will strictly be applicable to the dissolved phase of the contaminant. Similarly, traditional pump-and-treat remediation techniques will be partially successful with the dissolved phase of the contaminant. Knowing that over 70% of the initial mass remains as part of the LNAPL or DNAPL (i.e., only a small portion will propagate in dissolved form), and that these layers constitute a long term source of contamination to the aquifer, the appropriate remediation technique should attempt to remove them.

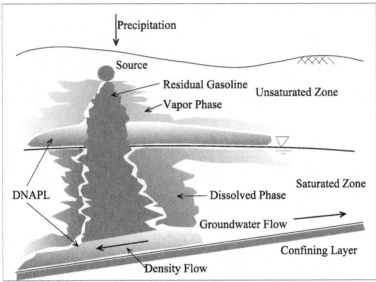

Figure 11.4: Spill of a Dense Non-Aqueous Phase Liquid

11.2. MODELING CONTAMINANT DISPERSION IN AQUIFERS

In this section we attempt to formulate fundamental equations describing contaminant transport in aquifers. The solution of these equations allow the hydrologist to predict qualitatively and quantitatively the propagation of a given contaminant in a system of aquifers. These predictions are essential in the assessment of the extent of a contamination problem, in the design of future monitoring networks, and in the design of possible remedial actions.

Consider initially a fixed control volume of saturated porous media contaminated with a conservative substance. Designate the volume as $V_T = A_T \times \Delta x$, where A_T is the cross-sectional area perpendicular to the regional groundwater flow, and Δx is the thickness (Figure 11.5). The regional groundwater pore velocity, u, is in the x direction. Recall that the mean pore velocity (or the seepage velocity, or the filtration velocity) is equal to q/n, where q is the specific discharge (or Darcy velocity), and n is the porosity (see chapter 5). If the aquifer is thin, as compared to its length, and the water table slope is mild, then Dupuit assumptions of nearly horizontal flow are valid, the hydraulic gradient approaches the water table slope, and the specific discharge is approximated as the product of the hydraulic conductivity times the hydraulic gradient (see chapter 5).

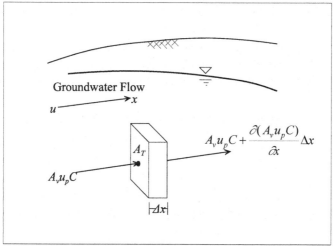

Figure 11.5: Aquifer Contaminant Transport through a Control Volume

Generally, the contaminant particles travel at speeds different from that of the fluid (i.e., the pore velocity, u). Designating the contaminant particle velocity as u_p, the substance mass rate entering the control volume is $A_v u_p C$, where A_v is the area of voids, and C is the contaminant concentration in the water (i.e., $m^2 \times (m/month) \times (kg/m^3) = kg/month$, or mass per month). Similarly, the solid mass rate leaving the control volume is $A_v u_p C + \partial(A_v u_p C)/\partial x . \Delta x$. In other words, the mass leaving the volume is equal to the mass entering it, plus the rate of change of mass with distance times distance. Now, the net contaminant mass rate is equal to that leaving the volume minus that entering it. In the absence of any transformation, the net mass rate must equal the change of mass within the volume per unit time, $\partial(A_T \Delta x C)/\partial t$. Thus, in words, the mass conservation statement is:

Net contaminant mass rate + change of mass within volume per unit time = zero

Noting that $A_v \Delta x = V_T n$, and dividing by V_T, then the above statement could be written mathematically as

$$\frac{\partial(nu_pC)}{\partial x}+\frac{\partial(nC)}{\partial t}=0 \tag{11.1}$$

An independent relationship is needed to transform the contaminant velocity into other measurable variables. This relationship is based on the *Fick's law of diffusion*:

$$n\left(u_p-u\right)C=-nD_x\frac{\partial C}{\partial x} \;\Rightarrow\; u_p=u-\frac{D_x}{nC}\frac{\partial C}{\partial x} \tag{11.2}$$

where

D_x = longitudinal dispersion coefficient ($m^2/month$)

This equation states that the contaminant moves relative to the fluid particles in a direction of decreasing concentration. In other words, contaminant propagate from regions of high concentration to regions of low concentration. In porous media, the dispersion coefficient is affected by several factors as will be seen shortly. Substituting equation (11.2) into (11.1), we obtain

$$\frac{\partial C}{\partial t}-\frac{\partial}{\partial x}\left(D_x\frac{\partial C}{\partial x}\right)+\frac{\partial(uC)}{\partial x}=0 \tag{11.3}$$

Advection, Diffusion, Dispersion, and Scale Dependency

Equation (11.3) illustrates the two fundamental physical processes governing the transport of contaminants in aquifers: *advection* and *hydrodynamic dispersion*. Advection is the physical drag of substance particles by water molecules traveling at an average pore velocity u. Dispersion is the spreading and mixing of the substance particles with uncontaminated water in the aquifer. Substance dispersion in a direction parallel to the flow velocity is called *longitudinal dispersion*. Dispersion that occurs normal to the pathway of the fluid flow is called *transverse* or *lateral dispersion*.

Small scale longitudinal dispersion (or *local dispersion*, usually a few meters in plume size) is caused by two main factors: *molecular diffusion* and *mechanical dispersion*. Molecular diffusion of a substance dissolved in water is the tendency of ions to migrate from regions of high concentration to regions of low concentration, as governed by Fick's law. In porous media, diffusion can not proceed as fast as in water because the ions must follow longer pathways as they travel around mineral grains.

In addition, diffusion can take place only through pore openings because mineral grains block many of the possible pathways. Therefore, molecular diffusion in porous media is determined as

$$D^* = \omega D \qquad (11.4)$$

where
D^* = porous media *effective diffusion coefficient* ($m^2/month$)
ω = empirical coefficient
D = *diffusion coefficient* ($m^2/month$)

Values of D are well known for electrolytes in water. For the major cations and anions in water, it ranges from 0.0025 to 0.0050 $m^2/month$. The coefficient ω is usually determined in laboratory experiments. For substances that are not adsorbed onto the mineral surface of the grains, it ranges from 0.01 to 0.5.

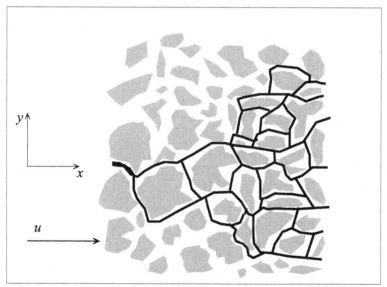

Figure 11.6: Porous Media Flow Paths and Mechanical Dispersion

The second factor affecting small scale longitudinal dispersion is called mechanical dispersion. As the substance moves through the pores, particles traveling through the center of the pores move faster than those traveling along the edges. In addition, some of the particles will travel in longer pathways than others. Finally, particles traveling through small pores will acquire a greater velocity than those moving through large pores. The result will be that some particles will travel at a greater velocity than that of the mean pore velocity u, and some will travel at a lower one. In addition to the longitudinal dispersion, these phenomena will cause transverse dispersion of the contaminant. Figure 11.6 illustrates how the random pore flow paths generate longitudinal and transverse dispersion of a contaminant. Customarily, mechanical dispersion is expressed as $a_L u$, where a_L is a factor called the *longitudinal dynamic dispersivity*. Small scale dispersivity values range from 0.3 to 10.0 m.

The transverse or lateral dispersion is caused by the branching to the side of contaminated fluid as it moves longitudinally. The transverse dispersion is then expressed as a factor of the longitudinal pore velocity, $a_T u$, where a_T is the *transverse dynamic dispersivity*. Some believe that the transverse dispersivity fluctuates around 10% of the longitudinal dispersivity, that is $a_T \approx 0.1 a_L$.

Small scale hydrodynamic dispersion is the summation of the two effects, molecular diffusion and mechanical dispersion:

$$D_x = D^* + a_L u$$

where
   D_x = small scale *longitudinal dispersion coefficient* ($m^2/month$)
   a_L = *longitudinal dynamic dispersivity* (m)
   u = groundwater pore velocity ($m/month$)

If plan view transverse dispersion is considered, and if we orient the x axis parallel ton the regional groundwater pore velocity, u, and the y perpendicular to it, then

$$D_y = D^* + a_T u \qquad (11.6)$$

where
   D_y = small scale *transverse dispersion coefficient* ($m^2/month$)
   a_T = *transverse dynamic dispersivity* (m)

Note that the y-direction dispersion coefficient is a function of the x-direction pore velocity, u. In general, we may also have transverse dispersion along the vertical z coordinate.

Figure 11.7 illustrates the relative effect of advection, molecular diffusion, and mechanical dispersion. A highly concentrated contaminant, represented in black, is released at time $t=0$. In the hypothetical case when there is only advection, caused by the pore velocity u in the x direction, the contaminant does not disperse. It moves at a velocity u. This situation rarely arises in nature. In the hypothetical case when there is only molecular diffusion, the contaminant grows radially, and at $t=1$ occupies a spherical section of a greater radius than that at $t=0$. However, the center of mass of the plume does not move. This situation is realistic in portions of an aquifer where the flow velocity is very small or zero, such as in the case of saturated clays. Finally, a realistic scenario occurs when advection, molecular diffusion, and mechanical dispersion are all present. In this case the center of mass of the plume moves at a velocity u (advection), it grows radially (molecular diffusion), and it disperses in the x, y, and z directions, with greater dispersion in the x than in the y direction (mechanical dispersion).

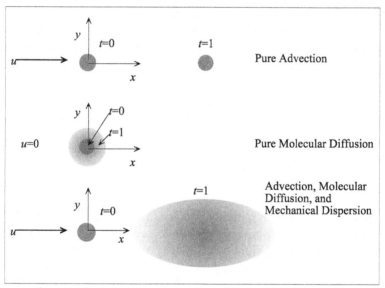

Figure 11.7: Advection, Molecular Diffusion, and Dispersion

Cases of interest in groundwater pollution usually exhibit groundwater flow velocities that make the mechanical dispersion component the predominant one. For this reason, many hydrologic studies neglect the molecular diffusion component. Advection, molecular diffusion, and mechanical dispersion are the most important physical processes affecting hydrodynamic dispersion of conservative substances in aquifers at the small scale. This usually refers to plume sizes ranging from one meter to a few tens of meters at the most. However, it has been observed that the dispersion coefficient significantly increases in magnitude as the contaminant plume grows in size, or alternatively, as the time after injection increases. This phenomenon has been termed the *scale dependency* of the dispersion coefficient. This suggests that the traditional small scale estimations of the dispersion coefficient, such as the ones obtained via laboratory experimentation on soil samples, will not be applicable to large scales, or long-term predictions.

It has been found that large-scale dispersion in aquifers depends not only on the physical processes described above, but also on large-scale aquifer heterogeneity in the hydraulic conductivity, aquifer recharge from rainfall, groundwater flow boundary conditions, and other factors. These factors cause an enhanced dispersion of the contaminant because of the variations in pore velocity. As a result, contaminant plumes will tend to occupy larger portions of an aquifer than those predicted by using small scale dispersion coefficients. Since aquifer heterogeneity in the hydraulic conductivity is difficult to describe, common approaches to the estimation of the field-scale dispersion coefficient focus on a statistical representation of the hydraulic conductivity. For example, one practical estimate of the field-scale dispersion coefficients is (Serrano, 1996)

$$\bar{D}_x(t) = D_x + \sigma_u^2 t$$

$$\bar{D}_y(t) = D_y + \frac{c\sigma_u^2 t}{l^2} \tag{11.7}$$

where
$\bar{D}_x(t)$ = *field-scale* longitudinal dispersion coefficient ($m^2/month$)
$\bar{D}_y(t)$ = field-scale transverse dispersion coefficient ($m^2/month$)
σ_u^2 = variance of the fluid pore velocity u ($m/month)^2$
l = transmissivity *correlation length* (m)
$c = 2.0 m^2$

To calculate the pore velocity variance, σ_u^2, an estimate of the transmissivity variance, σ_T^2 is needed. To this end, the hydrologist needs the magnitude of the aquifer transmissivity at several locations, from which the sample mean, $\bar{T}$, the variance, σ_T^2, and the correlation length, l, are computed using standard statistical formulae. The parameter l is a measure of correlation between individual values of transmissivity. For example, highly correlated transmissivity values, a homogeneous aquifer, reflect large values of l (e.g., 100 m). On the other hand, uncorrelated values of transmissivity, a heterogeneous aquifer, reflect low values of l (e.g., 10m). Strictly speaking, this number should be estimated from the transmissivity serial correlation coefficient, ρ, such that $l = 1/\rho$. However, the hydrologist rarely has a large sample for such a test, and instead has to rely on a limited number of punctual values. Knowing that the accuracy of the above estimate of the dispersion coefficient increases with the number of transmissivity samples, the hydrologist has to use common sense and experience in estimating statistical parameters.

Now the variance of the pore velocity, σ_u^2 is calculated from the above statistics of the transmissivity, and knowledge of the hydrologic conditions affecting the aquifer. For instance, for the classical unconfined aquifer bounded by two rivers of known head (see chapter 5), the variance of the pore velocity is given by (Serrano, 1995a)

$$\sigma_u^2 = \frac{\sigma_T^2 A^2}{n^2 h^2}$$

(11.8)

where
σ_T^2= variance of transmissivity $(m^2/month)^2$
n=porosity
h=hydraulic head with respect to the bottom of the aquifer (m)
A=parameter depending on recharge and boundary conditions

The hydraulic head for this aquifer is given by (see chapter 5)

$$h(x) = -\frac{R_g x^2}{2\overline{T}} + Ax + H_1$$

(11.9)

where
R_g = mean aquifer recharge $(m/month)$
$\overline{T}$= aquifer mean transmissivity $(m^2/month)$
x=distance from the left boundary (m)
H_1 = head at the left boundary (m)

Finally the parameter A in this aquifer is given by

$$A = \frac{H_2 - H_1}{l_x} + \frac{R_g l_x}{2\overline{T}}$$

(11.10)

where
H_2= head at the right boundary (m)
l_x= length of aquifer (m)

In the absence of recharge, the parameter A may be approximated as the mean regional hydraulic gradient. In conclusion, an estimation of the field scale dispersion coefficient requires knowledge of the hydrologic conditions of the aquifer in question (i.e., recharge, boundary conditions), as well as a statistical description of aquifer heterogeneity in the transmissivity or the hydraulic conductivity. Table 11.1 summarizes the physical processes affecting hydrodynamic dispersion of conservative contaminants in aquifers.

Table 11.1: Processes Affecting Hydrodynamic Dispersion in Aquifers

Small Scale	Large (Field) Scale
Advection	Aquifer Recharge
Molecular Diffusion	Flow Boundary Conditions
Mechanical Dispersion	Transmissivity Variability (Heterogeneity)

Example 11.1

A $1200m$ long unconfined aquifer is bounded by two rivers with average heads of $12m$ and $10m$, respectively, with respect to the bottom of the aquifer. The porosity is 0.15, the mean recharge is $0.01m/month$. A conservative contaminant with a diffusion coefficient of $0.005m^2/month$ is released in the aquifer, the longitudinal dispersivity is $1m$, the transverse dispersivity is $0.1m$, and random transmissivity measures taken in the aquifer are summarized in the following Table 11.2. Estimate longitudinal and transverse hydrodynamic dispersion coefficient $600m$ from the left river, and $12months$ after the injection.

Table 11.2: Point Transmissivity Values for Example 11.1

Sample i	$T_i(m^2/month)$	Sample i	$T_i(m^2/month)$
1	1250	6	1020
2	885	7	1130
3	1490	8	1055
4	1610	9	996
5	784	10	957

Solution

Let us first calculate the statistics of the transmissivity, the mean $\overline{T}$, the standard deviation σ_T, and the coefficient of variability C_v:

$$\overline{T} = \frac{1}{N}\sum_{i=1}^{N} T_i = 1118m^2/month$$

$$\sigma_T = \sqrt{\frac{1}{N-1}\sum_{i=1}^{N}(T_i - \overline{T})^2} = 262m^2/month$$

$$C_v = \frac{\sigma_T}{\overline{T}} = \frac{262m^2/month}{1118m^2/month} = 0.23(23\%)$$

With a coefficient of variability of 23% we conclude we have a mildly heterogeneous aquifer. We therefore assign a relatively low value of the correlation length parameter: $l=30m$. As will be seen, the effect of this parameter on the large-scale transverse dispersion coefficient is small. The parameter A is given from equation (11.10) as

$$A = \frac{H_2 - H_1}{l_x} + \frac{R_g l_x}{2\overline{T}} = \frac{10m - 12m}{1200m} + \frac{0.01m/month \times 1200m}{2 \times 1118m^2/month} = 0.0037$$

Now the head at $x=600m$ is calculated from equation (11.9):

$$h(x) = -\frac{R_g x^2}{2\overline{T}} + Ax + H_1$$

$$h(600) = \frac{0.01\dfrac{m}{month} \times 600^2 m^2}{2 \times 1118\dfrac{m^2}{month}} + 0.0037 \times 600m + 12m = 15.83m$$

The average pore velocity is calculated from Darcy's law:

$$u(x) \approx -\frac{\overline{T}}{nh(x)} \frac{dh(x)}{dx}$$

where the hydraulic gradient is calculated by differentiating equation (11.9) with respect to distance:

$$\frac{dh(x)}{dx} = -\frac{R_g x}{\overline{T}} + A = -\frac{0.01\dfrac{m}{month} \times 600m}{1118\dfrac{m^2}{month}} + 0.0037 = -0.0017 m/m$$

Thus, the mean pore velocity is

$$u(600) = \frac{1118m^2/month \times 0.0017}{0.15 \times 15.83m} = 0.8 \ m/month$$

Using equation (11.8) we now calculate the variance of the pore velocity:

$$\sigma_u = \frac{\sigma_T A}{nh} = \frac{262m^2/month \times 0.0037}{0.15 \times 15.83m} = 0.41 m/month$$

From equations (11.4) through (11.6) we calculate the small-scale dispersion coefficients, using a conservative value for the parameter ω:

$$D_x = \omega D + a_L u = 0.5 \times 0.005 \frac{m^2}{month} + 1m \times 0.8 \frac{m}{month} = 0.8025 \frac{m^2}{month}$$

$$D_y = \omega D + a_T u = 0.5 \times 0.005 \frac{m^2}{month} + 0.1m \times 0.8 \frac{m}{month} = 0.0825 \frac{m^2}{month}$$

Note that the transverse dispersion coefficient is about one order of magnitude smaller than the longitudinal one. Also the molecular diffusion component of the dispersion coefficient is negligible as compared to that of the mechanical dispersion. Finally, the large-scale dispersion coefficients are calculated from equation (11.7):

$$\bar{D}_x(t) = D_x + \sigma_u^2 t$$

$$\bar{D}_x(12) = 0.8025 \frac{m^2}{month} + 0.41^2 (\frac{m}{month})^2 \times 12month = 2.82 \frac{m^2}{month}$$

$$\bar{D}_y(t) = D_y + \frac{c\sigma_u^2 t}{l^2}$$

$$\bar{D}_y(12) = 0.0825 \frac{m^2}{month} + \frac{2m^2 \times 0.41^2 (\frac{m}{month})^2 \times 12month}{30^2 m^2} = 0.087 \frac{m^2}{month}$$

After twelve months, the large-scale longitudinal dispersion coefficient has grown by a factor of three with respect to the small-scale value. At the same time, the large-scale transverse dispersion coefficient has not grown significantly from the its small scale value. The dramatic increase in the the longitudinal dispersion parameter explains why contaminant plumes occupy a significantly larger portion of an aquifer than that estimated based on small-scale, or laboratory based, dispersion parameters.

Predicting Groundwater Pollution

Solutions to equation (11.3) subject to various initial and boundary conditions may be used to forecast groundwater pollution in an aquifer. In the simplest case of homogeneous aquifers, the dispersion coefficient may be assumed constant. If aquifer recharge is neglected, and the groundwater flow boundary conditions are not functions of time, then the groundwater pore velocity is constant. Thus, equation (11.3) reduces to

$$\frac{\partial C}{\partial t} - D_x \frac{\partial^2 C}{\partial x^2} + u \frac{\partial C}{\partial x} = 0 \qquad (11.11)$$

which is the classical *advection dispersion equation* governing the transport of conservative contaminants in homogenous one-dimensional aquifers. This equation is strictly applicable to controlled laboratory conditions where the above assumptions are valid. For this reason, it has been used in the past in laboratory experimentation aimed at the estimation of the dispersion coefficient. However, as we saw in the previous section, the large scale, or field scale, dispersion coefficient could be several orders of magnitude greater than that estimated via laboratory experimentation for the same soil. Nonetheless, the advection dispersion equation is an illustrative model of contaminant propagation in aquifers.

Boundary conditions imposed on equation (11.11) assume that the aquifer is very long and the substance concentration far from the area of interest is zero. Solutions to the advection dispersion equation depend on the form in which the contaminant is introduced into the aquifer. For example, if an *instantaneous spill* of a substance of mass M occurs, the solution to equation (11.11) is (Myint-U, 1987; Zauderer, 1983).

$$C(x, t) = \frac{M}{A_v \sqrt{4\pi D_x t}} e^{-\frac{(x-ut)^2}{4D_x t}} \qquad (11.12)$$

where
    M=initial mass (kg)
    $A_v = A_T \times n = w \times b \times n$ = contaminant-saturated voids area (Figure 11.8)

perpendicular to the direction of the flow u (m^2)

A_T= total cross-sectional area, including soil grains, saturated with the contaminant (m^2)

b=aquifer contaminated depth (m)

w=aquifer contaminated width (m)

n=porosity

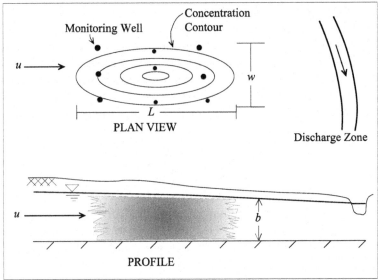

Figure 11.8: Well-Mixed Cross-Sectional Area of an Aquifer Spill

Equation (11.12) assumes that the contaminant is completely mixed across an area of the aquifer perpendicular to the regional groundwater flow velocity, u. Thus, the model provides an estimate of the average concentration per unit cross-sectional area of aquifer. Similar assumptions were adopted when considering the dispersion of contaminants along rivers (see chapter 9). However, in aquifers the contaminant will occupy the area of voids only, A_v. The extent of this area is not as obvious as in the case of rivers, where the flow cross-sectional area is easily identifiable. The hydrologist has to estimate the magnitude of this contaminant area from field observations. For example, a usual assumption of the vertical well-mixed depth, b, is to equate it to the aquifer thickness. As for the well-mixed width, w, water samples from a collection of piezometers at the spill site will help in the determination of this dimension. Figure 11.8 illustrates the approximation of the dimensions of a well-mixed cross-sectional area. Equation (11.12) assumes that this area remains constant. Clearly this assumption is incorrect, since lateral dispersion will cause a gradual increase in w over time. However, a one-dimensional model provides a simple approximation to the propagation of a contaminant in an aquifer. This approximation is a conservative one, since the predicted values will overestimate the concentration magnitude.

Now the initial mass, M, in equation (11.12) is usually estimated in an indirect way. The simplest case occurs when a known volume V_0 of a liquid containing a contaminant of a specified concentration C_0 is injected into the aquifer. The initial mass is $M=V_0 \times C_0$. If the injected fluid is composed of a pure chemical substance of density γ_s, then the initial mass is $M=V_0 \times \gamma_s$. Because of the accidental nature of most chemical spills, information on the initial volume and initial concentration is usually not available. The hydrologist has to estimate the initial mass based on a survey of the portion of the aquifer contaminated at the time of the investigation. This information is again deduced from water samples extracted from a network of monitoring wells drilled in the suspected area of contamination. Thus, if the portion of aquifer contaminated has a length L, a width w, and a depth b, and if the contaminated aquifer volume has an average concentration C_0, then the initial mass is $M=L \times w \times b \times n \times C_0$.

This is a practical approximation of the initial mass. The accuracy depends on the density of the monitoring network, and the analytical precision of chemical concentration measurements. Another factor to consider is that equation (11.12) assumes a point source initial condition, and predicts concentration a time t after the spill. Once the initial mass has been estimated as above, the time interval between the occurrence of the spill and the measurement date has to be estimated. During carefully planned aquifer tracer tests this is not a problem. However, in the case of accidental spills, this time interval has to be inferred based on accounts given by witnesses of the event, news papers, emergency response teams reports, or any other indirect procedure.

With the proper information at hand, equation (11.12) may be used to predict an aquifer contaminant plume evolution in space and time. At any given time, the shape of this equation may be recognized as that of a normal probability distribution with a mean equal to ut and a variance equal to $2D_x t$. Knowing the initial mass, the mean pore velocity, the mean cross-sectional area, and the dispersion coefficient, equation (11.12) may be used to estimate the substance concentration at a distance x from the spill and a time t time after the spill. We remark that the x coordinate has to be oriented parallel to the regional flow velocity u. The model could be used to simulate concentration *breakthrough curves*. A concentration versus distance curve is created by calculating the concentration magnitude for several locations along x, while keeping the time constant. This produces a picture of the shape of the contaminant plume at a fixed time after the spill.

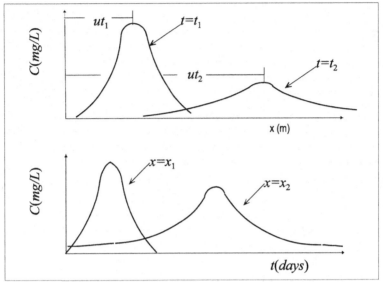

Figure 11.9: Dispersion Properties of Contaminant Plumes

Alternatively, a concentration versus time breakthrough curve is created by calculating the concentration magnitude for several times, while keeping the distance fixed. This will simulate the time evolution of a contaminant concentration as detected by an observer located at a fixed location in the aquifer. Equation (11.12) also illustrates the basic dispersion and dissipation properties of contaminants in aquifers. By plotting two concentration versus distance curves, one at time $t=t_1$, and one at time $t=t_2$, with $t_2>t_1$, one can easily observe that the center of mass of the first plume is located a distance ut_1 from the injection point, and the center of mass of the second plume is located a distance ut_2 from the injection point (Figure 11.9). This means that a contaminant plume travels at a mean velocity u. This physical drag of contaminant particles by the fluid particles having an average pore velocity u is called *advection*. Similarly, one may plot two concentration versus time curves, one at a distance x_1 from the injection point, and one at a distance x_2, with $x_2>x_1$ (Figure 11.9). Note that the peak concentration decreases in magnitude as it travels down gradient, while the "spread" (the dispersion, or the *plume variance*) simultaneously increases. The spread of contaminant particles away from its center of mass (up gradient and down gradient) is caused by mechanical dispersion forced by heterogeneity, and by molecular diffusion.

Example 11.2

$10m^3$ of a solution of a conservative substance with a concentration of $300mg/L$ was injected through a well in an unconfined aquifer with a thickness of $6m$. The aquifer hydraulic conductivity is constant and equal to $120m/month$, the hydraulic gradient in the direction of the regional groundwater flow velocity is $0.003m/m$, the porosity is 0.2, and the dispersion coefficient of the tracer is $0.5\,m^2/month$. Assuming that the contaminant will mix completely through the entire thickness of the aquifer, and across a width of $5m$ perpendicular to the flow, calculate the maximum contaminant concentration expected at a drinking water well located $6m$ from the injection point (in a direction parallel to the flow).

Solution

Choose the x coordinate as distance from the injection point, and in a direction parallel to the groundwater flow. The mean groundwater pore velocity is

$$u = \frac{q}{n} = -\frac{Ki}{n} = \frac{120m/month \times 0.003m/m}{0.2} = 1.8m/month$$

From equation (11.12), the maximum concentration at $x=6m$ occurs at $x=ut_p$, where t_p is the mean travel time (i.e., the time that makes the exponent zero, and the exponential equal to one). Therefore

$$t_p = \frac{x}{u} = \frac{6m}{1.8m/month} = 3.33month$$

Neglecting the large-scale component, due to our assumption of a homogeneous aquifer, we remark that in reality the maximum concentration will be somewhat smaller than that of these calculations. With this observation, the maximum concentration $C_{max} = C(x=6m,\ 3.33month)$ is

$$C_{max} = \frac{M}{A_v\sqrt{4\pi D_x t_p}} = \frac{V_0 C_0}{b \times w \times n \times \sqrt{4\pi D_x t_p}}$$

$$C_{max} = \frac{10m^3 \times 300mg/L}{6m \times 5m \times 0.2 \times \sqrt{4 \times \pi \times 0.5m^2/month \times 3.33month}} = 109.3mg/L$$

Example 11.3: Contaminant Spatial and Temporal Distribution
In Example 11.2, (1)in one graph plot the concentration versus time breakthrough curves at x=10, 20, and 30m, respectively; (2) the concentration versus distance breakthrough curves at t=12, 36, and 60$month$, respectively.

Solution
The following Maple worksheet programs equation (11.12)

```
> restart: V0:=10: C0:=300: b:=6: u:=1.8:
  n:=0.2: Dx:=0.5: w:=5:
  C:=(x,t)->V0*C0/(b*w*n*sqrt(4*Pi*Dx*t))
      *exp(-(x-u*t)^2/(4*Dx*t)):
  #(1)
  x1:=10.: x2:=20: x3:=30: Maxt:=26:
  G1:=plot(C(x1,t),t=0..Maxt,color=black,
      legend=`x=10m`):
  G2:=plot(C(x2,t),t=0..Maxt,color=black,
      legend=`x=20m`,linestyle=5):
  G3:=plot(C(x3,t),t=0..Maxt,color=black,
      legend=`x=30m`,linestyle=3):
  plots[display](G1,G2,G3,thickness=2,
      labeldirections=[HORIZONTAL,VERTICAL],
      symbol=box,labels=[`t (months)`,`C (mg/L)`],
      labelfont=[TIMES,ROMAN,16]);
```

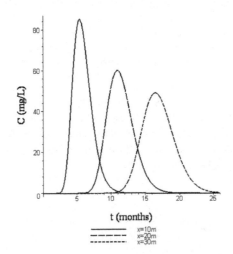

```
> #(2)
  t1:=12.: t2:=24: t3:=36: Maxx:=84:
  G4:=plot(C(x,t1),x=0..Maxx,color=black,
     legend=`t=12month`):
  G5:=plot(C(x,t2),x=0..Maxx,color=black,
     legend=`t=24month`,linestyle=5):
  G6:=plot(C(x,t3),x=0..Maxx,color=black,
     legend=`t=36month`,linestyle=3):
  plots[display](G4,G5,G6,thickness=2,
     labeldirections=[HORIZONTAL,VERTICAL],
     symbol=box,labels=[`x (m)`,`C (mg/L)`],
     labelfont=[TIMES,ROMAN,16]);
```

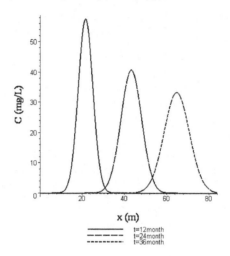

Non-Conservative Contaminants: Linear Decay

In their travel through porous media, many contaminants experience a chemical, biological or radioactive transformation. Certain aromatic hydrocarbons associated with petroleum products may be metabolized by bacteria present in the soil which, depending on the availability of dissolved oxygen, temperature, contaminant concentration and other factors, transform the original substance into a series of by-products. The resulting compounds may also be toxic. Halogenated organic solvents dissolved in groundwater undergo transformations with the compounds suffering progressive dehalogenation. The following classes of organic compounds have been found to undergo either biotic or abiotic degradation: chlorinated methanes, chlorinated ethanes, chlorinated propanes, chlorinated butanes, chlorinated ethenes, bromonated methanes, bromonated ethenes, alkylbenzenes, bromochloropropanes, halogenated acetates, and various aromatics such as benzene and toluene. These are common groundwater contaminants which may undergo substitution reactions, dehydrohalogenation, oxidations and reductions. Radioactive contaminants are subject to a gradual decay resulting from nuclear reactions stabilizing with the continuous energy emissions.

The degradation of groundwater contaminants causes a decrease in the concentration. Given the complexity of the physical, chemical and biological processes involved, the hydrologic prediction of contaminant propagation of degradable contaminants has been approached from the macroscopical point of view with the aid of empirical equations which attempt to replicate the resulting decrease in contaminant concentration. Referring once again to a control volume in an aquifer (Figure 11.5), the mass conservation statement in the presence of a degradable contaminant is:

Net contaminant mass rate + change of mass within volume per unit time = mass rate loss due to transformation

Following the same procedure we adopted for degradable contaminants in surface waters, we conceive that the substance decays according to a first order reaction. In other words, the mass rate loss of the substance is proportional to the substance concentration. Thus, for a homogeneous aquifer with constant flow velocity, equation (11.11) becomes

$$\frac{\partial C}{\partial t} - D_x \frac{\partial^2 C}{\partial x^2} + u \frac{\partial C}{\partial x} + KC = 0 \qquad (11.13)$$

where
K=decay rate of the substance ($month^{-1}$)

It is interesting to compare the equation of dispersion in rivers, equation (9.22), with that in aquifers, equation (11.13). Although the equations are mathematically identical, they exhibit fundamental differences in their parameters. The dispersion coefficient in rivers is caused by molecular diffusion and turbulent flow dispersion, whereas the dispersion coefficient in aquifers is caused by mechanical dispersion within the porous media, besides molecular diffusion. The flow velocity in rivers represents an average over the river cross-sectional area. The flow velocity in aquifers represents an average over the cross-sectional area occupied by the pores only. If an instantaneous spill of a substance of mass M occurs, the solution to equation (11.13) is (Myint, 1987; Zauderer, 1983).

$$C(x,\ t) = \frac{M}{A_v\sqrt{4\pi D_x t}} e^{-\frac{(x-ut)^2}{4D_x t} - Kt} \tag{11.14}$$

Example 11.4:Effect of Linear Contaminant Decay

$40 m^3$ of a solution of arsenic acid with a concentration of $600 mg/L$ were injected through a well in an unconfined aquifer $5m$ in thickness. The mean groundwater pore velocity is $0.4m/month$, the porosity is 0.15, and the dispersion coefficient for the tracer is $1\,m^2/month$. Assume the contaminant will mix completely through the entire thickness of the aquifer, and across a width of $10m$ perpendicular to the flow. (1) Assuming no decay, calculate the contaminant concentration expected at a drinking water well located $10m$ from the injection point (in a direction parallel to the flow) one year after injection. (2) Repeat (1) if a decay rate of $0.05\,month^{-1}$ is assumed.

Solution

(1) Choosing the x coordinate as distance from the injection point in a direction perpendicular to the groundwater flow, the concentration is given from equation (11.14):

$$C(x,\ t) = \frac{M}{A_v\sqrt{4\pi D_x t}} e^{-\frac{(x-ut)^2}{4D_x t} - Kt} = \frac{V_0 C_0}{b \times w \times n \times \sqrt{4\pi D_x t}} e^{-\frac{(x-ut)^2}{4D_x t} - Kt}$$

$$C(10,\ 12) = \frac{40 m^3 \times 600\frac{mg}{L}}{5m \times 10m \times 0.15 \times \sqrt{4\times\pi\times1\frac{m^2}{month}\times12month}}$$

$$\times\exp\left(-\frac{(10m - 0.4\frac{m}{month}\times12month)^2}{4\times1\frac{m^2}{month}\times12month}\right)$$

$$C(10,\ 12) = 260.06\frac{mg}{L}\times e^{-0.56} = 148.4 mg/L$$

(2) If we consider arsenic acid to be a degradable substance, then the estimated concentration at the well will be

$$C(x, t) = \frac{V_0 C_0}{b \times w \times n \times \sqrt{4\pi D_x t}} e^{-\frac{(x-ut)^2}{4D_x t} - Kt}$$

$$C(10, 12) = 260.06 mg/L \times e^{-0.56 - 0.192 month^{-1} \times 12 month} = 81.4 mg/L$$

Thus, degradation substantially reduces contaminant concentration.

Table 11.2: Values of Degradation Constant K of Some Pesticides in Soil

Pesticide	K (month^{-1})	Pesticide	K (month^{-1})
Fungicides		**Insecticides**	
BAS 3460F	2.466	Aldrin	0.774
Benomyl	4.458	Azinphosmethyl	1.599
		BHC	0.420
Herbicides		Bromophos	0.594
Alachlor	1.152	Chlordane	0.060
Amitrole	2.304	Diazinon	0.990
Arsenic Acid	0.192	Dieldrin	0.561
Asulam	1.158	Dioxathion	0.468
Atrazine	0.393	p,p'-DDT	0.144
Butralin	0.231	Endosulfan	0.486
Cyanazine	0.192	Ethion	0.096
Dicamba	6.420	Heptachlor	0.084
2,4-D	5.199	Lindane	0.792
Fluchloralin	0.210	Malathion	> 40.0
Metobromuron	0.744	Parathion	8.886
Nitralin	0.465	Phorate	1.089
Picloram	2.316	Zinophos	0.732
Simazine	0.348		
Tebuthiuron	1.281	**Nematicides**	
2,4,5-T	1.524	Trichloronate	0.150
Trifluralin	1.188		

Source: Nash, R.G., 1989. Dissipation Rate of Pesticides from Soils. CREAMS User Manual, USDA

Few studies have been conducted on the values of the degradation constant. Laboratory experiments on degradation are usually difficult to extrapolate to complex field conditions. It has been found that the degradation rate is a function of many parameters, including contaminant concentration, temperature, soil organic content, dissolved oxygen, and type and quantity of bacteria present. As a result, one contaminant may exhibit a range of values depending on the field conditions. For example, typical degradation rates for polyvinyl alcohol range between 18.9 and 75.0 $month^{-1}$; for benzoic acid, between 2.28 and 30.0 $month^{-1}$; and for chloropropham, between 0.3 and 0.9 $month^{-1}$. Table 11.2 summarizes typical values of the degradation constant for some pesticides in soil. In practice, however, the hydrologist uses the degradation constant in accordance with the project objectives. For instance, the worst possible contamination scenario is one in which no degradation exists (i.e., $K=0$).

Example 11.5: Effect of Linear Decay on Contaminant Distribution

In Example 11.4, in one graph plot the concentration versus time breakthrough curves at the well for (1) the case of no decay, and (2) when the decay rate is $0.05\,month^{-1}$.

Solution

Modify the program in Example 10.3 as follows:

```
> restart: V0:=40: C0:=600: b:=5: u:=0.4:
  n:=0.15: Dx:=1.: w:=10: X:=10: Maxt:=120:
  C:=(x,t)->V0*C0/(b*w*n*sqrt(4*Pi*Dx*t))
       *exp(-(x-u*t)^2/(4*Dx*t)-K*t):
  #(1)
  K:=0.0:
  G1:=plot(C(X,t),t=0..Maxt,color=black,
       legend=`K=0.0`):
  #(2)
  K:=0.05:
  G2:=plot(C(X,t),t=0..Maxt,color=black,
       legend=`K=0.05`,linestyle=3):
  plots[display](G1,G2,thickness=2,
       labeldirections=[HORIZONTAL,VERTICAL],
       symbol=box,labels=[`t (months)`,`C (mg/L)`],
       labelfont=[TIMES,ROMAN,16]);
```

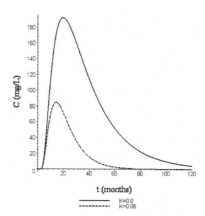

Non-Conservative Substances: Nonlinear Decay

In the general case of substances undergoing nonlinear biological or radioactive decay, the substance decay rate has the form

$$C_f = K.C^\beta \qquad (11.15)$$

where

C_f = substance decay rate ($(mg/L)/month$)
C = liquid-phase concentration (mg/L)
β = the nonlinear parameter
K = decay rate constant ($(mg/L)^{1-\beta}/month$))

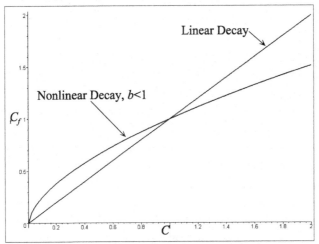

Figure 11.10: Comparison between linear and nonlinear decay relationship, $\beta<1$. For $C<1$ nonlinear decay is greater than that of linear. When $C>1$ the opposite is true

When $\beta=1$ (i.e., linear decay), K has the dimensions of ($month^{-1}$). Figure 11.10 shows the shape of equation (11.15) for the linear ($\beta=1$) and nonlinear ($\beta=0.6$) cases when $K=1 (mg/L)^{1-\beta}/month$). With $\beta<1$, the nonlinear decay curve has the shape shown in Figure 11.10. For concentration less than 1, the amount of substance decayed is greater than that exhibited by a linear decay rate. Conversely, for concentrations greater than 1, the amount of substance decayed is less than that exhibited by a linear decay rate. Thus, when $\beta<1$ spilled chemical with large concentrations ($C>>1$) should experience less decay than that of linear plumes. Under nonlinear decay, equation (11.13) becomes

$$\frac{\partial C}{\partial t} - D\frac{\partial^2 C}{\partial x^2} + u\frac{\partial C}{\partial x} + KC^\beta = 0 \qquad (11.16)$$

There are few solutions to equation (11.16). For the case of an instantaneous spill of a substance of mass M, Serrano (2003c) obtained an approximate analytical solution of the form:

$$C(x,\ t) \approx C_0(x,\ t) e^{-\dfrac{2KtC_0(x,\ t)^{\beta-1}}{\beta+1}} \qquad (11.17)$$

where

$C_0 =$ solution to the advective-dispersive equation subject to no decay (equation (11.12)

Equation (11.17) is subject to $\beta > 0$ and $M/A_v > 1$, where A_v is the contaminant-saturated voids area (Figure 11.8) perpendicular to the direction of the flow.

Example 11.6: Effect of Nonlinear Decay on Plume Distribution

In the Spill of Example 11.4, in one graph plot the concentration versus distance breakthrough curves at $t=12months$ for the following conditions: (1) no-decay; (2) linear decay with $K=1/month$; and (3) nonlinear decay with $K=0.05\,(mg/L)^{1-\beta}/month$, and $\beta=0.6$.

Solution

The following Maple worksheet programs equations (11.12), (11.14), and (11.17), respectively for the three conditions.

```
> restart: V0:=40: Cin:=600: b:=5: u:=0.4: K:=0.05:
  n:=0.15: Dx:=1.: w:=10: T:=12: beta:=0.6:
  L:=sqrt(8*Dx*T): Xmin:=u*T-2*L: Xmax:=u*T+2*L:
  C0:=(x,t)->V0*Cin/(b*w*n*sqrt(4*Pi*Dx*t))
      *exp(-(x-u*t)^2/(4*Dx*t)):
  Clin:=(x,t)->V0*Cin/(b*w*n*sqrt(4*Pi*Dx*t))
      *exp(-(x-u*t)^2/(4*Dx*t)-K*t):
  Cnlin:=(x,t)->C0(x,t)
      *exp(-2*K*t*C0(x,t)^(beta-1)/(beta+1)):
  #(1) no decay
  G1:=plot(C0(x,T),x=Xmin...Xmax,color=black,
      legend=`No Decay`):
  #(2) linear decay
  G2:=plot(Clin(x,T),x=Xmin...Xmax,color=black,
      legend=`Linear Decay`,linestyle=3):
  #(3) nonlinear decay
  G3:=plot(Cnlin(x,T),x=Xmin...Xmax,color=black,
      legend=`Nonlinear Decay`,style=point):
  plots[display](G1,G2,G3,thickness=2,
      labeldirections=[HORIZONTAL,VERTICAL],
      symbol=box,labels=[`x (m)`,`C (mg/L)`],
      labelfont=[TIMES,ROMAN,16]);
```

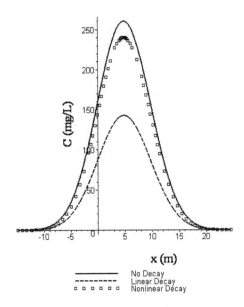

x (m)

————— No Decay
--------- Linear Decay
□ □ □ □ □ □ Nonlinear Decay

In this example, the nonlinear plume is somewhere between those of no decay and nonlinear decay.

Contaminant Transport and Linear Sorption

Changes in the concentration of contaminants traveling through aquifers can occur because of chemical reactions within the liquid phase, or because of the transfer of the solute to or from other phases, such as the solid matrix of the porous media, or the gas phase in the unsaturated zone. Among the many kinds of chemical or biological reactions that may occur are: *adsorption-desorption* reactions, acid-base reactions, solution-precipitation reactions, oxidation-reduction reactions, ion pairing or complexation, and microbial cell synthesis. In this section we focus on adsorption processes, which lend themselves better to hydrologic analysis. Other chemical reactions are part of the chemistry of natural waters and are outside the scope of this book.

Adsorption is the migration of charged dissolved contaminant ions to the soil grain surfaces. The surface of solids have an electrical charge due to isomorphous replacement, broken bonds, or lattice effects. The electrical charge is imbalanced and may be satisfied by adsorbing a charged ion. This phenomenon is especially important in clays, since they have a large surface area per unit volume and significant electrical charges at the surface. The adsorption may be relatively weak. It is essentially a physical process caused by van der Waals forces. The process may be reversible. As concentrations in the liquid phase decrease due to other transport mechanisms, a return of the ions to the liquid phase, or desorption, may occur (i.e., *reversible reaction*).

The effect of adsorption is to decrease the contaminant concentration in the liquid phase. The hydrologist is interested in the analysis and prediction of the concentration in the field for environmental analysis. Referring once again to a control volume in an aquifer (Figure 11.5), the mass conservation statement in the volume under adsorption is:

Net contaminant mass rate + change of mass within volume per unit time = mass rate loss due to adsorption

If we express the mass rate loss as the change in the mass of the chemical constituent adsorbed by the solid part of the porous media per unit mass of solids (i.e., concentration in the solid phase), then for a homogeneous aquifer with constant flow velocity, equation (11.11) becomes

$$\frac{\partial C}{\partial t} - D_x \frac{\partial^2 C}{\partial x^2} + u \frac{\partial C}{\partial x} = \frac{\rho_b}{n} \frac{\partial C_s}{\partial t} \tag{11.18}$$

where

C = concentration in the liquid phase (kg/m^3)
C_s = concentration in the solid phase (kg/kg)
ρ_b = dry bulk density of the porous media (kg/m^3)

$\partial C_s / \partial t$ is the rate at which the constituent is adsorbed ($kg/(kg.month)$), and $(\rho_b/n).\partial C_s / \partial t$ is the change in liquid-phase concentration in due to adsorption or desorption ($kg/(m^3.month)$).

It is commonly assumed that adsorption of contaminants in groundwater occur rapidly relative to the flow velocity. To express solid-phase concentration in terms of that in the liquid phase in equation (11.18), we note that the amount of contaminant that is adsorbed by the solids, or the concentration in the solid phase, is a function of the concentration in the liquid phase. That is $C_s = f(C)$. Therefore,

$$\frac{\partial C_s}{\partial t} = -\frac{\partial C_s}{\partial C} \cdot \frac{\partial C}{\partial t} \tag{11.19}$$

where

$\partial C_s / \partial C$ = contaminant partitioning between solids and solution

The *partitioning* of solutes between solid and liquid phases in an aquifer is determined in laboratory experiments. The results are commonly expressed in a graph, called the *isotherm* (i.e, experiments are conducted at constant temperature), showing solid concentration versus liquid concentration. Customarily, the results of adsorption experiments are plotted in double-logarithmic paper, and straight graphical relationships are commonly obtained. In such cases,

$$\log C_s = \beta \log C + \log K_d \Rightarrow C_s = K_d C^\beta \qquad (11.20)$$

where
   K_d, β = coefficients function of the substance and porous media

Equation (11.20) is called the *Freundlich sorption isotherm* (Fetter, 1993). The constant β is the slope of the logarithmic relation. If $\beta=1$ (i.e., 45° of slope in the logarithmic graph), then C_s versus C also plots as a straight line on an arithmetic graph. Such relationship is called a *linear isotherm*, and

$$\frac{dC_s}{dC} = K_d \qquad (11.21)$$

where
   K_d = *distribution coefficient* (m^3/kg)

K_d is a valid representation of the partitioning of contaminants between the solid and liquid phases if the partitions reactions are fast and reversible, and if the isotherm is linear. Fortunately many contaminants of interest approximately meet these requirements. Substituting equations (11.19) and (11.21) into equation (11.18) we obtain

$$\frac{\partial C}{\partial t} - D_x \frac{\partial^2 C}{\partial x^2} + u \frac{\partial C}{\partial x} = -\frac{\rho_b K_d}{n} \frac{\partial C}{\partial t} \qquad (11.22)$$

Now factorizing $\partial C/\partial t$,

$$\frac{\partial C}{\partial t} - \frac{D_x}{R} \frac{\partial^2 C}{\partial x^2} + \frac{u}{R} \frac{\partial C}{\partial x} = 0 \qquad (11.23)$$

where
   $R = 1 + (\rho_b/n).K_d$ = *retardation factor*

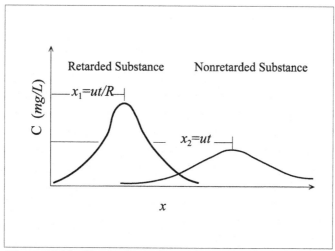

Figure 11.11: $C(\bullet, t)$ of Reactive and Non-reactive Substances

As the name implies, the effect of R is to retard the dispersion of a contaminant. By comparing the transport equation for a non-reactive contaminant, equation (11.11), with that for a reactive one, equation (11.23), one can easily observe that the reactive contaminant is governed by an equation whose dispersion coefficient and velocity coefficient, D_x and u respectively, are reduced by a factor of R. This phenomenon may be observed by comparing the concentration versus distance curves of two tracers, one reactive and one non-reactive, some time after being simultaneously released at a point in an aquifer. Figure 11.11 illustrates this experiment. At time t after the release, the non-reactive substance has a center of mass located at a distance $x_2 = ut$, whereas the reactive one has a center of mass located at a distance $x_1 = ut/R$. Thus, the mean contaminant velocity of the reactive contaminant is retarded by a factor of R. At the same time, the non-reactive contaminant has a greater dispersion around its center of mass and correspondingly a lower peak concentration (if the initial masses were the same). In comparison, the reactive contaminant exhibits less dispersion around its center of mass and a greater peak concentration. Thus, the dispersion coefficient of the reactive contaminant is reduced by a factor of R.

Information from C versus x curves may be used to approximate the value of R. Thus, if Figure 11.11 represents the results from such an experiment, clearly $u = x_2/t$, and $R = ut/x_1$. Retardation factors of about one, imply that the contaminant is non-reactive. The higher the value of R the more reactive or adsorbable the contaminant. Another approach to estimate R is via an experimental determination of the partition coefficient K_d (i.e., the isotherm). Values of K_d range from about zero for non-reactive contaminants to $1m^3/kg$ or more. This latter value would produce retardation factors between 5 and 10. For values of K_d greater than $1m^3/kg$, the solute is essentially immobile. Clays usually have the largest K_d values for specific inorganic solutes, due to the large surface areas and numerous ion exchange sites. Substances such as chloride may be only very weakly adsorbed. Sodium is weakly attenuated. Potassium, ammonia, magnesium, silicon, and iron are moderately attenuated. Lead, cadmium, mercury, and zinc can be strongly adsorbed.

For the hydrologist, the value of R represents the seriousness of a contamination problem in relation to project objectives. In a contamination assessment project, the lower the value of R, the more rapidly the contaminant may travel through the aquifer and the more serious is the pollution problem. In an aquifer restoration project, the higher the value of R, the more difficult is the contaminant extraction. Since a good portion of the contaminant is in the solid phase, conventional hydraulic gradient control techniques, such as pump-and-treat methods, are not likely to be successful. Other techniques such as the injection of *surfactants* that cause the return of the contaminant to the liquid phase should be attempted before any hydraulic control.

Example 11.7
Two tracers, one reactive and one non-reactive, are simultaneously injected through a well into an aquifer. One month later, the center of mass of the reactive contaminant is located $6m$ from the well, and the center of mass of the non-reactive contaminant is located $20m$ from the well. If the aquifer porosity is 0.3 and the dry bulk density is 1,600 kg/m^3, estimate the retardation coefficient and the partition coefficient.

Solution
We first estimate the mean pore velocity from the non-reactive plume:

$$u = \frac{x_2}{t} = \frac{20m}{1month} = 20m/month$$

The retardation coefficient is then estimated from the reactive plume:

$$R = \frac{ut}{x_1} = \frac{20m/month \times 1month}{6m} = 3.33$$

Finally the partition coefficient is given by

$$R=1+\frac{\rho_b}{n}K_d \Rightarrow K_d=\frac{(R-1)n}{\rho_b}=\frac{(3.33-1)\times0.3}{1,600\frac{kg}{m^3}}=4.37\times10^{-4}\frac{m^3}{kg}=0.44\frac{mL}{g}$$

Synthetic organic contaminants in solution may be adsorbed by the organic carbon in the soil. An important consideration in this case is the solubility of the organic compound in water. The relative tendency of an organic compound to remain dissolved in water, rather than to be adsorbed onto soil organic carbon is related to the *octanol-water partition coefficient* of that chemical, which is the tendency of a chemical to be dissolved into either water or *n*-octanol when shaken in a solution of the two. The *soil-water partition coefficient*, K_w, can be estimated from either the water solubility or the octanol-water partition coefficient. Table 11.3 gives the soil-water partition coefficient for several organic chemicals that are potential groundwater contaminants. Thus, the value of K_d for an organic compound in a specific soil is estimated a

$$K_d=K_w f \qquad (11.24)$$

where
   K_w=soil-water partition coefficient (m^3/kg)
   f=weight fraction of organic carbon in the soil (e.g., 0.01)

In cases of contamination by a source of multiple substances, each with a particular retardation coefficient or partition coefficient, there will be a number of solute fronts. The resulting plume may be a complex combination of different contaminants segregated according to their mobility properties.

Contaminant Transport and Nonlinear Sorption
Consider the problem of contaminant dispersion in a long aquifer subject to a general nonlinear Freundlich isotherm of the form given by equation (11.20). In this case $\beta \neq 1$ and K_d has the dimensions of $(mg/L)^{-\beta}$. Thus equation (11.18) becomes

$$\frac{\partial C}{\partial t}-D\frac{\partial^2 C}{\partial x^2}+u\frac{\partial C}{\partial x}+rC^{\beta-1}\frac{\partial C}{\partial t}=0, \qquad r=\frac{\rho_b K_d \beta}{n} \qquad (11.25)$$

An approximate analytical solution to this problem is given by (Serrano, 2003c)

$$C(x,\ t) \approx \frac{Me^{-\frac{(x-u\varphi(x,\ t))^2}{4D_x\varphi(x,\ t)}}}{A_v\sqrt{4\pi D_x\varphi(x,\ t)}}, \qquad \varphi(x,t) = \int_0^t \frac{d\tau}{1+rC_0(x,\ \tau)^{\beta-1}} \qquad (11.26)$$

where C_0 is the solution to the advective-dispersive equation subject to no decay (given by equation (11.12)), and φ must be evaluated using numerical integration.

Example 11.8: Effect of Nonlinear Sorption on Plume Shape

$100 m^3$ of a solution of a substance with a concentration of $1000 mg/L$ were injected through a well in an unconfined aquifer $10m$ in thickness. The mean groundwater pore velocity is $0.1 m/month$, the porosity is 0.2, the soil dry bulk density is $1,000\ kg/m^3$, and the dispersion coefficient for the tracer is $0.1\ m^2/month$. Assume the contaminant will mix completely through the entire thickness of the aquifer, and across a width of $10m$ perpendicular to the flow. Write a program to simulate the contaminant spatial distribution $360 months$ after injection, according to the following scenarios: (1) No sorption; (2) under a linear sorption isotherm with $K_d = 1 \times 10^{-6}(L/mg)$; (3) under a nonlinear sorption isotherm with $K_d = 1 \times 10^{-7}(L/mg)^{-\beta}$ and $\beta = 0.8$; and (4) under a nonlinear sorption isotherm with $Kd = 1 \times 10^{-7}(mg/L)^{-\beta}$ and $\beta = 1.2$.

Solution

The following Maple worksheet illustrates the simulations. Note that ρ_b is multiplied by 10^3 to transform it from kg/m^3 to mg/L. For part (1), equation (11.12) is programmed; for part (2), equation (11.23) is used; and for parts (3) and (4) equation (11.26) is applied for their corresponding values of β, using Maple numerical integration routines for $\varphi(x,\ t)$. Note that for part (3) C is calculated at 1-m intervals, instead of continuously. This is necessary to reduce computing time because when $\beta < 0$, the calculation of φ becomes too slow. All plumes are plotted in a single figure for comparison purposes.

The comparison between linear $(R = 1 + rb)$ and non-linear profiles is only qualitative since the dimensions of K_d depend on β. Yet it is possible to see that when $\beta < 1$ and $C > 1$ the nonlinear plume suffers retardation of the processes of advection and dispersion, but not as severe as that of the linear one. This retardation reduces the velocity of the plume center of mass and the plume variance, the degree of which is controlled by the magnitude of β. The same observations related to non-linear decay discussed previously are applicable here: If one interprets Figure 11.11

as a Freundlich isotherm with β<1, portions of the nonlinear plume with
C>1 suffer less sorption (i.e., less retardation, or more mobility) than that
of the linear plume.

```
> restart: V0:=100: Cin:=1000: b:=10: u:=0.1: Kd:=1E-6:
  n:=0.2: Dx:=0.1: w:=10: T:=360: rhob:=1000:
  R:=1+rhob*10^3*Kd/n: r:=rhob*10^3*Kd*beta/n:
  Xmin:=-10: Xmax:=60:
  C0:=(x,t)->V0*Cin/(b*w*n*sqrt(4*Pi*Dx*t))
       *exp(-(x-u*t)^2/(4*Dx*t)):
  Clin:=(x,t)->V0*Cin/(b*w*n*sqrt(4*Pi*Dx/R*t))
       *exp(-(x-u/R*t)^2/(4*Dx/R*t)):
  Phi:=x->evalf(Int(1/((1+r*C0(x,tau)^(beta-1))),tau=0..T)):
  CNlin:=(x,t)->V0*Cin/(b*w*n*sqrt(4*Pi*Dx*Phi(x)))
       *exp(-(x-u*Phi(x))^2/(4*Dx*Phi(x))):
  #(1)no sorption
  G1:=plot(C0(x,T),x=Xmin...Xmax,color=black,
       legend=`No Sorption`):
  #(2)linear Isotherm
  G2:=plot(Clin(x,T),x=Xmin...Xmax,color=black,
       legend=`Linear Isotherm`,linestyle=3):
  #(3)nonlinear sorption, beta=0.8
  beta:=0.8:
  for i from -10 to Xmax do
    c1[i]:=evalf(CNlin(i)):
  end do:
  CN:=[seq([i,c1[i]],i=-10..Xmax)]:
  G3:=plot(CN,color=black,style=point,symbol=circle,
       legend=`Nonlinear Sorption, beta=0.8`):
  #(4)nonlinear sorption, beta=1.2
  beta:=1.2:
  G4:=plot(CNlin(x,T),x=Xmin...Xmax,color=black,
       linestyle=2,legend=`Nonlinear Sorption, beta=1.2`):
  plots[display](G1,G2,G3,G4,thickness=2,
       labeldirections=[HORIZONTAL,VERTICAL],
       symbol=box,labels=[`x (m)`,`C (mg/L)`],
       labelfont=[TIMES,ROMAN,16]);
```

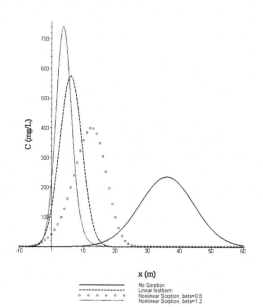

x (m)

No Sorption
Linear Isotherm
Nonlinear Sorption, beta=0.8
Nonlinear Sorption, beta=1.2

This example also shows that when $\beta>1$ and $C>1$ the nonlinear plume suffers retardation of the processes of advection and dispersion that are more pronounced than that of the linear one. This occurs because in this region of the isotherm the nonlinear plume suffers more sorption than that of the linear one. When $C<1$, the effect of β on plume shape with respect to the linear plume is expected to be the opposite of that when $C>1$ as a result of the nonlinear relationship between sorption and concentration. Finally, the simulations show the well-known phenomenon that linear plumes are symmetric with respect to their center of mass, whereas nonlinear ones are not. Thus (11.26) reproduces the well-known features of Freundlich sorption, namely the sharp leading edges and the "tailed" hind edges reported in field studies.

From the above example, we observe that a plume traveling under nonlinear Freundlich sorption loses its symmetry with respect of its center of mass thus resulting in a sharp front tail accompanied by a prolonged back tail. In addition, the Freundlich plume suffers retardation of the processes of advection and dispersion, the degree of which is controlled by the magnitude of the nonlinear parameter β and by the position in the isotherm. Other representations of nonlinear reactions are possible. For example, in concert with a Freundlich model, a plume traveling under nonlinear *Langmuir sorption* experiences a decrease in the velocity of the plume center of mass, and a corresponding increase in the magnitude of the maximum concentration with respect to the no sorption plume (Serrano, 2003c). This reduction in the center of mass, and corresponding increase in maximum concentration, is not as drastic as that of the linear plume. The Langmuir plume also exhibits the same non-symmetrical features of the Freundlich. A plume propagating under *reversible kinetic sorption* experiences a partial contaminant return to the *mobile phase*, the degree of which is controlled by the magnitude of the backward constant relative to that of the forward constant. If in addition the forward reaction is nonlinear, the shape of the plume may be significantly re-scaled. As before, the degree of plume re-scaling depends on the magnitude of the nonlinear parameter β. On the other hand, the direction of plume re-scaling, either up or down, is controlled by the position in which a particular plume region stands in the solid-phase liquid-phase relationship (Serrano, 2003c).

Modeling Groundwater Pollution in Two Dimensions

For the case of linear plumes, solutions to equation (11.23) are mathematically identical to those of equation (11.11), when the dispersion coefficient and velocity terms are reduced by a factor of R. To extend the one-dimensional models to the problem of two-dimensional (plan view) contaminant dispersion in a homogeneous aquifer, a corresponding advection-dispersion equation subject to degradation and adsorption should be considered. A mass conservation statement should include dispersion in the y as well as in the x direction. By analogy with equations (11.13) and (11.23), the two-dimensional dispersion equation is given by

$$\frac{\partial C}{\partial t} - \frac{D_x}{R}\frac{\partial^2 C}{\partial x^2} - \frac{D_y}{R}\frac{\partial^2 C}{\partial y^2} + \frac{u}{R}\frac{\partial C}{\partial x} + KC = 0 \tag{11.27}$$

where
    C=average-over-depth concentration (mg/L)
    D_y= transverse (y direction) dispersion coefficient ($m^2/month$)
    y=plan view distance perpendicular to the flow (m)

We remark that the concentration depicted by equation (11.27) is the liquid-phase solute concentration averaged over the contaminated depth of the aquifer. If the entire aquifer thickness is contaminated (i.e., complete dilution over the depth), then the contaminated depth is simply $b \times n$. Another point to remember is that the x axis has been selected to coincide with the direction of the pore velocity u. If an instantaneous spill of a substance of mass M occurs, the solution to equation (11.27) is

$$C(x,\ t) = \frac{M}{bn\sqrt{4\pi\frac{D_x}{R}t}\sqrt{4\pi\frac{D_y}{R}t}}\, e^{-\frac{(x-\frac{u}{R}t)^2}{4\frac{D_x}{R}t} - \frac{y^2}{4\frac{D_y}{R}t} - Kt} \tag{11.28}$$

Equation (11.28) may be used to predict concentration as a function of space and time. Often the presentation of the results are in graphical form. For instance, a concentration contour map (i.e., a graph of lines of equal concentration) may be obtained by keeping the desired simulation time constant while calculating concentration as a function of (x, y). In practice this is accomplished via a computer program that sweeps the (x, y) field and calculates C while keeping t constant. The numerical results are linked to a standard contouring software and plotted. The contour map gives a visual representation of the plume at the desired time. By repeating the procedure for several future times, the hydrologist may estimate the space-time evolution of the contaminant plume. The visual representation of the contamination evolution helps in the design of monitoring networks, in the construction of containment or remedial actions, and in the adoption of important aquifer management decisions.

Table 11.3: Soil-Water Partition Coefficient, K_w, for Some Common Organic Compounds

Compound	$K_w(m^3/kg\times10^{-3})$	Mobility Class
1,4-Dioxane	1	very high
acetone	1	very high
tetrahydrofuran	1	very high
ethyl ether	8	very high
benzyl alcohol	12	very high
2-methylphenol	15	very high
phenol	27	very high
chloroform	34	very high
1,2-dichloroethane	36	very high
chloroethane	42	very high
chloromethane	43	very high
1,1,2-trichloroethane	49	very high
benzoic acid	64	high
benzene	97	high
trichloroethene	152	moderate
carbon tetrachloride	232	moderate
toluene	242	moderate
tetrachloroethylene	303	moderate
chlorobenzene	318	moderate
1,2-dichlorobenzene	343	moderate
1,4-dichlorobenzene	594	low
ethyl benzene	622	low
pentachlorofenol	900	low
1,2,4-trichlorobenzene	1080	low
naphtalene	1300	low
dibenzofuran	2140	slight
hexachloroethane	2450	slight
hexachlorobenzene	3910	slight
fluorene	5835	slight
endosulfan II	19623	slight
endosulfan sulfate	22788	immobile
anthracene	26000	immobile
chlordane	53200	immobile
pyrene	63400	immobile
PCB-1254	63914	immobile
benzo(a)anthracene	125719	immobile
4,4'-DDT	238000	immobile

Source: Roy, W.R., and Griffin, RA., 1985. *Mobility of Organic Solvents in Water-Saturated Soil Materials*. Envr. Geol. Water Sci., 7:241-247.

Example 11.9: Modeling Plume Two-Dimensional Spatial Distribution

$100\,m^3$ of a solution of a substance with a concentration of $1000\,mg/L$ were injected through a well in an unconfined aquifer $10m$ in thickness. The mean groundwater pore velocity is $1.0\,m/month$, the porosity is 0.2, and the soil dry bulk density is $1,000\,kg/m^3$. The longitudinal dispersion coefficient (i.e., parallel to the groundwater flow direction) is $1.0\,m^2/month$. Assuming that the contaminant will mix completely through the entire thickness of the aquifer, that the transverse dispersion coefficient is 10% of the longitudinal value, that there is no decay, and no sorption, write a program to simulate the contaminant spatial distribution $120\,months$ after injection (1) as a three-dimensional plot, and (2) as a plan view, two-dimensional, contour plot.

Solution

The following Maple worksheet programs equation (11.28). A plotting window $(X_{max}-X_{min},\ Y_{max}-Y_{min})$ is calculated based on an estimation of the area covered by the plume at a given time. The three-dimensional plot in part (1) provides a range in contaminant concentration, which is then used in selecting concentration contours (i.e., lines of equal concentration) every 10 mg/L in part (2).

```
> restart: with(plots):
  V0:=100: Cin:=1000: b:=10: u:=1:
  n:=0.2: Dx:=1: Dy:=0.1*Dx: T:=120: rhob:=1000:
  K:=0: R:=1: M:=V0*Cin:
  #Calculate the size of the plotting window
  Lx:=sqrt(8*Dx*T): Xmin:=u*T-2*Lx: Xmax:=u*T+2*Lx:
  Ly:=sqrt(4*Dy*T): Ymin:=-2*Ly: Ymax:=2*Ly:
  X:=(x,t)->exp(-(x-u/R*t)^2/(4*Dx/R*t)-K*t)/sqrt(4*Pi*Dx/R*t):
  Y:=(y,t)->exp(-y^2/(4*Dy/R*t))/sqrt(4*Pi*Dy/R*t):
  C:=(x,y,t)->M/(b*n)*X(x,t)*Y(y,t):
  #(1)3D plot
  plot3d(C(x,y,T),x=Xmin..Xmax,y=Ymin..Ymax,
      labels=[`x (m)`,`y (m)`,`C (mg/L)`],
      labeldirections=[HORIZONTAL,HORIZONTAL,VERTICAL],
      labelfont=[TIMES,ROMAN,16],axes=normal,
      orientation=[-120,60],shading=ZGRAYSCALE);
```

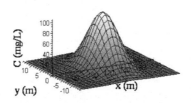

```
> #(2)2D contour plot
  contourplot(C(x,y,T),x=Xmin..Xmax,y=Ymin..Ymax,
      labels=[`x (m)`,`y (m)`],
      labeldirections=[HORIZONTAL,VERTICAL],color=black,
      labelfont=[TIMES,ROMAN,16],scaling=constrained,
      contours=[10,20,30,40,50,60,70,80,90,100]);
```

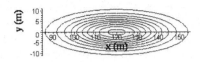

Example 11.9 assumed that the small scale dispersion coefficient is adequate to simulate field scale plumes. However, from equation (11.7) we learned that field scale dispersion coefficients are functions of time after a spill and aquifer heterogeneity, as represented by the statistical properties of aquifer transmissivity and pore velocity. Hence, if field-scale dispersion coefficient are used , equation (11.27) becomes

$$\frac{\partial C}{\partial t}-\frac{\bar{D}_x}{R}\frac{\partial^2 C}{\partial x^2}-\frac{\bar{D}_y}{R}\frac{\partial^2 C}{\partial y^2}+\frac{u}{R}\frac{\partial C}{\partial x}+KC=0 \qquad (11.29)$$

where
$\bar{D}_x(t)$ = field-scale longitudinal dispersion coefficient (equation (11.7))
$\bar{D}_y(t)$ = field-scale transverse dispersion coefficient (equation (11.7))

Once again the terms *longitudinal* and *transverse* refer to x and y directions, respectively, when the x coincides with the regional groundwater flow direction, u, and y is perpendicular to it. For an instantaneous point spill of mass M at $x=0, y=0$, and $t=0$, the solution to equation (11.29) is given by (Serrano, 1996)

$$C(x, t)=\frac{M}{bn}X(x, t)Y(y, t)e^{-Kt}$$

$$X(x, t)=\frac{e^{-\frac{\left(x-\frac{u}{R}t\right)^2}{4\frac{\varphi_x(t)}{R}}}}{\sqrt{4\pi\frac{\varphi_x(t)}{R}}}, \quad Y(y, t)=\frac{e^{-\frac{y^2}{4\frac{\varphi_y(t)}{R}}}}{\sqrt{4\pi\frac{\varphi_y(t)}{R}}} \qquad (11.30)$$

where
$\varphi_x(t)$, $\varphi_y(t)$ = time integrals of equation (11.7) given as

$$\varphi_x(t)=D_x t+\sigma_u^2\frac{t^2}{2}, \quad \varphi_y(t)=D_y+\frac{c\sigma_u^2 t^2}{2l^2} \qquad (11.31)$$

Example 11.10: Field-Scale Plume Spatial Distribution

In Example 11.9 it is suspected that aquifer heterogeneity significantly affects field-scale plume distribution. Modify the model and rerun the simulations if the standard deviation of the pore velocity is $0.1m/month$, and the transmissivity correlation length is $10m$ (i.e., a highly heterogeneous aquifer).

Solution

The program now uses equations (11.30) and (11.31) to forecast the contaminant spatial distribution.

```
> restart: with(plots):
  V0:=100: Cin:=1000: b:=10: u:=1:
  n:=0.2: Dx:=1: Dy:=0.1*Dx: T:=120: rhob:=1000:
  K:=0.0: R:=1: M:=V0*Cin: sigmau:=0.1: l:=10: c:=2.:
  #Field dispersion coeficients
  Phix:=t->Dx*t+sigmau^2*t^2/2:
  Phiy:=t->Dy*t+c*sigmau^2*t^2/(2*l^2):
  #Calculate the size of the plotting window
  Lx:=sqrt(8*Phix(T)): Xmin:=u*T-2*Lx: Xmax:=u*T+2*Lx:
  Ly:=sqrt(4*Phiy(T)): Ymin:=-2*Ly: Ymax:=2*Ly:
  X:=(x,t)->exp(-(x-u/R*t)^2/(4*Phix(t)/R)-K*t)
      /sqrt(4*Pi*Phix(t)/R):
  Y:=(y,t)->exp(-y^2/(4*Phiy(t)/R))/sqrt(4*Pi*Phiy(t)/R):
  C:=(x,y,t)->M/(b*n)*X(x,t)*Y(y,t):
  #(1) 3D plot
  plot3d(C(x,y,T),x=Xmin..Xmax,y=Ymin..Ymax,
      labels=[`x (m)`,`y (m)`,`C (mg/L)`],
      labeldirections=[HORIZONTAL,HORIZONTAL,VERTICAL],
      labelfont=[TIMES,ROMAN,16],axes=normal,
      orientation=[-120,60],shading=ZGRAYSCALE);
```

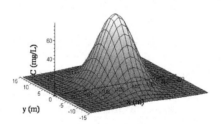

```
> #(2) 2D contour plot
  contourplot(C(x,y,T),x=Xmin..Xmax,y=Ymin..Ymax,
      labels=[`x (m)`,`y (m)`],
      labeldirections=[HORIZONTAL,VERTICAL],color=black,
      labelfont=[TIMES,ROMAN,16],scaling=constrained,
      contours=[10,20,30,40,50,60,70,80,90,100]);
```

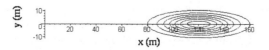

Taking into consideration aquifer heterogeneity, the field-scale plume in this example contaminates a larger portion of the aquifer, with a lower concentration magnitude, than the small-scale one in Example 11.9.

Applications to Spills Originated in the Unsaturated Zone

More complex solutions of equation (11.27) respond to situations where the contaminant is introduced in the aquifer in ways different from an instantaneous spill (see Charbeneau, 2000 for more details). This *initial condition*, as it is usually called in mathematical modeling, includes cases where the contaminant is released over a long time in the aquifer, rather than "instantaneously" (e.g., a sanitary landfill leachate); cases where the original spill occupies a large area (i.e., a non-point source); or cases where the spill originated in the unsaturated zone and subsequently propagated in the saturated zone. In the latter case, the equation of dispersion in the unsaturated zone is analogous to equation (11.27), except that the variable water content, rather than a constant porosity, is imbedded in the equation. In addition, the advection term is constituted by the infiltration from rainfall and points downward in the vertical direction. Even more difficult groundwater pollution problems arise in the presence of layered soils, each with distinct properties. In such cases the coupling of several equations, one per layer, is necessary. Solutions to those systems of equations are difficult to generalize. Finally, contamination problems where fractured flow exists are difficult to analyze quantitatively at the present state of the art, since the fundamental assumption of laminar flow is no longer valid.

In summary, initial conditions or contamination sources in groundwater may be classified as follows: (1) According to the hydrologic zone of origin, unsaturated-zone sources or saturated zone sources. (2) According to the timing of the source, *instantaneous spills* or *stationary spills*. (3) According to the area covered by the source, *point sources* or *non-point sources*.

Most groundwater pollution models are in the form of numerical solutions. For additional details see Pinder and Gray (1987); Bear and Veruijt (1987). For the use of models in the design of remedial actions see Boutwell et al. (1986). These models usually require expertise in numerical modeling and are usually inaccessible to the average applied hydrologist. Numerical models need the generation of grid data at discrete points in an aquifer. This usually requires thousands of field measurements and input data tasks with their associated massive matrix calculations, computing time, and numerical debugging. An additional difficulty is that most numerical codes have been written for either the unsaturated zone or the saturated zone. The communication between the two is not simple. This precludes the hydrologist from studying a soil spill that subsequently propagates in the saturated zone. Nevertheless, a large variety of numerical codes have been implemented with the addition of friendly end-user interfaces and graphical post-processor routines. With these improvements and the ever increasing speed of digital processors, numerical codes have become the models of choice (Zheng and Bennet, 1995). One of the most popular numerical models for groundwater flow and pollution is MODFLOW (Waterloo Hydrogeologic, 2004).

In this section we attempt a description of contaminant propagation in the unsaturated zone. For that purpose consider the case of a shallow aquifer contaminated by an instantaneous and point source of mass M at $t=0$. Assume that the soil is homogeneous and isotropic in the dispersion coefficient; the contaminant loss due to evapotranspiration is negligible; the concentration at the water table does not affect that in the unsaturated soil; the plume center of mass moves as a result of advection from recharge; and that dispersion in the horizontal direction is greater than that in the vertical. The governing differential equation is (Serrano, 1995b)

$$\frac{\partial C'}{\partial t} - \frac{D'_x}{R}\frac{\partial^2 C'}{\partial x^2} - \frac{D'_y}{R}\frac{\partial C'}{\partial y^2} - \frac{D'_z}{R}\frac{\partial C'}{\partial z^2} + \frac{R_g}{\theta R}\frac{\partial C'}{\partial z} + KC' = 0$$

$$-\infty < x < \infty, \quad -\infty < y < \infty, \quad -W < z < S_d, \quad 0 < t \tag{11.32}$$

$$C'(\pm\infty, \pm\infty, \pm\infty, t) = 0; \quad C'(x, y, z, 0) = M\delta(x)\delta(y)\delta(z)$$

where
C' = unsaturated soil solute concentration (mg/kg, or kg/m^3)
x, y = horizontal distance from the spill (m), with x parallel to the
    regional groundwater flow direction, u (m)
z = vertical distance from the spill, positive upwards (m)
S_d = source depth below the ground surface (m)
W = depth of water table (m)
t = time after the spill (*months*)
$D'_x = D'_y$ = unsaturated horizontal dispersion coefficient ($m^2/month$)
D'_z = unsaturated-zone vertical dispersion coefficient ($m^2/month$)
R_g = mean monthly recharge from rainfall ($m/month$)
θ = unsaturated soil volumetric water content
M = initial contaminant mass (kg)

K=contaminant decay rate ($month^{-1}$)

R=unsaturated soil retardation factor given by(see equation (11.23))

$$R=1+\frac{\rho_b}{\theta}K_d \tag{11.33}$$

where

K_d= distribution coefficient (m^3/kg)

ρ_b = dry bulk density (kg/m^3)

Notice equation (11.32) uses the soil water content, rather than the porosity, since the soil is unsaturated (see Chapter 4). This is a variable quantity which needs to be approximated to a constant average, such as the soil field capacity, or an effective porosity, if we are to retain a simple model. This approximation has been found to be reasonable in some studies (Charbeneau, 2000). The solution to equation (11.32) is given by (Serrano, 1988a)

$$C'(x,\ y,\ z\ t)=MX'(x,\ t)Y'(y,\ t)Z'(z,\ t)\ e^{-Kt}, \quad -W\leq z\leq S_d$$

$$X'(x,\ t)=\frac{e^{-\frac{x^2}{4\frac{D'_x}{R}t}}}{\sqrt{4\pi\frac{D'_x}{R}t}},\ Y'(y,\ t)=\frac{e^{-\frac{y^2}{4\frac{D'_y}{R}t}}}{\sqrt{4\pi\frac{D'_y}{R}t}},\ Z'(z,\ t)=\frac{e^{-\frac{(z+\frac{R_g}{\theta R}t+S_d)^2}{4\frac{D'_z}{R}t}}}{\sqrt{4\pi\frac{D'_z}{R}t}} \tag{11.34}$$

Equation (11.34) may be used to forecast concentration contours in the unsaturated zone between the ground surface and the water table. The liquid phase of an initial point source in the unsaturated zone will spread radially and its center of mass will travel vertically due to recharge. With time the contaminant will become a non-point source at the interface with the saturated zone, where it will propagate according to advection and dispersion, as described before. As before, we may also consider retardation, decay, and scale dependency in the dispersion coefficients due to aquifer heterogeneity in the hydraulic conductivity. Thus, the governing equation of contaminant propagation in the saturated zone is given by equation (11.29), subject to a distributed source at the water table:

$$\frac{\partial C}{\partial t} - \frac{\overline{D}_x}{R}\frac{\partial^2 C}{\partial x^2} - \frac{\overline{D}_y}{R}\frac{\partial^2 C}{\partial y^2} + \frac{u}{R}\frac{\partial C}{\partial x} + KC = f_m C'(x, y, -W, t) \qquad (11.35)$$

where

$f_m = \rho_b \times 10^{-3}/n =$ conversion from mg of contaminant per kg of soil to mg per L of solution (kg/L)

$b =$ saturated zone thickness (m)

The right-hand side of equation (11.35) represents the contaminant forcing function given by the unsaturated zone liquid-phase concentration equation (11.34) evaluated at the water table depth $z=-W$. The solution to equation (11.35) is given by (Serrano, 1995b)

$$C(x, y, t) = \frac{f_m}{b} e^{-kt} \int_0^t \overline{X}(x, t, \tau)\overline{Y}(y, t, \tau)Z'(-W, \tau)d\tau$$

$$\overline{X}(x,t,\tau) = \frac{e^{-\frac{[x-\frac{u}{R}(t-\tau)]^2}{\frac{4}{R}[\varphi_x(t-\tau)+D_x'\tau]}}}{\sqrt{\frac{4\pi}{R}[\varphi_x(t-\tau)+D_x'\tau]}}, \quad \overline{Y}(y,t,\tau) = \frac{e^{-\frac{y^2}{\frac{4}{R}[\varphi_y(t-\tau)+D_y'\tau]}}}{\sqrt{\frac{4\pi}{R}[\varphi_y(t-\tau)+D_y'\tau]}} \qquad (11.36)$$

where φ_x, φ_y are given by equation (11.31), Z' is given by equation (11.34), and the time integral must be solved numerically.

Example 11.11: Unsaturated-Saturated Zone Transport Modeling

An underground storage tank buried $0.5m$ below the ground surface released an unknown quantity of a contaminant. Field investigation revealed that the contaminated soil included a surface area of $5m \times 5m$ and a depth of $0.5m$ with an average concentration of $400mg/kg$. Using the data in Table 11.4, (1) plot the unsaturated zone concentration contours (mg/kg) at $t=6months$ after the spill, and (2) the plan view concentration contours (mg/L) in the saturated zone at $t=24months$ after the spill.

Solution

The following Maple program illustrates the solution. For part (1), equation (11.34) is programmed. Before the contour plotting routine is called, a breakthrough curve $C'(0, 0, z, t=6)$, $-W \le z \le S_d$ (not shown) is plotted to identify appropriate contour-line values. Then contour lines from 18 to $24mg/kg$ are plotted at $1mg/kg$ intervals. The contour map shows a vertical section of the soil at $y=0$. Notice the plume center of mass has descended from it initial value located $0.5m$ below the ground surface. For part (2), equations (11.31) and (11.36) are programmed. Before the contour plotting routine is called, a breakthrough curve $C(x, 0, t=6)$ (not shown) is plotted to identify appropriate contour-line values. Then contour lines from 5 to $35mg/L$ are plotted at $5mg/L$ intervals. The time integral in equation (11,36) is easily solved with the evalf(Int(,)) command, which has access to several quadrature routines. The contour map shows a plan view of the concentration spatial distribution at $t=6months$ after the spill. Observe that the center of mass of the plume has slightly moved down gradient. However, the plume center will remain close to the origin for a long time until the distributed contaminant load coming from the unsaturated zone has completely receded. Only then the plume will begin to move significantly away from the origin. Of course this depends on the parameter values and in the case of substantial retardation the contaminant shall remain in the immobile phase.

Table 11.4: Soil and Aquifer Data for Examples 11.11 and 11.12

UNSATURATED ZONE	Name	Value
Horizontal Dispersion Coefficient	$D_x'=D_y'$	$1.0\,m^2/month$
Vertical Dispersion Coefficient	D_z'	$0.1D_x'$
Soil Porosity	n	0.1
Recharge from Rainfall	R_g	$0.01\,m/month$
Water Table Depth	W	$1.0m$
Source Depth	S_d	$0.5m$
Distribution Coefficient	K_d	$1\times10^{-6}m^3/kg$
Decay Rate	K	$0.0/month$
Dry Bulk Density	ρ_b	$1,600\,kg/m^3$
SATURATED ZONE	**Name**	**Value**
Longitudinal Dispersion Coefficient	D_x	$0.1\,m^2/month$
Transverse Dispersion Coefficient	D_y	$0.1D_x$
Seepage (pore) Velocity	u	$0.2m/month$
Pore Velocity Variance	σ_u^2	$0.1\,(m/month)^2$
Transmissivity Correlation Length	l	$10.0m$
Aquifer Thickness	b	$10.0m$

The first edition of this book included the KYSPILL software, which executed solutions of the contaminant transport equation in the saturated zone and the saturated zone according to various initial conditions. With the advances in computing technology, programming and execution of these equations is easily accomplished by using a standard mathematics software, such as Maple. For many practical situations in groundwater pollution modeling, the use of specialized software is no longer necessary, except in complex contamination scenarios.

```
> restart: with(plots):
  Dxp:=1: Dzp:=0.1*Dxp: n:=0.1: Rg:=0.01:
  W:=1.0: Sd:=0.5: T:=6: K:=0.0: Kd:=1E-6:
  rhob:=1600: R:=1+rhob*Kd/n: Dyp:=Dxp:
  Cin:=400: V0:=5*5*0.5: M:=Cin*V0:
  #(1) Unsaturated zone module
  Xp:=(x,t)->exp(-x^2/(4*Dxp/R*t))/sqrt(4*Pi*Dxp/R*t):
  Yp:=(y,t)->exp(-y^2/(4*Dyp/R*t))/sqrt(4*Pi*Dyp/R*t):
  Zp:=(z,t)->exp(-(z+Rg/R/n*t-Sd)^2/(4*Dzp/R*t))
      /sqrt(4*Pi*Dzp/R*t):
  Cp:=(x,y,z,t)->M*Xp(x,t)*Yp(y,t)*Zp(z,t)*exp(-K*t):
  #Initial plot to determine contour values
  plot(Cp(0,0,z,T),z=-W..Sd):
> #Unsaturated zone profile contour plot (mg/kg)
  Lxp:=sqrt(8*Dxp*T): Xpmin:=-2*Lxp: Xpmax:=2*Lxp:
  contourplot(Cp(x,0,z,T),x=Xpmin..Xpmax,z=-W..Sd,
      labels=[`x (m)`,`z (m)`],
      labeldirections=[HORIZONTAL,VERTICAL],color=black,
      contours=[18,19,20,21,22,23,24],
      labelfont=[TIMES,ROMAN,16],scaling=constrained,axes=boxed);
```

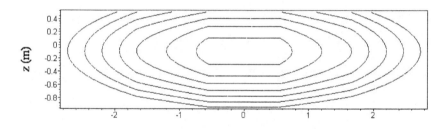

x (m)

```
  #Field dispersion coeficients for the saturated zone
  Phix:=t->Dx*t+sigmau^2*t^2/2:
  Phiy:=t->Dy*t+c*sigmau^2*t^2/(2*1^2):
  X:=(x,t,tau)->exp(-(x-u/R*(t-tau))^2/(4*Phix(t-tau)/R+Dxp/R*tau))
      /sqrt(4*Pi*(Phix(t-tau)/R+Dxp/R*tau)):
  Y:=(y,t,tau)->exp(-y^2/(4*Phiy(t-tau)/R+Dyp/R*tau))
      /sqrt(4*Pi*(Phiy(t-tau)/R+Dyp/R*tau)):
  G:=(x,y,t,tau)->fm*M*X(x,t,tau)*Y(y,t,tau)
      *Zp(-W,tau)*exp(-K*t):
  C:=(x,y)->evalf(Int(G(x,y,T,tau),tau=0..T)):
  Lx:=sqrt(8*Phix(T)): Xmin:=-2*Lx: Xmax:=4*Lx:
  Ly:=sqrt(8*Phiy(T)): Ymin:=-4*Ly: Ymax:=4*Ly:
  #Initial plot to determine contour values
  plot(C(x,0),x=Xmin..Xmax);
> #Saturated zone plan view contours (mg/L)
  contourplot(C(x,y),x=Xmin..Xmax,y=Ymin..Ymax,
      labels=[`x (m)`,`y (m)`],
      labeldirections=[HORIZONTAL,VERTICAL],color=black,
      labelfont=[TIMES,ROMAN,16],scaling=constrained,axes=boxed,
      contours=[25,50,75,100,125,150,175,200,225,250],
      numpoints=3000);
```

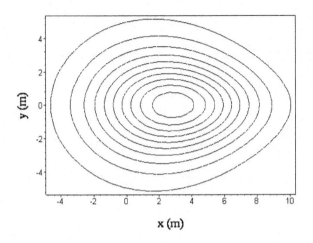

x (m)

For more details on the theory of dispersion in unsaturated soils, see Charbeneau (2000) and Fetter (1993). Until now we have considered instantaneous spills. Another scenario of interest is the case of stationary spills, that is when a contaminant is released in the soil or the aquifer over a long time. Assuming that the soil is initially uncontaminated, and that a point source is introduced continuously at the origin at a rate $C_i q$, where C_i is contaminant concentration at the source and q the flow rate, the governing equation of contaminant dispersion in an unsaturated soil is, from equation (11.32),

$$\frac{\partial C'}{\partial t} - \frac{D_x'}{R}\frac{\partial^2 C'}{\partial x^2} - \frac{D_y'}{R}\frac{\partial C'}{\partial y^2} - \frac{D_z'}{R}\frac{\partial C'}{\partial z^2} + \frac{R_g}{\theta R}\frac{\partial C'}{\partial z} + KC' = C_i q\delta(x)\delta(y)\delta($$

$$-\infty < x < \infty, \quad -\infty < y < \infty, \quad -W < z < S_d, \quad 0 < t,$$ (11.37)

$$C'(\pm\infty,\pm\infty,\pm\infty,t)=0; \quad C'(x,y,z,0)=0$$

If the release rate is constant, the solution to this equation is given by

$$C'(x,y,z,t) = \frac{C_i q}{f_m}\int_0^t X'(x,t-t_1)Y'(y,t-t_1)Z'(z,t-t_1)e^{-K(t-t_1)}dt_1 \quad (11.38)$$

where
  C'=unsaturated zone contaminant concentration (mg/kg)
  C_i= source concentration (mg/L)
  q=contaminant flow rate at the source ($m^3/month$)

$$X'(x,\ t)=\frac{e^{-\dfrac{x^2}{4\dfrac{D'_x}{R}t}}}{\sqrt{4\pi\dfrac{D'_x}{R}t}},\quad Y'(y,\ t)=\frac{e^{-\dfrac{y^2}{4\dfrac{D'_y}{R}t}}}{\sqrt{4\pi\dfrac{D'_y}{R}t}},\quad Z'(z,\ t)=\frac{e^{-\dfrac{(z+\frac{R_g}{\theta R}t+S_d)^2}{4\dfrac{D'_z}{R}t}}}{\sqrt{4\pi\dfrac{D'_z}{R}t}} \qquad (11.39)$$

and the time integral in equation (11.38) must be solved numerically. Once the contaminant reaches the capillary fringe, that is the interface with the saturated zone, it will become a stationary non-point source to the regional aquifer. The governing equation of contaminant transport in the aquifer is given by equation (11.35) and its solution is given by

$$C(x,\ y,\ t)=\frac{C_i q}{b}\int_0^t\int_0^{t_1}\bar{X}(x,t,t_1,t_2)\bar{Y}(y,t,t_1,t_2)Z'(-W,t_1-t_2)e^{-K(t-t_2)}dt_2,$$

$$\bar{X}(x,t,t_1,t_2)=\frac{e^{-\dfrac{[x-\frac{u}{R}(t-t_1)]^2}{\frac{4}{R}[\varphi_x(t-t_1)+D'_x(t_1-t_2)]}}}{\sqrt{\dfrac{4\pi}{R}[\varphi_x(t-t_1)+D'_x(t_1-t_2)]}} \qquad (11.40)$$

$$\bar{Y}(y,t,t_1,t_2)=\frac{e^{-\dfrac{y^2}{\frac{4}{R}[\varphi_y(t-t_1)+D'_y(t_1-t_2)]}}}{\sqrt{\dfrac{4\pi}{R}[\varphi_y(t-t_1)+D'_y(t_1-t_2)]}}$$

where Z' is given by equation (11.39) and the double integrals must be solved numerically.

Example 11.12: Unsaturated-Saturated Zone Stationary Source
An underground storage tank buried $0.5m$ below the ground surface

contains a chemical with a concentration of 100*mg/L* and leaks at a rate of about 0.1 m^3/*month*. Using the soil and aquifer data in Table 11.4, (1) plot the unsaturated zone concentration contours (*mg/kg*) at *t=6months* after the spill, and (2) the plan view concentration contours (*mg/L*) in the saturated zone at *t=24months* after the spill.

Solution

A slight modification of the program in Example 11.11 is necessary. For part (1), equations (11.38) and (11.39) are used. For part (2), equation (11.40) are used. The double integration requires a more CPU time than any other program in this book and may take a few minutes, depending on processor speed. Since the tank leaks permanently, the plume center of mass remains near the origin, but the contaminant covers a significantly larger portion of the soil and aquifer than a comparable instantaneous spill.

```
> restart: with(plots):
  Dxp:=1: Dzp:=0.1*Dxp: n:=0.1: Rg:=0.01:
  W:=1.0: Sd:=0.5: T:=24: K:=0.0: Kd:=1E-6:
  rhob:=1600: R:=1+rhob*Kd/n: Dyp:=Dxp: fm:=rhob/(1000*n):
  Cin:=100: q:=1: M:=Cin*q:
  #(1) Unsaturated zone module
  Xp:=(x,t,tau)->exp(-x^2/(4*Dxp/R*(t-tau)))
      /sqrt(4*Pi*Dxp/R*(t-tau)):
  Yp:=(y,t,tau)->exp(-y^2/(4*Dyp/R*(t-tau)))
      /sqrt(4*Pi*Dyp/R*(t-tau)):
  Zp:=(z,t,tau)->exp(-(z+Rg/R/n*(t-tau)-Sd)^2
      /(4*Dzp/R*(t-tau)))/sqrt(4*Pi*Dzp/R*(t-tau)):
  G:=(x,y,z,t,tau)->M/fm*Xp(x,t,tau)*Yp(y,t,tau)
      *Zp(z,t,tau)*exp(-K*(t-tau)):
  Cp:=(x,y,z)->evalf(Int(G(x,y,z,T,tau),tau=0..T)):
  #Initial plot to determine contour values
  plot(Cp(x,0,-W),x=-10..10):
> #Unsaturated zone profile contour plot (mg/kg)
  Lxp:=sqrt(8*Dxp*T): Xpmin:=-2*Lxp: Xpmax:=2*Lxp:
  contourplot(Cp(x,0,z,T),x=Xpmin..Xpmax,z=-W..Sd,
      labels=[`x (m)`,`z (m)`],
      labeldirections=[HORIZONTAL,VERTICAL],color=black,
      contours=[0.05,0.1,0.15,0.2,0.25,0.3],
      labelfont=[TIMES,ROMAN,16],scaling=constrained,
      numpoints=1000,axes=boxed);
```

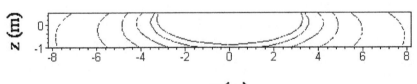

```
> #(2) Saturated zone Module
  Dx:=0.1: Dy:=0.1*Dx: u:=0.2: sigmau:=0.1: c:=2.: l:=10:
  b:=10.: T:=24:
  #Field dispersion coeficients for the saturated zone
  Phix:=t->Dx*t+sigmau^2*t^2/2:
  Phiy:=t->Dy*t+c*sigmau^2*t^2/(2*l^2):
  X:=(x,t,t1,t2)->exp(-(x-u/R*(t-t1))^2
     /(4/R*(Phix(t-t1)+Dxp*(t1-t2))))
     /sqrt(4*Pi/R*(Phix(t-t1)+Dxp*(t1-t2))):
  Y:=(y,t,t1,t2)->exp(-y^2/(4/R*(Phiy(t-t1)+Dyp*(t1-t2))))
     /sqrt(4*Pi/R*(Phiy(t-t1)+Dyp*(t1-t2))):
  G:=(x,y,t,t1,t2)->M/(b*n)*X(x,t,t1,t2)*Y(y,t,t1,t2)
     *Zp(-W,t1,t2)*exp(-K*(t-t2)):
  C:=(x,y)->evalf(Int(Int(G(x,y,T,t1,t2),t2=0..t1),t1=0..T)):
  Lx:=sqrt(8*Phix(T)): Xmin:=-2*Lx: Xmax:=4*Lx:
  Ly:=sqrt(8*Phiy(T)): Ymin:=-6*Ly: Ymax:=6*Ly:
  #Initial plot to determine contour values
  Cx:=[seq([i,C(i,0)],i=floor(Xmin)..ceil(Xmax))]:
  plot(Cx);
> #Saturated zone plan view contours (mg/L)
  contourplot(C(x,y),x=Xmin..Xmax,y=Ymin..Ymax,
     labels=[`x (m)`,`y (m)`],
     labeldirections=[HORIZONTAL,VERTICAL],color=black,
     labelfont=[TIMES,ROMAN,16],
     scaling=constrained,axes=boxed,
     contours=[5,10,15,20,25,30,40,45,50]);
```

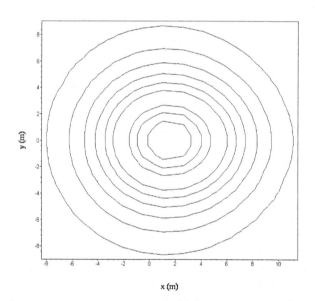

x (m)

11.3 MONITORING GROUNDWATER QUALITY

A successful diagnosis and analysis in groundwater pollution depends on an appropriate strategy of groundwater quality sampling and groundwater monitoring. Assessment of the extent of contamination, groundwater pollution modeling, and remedial actions design, are based on a comprehensive measurement program of the groundwater quality at the site. The hydrologist is usually involved in the collection of water samples in the field. These samples are shipped to a specialized analytical laboratory for specific chemical analyses.

The sampling program has to be carefully planned. The specific objectives of the sampling program must be clearly defined. For instance, the objective may be to identify the presence of a certain contaminant, to define the basic water chemistry, to assess if drinking water norms are met, or to determine if the unsaturated zone and surface waters are also contaminated. In compliance with the objectives, the hydrologist must decide on the number of sampling points, the frequency of the sampling (i.e., seasonally, annually, etc.), and the number of samples per sampling point. Keeping in mind that the cost increases as the number of samples increases, the number and frequency of sampling should be minimum such that project objectives are satisfied.

An important decision is the determination of the chemical substances to test, and the lowest limit to quantify. Below this limit, the hydrologist may request the detection of particular substances, but without quantitative evaluation. Again these decisions must be taken in agreement with the objectives. The hydrologist must assess the effectiveness of an analytical laboratory to detect and correctly quantify certain substances. This is traditionally done by submitting a set of samples of known concentration to the laboratory, and by submitting a portion of duplicate samples from the same source. The duplicate sample should be thoroughly mixed before being split for shipment to the laboratory, and of course laboratory personnel should not be aware of which samples are duplicates.

To assess field sampling procedures, blank samples of highly purified water are run through the sampling devices, placed in sample containers, and shipped to the laboratory for analysis. If substance trace amounts are reported in both the samples and the field blanks, there is reason to believe that the substance is not present in the groundwater, and there is a problem with the sampling methodology or the laboratory procedures.

Sampling devices must be thoroughly rinsed with distilled water before use to prevent residues from contaminating the water sample. If acetone is used in the cleaning of the sampling device, it should be rinsed with distilled water and then autoclaved to volatilize any acetone residue. Sampling protocols have been developed by Ford et al. (1983), and Keith

(1996).

Groundwater monitoring wells are installed today to test water quality in places near spills, underground storage tanks, waste disposal facilities, mines, or areas suspected of groundwater contamination. The construction of monitoring wells follow specific steps summarized in chapter 5. Special precautions must be taken in the design of wells for the specific purpose of water quality sampling. In particular the well construction material must be made of inert substances to prevent well residues from contaminating water samples. The casing and screens are usually built of stainless steel because of durability and chemical stability. PVC pipes are commonly used because of low cost. However, threaded joints must be used, instead of solvent-welded joints, to prevent the contamination of water samples by organic residues. Figure 5.24, Chapter 5, illustrates a typical groundwater monitoring well.

If sampling at different depths in the aquifer is required, then a multilevel monitoring well is necessary. Figure 11.12 illustrates a typical multilevel groundwater sampling device. It consists of a rigid PVC pipe, inside of which are multiple tubes, each ending at a sampling port at a different depth. It could be used to collect groundwater samples at elevations separated by about 30cm. A small sample of water is withdrawn to prevent vertical mixing. The result is a detailed picture of the vertical contaminant distribution.

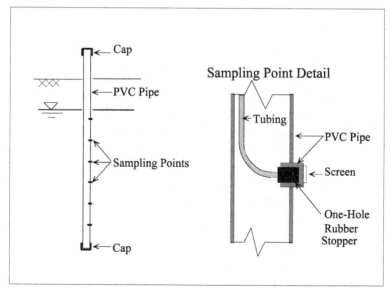

Figure 11.12: Groundwater Sampling at Several Depths

Once a monitoring well is installed and developed, a method for collecting water samples is needed. There are many commercially available pumping devices. A pump selected to collect water quality samples must satisfy special requisites. For instance, the pump material should not have substances that may contaminate the water sample, or alter its chemistry in any way. A pump intended to be used in other wells should be easy to clean for residues from previous wells. The method of pumping is important since a strong vacuum may produce a strong change in the water sample pressure while being delivered to the surface. This may result in a loss of dissolved gases.

Monitoring devices designed to collect gas and water samples in the unsaturated zone require special considerations that fall outside the scope of the present treatment. For a more detailed description of subsurface contamination, including monitoring and remediation techniques see Keith (1996), Wilson (1995), Fetter (1993), Devinny et al. (1990), Schwendeman and Wilcox (1990), and Schwille (1988). For a more in depth description of the design of a sampling strategy see Gilbert (1987). For specialized description of soil and groundwater remediation engineering see Bedient et al. (1999), Kuo (1999), Suthersan (1997), and Roy F. Weston, Inc. (1990).

QUESTIONS AND PROBLEMS

11.1 Which dispersion physical processes are most important in clays? Which in sands?

11.2 Select a highly mobile organic contaminant from Table 11.3. Find the contaminant maximum concentration in drinking water from Table 8.2. Speculate about the potential damage a spill of a $0.5\text{-}m^3$ drum containing this contaminant may cause to the aquifer. Repeat the exercise for an immobile contaminant. Which contaminant causes the greatest damage and why? Which contaminant will be more difficult to clean and why?

11.3 What is the effect of rainfall on contaminant propagation in the unsaturated zone? What is its effect in the saturated zone? In which parameters is rainfall indirectly present in contaminant transport equations?

11.4 How does an aquifer regional hydraulic gradient affect contaminant propagation in the saturated zone? In which parameter is the gradient indirectly imbedded in the contaminant transport equations?

11.5 What effect do contaminant chemical reactions have on plume shape and plume propagation in aquifers? Which parameters represent chemical reactions in sub-surface contaminant transport equations?

11.6 What effect does contaminant degradation have on plume shape and plume propagation? Which parameter represents degradation in contaminant transport equations?

11.7 Describe the effect that nonlinear contaminant decay has on contaminant spatial distribution.

11.8 Describe the effect that nonlinear sorption has on contaminant spatial distribution.

11.9 Describe the effect that nonlinear sorption has on plume shape.

11.10 What are the main sub-surface propagation features of $LNAPL$'s and $DNAPL$'s?

11.11 What is the effect of aquifer heterogeneity in the hydraulic conductivity on contaminant dispersion? Which contaminant transport parameter is affected the most and in what way?

11.12 A $1000m$ long unconfined aquifer is bounded by two rivers with average heads of $11m$ and $10m$, respectively, with respect to the bottom of the aquifer. The porosity is 0.25, the mean recharge is $0.015m/month$. A conservative contaminant with a diffusion coefficient of $0.004m^2/month$ is released in the aquifer; the longitudinal dispersivity is $1.5m$; the transverse dispersivity is $0.2m$; and transmissivity measures taken at random in the aquifer are summarized in Table 11.4. Assuming a transmissivity correlation length of 20m, estimate longitudinal and transverse hydrodynamic dispersion coefficient $500m$ from the left river, and $18months$ after the injection.

Table 11.4: Transmissivity Data for Problem 11.12

Sample i	T_i ($m^2/month$)	Sample i	T_i ($m^2/month$)
1	650	6	1020
2	885	7	792
3	990	8	823
4	1102	9	996
5	784	10	957

11.13 $15m^3$ of a solution of a conservative substance with a concentration of $400mg/L$ is injected through a well into an unconfined aquifer $6m$ in thickness. The aquifer hydraulic conductivity is constant and equal to $120 m/month$, the hydraulic gradient in the direction of the regional groundwater flow velocity is $-0.003 m/m$, the porosity is 0.1, and the dispersion coefficient for the tracer is $0.6 m^2/month$. Assuming that the contaminant will mix completely through the entire thickness of the aquifer, and across a width of $6m$ perpendicular to the flow, calculate the maximum contaminant concentration expected at a drinking water well located $50m$ from the injection point (in a direction parallel to the flow).

11.14 For Problem 11.13, (1) plot the concentration versus time breakthrough curve at the well; and (2) in one graph plot the concentration versus distance breakthrough curves 12, 24, and $36 months$ after the spill. *Hint*: Modify the program in Example 11.3.

11.15 $40 m^3$ of a chemical solution with a concentration of $700 mg/L$ is injected through a well in an unconfined aquifer $5m$ in thickness. The mean groundwater pore velocity is $0.4 m/month$, the porosity is 0.1, and the dispersion coefficient for the tracer is $1.2 m^2/month$. Assume that the contaminant will mix completely through the entire thickness of the aquifer, and across a width of $10m$ perpendicular to the flow. (1) Calculate the contaminant concentration expected at a drinking water well located $10m$ from the injection point (in a direction parallel to the flow) one year after injection if decay is negligible. (2) Repeat (1) if a decay rate of $0.1\, month^{-1}$ is assumed.

11.16 In Problem 11.15, in one graph plot the concentration versus time breakthrough curves at the well for (1) the case of no decay, and (2) when the decay rate is $0.1\, month^{-1}$. *Hint*: Modify the program in Example 11.5.

11.17 In the Spill of Problem 11.15, in one graph plot the concentration versus distance breakthrough curves at $t=12 months$ for the following conditions: (1) no-decay; (2) linear decay with $K=0.1/month$; and (3) nonlinear decay with $K=0.1\,(mg/L)^{1-\beta}/month$, and $\beta=0.6$. *Hint*: Modify the program in Example 11.6.

11.18 Two tracers, one reactive and one non-reactive, are simultaneously injected through a well into an aquifer. One month later, the center of mass of the reactive contaminant is located $5m$ from the well, and the center of mass of the non-reactive contaminant is located $25m$ from the well. If the aquifer porosity is 0.33 and the dry bulk density is $1,650\, kg/m^3$, estimate the retardation coefficient and the partition coefficient.

11.19 Solve Example 11.8 with the same data, except that for part (3), $\beta=0.6$, and for part (4), $\beta=1.5$. State your conclusions.

11.20 Solve Example 11.9 with the same data, but run the simulations for a time $t=240 month$.

11.21 Solve Example 11.10 with the same data if the standard deviation of the pore velocity is $0.5m/month$. What is the effect of this parameter on plume spatial distribution?

11.22 Solve Example 11.11 with the same data, but run the saturated zone simulations for a time $t=60months$.

11.23 Solve Example 11.12 with the same data, but run the saturated zone simulations for a time $t=60months$.

APPENDIX A: CONVERSION FACTORS

LENGTH

1 foot=12 inches

1 inch=2.54 centimeters

1 kilometer=1000 meter

1 meter=100 centimeters

1 centimeter=10 millimeters

1 foot=0.3048 meters

1 yard=0.9144 meters

1 mile=1609 meters

VELOCITY

1 foot per second=0.3048 meters per second

1 mile per hour=1.609 kilometers per hour

1 knot=1.852 kilometers per hour

AREA

1 acre=0.4047 hectares

1 acre=4047 square meters

1 acre=43560 square feet

1 square mile=259 hectares

1 square mile=2.59 square kilometers

1 square kilometer=247.1 acres

1 square foot=0.0929 square meters

FLOW RATE

1 cubic foot per second

    =0.02832 cubic meters per second

1 cubic meter per second

    =15800 gallons per minute

1 million U.S. gallons per day

    =694.4 U.S. gallons per minute

1 million U.S. gallons per day

    =3785 cubic meters per day

VOLUME

1 U.S. gallon=0.134 cubic feet

1 U.S. gallon=0.00379 cubic meters

1 cubic meter=1000 liters

1 acre foot=1233 cubic meters

1 million gallons=3785 cubic meters

PRESSURE

1 foot of water=0.883 inches of mercury

1 inch of mercury=25.40 millimeters of mercury

1 millibar=0.7501 millimeters of mercury

1 kilopascal=1000 newtons per square meter

1 kilopascal=10 millibars

1 pound per square inch

    =703.1 kilograms per square meter

ENERGY

1 calorie=4.186 joules

1 calorie=3.087 feet-pounds

1 British thermal unit (60 degrees Fahrenheit)

    =252 calories

1 joule=0.7376 Feet-pounds

1 kilowatt-hour=3413 British thermal units

1 kilowatt-hour

    =860100 calories 1.341 horsepower-hours

1 Horsepower-hour=2542 British thermal units

1 horsepower-hour=641437 calories

APPENDIX B: ANSWERS TO PROBLEMS

Chapter 1
1.6 $A \approx 6512.0 km^2$

1.7 $P = 1636.4 mm$

1.8 $ET = 3.190 \times 10^8 m^3/year$

1.9 $Q = 4.5 \times 10^7 m^3/year$

1.10 $S(t=4) = 3,010,800 m^3$

1.11 $S(t=4) = 12,028,800 m^3$

1.12 $Q_o = 2,572,128 m^3/day$

1.13 $Q_o = 4,372,013 m^3/day$

1.14 $Q_o = 2,874,528 m^3/day$ 1

1.15 $E = 7.3 mm/day$

1.16 $E = 13.5 mm/day$

1.19.

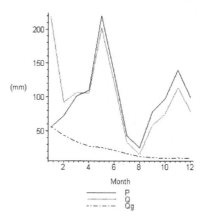

20.

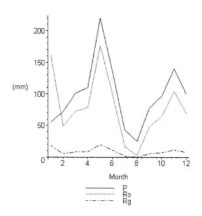

Chapter 2

2.1 There appears to be a break in 1990. The line slope prior to the break is $a=0.93$; the line slope after the break is $b=0.75$. Correction for series prior to 1990 is $c=b/a=0.75/0.93=0.806$

2.2 There appears to be a line break in 1982. Line slope prior to the break is $a=1.12$; line slope after the break is $b=0.878$; correction for the series before the break is $c=b/a=0.878/1.12=0.78$

2.3 $P_1=73.7mm$

2.4 $P_1=80.6mm$

2.5 $P_{max}=2.7mm/hour$; $t_d=5.0hours$; total $P=8.0mm$

2.6

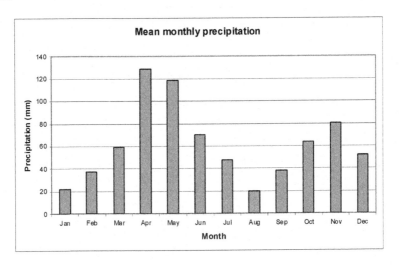

2.7

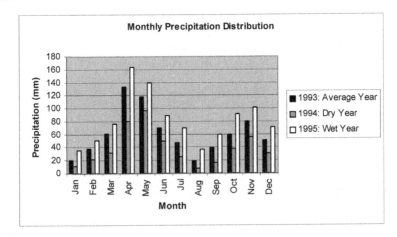

2.8 (2)$\bar{P}$=576.4*mm*.

    (3) Medium years: 1966-1967, 1972, 1984-1985. Dry years: 1968-1970, 1973-1983. Wet years: 1965-1967, 1971-1972, 1986-1996.

    (4) The average period of precipitation oscillation is 10 years.

    (5) σ_P=360*mm*.

    (6) $\bar{P}+\sigma_p$=936*mm*, $\bar{P}-\sigma_p$=216*mm*

2.9 The longer the period of calculation for the moving average, the "smoother" (i.e., less fluctuating) the curve.

2.11(1) $\bar{P}$=16.3*mm*, (2) $\bar{P}$=20.2*mm*, (3) $\bar{P}$=20.5*mm*

2.12 P=25.6*mm*

2.13(2) $P(T=2, t_s=12)=7mm$

    (2) $p(T=2, t_s=12)=7mm/hour$

    (3) $P(T=2.33, t_s=12)=7mm/hour$; $P=84mm$

2.14

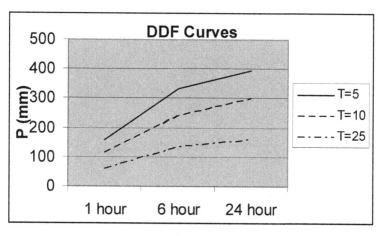

2.15 P=4.5*mm/hour*

Chapter 3:

3.1 r=81%

3.5 E=1.56*mm*

3.6 E=2.74*mm/day*

3.7 For the first day, E=3.44*mm/day*

3.8 E=3.6*mm/day*

3.9 E=3.9*mm/day*

3.10 E=3.9*mm/day*

3.11 New evaporation rate is E=5.9*mm/day*

3.12 PET=4.4*mm/day*

3.13 PET=848.37*mm* for the growing season only

3.15 $PET=6.6mm/day$

Chapter 4:
4.1 Gravelly Loam
4.2 $\rho_b=1646.8kg/m^3$, $n=0.38$, $\theta=0.15$
4.4

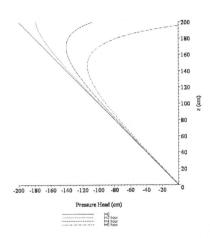

4.5

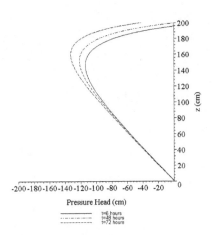

4.6 (1) $P(8)=279mm$. (2) $I(8)=161mm$. (3) $R_o=118mm$
4.7 (1) $f(4)=10.4mm$. (2) $F(6)=108mm$
4.8 $k=0.21$
4.9 $k=0.257hour^{-1}$
4.10 $i(3)=1.5mm/hour$, $i(4)=27.2mm/hour$

Chapter 5:

5.1 K_x=117.17$m/month$, $\bar{K}_z$=74.3$m/month$

5.2 (2) $Q(0)$=-5.64$m^3/month$, $Q(1000)$=9.04$m^3/month$

    (3) Groundwater divide located at x=351m

5.3 (2) t=560.5$months$

5.4 (2) ΔS_g=2058.69m^3/m

5.6 (2) $Q_x(0)$=-1.199$m^3/month$

5.7 (1)

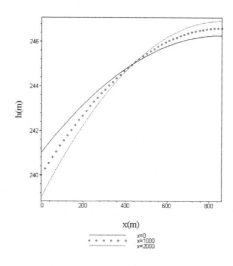

x(m)

········ x=0
········ x=1000
········ x=2000

5.8 q=0.0321$m/month$, u=0.161$m/month$, and θ=3.65 degrees with respect to the negative x axis.

5.10

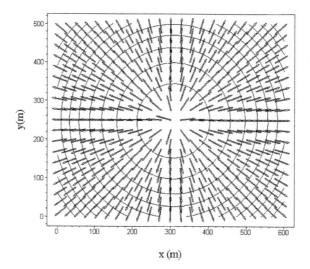

x (m)

5.12 $\overline{Q}_g$=8.25×10^{6}m^3/year

5.13 Q_p=715.9m^3/day

5.14 R=10,243.7m

5.15 K_r=0.0525m/day, R=3,354.97

5.16

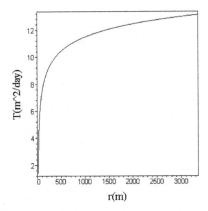

5.17 Q_p=316.91m^3/day

5.18 Q_p=414.25m^3/day

5.19 T=3074.5m^2/day, S=0.00017

5.20 T=1311.88m^2/day, S=6.9×10^{-5}

5.21 T=905.2m^2/day, S=7.87×10^{-5}

Chapter 6:

6.3 (1) t=16 and t=19 *hours.* (2) k=14.96*hour*

6.4 (1) S_r=153,288m^3. (2) R_o=10.2mm

6.5 (1) I=34.4mm. (2) Δh=98.3mm

6.6 (1) R_o=13.9mm

6.11

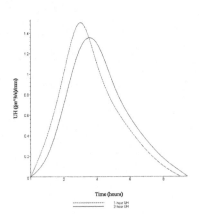

6.15

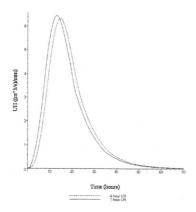

6.17

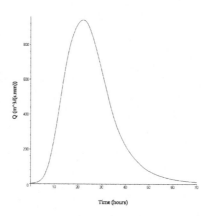

6.18

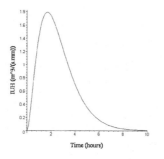

Chapter 7:
7.1 ΔQ=33.3%, Time Phase=12$hour$

7.3

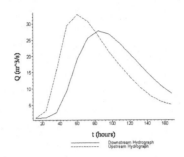

7.4 $\hat{k}$=23.9*hour*, $\hat{x}$=0.2
7.5 $\hat{k}$=24.0*hour*, $\hat{x}$=0.2
7.6 ΔQ=31%, Time Phase=1*day*
7.7 O_{max}=345m^3/s
7.8

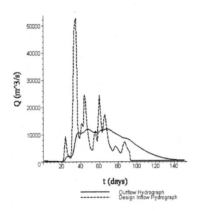

7.9

```
> restart: with(stats):
  #Enter data; calculatye initial storage constants
  In:=[2.0,15.0,40.0,25.5,17.6,12.8,9.0,6.0,3.4,2.0,
       seq(2.0,j=1..60)]:
  N:=describe[count](In): On[1]:=In[1]: dt:=1: a:=1.4:
  w:=40: A:=5*10^6: dt:=8.64*10^4: c:=1.656:
  eq1:=O=c*w*H^1.5:              #O(H) relation
  sols:=[solve(eq1,H)]:         #solve for H
  eq2:=S1=2*A*sols[1]/dt+O:     #2S/dt+O using first real solution
  S:=unapply(op(2,%),O):        #equate the rhs to S
  Sp[1]:=evalf(S(On[1])):       #Initial 2S/dt+O
  Sm[1]:=Sp[1]-2*On[1]:         #Initial 2S/dt-O
> step:=proc(j)                 #Basic iteration time step
    global Sm, Sp, S, Q, In, On, eq3;
    Sp[j+1]:=In[j]+In[j+1]+Sm[j]:
    eq3:=S(O)=Sp[j+1]:
    On[j+1]:=fsolve(eq3,O):
    Sm[j+1]:=Sp[j+1]-2*On[j+1]:
    On[j+1]:
  end:
  Apply routing equation iteratively. Store output in array and plot.
> for i from 1 to 15 do step(i) end do:
  Qin:=[seq([i,In[i]],i=1..15)]:
  Qout:=[seq([i,On[i]],i=1..15)]:
  plot(Qin,color=black,linestyle=3,thickness=2,
       legend='Design Inflow Hydrograph'):
  plot(Qout,color=black,thickness=2,legend='Outflow Hydrograph'):
  plots[display](%,%%,labels=['t (days)','Q (m^3/s)'],
       labeldirections=[HORIZONTAL,VERTICAL],
       labelfont=[TIMES,ROMAN,16]);
```

7.10 $Q(T=50)=29,000\,m^3/s$. Not a good fit
7.11 $Q(T=50)=31,774\,m^3/s$
7.12 $Q(T=50)=31,420\,m^3/s$
7.13 $Q(T=50)=29,770\,m^3/s$
7.14 $Q(T=25)=821\,m^3/s$
7.15 $Q(T=25)=1,227\,m^3/s$
7.16 $Q(T=25)=1,010\,m^3/s$
7.17 $Q_{100}=32,424m^3/s$. For a conservative design, select that from Example 7.10
7.18 $Q_p(Area\ IV)=5.04m^3/s$

Chapter 8:
8.9 $VSS=149mg/L$
8.10 $BOD_u=165mg/L$
8.11 $TS=700mg/L,\ VS=500mg/L,\ FS=200mg/L$
8.12 $TSS=33\%$, and $TDS=67\%$ of TS
8.13 $VSS=960,\ FSS=76.8,\ FDS=364.8,\ VDS=278.4mg/L$

Chapter 9:
9.1 $DO_{crit}=0.8mg/L,\ X_{crit}=2.0km$
9.2

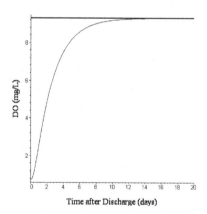

Time after Discharge (days)

9.3 $DO_{crit}=0.0mg/L,\ X_{crit}=14.3km$
9.4 The DO reaches its minimum value of $0mg/L$ quickly after release, and takes about 20 days to recover
9.5 Reduce waste by 38% to a chloride concentration $C'_w=386mg/L$, or increase the tributary flow rate to $Q'_T=11.79m^3/s$
9.6 $K=46.14/day$
9.7 $C_r(9)=3.407\times10^6N/L$; disinfection is necessary
9.8 $C_{max}=1.02mg/L,\ t_p=8.7days,\ t_1=7.6days,\ t_2=9.7days$

9.10 $C_r(x=35km)=5.01mg/L$

Chapter 10:
10.1 $\overline{C}=0.115mg/L$
10.2

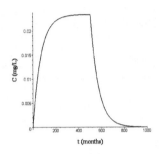

10.3 $C(t)=0.0327+0.0243e^{-0.0113t}$
10.4

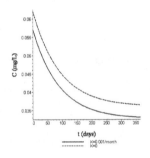

10.5 $63,505kg/day$
10.6

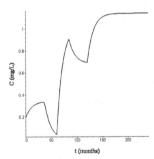

10.7   Maximum $C=1.51mg/L$; $t'=20.19months$
10.8   Maximum $C=3.01mg/L$; $t'=9.41months$
10.9 $F_s=21,918kg/day$
10.10 $A=230.72km^2$

10.11   (1) $C(t)=0.021e^{-0.0043t}$, (2)$C(t) = e^{-0.0643t}$, $t=months$
10.12 $t'=175.5 month$
10.13 $M=5.65\times10^{10}kg$

Chapter 11:

11.12 $\bar{D}_x=2.274$, $\bar{D}_y=0.068m^2/month$
11.13 $C_{max}=162.9mg/L$
11.15   (1) $C(10, 12)=260.3mg/L$. (2) $C(10, 12)=78.4mg/L$
11.18 $R=5$, $K_d=0.8mL/g$
11.19

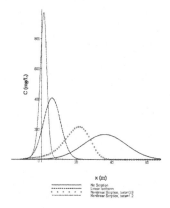

BIBLIOGRAPHY

Abbaoui, K., and Cherruault, Y., 1994. *Convergence of Adomian's Method Applied to Differential Equations.* Comp. Math. Applic., 28(5):103-109.

Adomian, G., 1994. *Solving Frontier Problems in Physics-The Decomposition Method.* Kluwer Acad. Pub., Dordrecht, The Netherlands.

Adomian, G., 1991, *A Review of the Decomposition Method and Some Recent Results for non Linear Equations.* Comp. Math. Applic. 21(5), 101-127.

Adomian, G., 1983. *Stochastic Systems.* Academic Press, New York, NT.

Adomian, G., and Serrano, S.E. (1998). *Stochastic contaminant transport equation in Porous media.* Appl. Math Letters, 1191, 53-55.

Alley, W. M., 1984. *Treatment of Evapotranspiration, Soil Moisture Accounting and Aquifer Recharge in Monthly Water Balance Models.* Water Resour. Res., 20(8):1137-1149.

Anderson, M. P., 1992. *Applied Groundwater Modeling.* Academic Press, New York, NY

Aral, M. M., 1989. *Groundwater Modeling in Multilayer Aquifers. Steady Flow.* Lewis Publishers, Chelsea, MI.

Aral, M. M., 1989. *Groundwater Modeling in Multilayer Aquifers. Unsteady Flow.* Lewis Publishers, Chelsea, MI.

Avila, A., Neal, C., and Terradas, J., 1996. *Climate Change Implications for Streamflow and Streamwater Chemistry in a Mediterranean Catchment.* Journal of Hydrology, 177(1-2):99-11.

Bartholomew, A., 2005. *Hidden Nature. The startling Insights of Viktor Schauberger.* Adventures Unlimited Press, Kempton, IL.

Battan, L. J., 1974. *Radar Observation of the Atmosphere.* University of Chicago Press. Chicago, IL.

Bear, J., 1979. *Hydraulics of Groundwater.* McGraw-Hill, New York, NY.

Bear, J., and Verruijt, A., 1987. *Modeling Groundwater Flow and Pollution.* D. Reidel Publishing Co., Dordrecht, Holland.

Bedient, P. B., and Huber, W. C., 2002. *Hydrology and Floodplain Analysis, 3rd ed*. Prentice Hall, Upper Saddle River, NJ.

Bedient, P. B., Rifai, H. S., and Newell, C. J., 1999. *Groundwater Contamination. Transport and Remediation*. 2nd Ed. Prentice Hall, Upper Saddle River, NJ.

Bender, D. L., and Robertson, J. A., 1965. *The Use of Dimensionless Unit Hydrograph to Derive Unit Hydrograph for some Pacific Northwest Basins*. J. Geophys. Res., 66(2):521-527.

Beven, K., 1984. *Infiltration into a Class of vertically non-uniform Soils*. Hydrological Sciences J., 29:425-434.

Biazar, J., Babolian, E., Kember, G., Nouri, A., and Islam, R.. (2003). *An Alternate algorithm for Computing Adomian Polynomials in Spectral Cases*. Appl. Math. and Comp., 138, 523-529.

Biswas, A. K., 1970. *History of Hydrology*. North-Holland Publishing Co., Amsterdam, The Netherlands.

Blaney, H. F., and Criddle, W.D., 1962. *Determining Consumptive Use of Irrigation Water Requirements*. U.S. Dept. of Agriculture Technical Bulletin No. 1275, Washington, D.C.

Blaney, H. F., and Criddle, W.D., 1950. *Determining Water Requirements in Irrigated Areas from Climatological and Irrigation Data*. U.S. Dept. of Agriculture Irrigation and Water Conservation, SCS TP-96.

Bobbald, J., 2006. *Viktor Schauberger. A Life of Learning from Nature*. Floris Books, Edinburgh, U.K.

Bonnor, G. M., 1975. *The Error of Area Estimates from Dot Grids*. Canadian J. Forestry Res., 5:10-17.

Botkin, D. B., and Keller, E.A., 2005. *Environmental Science*. Fifth Edition. John Wiley & Sons., Hoboken, NJ.

Boutwell, S. H., Brown, S.M., Roberts, B.R., and Atwood, D.F., 1986. *Modeling Remedial Actions at Uncontrolled Hazardous Waste Sites*. Pollution Technology Review No. 130. Noyes Publications, Park Ridge, NJ.

Bowen, I. S., 1926. *The Ratio of Heat Losses by Conduction and by Evaporation from Any Water Surface*. Physics Rev., 27:779-787.

Bras, R. L., 1990. *Hydrology.* Addison-Wesley, New York, NY.

Broadbridge, P., and White, L., 1988. *Constant Rate Rainfall Infiltration: A Versatile Non-Linear Model. 1. Analytical Solution.* Water Resour. Res., 24(1):145-154.

Brooks, R. H., and Corey, A. T., 1966. *Properties of Porous Media Affecting Fluid Flow.* Proc. ASCE J. Irrigation Drainage Div., Ir2, 61-68.

Bouwer, H., 1986. *Intake Rate: Cylinder Infiltrometer.* In A. Klute, ed., Methods of Soil Analysis; Part I:Physical and Mineralogical Methods. Soil Sci. Soc. Am., Madison, WI.

Bruce, J. P., and Rodgers, G. K., 1962. *Water Balance in the Great Lakes System, Great Lakes Basin.* American Assoc. Adv. Sci., 71, Washington, D.C.

Chadwick, O. A., Gavenda, R. T., Kelly, E. F., Ziegler, K., Olson, C. G. W., Elliott, C. and Hendricks, D. M., 2003. *The Impact of Climate on the Biogeochemical Functioning of Volcanic Soils.* Chemical Geology, 202(3-4):195-223.

Chapra, S. C., and Canale, R. P., 1988. *Numerical Methods for Engineers.* Second Ed., Mc-Graw-Hill, New York, NY.

Chapra, S., and Reckhow, K. H., 1983. *Engineering Approaches for Lake Management, Volume 2: Mechanistic Modeling.* Butterworth, Boston, MA.

Charbeneau, R. J., 2000. *Groundwater Hydraulics and Pollutant Transport.* Prentice Hall, Upper Saddle River, NJ.

Cherruault, Y., 1989. *Convergence of Adomian's Method.* Kybernetes, 18(2):31-38.

Cherruault, Y., Saccomardi, G., and Some, B., 1992. *New Results for Convergence of Adomian's Method Applied to Integral Equations.* Math. Comput. Modelling, 16(2):85-93.

Chiew, F. H. S., and McMahon, T. A., 1990. *Estimating Groundwater Recharge Using a Surface Watershed Modelling Approach.* J. Hydrol., 114:285-304.

Chiew, F. H. S., Whetton, P. H., McMahon, T. A., and Pittock, A. B., 1995. *Simulation of the Impacts of Climate Change on Runoff and Soil Moisture in Australian Catchments.* Journal of Hydrology, 167(1-4):121-147.

Chow, V. T., 1959. *Open Channel Hydraulics.* McGraw-Hill, New York, NY.

Chow, V. T., Maidment, D. R., and Mays, L. W., 1988. *Applied Hydrology.* McGraw-Hill, New York, NY.

Chu, S. T., 1978. *Infiltration during an Unsteady Rain.* Water Resour. Res., 14:461-466.

Collier, C. G., 1985. *Remote Sensing for Hydrologic Forecasting.* In: Facets of Hydrology II, edited by J.C. Rodda. John Wiley, New York NY.

Commons, G., 1942. *Flood Hydrographs.* Civil Engineering, 12:571-572.

Crawford, N. H., and Linsley, R. K., 1966. *Digital Simulation in Hydrology, Stanford Watershed Model IV.* Tec. Rep. 39, Civil Engr. Dept., Stanford University, Stanford, CA

Creutin, J. D., and Obled, C., 1962. *Objective Analysis and Mapping Techniques for Rainfall Fields: An Objective Comparison.* Water Resour. Res., 18:413-431.

Dalton, G., 1802. *Experimental Essays on the Constitution of Mixed Gases; on the Force of Steam or Vapor from Water and Other Liquids, Both in a Torricellian Vacuum and in Air; on Evaporation; and on the Expansion of Gases by Heat.* Manchester Literary and Philosophical Society Proceedings, 5:536-602, UK.

Debo, T. N., and Reese, A. J., 1995. *Municipal Storm Water Management.* Lewis Publishers, Boca Raton, FL.

DeGroot, W., ed., 1982. *Stormwater Detention Facilities.* Proceedings of the conference American Society of Civil Engineers, New York (now Reston, VA), August.

Dept. Of Commerce-Dept. Of Defense., 1972. *Radiosonde Observation Computation Tables.* Washington, D.C.

De Marsily, G., 1986. *Quantitative Hydrogeology.* Academic Press, San Diego, CA.

Devinny, J. S., Everett, L.G., Lu, J.C.S., and Stollar, R.L., 1990. *Subsurface*

Migration of Hazardous Wastes., Van Nostrand Reinhold, New York, NY.

DeVries, J. J., and Hromadka, T. V., 1993. *Computer Models for Surface Water.* In *Handbook of Hydrology.* D.R. Maidment, ed., McGraw-Hill, New York, NY.

Dingman, S. L., 1994. *Physical Hydrology.* Macmillan, New York, NY.

Dooge, J., 1973. *Linear Theory of Hydrologic Systems.* Agr. Res. Serv., U.S. Depth Agric., Tech. Bull. 1468, Washington, DC.

Dooge, J., 1959. *General Theory of the Unit Hydrograph.* J. Geophys. Res., 64(2):241-256.

Dooge, J., Lloyd, E., O'Donnel, T., and Wilkinson, J., 1979. *Deterministic Input-Output Models.* In The Mathematics of Hydrology. Academic Press, London, UK.

Doorenbos, J., and Pruitt, W.O., 1977. *Guidelines for Predicting Crop Water Requirements.* Irrigation and Drainage Paper 24, FAO, Rome.

Dunne, T., and Leopold, L.B., 1978. *Water in Environmental Planning.* Freeman and Co., San Francisco, CA.

England, C. B., 1970. *Land Capability: A Hydrologic Response Unit in Agricultural Watersheds.* U.S. Dept. Agric., ARS 41-172.

English, N. B. , Weltzin, J. F., Fravolini, A.. Thomas, L. and Williams, D. G. *The Influence of Soil Texture and Vegetation on Soil Moisture under Rainout Shelters in a Semi-desert Grassland.* J. of Arid Envir., 63(1):324-343.

Environmental Protection Agency (EPA), 1979. *Methods of Chemical Analysis of Water and Wastes.*, EPA 600/4-79-020, Washington, D.C.

Eltahir, E. A. B., Yeh, P. J.-F., 1999. *On the Asymmetric Response of Aquifer Water Level to Floods and Droughts in Illinois.* Water Resources. Research, 35(4):1199-1218.

Fetter, C. W., 1994. *Applied Hydrogeology.* Third Ed., Macmillan, New York, NY.

Fetter, C. W., 1993. *Contaminant Hydrogeology.* Macmillan, New York, NY.

Fischer, H. B., List, E. J., Koh, R. C. Y., Imberger, J., and Brooks, N.H., 1979. *Mixing in Inland and Coastal Waters*. Academic, New York, NY.

Fischer, H. B., 1968. *Dispersion Predictions in Natural Streams*. J. Sanit. Engr. Div., Proc. ASCE, 94(SA5):927-944.

Ford, P. A., Turina, P. J., and Seely, D. E., 1983. *Characterization of Hazardous Waste Sites - A Methods manual, Volume II, Available Sampling Methods*. U.S. Environmental Protection Agency, EPA-600/4-83-040.

Freeze, R. A., and Cherry, J.A., 1979. *Groundwater*. Prentice-Hall, Englewood Cliffs, NJ.

Freeze. R. A., 1971. *Three-Dimensional, Transient, Saturated-Unsaturated Flow in a Groundwater Basin.*, Water Resour. Res., 7(2):347-366.

Freyberg, D. L., Reeder, J. W., Fanzini, J. B., and Remson, I., 1980. *Application of the Green and Ampt Model to Infiltration under Time-Dependent Surface Water Depths*. Water Resour. Res., 16:517-528.

Fuhrer, J., 2003. *Agroecosystem Responses to Combinations of Elevated CO_2, Ozone, and Global Climate Change*. Agriculture, Ecosystems & Environment, (1-3)(97):1-20.

Gabet, L., 1994. *The Decomposition Method and Distributions*. Computers Math. Applic., 27(3):41-49.

Gabet, L., 1993. *The Decomposition Method and Linear Partial Differential Equations*. Math. Comput. Modelling, 17(6):11-22.

Gabet, L., 1992. *Equisse d'une Théorie Décompositionnelle et Application aux Equations aux Dérivées Partialles*. Dissertation, Ecole Centrale de Paris, France.

Gardner, W. R., Hillel, D., and Benyamini, Y., 1970. *Post Irrigation Movement of Soil Water: I. Redistribution*. Water Resour. Res., 6(3):851-861

Gardner, W. R., 1960. *Soil Water Relations in Arid and Semi-arid Conditions*. Unesco, 15:37-61.

Gardner, W. R., and Mayhugh, M. S., 1958. *Solutions and Tests of the Diffusion Equation for the Movement of Water in Soil*. Soil Sci. Soc. Am. Proc., 22:197-201.

Gilbert, R. O., 1987. *Statistical Methods for Environmental Pollution Monitoring*. Van Nostrand Reinhold, New York, NY.

Gosnold, W. D., Todhunter, P. E., and Schmidt, W., 1997. *The Borehole Temperature Record of Climate Warming in the Mid-continent of North America*. Global and Planetary Change, 15(1-2):33-45.

Goyal, R. K., 2004. *Sensitivity of Evapotranspiration to Global Warming: a Case Study of Arid Zone of Rajasthan (India)*. Agricultural Water Management, 69(1):1-11.

Gray, D. M. (ed.), 1973. *Handbook on the Principles of Hydrology*. National Research Council of Canada, Water Information Center, Inc., Port Washington, NY.

Gray, D. M., 1961. *Synthetic Unit Hydrograph for Small Watersheds*. Am. Soc. Civil Engr. J. Hydraul. Engr., 87(HY4):33-53.

Green, W. H., and Ampt, G., 1911. *Studies in Soil Physics, Part I: The Flow of Air and Water through Soils*. J. Agric. Sci., 4(1):1-24.

Greenberg, M. D., 1971. Applications of Green's Functions in Science and Engineering. Prentice-Hall, Englewood Cliffs, NJ.

Gunlach, D. L., and Thomas, W.A., 1977. *Guidelines for Calculating and Routing a Dam-Break Flood*. Research Note 5, Hydrologic Engineering Center, U.S. Army Corps of Engr., Davis, CA.

Gupta, R. S., 1989. *Hydrology and Hydraulic Systems*. Prentice Hall, Englewood Cliffs, NJ.

Haan, C. T., 1977. *Statistical Methods on Hydrology*. The Iowa State University Press, Ames, Iowa.

Haan, C. T., 1972. *A Water Yield Model for Small Watersheds*. Water Resour. Bull. 8(1):58-69.

Haestad Methods Inc., 2002. *Computer Applications in Hydraulic Engineering*. 5th ed. Haestad Press. Waterbury, CT.

Hantush, M. S., 1964. *Hydraulics of Wells*. In Advances in Hydroscience, Vol. I, ed. V.T. Chow, Academic Press, New York, NY.

Harbeck, G. E., 1962. *A Practical Field Technique for Measuring Reservoir Evaporation Utilizing Mass Transfer Theory.* U.S. Geological Survey, Professional Paper 272-E, Washington, DC.

Herman, B., 1986, *Intake Rate: Cylindrical Infiltrometer.* In Klute, A., Methods of Soil Analysis (2nd ed.), Madison, Wisconsin: Soil Sci. Soc. Am.:825–843

Hermance, J.F., 1999. *A Mathematical Primer on Groundwater Flow.* Prentice Hall, Upper Saddle River, NJ

Hershfield, D.M., 1961. *Estimating Probable Maximum Precipitation.* Proc. ASCE J. Hydraul. Div., 87(HY5):99-116.

Hickok, R. B., Keppel, R.V., and Rafferty, B.R., 1959. *Hydrograph Synthesis for Small Aridland Watersheds.* Agricultural Engineering, 40:608-615.

Hillel, D., 1980. *Fundamentals of Soil Physics.* Academic Press, New York, NY.

Hoggan, D. H., 1997. *Computer-Assisted Floodplain Hydrology and Hydraulics,* 2nd ed., McGraw-Hill, New York, NY.

Hoggan, D. H., 1989. *Computer Assisted Floodplain Hydrology & Hydraulics.* McGraw-Hill, New York, NY.

Holbrook, N. M., and Zwieniecki, M. A., 2008. *Transporting Water to the Tops of Trees.* Physics Today, 61(1):76-77

Holtan, H. N., 1965. *A Model for Computing Watershed retention from Soil Parameters.* J. Soil Water Conserv., 20(3):91-94.

Holtan, H. N., 1961. *A Concept for Infiltration Estimates in Watershed Engineering.* U.S. Dept. of Agric., ARS 41-51, Washington, DC.

Holtan, H. N., Stiltner, G.J., Henson, W. H., and Lopez N.C., 1975. *USDAHL-74 Revised Model of Watershed Hydrology.* U.S. Dept. of Agric., ARS Tech. Bull. 1518, Washington, DC.

Horner, R. R., Skupien, J.J., Livingston, E. H., and Shaver, H.E., 1994. *Fundamentals of Urban Runoff Management: Technical and Institutional Issues.* Terrene Institute, Alexandria, VA.

Horton, R. E., 1935. *Surface Runoff Phenomena: Part I, Analysis of the Hydrograph.* Horton Hydrol. Lab. Pub. 101. Ann Arbor MI: Edwards Bros.

Hostetler, S. W., and Giorgi, F., 1993. *Use of Output from High-resolution Atmospheric Models in Landscape-scale Hydrologic Models: an Assessment.* Water Resources Research, 29(6):1685-1696.

Hromadka II, T. V., McCuen, R. H., and Yen, C.-C., 1987. *Computational Hydrology in Flood Control Design and Planning.* Lighthouse Publications, Mission Viejo, CA.

Huber. W. C., and Dickinson, R. E., 1988. *Storm Water Management Model, Version 4, User's Manual.* EPA/600/3-88/001a (NTIS PB88-236641/AS), Environmental Protection Agency, Athens, GA.

Huggins, L. F., and Monke, E. J., 1966. *The Mathematical Simulation of the Hydrology of Small Watersheds.* Purdue University, Water Res. Center, Tech. Rept. 1, Lafayette, IN.

Hunt, B., 1983. *Mathematical Analysis of Groundwater Resources.* Butterworths, London, England.

Hutchinson, G. E., 1967. *A Treatise on Limnology. Vol. II. Introduction to Lake Biology and Limnoplankton.* John Wiley & Sons, New York, NY.

Hutchinson, G. E., 1957. *A Treatise on Limnology. Vol. I. Geography, Physics and Chemistry.* John Wiley & Sons, New York, NY.

Huyakorn, P. S., and Pinder, G. F., 1983. *Computational Methods in Subsurface Flow.* Academic Press, New York, NY.

Hydrologic Engineering Center, 1998. *HEC-HMS Hydrologic Modeling System.* U.S. Army Corps of Engineers, Davis, CA

Hydrologic Engineering Center, 1981. *HEC-1 Flood Hydrograph Package: User's Manual and Programmer's Manual.* U.S. Army Corps of Engineers, Davis, CA.

Hydrologic Engineering Center, 1975. *Urban Storm Water Runoff: STORM, Generalized Computer Program.* 723-58-L2520. U.S. Army Corps of Engineers, Davis, CA.

Jacob, C. E., 1950. *Flow of Ground-Water.* In Engineering Hydraulics, ed. H. Rouse, John Wiley & Sons, New York, NY.

James, W., and James, R. C., 1998. *Water Systems Models 1 Hydrology, User's*

Guide to SWMM4. Computational Hydrologic Int., Ontario, Canada.

James, W., and James, R. C., 1998. *Water Systems Models 2 Hydraulics, User's Guide to SWMM4*. Computational Hydrologic Int., Ontario, Canada.

Johanson, R. C., Imhoff, J. C., and Davis, H.H., 1980. *Users manual for Hydrologic Simulation Program-FORTRAN (HSPF)*. EPA-600-9-80-015, U.S. EPA, Athens, GA.

Johansson, P.-O., 1987. *Estimation of Groundwater Recharge in Sandy Till with Two Different Methods Using Groundwater Level Fluctuations*. J. Hydrol., 90:183-198.

Johnson, A. I., 1963. *A Field Method for Measurement of Infiltration*. U.S. Geological Surv., Water Supply Paper 1544-F, Washington, D.C.

Keith, L. H., 1996. *EPA's Sampling and Analysis Methods*. Lewis Publishers, Boca Raton, FL.

Kibler, D. F. (Ed.), 1982. *Urban Stormwater Hydrology*. Water Resources Monographs 7, American Geophysical Union, Washington, D.C.

Kirpich, Z. P., 1940. *Time of Concentration of Small Agricultural watersheds*. Civil Engineering 10(6):362.

Kottegoda, N. T., 1980. *Stochastic Water Resources Technology*. Macmillan Press, London, UK.

Kresic, N., 1997. *Quantitative Solutions in Hydrogeology and Groundwater Modeling*. Lewis Publishers, New York, NY.

Kuhnel, V., Dooge, J. C. I., Sander, G. C., and O'Kane, J. P. J., 1990. *Duration of Atmosphere-Controlled and Soil-Controlled Phases of Infiltration of Constant Rainfall at a Soil Surface*. Annals Geophysicae, 8:11-20.

Kuo, J., 1999. *Practical Design Calculations for Groundwater Soil Remediation*. Lewis Publishers, Boca Raton, FL.

Laiho, R., Laine, J., Trettin, C. C., and Finér, L. 2004. *Scots Pine Litter Decomposition along Drainage Succession and Soil Nutrient Gradients in Peatland Forests, and the Effects of Inter-annual Weather Variation*. Soil Biol. and Biochem., 36(7):1095-1109.

Laliberte, G. E., 1969. *A Mathematical Function Describing for Describing Capillary Pressure-desaturation Data.* Bull. Int. Assoc. Sci. Hydrol., 14(2):131-149.

Lerman, A., Ed., 1978. *Lakes, Chemistry, Geology, Physics.* Springer-Verlag, New York, NY.

Lettenmaier, D. P., McCabe, G., and Stakhiv, E. Z., 1996. *Chapter 29 Global Climate Change: Effect on Hydrologic Cycle.* Water Resources Handbook. L. W. Mays Editor. McGraw-Hill, New York NY

Li, T., Grant, R. F., and Flanagan, L. B., 2004. *Climate Impact on Net Ecosystem Productivity of a Semi-arid Natural Grassland: Modeling and Measurement.* Agricultural and Forest Meteorology, 126(1-2):99-116.

Liakopoulos, A. C., 1965. *Theoretical Solution of the Unsteady Unsaturated Flow Problems in Soils.* Bull. Int. Assoc. Sci. Hydrol., 10:5-39.

Ligget , J. A., and Liu, P. L-F., 1983. *The Boundary Integral Equation Method for Porous Media Flow.* George Allen & Unwin, London, England.

Linsley, R. K., Franzini, J. B., Freyberg, D. L., and Tchobanoglous, G., 1992. *Water-Resources Engineering.* McGraw-Hill, New York, NY.

Linsley, R. K., Kohler, M. A., and Pulhus, J. L. H., 1982. *Hydrology for Engineers.* 3rd. Ed., McGraw-Hill, New York, NY.

Loucks, D.P., Stedinger, J. R., and Haith, D. A., 1981. *Water Resource Systems Planning and Analysis.* Prentice-Hall, Englewood Cliffs, NJ.

Maidment, D. R., 1993. *Handbook of Hydrology.* McGraw-Hill, New York, NY.

Mariño, M. A., and Luthin, J. N., 1982. *Seepage and Groundwater.* Development in Water Science Series No. 13. Elsevier Sci., New York, NY.

Martin, J. L, and McCutcheon, S. C., 1999. *Hydrodynamics and Transport for Water Quality Modeling.* Lewis Publishers , Boca Raton, FL.

Mays, L. W., 2001. *Stormwater Collection Systems Design Handbook.* McGraw Hill, New York, NY.

McCuen, R. H., 1998. *Hydrologic Analysis and Design.* 2nd Ed., Prentice Hall, Upper Saddle River, NJ.

McCuen, R. H., 1989. *Hydrologic Analysis and Design.* Prentice Hall, Englewood Cliffs, NJ.

McCuen, R. H., Wong, S. L., and Walter, J. R., 1984. *Estimating Urban Time of Concentration.* Am. Soc. Civil Engr., J. Hydraul. Engr., 10(7).

McPherson, M. B., 1969. *Some Notes on the Rational Method of Storm Drain Design.* Tech. Memo No. 6., Am. Soc Civil Engr., Water Resources Research Program, Harvard University, Cambridge, MA.

McQueen, I. S., 1963. *Development of a Hand-Portable Rainfall Simulator Infiltrometer.* U.S. Geological Survey, Circular 482, Washington, DC.

Metcalf and Eddy Inc., 1991. *Waste Water Engineering, Treatment/Disposal/Reuse.*, 3rd ed., McGraw-Hill, New York, NY.

Metcalf & Eddy, Inc., University of Florida, Gainesville, and Water Resources Engineers, Inc., 1971. *Storm Water Management Model, for Environmental Protection Agency.* 4 Volumes, EPA Rep Nos. 11024DOC07/71, 11024DOC08/71, 11024DOC09/71, 11024DOC10/71.

Meyer, A. F., 1944. *Evaporation from Lakes and Reservoirs.* Minnesota Resources Commission, St. Paul, MN.

Mimikou, M. A., 1995. *Climate Change.* In Environmental Hydrology, Edited by V.P. Singh. Kluwer Academic, Boston, MA.

Mitchell, W. D., 1948. *Unit Hydrographs in Illinois.* Division of Water Ways, State of Illinois, Springfield, Illinois.

Myint-U, T., and Debnath, L., 1987. *Partial Differential Equations for Scientists and Engineers.* Third Ed., North Holland, New York, NY.

Nace, R. L., 1974. *General Evolution of the Concept of the Hydrologic Cycle.* In: Three Centuries of Scientific Hydrology, 40-48. UNESCO-World Meteorological Organization-International Association of Hydrological Sciences, Paris, France.

Nash, J. E., 1957. *The Form of the Instantaneous Unit Hydrograph.* Int. Assoc. Sci. Hydrol. Pub. 45(3).

National Assessment Synthesis Team., 2000. *Climate Change Impacts on the United States. U.S. Global Change Research Program.* Cambridge

University Press, Cambridge, U.K.

Newton, D. W., and Vinyard, J.W., 1967. *Computer Determined Unit Hydrographs from Floods*. Am. Soc. Civil Engr. J. Hydraul. Engr., HY5:219-235.

Nielsen, D. M., Ed., 1991. *Practical Handbook of Groundwater Monitoring*. Lewis Publishers, Chelsea, MI.

O'Kane, J. P. J., and Dooge, J. C. I., 1977. *PICOMO: A Program for the Identification of Conceptual Models*. Workshop on Mathematical Models in Hydrology. Pisa, December, 1974. Published by Ciriani, Marioni and Wallis (ed.). Mathematical Models for Surface Water Hydrology. Wiley Interscience, London, UK.

Omernik, J. M., and Kinney, A. J., 1983. *An Improved Technique for Estimating Mean Depth of Lakes*. Water Res., 11:1603-1607.

Overton, D. E., and Meadows, M. E., 1976. *Storm Water Modeling*. Academic Press, New York, NY.

Palmer, W. C., 1965. *Meteorological Drought*. Research paper 45, U.S. Weather Bureau, Washington, DC.

Panagoulia, D., and Dimou, G., 1997. *Linking Space–time Scale in Hydrological Modelling with Respect to Global Climate Change: Part 2. Hydrological Response for Alternative Climates*. Journal of Hydrology, 194(1-4):38-63.

Parlange, J. Y., 1971. *Theory of Water Movement in Soils: I. One-Dimensional Absorption*. Soil Sci., 111(2):134-137.

Patel, A., and Serrano, S. E., 2011. *Decomposition Solution of Multidimensional Groundwater Equations*. J. of Hydrol.,397:202-2109. http://dx.doi.org/10.1016/j.jhydrol.2010.11.032

Penman. H.L., 1948. *Natural Evaporation from Open Water, Bare Soil and Grass*. Proceedings of the Royal Society, 193:120-145, London, England.

Philip, J. R., 1972. *On Solving the Unsaturated Flow Equation: 1. The Flux-Concentration Relation.*, Soil Sci., 16(5):328-335.

Philip, J. R., 1957. *The Theory of Infiltration: 1. The Infiltration Equation and its Solution*. Soil Sci., 83:345-357.

Philip, J. R., 1955. *Numerical Solution of Equations of the Diffusion Type with Diffusivity Concentration-Dependent.* Trans. Faraday Soc., 51(7), 391.

Philip, J. R., and Knight, J. H., 1974. *On Solving the Unsaturated Flow Equation: 3. New Quasi-Analytical Technique.*, Soil Sci., 117(1):1-13.

Pickard, W. F., 1981. *The Ascent of Sap in Plants.* Prog. Biophys. Mol. Biol., 37:181.

Pinder, G. F., and Gray, W.G., 1979. *Finite Element Simulation in Surface and Subsurface Hydrology.* Academic Press, New York, NY.

Poertner, H. G., ed., 1981. *Urban Stormwater Management.* Special Report No. 49. American Public WorksAssociation, Chicago, IL.

Ponce, V. M., 1989. *Engineering Hydrology.* Prentice Hall, Englewood Cliffs, NJ.

Powers, D. L., 1979. *Boundary Value Problems.* Second Ed., Academic Press, New York, NY.

Rao, R. A., Delleur, J. W., and Sarma, B., 1972. *Conceptual Hydrologic Models for Urbanizing Basins.* Proc. Am. Soc. Civil Engr., Hyd. Div. (HY7), July, 1972.

Reckhow, K. H., and Chapra, S. C., 1983. *Engineering Approaches for lake Management. Vol. 1: Data Analysis and empirical Modeling.* Buterworth, Boston, MA.

Reed, J. E., 1980. *Type Curves for Selected Problems of Flow to Well in Confined Aquifers.* Techniques of water Resources Investigations, Chap. B3, Book 3, U.S., Geological Survey, Washington, D.C.

Rodríguez-Iturbe, I., and Porporato, A., 2004. *Ecohydrology of Water-Controlled Ecosystems: Soil Moisture and Plant Dynamics.* Cambridge University Press, Cambridge, UK.

Roy F. Weston, Inc., 1990. *Remedial Technologies for Leaking Underground Storage Tanks.* Lewis Publishers, Boca Raton, FL.

Sander, G. C., Parlange, J. Y., Kuhnel, V., Hogarth, W. L., Lockington, D., and O'Kane, J. P. J., 1988. *Exact Non-linear Solution for Constant Flux Infiltration.* Short Note., J. Hydrol., 97:341-346.

Sarino, and Serrano, S. E., 1990. *Development of the Instantaneous Unit Hydrograph Using Stochastic Differential Equations.* Stoch. Hydrol. and Hydraul., 4(2):151-160

Sawyer, C. N., and McCarty, P. L., 1978. *Chemistry for Environmental Engineering,* 3rd ed., Mc-Graw-Hill, New York, NY.

Schauberger, V., 1998. *The Water Wizard. The Extraordinary Properties of Natural Water.* Translated and Edited by Callum Coats. Gateway Books, Bath, UK.

Schmid, B., 1990. *Derivation of an Explicit Equation for Infiltration on the Basis of the Mein-Larson Model.* Hydrological Sci. J., 35:197-208.

Schueler, T. R., 1987. *Controlling Urban Runoff: A Practical Manual for Planning and Designing Urban BMPs.* Dept. of Environmental Programs, Metropolitan Washington Council of Governments, Washington, D.C., July (available from Water resources Publications, Highlands Ranch, CO).

Schwendeman, T. G., and Wilcox, H. K., 1990. *Underground Storage Systems. Leak Detection and Monitoring.* Lewis Publishers, Boca Raton, FL.

Schwille, F., 1988. *Dense Chlorinated Solvents in Porous and Fracture Media. Model Experiments.* Lewis Publishers, Boca Raton, FL.

Serrano, S. E., 2011. *Engineering Uncertainty and Risk Analysis. Second Edition. A Balanced Approach to Probability, Statistics, Stochastic Models, and Stochastic Differential Equations.* HydroScience Inc., Ambler, PA.

Serrano, S. E., 2006. *Development and Verification of an Analytical Solution for Forecasting Nonlinear Kinematic Flood Waves.* ASCE J. of Hydrol. Engr, 11(4):347-353.

Serrano, S. E., 2004. *Modeling Infiltration with Approximate Solutions to Richard's Equation.* ASCE J. of Hydrol. Engr, 9(5):421-432.

Serrano, S. E., 2003a. *Modeling Groundwater Flow under a Transient Non-linear Free Surface.* ASCE J. of Hydrol. Engineering, 8(3):123-132.

Serrano, S. E., 2003b. *Improved Decomposition Solution to Green and Ampt Equation.* ASCE J. of Hydrol. Engr., 8(3):158-160.

Serrano, S. E., 2003c. *Propagation of Nonlinear Reactive Contaminants in*

Porous Media. Water Resour. Res., American Geophysical Union, 39(8):1228-1242.

Serrano, S. E., 2001b. *An Explicit Solution to the Green and Ampt Infiltration Equation*. ASCE J. of Hydrol. Engr., 6(4):336-340.

Serrano, S. E., 1998. *Analytical Decomposition of the Non-Linear Infiltration Equation*. Water Resour. Res., 34(3):397-407.

Serrano, S. E., 1997a. *The Theis Solution in Heterogeneous Aquifers*. Ground Water, 35(3):463-467.

Serrano, S. E., 1997b. *Non-Fickian Transport in Heterogeneous Saturated Porous Media*. ASCE J. of Engr. Mech., 123(1):70-76.

Serrano, S. E., 1996. *Hydrologic Theory of Dispersion in Heterogeneous Aquifers*. ASCE J. of Hydrol. Engr., 1(4):144-151

Serrano, S. E., 1995a. *Analytical Solutions of the Nonlinear Groundwater Flow Equation in Unconfined Aquifers and the Effect of Heterogeneity*. Water Resour. Res., 31(11):2733-2742.

Serrano, S. E., 1995b. *Forecasting Scale-Dependent Dispersion from Spills in Heterogeneous Aquifers*. J. Hydrol., 169:151-169.

Serrano. S. E., 1992. *Semi-Analytical Methods in Stochastic Groundwater Transport*. Appl. Math. Mod., 16:181-191.

Serrano, S. E., 1990a. *Modeling Infiltration in Hysteretic Soils*. Adv. Water Resour., 13(1):12-23.

Serrano, S. E., 1990b. *Stochastic Differential Equation Models of Erratic Infiltration*. Water Resour. Res., 26(4):703-711.

Serrano, S. E., 1988a. *General Solution to Random Advective-Dispersive Equation in Porous Media. Part I: Stochasticity in the Sources and in the Boundaries*. Stoch. Hydrol. and Hydraul., 2(2):79-98.

Serrano, S. E., 1988b. *General Solution to Random Advective-Dispersive Equation in Porous Media. Part II: Stochasticity in the Parameters*. Stoch. Hydrol. and Hydraul., 2(2):99-112.

Serrano, S. E., and Workman, S. R., 2008. *Experimental Verification of Models of Nonlinear Stream Aquifer Transients.* ASCE J. of Hydrol. Engr., 13(12):1119-1124

Serrano, S. E., Workman, S. R., Srivastava, K., and Miller-Van Cleave, B., 2007. *Models of Nonlinear Stream Aquifer Transients.* J. of Hydrol., 336(1-2):199-205. http://dx.doi.org/10.1016/j.jhydrol.2007.01.016

Serrano, S. E., and Adomian, G., 1996. *New Contributions to the Solution of Transport Equations in Porous Media.* Math. Comput. Mod., 24(4):15-25.

Serrano, S. E., and Unny, T.E., 1987. *Semigroup Solutions of the Unsteady Groundwater Flow Equation with Stochastic Parameters.* Stoch. Hydrol. Hydraul., 1(4):281-296.

Serrano, S. E., and Workman, S.R., 2008. Experimental Verification of Models of Nonlinear Stream Aquifer Transients. *ASCE J. of Hydrol. Engr.,* 13(12):1119-1124.

Serrano, S. E., and Workman, S.R., 1998. *Modeling Transient Stream/Aquifer Interaction with the Non-Linear Boussinesq Equation and its Analytical Solution.* J. of Hydrol., 206:245-255.

Serrano, S. E., Workman, S.R., Srivastava, K., and Miller-Van Cleave, B., 2007. *Models of Nonlinear Stream Aquifer Transients.* J. of Hydrol, 336(1-2):199-205.

Serrano, S., Whiteley. H. R., and Irwin, R., 1985. *Drainage Effects on Streamflow in the Middle Thames River, 1949-1980.* Canadian J. Civil Engr., 12:875-885.

Shaw, E. M., 1988. *Hydrology in Practice* (2nd ed.). Van Nostrand-Reinhold, London, UK.

Shaw, E. M., and Lynn, P.P., 1972. *Areal Rainfall Evaluation Using Two Surface Fitting Techniques.* Hydrol. Sci. Bull., 17:419-433.

Sherman, L. K., 1942. *The Unit Hydrograph Method.* In Physics of the Earth-Hydrology, Chap. X-IE, ed. O. E. Meinzer. McGraw-Hill, New York, NY.

Sherman, L. K., 1932. *Streamflow from Rainfall by the Unit-Graph Method.* Engr. News Record, 108:501-502.

Shineldecker, C. L., 1992. *Handbook of Environmnetal Contaminants.* Lewis

Publishers, Boca Raton, FL.

Singh, V. P., 1996. Kinematic Wave Modeling in Water Resources: Surface Water Hydrology. Wiley, NY.

Singh, V. P., 1988. *Hydrologic Systems. Volume I, Rainfall-Runoff Modeling.* Prentice-Hall, Englewood Cliffs, NJ.

Snyder, F. F., 1938. *Synthetic Unit Graphs.* Trans. Am. Geophys. Union, 19:447-454.

Soil Conservation Service, 1984. *Computer Program for Project Formulation, Hydrology.* Tech Release No. 20, U.S. Department of Agriculture, Washington, D.C.

Srivastava, K., and Serrano, S. E., 2007. *Uncertainty Analysis of Linear and Nonlinear Groundwater Flow in a Heterogeneous Aquifer.* ASCE J. of Hydrol. Engr., 12(3):306-318.

Srivastava, K., Serrano, S. E., and Workman, S. R., 2006. *Stochastic Modeling of Stream-Aquifer Interaction with the Nonlinear Boussinesq Equation.* J. of Hydrol., 328:538-547.

Stallman, R. W., 1971. *Aquifer-Test Design Observation and Data Analysis.* Techniques of Water Resources Investigations, Chap. B1, Vol. 3, U.S. Geological Survey, Washington, D.C.

Steel, E. W., and McGhee, T. J., 1979. *Water Supply and Sewerage,* 5th ed., McGraw-Hill Book Co., New York, NY.

Steenhuis, T. S., and Van Der Molen, 1986. *The Thornthwaite-Mather Procedure as a Simple Engineering Method to Predict Recharge.* J. Hydrol., 84:221-229.

Stephenson, D., and Meadows, M., 1986. *Kinematic Hydrology and Modeling.* Elsevier Sci., New York, NY.

Steenhuis, T. S., Jackson, C.D., Kung, S. K. J., and Brutsaert, W., 1985. *Measurement of Groundwater Recharge on Eastern Long Island, New York, U.S.A.* J. Of Hydrol., 79:145-169.

Strack, O. D. L., 1989. *Groundwater Mechanics.* Prentice-Hall, Englewood Cliffs, NJ.

Strangeways, I. C., 1985. *Automatic Weather Stations.* In: Facets of Hydrology II, edited by J. C. Rodda. John Wiley, New York, NY.

Su, C., and Brooks, R. H., 1975. *Soil Hydraulic Properties from Infiltration Tests.* Watershed Management Proceedings, ASCE Irrigation and Drainage Div., Logan, Utah, August 11-13, Pp. 516-542.

Sulkava, P., and Huhta, V., 2003. *Effects of Hard Frost and Freeze-thaw Cycles on Decomposer Communities and N Mineralization in Boreal Forest.* Applied Soil Ecology, 22(3):225-239.

Suthersan, S. S., 1997. *Remediation Engineering Design Concepts.* Lewis Publishers, Coca Raton, FL.

Szép, I. J., Mika, J., and Dunkel, Z., 2005. *Palmer Drought Severity Index as Soil Moisture Indicator: Physical Interpretation, Statistical Behaviour and Relation to Global Climate.* Physics and Chemistry of the Earth, Parts A/B/C, 30(1-3):231-243.

Tabios, G. Q., and Salas, J. D., 1982. *A Comparative Analysis of Techniques for Spatial Interpolation of Precipitation.* Water Resour. Bull., 21:365-380.

Taylor, A. B., and Schwartz, H. E., 1952. *Unit Hydrograph Lag and Peak Flow Related to Basin Characteristics.* Trans. Am. Geophys. Union, 33:235-243.

Terstriep, M. L., and Stall, J. B., 1974. *ILLUDAS.* Bull. 58, Illinois Water Survey, Urbana, IL.

Theis, C.V ., 1935. *The Relation Between the Lowering of the Piezometric Surface and the Rate and Duration of Discharge of a Well Using Groundwater Storage.* Trans. Am. Geophys. Union, 16:519-524.

Thiery, D., 1988. *Forecast of Changes in Piezometric Levels by a Lumped Hydrological Model.* J. of Hydrol., 97:129-148.

Thomann, R. V., and Mueller, J. A., 1986. *Principles of Surface Water Quality Modeling and Control.* Harper & Row, New York, NY.

Thomas, H. A., 1981. *Improved Methods for National Water Assessment.* Report, Contract WR 15249270, Harvard Water Resources Group, Harvard University, Cambridge, MA.

Thornthwaite, C. W. and Mather, J.R ., 1955. *The Water Balance.* Publication of the Climatology Lab., Climatology Drexel Institute of Technology, 8(1).

Thornthwaite, C. W., and Wilm, H. G., 1944. *Report of the Committee on Transpiration and Evaporation, 1943-1944.* Trans., Am. Geophys. Union, 25(5):683-693.

Tonkov, S., 2003. *Holocene Palaeovegetation of the Northwestern Pirin Mountains (Bulgaria) as Reconstructed from Pollen Analysis.* Review of Palaeobotany and Palynology, 124(1-2):51-61.

Todd, D. K., 1980. *Groundwater Hydrology, 2nd Ed.* John Wiley & Sons, New York, NY.

Tricker, A. S., 1979. *The Design of a Portable Rainfall Simulator Infiltrometer.* J. of Hydrol., 41:143-147.

Turc, L., 1955. *Le Bilan d'Eau des Sols. Relations entre les Precipitations, l'Evaporation* et *l'Ecoulement.* Ann. Agron., 6:5-131.

Turc, L., 1954. *Calcul du Bilan de l'Eau Evaluation en Fonction des Precipitations et des Temperatures.* IASH Symp. 111 Pub No. 38:188-202.

Urbonas, B., and Stahre, 1993. *Stormwater: Best Management Practices and Detention for Water Quality, Drainage, and CSO Management.* Prentice Hall, Englewood Cliffs, NJ.

U.S. Army Corps of Engineers, 1981. *HEC-1 Flood Hydrograph Package, Users Manual.* Hydrologic Engineering Center, Davis, CA.

U.S. Dept. Agric., Soil Conservation Service, 1968. *Hydrology.* Suppl. A to Section 4, Washington, DC.

U.S. Geological Survey, 1970. *Measurement of the Travel Time and Dispersion by Dye Tracing*, preliminary Report, Book 3, Chapter A9. In: Techniques of Water Resources Investigations, by F. A. Kilpatrick, L. A. Martens, and J. F. Wilson.

U.S. Soil Conservation Service, 1986. *Urban Hydrology for Small Watersheds.* U.S. Dept. Agric., revised Tech. Rel. 55, Washington, D.C.

U.S. Water Resources Council, 1981. *Guidelines for Determining Flood Frequency.* Water Resources Council, Hydrology Committee, Bulletin 17B, Washington, D.C.

U.S. Soil Conservation Services, 1975a. *Engineering Field Manual of Soil Conservation Practices.* Chap. 14, U.S. Dept. Agric., Washington, D.C.

U.S. Soil Conservation Service, 1975b. *Urban Hydrology for Small Watersheds.* U.S. Dept. Agric., Tech. Rel. 55, Washington, D.C.

U.S. Weather Bureau, 1960. *Generalized Maps of Maximum Possible Precipitation for the United States West of the 105 Meridian.* Tech. Paper 38, U.S. Weather Bureau, Washington, D.C.

U.S. Weather Bureau, 1956. *Seasonal Variation of the Probable Maximum Possible Precipitation, East of the 105 meridian for Areas from 10 to 1000 Square Miles and Durations of 6, 12, 24, and 48 hours.* Hydrometeorology Report 35, Washington, D.C.

U.S. National Weather Service, 1982. *Application of Probable Maximum Precipitation Estimates- U.S. East of the 105 Meridian.* Hydrometeorology Report 52, Nal. Ocean. Atmosph. Adm., U.S. Dept. of Commerce, Washington, D.C.

U.S. National Weather Service, 1980. *Seasonal Variation of 10-Sq. Mi. Probable Maximum Precipitation Estimates - U.S. East of the 105 Meridian.* Hydrometeorology Report 53, National Oceanic and Atmospheric administration, U.S. Dept. of Commerce, Washington, D.C.

U.S. National Weather Service, 1978. *Probable Maximum Precipitation Estimates - U.S. East of the 105 Meridian.* Hydrometeorology Report 51, National Oceanic and Atmospheric administration, U.S. Dept. of Commerce, Washington, D.C.

U.S. Soil Conservation Service, 1957. *Engineering Handbook, Section 4, Hydrology.* Supplement A, U.S. Dept. Agric., Washington, D.C.

Van Genuchten, R., 1978. *Calculating the Unsaturated Hydraulic Conductivity with a New Closed-form Analytical Model.* Publication of the Water Resour. Prog. Dept., Civil Eng., Princeton, University, Princeton, NJ.

Venugopal, V., Foufoula-Georgiou, E., and Sapozhnikov, V., 1999. *A Space-time Downscaling Model for Rainfall.* J. Geophys. Res., 104(D16):19705-1972.

Viessman, W., and Lewis, G., 1996. *Introduction to Hydrology,* Fourth Edition. Harper Collins, New York, NY.

Viessman, W., Lewis, G. L., and Knapp, J. W., 1989. *Introduction to Hydrology*. Third Edition. Harper and Row, New York, NY.

Visser, W. C., 1966. *Progress in the Knowledge about the Effect of Soil Moisture Content on Plant Production*. Inst. of Land Water Management, Wagenigen, the Netherlands, Tech. Bull. 45.

Wallis J. R., and Bowden, K.L., 1962. *A Rapid Method for Getting Area-Elevation Information*. U.S. Forest service Pacific Southwest Forest and Range Experiment Station., Research Note 208, Berkeley, CA.

Walton, W. C., 1989. *Numerical Groundwater Modeling*. Lewis Publishers, Chelsea, MI.

Wang, H. F., and Anderson, M.P., 1982. *Introduction to Groundwater Modeling*. W. H. Freeman and Co., San Francisco, CA.

Water Environment Federation and American Society of Civil Engineers, 1992. *Urban Runoff Quality Management*. WEF Manual of Practice No. 23, ASCE Manuals and Reports of Engineering Practice No. 87. Water Environment Federation , Alexandra, VA.

Water Pollution Control Federation, 1989. *Combined Sewer Overflow Pollution Abatement*. Manual of Practice No. FD-17, Alexandra, VA.

Water Pollution Control Federation, 1989a. *Standard Methods for the Examination of Water and Waste Water.*, 17th ed., WPCF, Alexandria, VA.

Water Pollution Control Federation, 1977. *Water Treatment Plant Design.*, WPCF Manual of Practice No. 8, Alexandria, VA.

Waterloo Hydrogeologic, 2004. *Visual MODFLOW*. Waterloo Hydrogeologic Inc., Waterloo, Ontario, Canada, www.waterloohydrogeologic.com

Wazwaz, A. M., and Gorguis A., 2004. *Exact Solutions for Heat like and Wave like Equations with Variable Coefficients*. Applied Math. and Comp., 149, 15-29.

Wazwaz, A.-M., 2000. *A New Algorithm for Calculating Adomian Polynomials for Nonlinear Operators*. Appl. Math. Comput., 111:53-69.

Wenzel, L. K., 1942. *Methods for Determining Permeability of Water-Bearing Materials*. U.S. Geological Survey, Water Supply Paper 887.

Webb, E. K., 1966. *A Pan-Lake Evaporation Relationship*. J. of Hydrol., 4:1-11.

Wellings, S. R., 1984. *Recharge of a Chalk Aquifer at a Site in Hampshire, England-1. Water Balance and Unsaturated Flow*. J. of Hydrol., 69:259-273.

Wetzel, R. G., 1975. *Limnology*. W.B. Suanders Co., Philadelphia, PA.

White, N. F., Duke, H. R., Sunada, D. K., and Corey, A. T., 1970. *Physics of Desaturation in Porous Materials*. Proc. ASCE J. Irrigation Drainage Div., Ir2, 165-191.

Wilcock, D. N., and Essery, C. I., 1984. *Infiltration Measurements in a Small Lowland Catchment*. J. Hydrol., 74:191-204.

Wilson, N., 1995. *Soil and Ground Water Sampling*. Lewis Publishers, Boca Raton, FL.

Williams, H. M., 1945. *Discussion on Military Airfields: Design of Drainage Facilities*. Trans. Am. Soc. Civil Engr., 110:820-826.

Workman, S. R., Serrano, S. E., and Liberty, K., 1997. *Development and Application of an Analytical Model of Stream/Aquifer Interaction*. J. of Hydrol., 200:149-163

Wurbs, R. A., and James, W. P., 2002. *Water Resources Engineering*. Prentice Hall, Upper Saddle River, NJ.

Zauderer, E., 1983. Partial Differential Equations of Applied Mathematics. John Wiley, New York, NY.

Zheng C., and Bennet, G. D., 1995. *Applied Contaminant Transport Modeling: Theory and Practice*. Van Nostrand Reinhold, New York, NY.

INDEX

Simple, integrated, treatment of probability & statistics:

ENGINEERING UNCERTAINTY AND RISK ANALYSIS
A Balanced Approach to
Probability, Statistics, Stochastic Modeling,
and Stochastic Differential Equations
SECOND EDITION, COMPLETELY REVISED
Sergio E. Serrano, Ph.D.

Engineering Uncertainty and Risk Analysis is the much needed, well rounded, introduction to probability, statistics, risk assessment, and stochastic modeling every engineer must have, regardless of his/her field.

- Prepares the reader for today's problems in engineering analysis, modeling, and design under uncertainty
- Clear presentation of concepts. Practical engineering examples. No cards, no dice, no colored balls
- Integrated treatment of probability, statistics, and stochastic modeling
- Includes numerical (Monte Carlo) simulations and analytical modeling
- Intuitive and graphical introduction to stochastic processes
- Practical introduction to applied stochastic differential equations
- New analytical methods for solving nonlinear equations
- Simple methods to solve and graph boundary-value problems in several dimensions
- 478 pages, 177 solved examples, 147 proposed problems, 174 illustrations, 69 short computer programs, 51 data and statistical tables, 155 answers to problems. Softcover, ISBN: 9780965564311

Engineering Uncertainty and Risk Analysis offers an integrated coverage of the subjects of probability, statistics, Monte Carlo simulation, descriptive and inferential statistics, design of experiments, systems reliability, fitting random data to models, analysis of variance (ANOVA), stochastic processes, and stochastic differential equations. While these subjects are normally covered in different treatises or college courses, the author for the first time presents an introduction to the broad field of engineering uncertainty analysis in one comprehensive, friendly, coverage.

Engineering Uncertainty and Risk Analysis illustrates practical applications with the use of modern computer algebra software, such as Maple. However, **no prior knowledge of Maple is needed.**

HydroScience Inc.
E-mail: hydroscience@earthlink.net
http://home.earthlink.net/~hydroscience

CPSIA information can be obtained at www.ICGtesting.com
Printed in the USA
BVOW06s0027290816

460412BV00004B/7/P